CONSTELLATIONS: 2

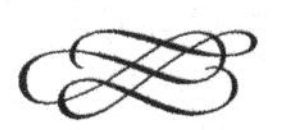

CONSTELLATIONS: 2

AN EXQUISITE CORPSE OF DREAMS

JOSHUA D. LUNDELL

Crafted with loving kindness at:

76 Divisadero St.

San Francisco, California 94117

Cover design by David Ortel

For Maximus Arthur

With doves from my heart.

"This is an evolutionary blueprint of the psyche.
This is the song of the soul.
Samely singeth the Spirit."

— UNKNOWN [1419.1 / 3858]

CONTENTS

GENTLE REMINDERS

Constellation: *(noun)*

1. An area in which a group of visible stars forms a perceived outline or pattern.
2. A configuration of related ideas, feelings, characteristics, objects, etc.
3. *In this work,* small clusters of dream journal entries *(and subordinated characters).*

Exquisite Corpse: *(noun)*

1. A surrealist technique by which a collection of words/images is collectively assembled.
2. *In this work,* the author acts as a daily de novo contributor using a journal entry convention to frame a simple multi-year inquiry: ***"What do I dream about? How much can I remember?"***

Dream: *(noun)*

1. Images, ideas, and sensations that usually occur involuntarily in the mind during certain stages of sleep. The content and purpose of dreams are not fully understood.

* * *

This is a work of fiction. It is not based on any conscious waking-life human interactions. Space and time have been rearranged. Some imagined events have been compressed, and **all** dialogue has been recreated. Some elements may include mature, and occasionally graphic themes. While the author intends such subject matter is dealt with in a candid, compassionate and radically responsible manner, it may be troubling for some readers. Discretion is advised.

1. Names of people familiar to the author have been changed.
2. Public figures *(referred to as "Zeitgeist Valences")* and resemblance to persons living or dead is purely coincidental. Expressed opinions, taboos, and non-sequiturs are those of imaginal characters, not be confused with the author's. Roles, actions, and attitudes mentioned in dream narratives are entirely fictional and drawn from dream realm experiences.

3. "Amalgams, Hybrids, and Spirits" appearing within the work have provided their preferred names for publication.

INTRODUCTION

Welcome to you, THE DREAMER!

I'm delighted at the fortune of meeting *(again)* for the first time. I've held it true in my heart from the start of this journey that it all could be said perfectly. Admittedly, I also must tend toward hallucination. As a helpful character will tell you: *"You're about to embark on a journey of massive self-discovery."* [0143.1 / 0334]. I'll take a cue from an influential *(and arguably troublesome)* person turned dense meme and declare, *"I'm simply going to say what needs to be said, concern free."* [0609.1 / 1539].

This work has found its way to you, its invitations are many, and it comes with a unique set of responsibilities *(and inherent risk of possible frustration)*. You have the opportunity to plot your course in the manner of best fit, though a clue would be to interact with it ***intuitively***. Open to any page. Flip around. Start where you are and then choose where to go next. You have the freedom to jump through this catalog at will and engage in some *"Whimsical Literary Gold Panning."*

This is not just preferred, but highly encouraged.

As THE DREAMER, you choose the path. A few options to frame your journey may be:

1. Read cover to cover *(though it may drive the analytical mind mad)*.
2. Consume as much *(or as little)*, as frequently *(or infrequently)* as desired.
3. Keep this bedside and read an entry *(or two)*, to prime your launch into dream realm.
4. Use vignettes as prompts for your own creative expressions and remembrance.
5. Follow a constellation *(Major, Minor, 1100+ total)* ...they'll appear shortly.
6. Simply open to any page and jump to any point from there.

"All models lack correctness, though some may be useful...for a time." [0536.2 / 1319]. A simple orientation found on **page 17** will assist with grounding into the ontological oneiric frame that's presented itself for our shared purpose: **to remember what we've forgotten.**

The abundant content with fractional context is purposeful. Mathematically, it may be that no one will ever have the same experience as you. The group theory work hasn't been done, though I've imagined there could be more many-to-many combinations a dreamer could navigate in the pages that follow than could be read in an entire linear lifetime.

Meaning can be derived looking back at paths trodden, so journey onward. Consider each dream the dip of a thimble into an infinite river, generous with its gifts and firm in its tutelage.

Who are you, really? What have you left out? I tend to forget most of it, until gently guided back. Perhaps interacting with this work will spark an inner fire that inspires unique pursuits of things you determine to be good, true and beautiful.

Ideally more of us will stay awake! Make art! Build stuff! Serve others!

I believe: In sleep exists the potential to wake up more fully.

Though I don't know much, I trust the following are arguably certain:

1. We are in space.
2. No one knows what's going on.
3. I love you.

-THE APERTURE

⁂ MAJOR CONSTELLATIONS (22) ⁂

~Most frequently encountered reflections ~
*Follow a constellation by turning to their dream of origin (**#0000**).*

⁂ 0 - **THE WEAVER** ⁂ *Encountered in 262 dreams beginning with **#0010**.*

⁂ 1 - **THE CARPENTER** ⁂ *Encountered in 207 dreams beginning with **#0012**.*

⁂ 2 - **THE DANCER** ⁂ *Encountered in 173 dreams beginning with **#0002**.*

⁂ 3 - **THE CHILD** ⁂ *Encountered in 107 dreams beginning with **#0102**.*

⁂ 4 - **THE CONNECTOR** ⁂ *Encountered in 62 dreams beginning with **#0071**.*

⁂ 5 - **THE LAWYER** ⁂ *Encountered in 54 dreams beginning with **#0080**.*

⁂ 6 - **THE PILOT** ⁂ *Encountered in 37 dreams beginning with **#0129**.*

⁂ 7 - **THE WORLDBRIDGER** ⁂ *Encountered in 35 dreams beginning with **#0010**.*

⁂ 8 - **THE ATHEIST** ⁂ *Encountered in 35 dreams beginning with **#0020**.*

⁂ 9 - **THE FIDUCIARY** ⁂ *Encountered in 30 dreams beginning with **#0007**.*

⁂ 10 - **THE ACTOR** ⁂ *Encountered in 29 dreams beginning with **#0066**.*

⁂ 11 - **GRANDMA** ⁂ *Encountered in 27 dreams beginning with **#0013**.*

⁂ 12 - **THE LITTLE PRINCE** ⁂ *Encountered in 25 dreams beginning with **#0915**.*

⁂ 13 - **THE NURSE** ⁂ *Encountered in 24 dreams beginning with **#0026**.*

⁂ 14 - **THE MAGICIAN** ⁂ *Encountered in 22 dreams beginning with **#0472**.*

⁂ 15 - **THE ROMANTIC** ⁂ *Encountered in 21 dreams beginning with **#0318**.*

⁂ 16 - **THE CONFIDANT** ⁂ *Encountered in 20 dreams beginning with **#0022**.*

⁂ 17 - **THE LOBBYIST** ⁂ *Encountered in 18 dreams beginning with **#0129**.*

⁂ 18 - **THE PUBLIC MEDIUM** ⁂ *Encountered in 17 dreams beginning with **#0028**.*

⁂ 19 - **THE TRANSLATOR** ⁂ *Encountered in 17 dreams beginning with **#0322**.*

⁂ 20 - **THE HEALER** ⁂ *Encountered in 16 dreams beginning with **#0010**.*

⁂ 21 - **THE KIND HEART** ⁂ *Encountered in 15 dreams beginning with **#0179**.*

⁂ MINOR CONSTELLATIONS (31) ⁂

~Less frequently encountered reflections~

***Reflections of Creativity & Will** (8) - (♣)*

THE FEELER: #0094
THE COUTURIER: #0204
THE GUITARIST: #0025
THE HILLBILLY: #0014
THE POSTMASTER: #0201
THE CATHOLIC: #0678
THE DULCE DE LECHE: #0363
THE VEGAN: #0837

***Reflections of The Material World** (8) - (♦)*

THE JESTER: #0127
THE RAPTOR: #0176
THE NUN: #0165
THE LALA: #0561
THE VIKING ELF: #0117
THE WARD OF GAIA: #0010
THE AYURVEDIC: #0002
THE WHITE RABBIT: #0014

***Reflections of Reason** (7) - (♠)*

THE DEVOTEE: #0384
THE PSYCHIATRIST: #0259
THE THINKER: #0056
THE PIXIE: #0115
THE KANGAROO: #0279
THE REVOLUTIONARY: #0069
THE DESIGNER: #0472

***Reflections of Emotion & Love** (8) - (♥)*

THE ROBOT: #0176
THE ARCHITECT: #0198
GRANDPA: #0014
THE EPICUREAN: #0233
THE FARMHAND: #0201
THE FIREFIGHTER: #0668
THE RECONCILIATOR: #0317
THE NEUTRAL GUIDE: #0010

*Follow a constellation by turning to their dream of origin (**#0000**).*

ORIENTATION

As illustrated below, an ascending numerical index *(date, time, and physical location)* can assist THE DREAMER orient and navigate experiences of THE UNCONSCIOUS.

#0000 - October 4, 1582 @ 00:00 (Someplace, Somewhere)
** General commentary from THE APERTURE will be found beneath the index, if relevant **

[0000.1 / 0001] [Bracketed text indicates a dream component. Occasionally, a MAJOR or MINOR CONSTELLATION may appear, who can be followed to their next dream interaction. Encounters with ZEITGEIST VALENCES are also possible, though less frequent.

Various ALTERNATIVES beneath each entry allow THE DREAMER to take directed *"jumps"* between dreams. Follow a concept by turning to the index number provided (#0000) *...if so desired.*]

Note: *Characters advance prospectively. At the end of their journey, no further option is listed. Indexes provided at the back of the book help THE DREAMER locate initial character encounters.*

[0000.2 / 0002] [*"Asterisms and Bright Stars"* appear less frequently than constellations.]

[0000.3 / 0003] ["Amalgams , Hybrids, & Spirits " are *(mostly)* underlined or in quotations.]

[0000.4 / 0004] [***"Dialog contributed by THE DREAMER looks like this."***
Double hash marks indicate the end of a dream]. //

⁂

Maj. = 1- THE MAJOR CONSTELLATION(S): #2222
Min. = ♣♠♦♠ - THE MINOR CONSTELLATION(S): #3333
THE ZEITGEIST VALENCE: #4444
ALTERNATIVE: #5555
THE ASTERISM or THE BRIGHT STAR: #6666

⁂

ORIENTATION

Before every journey, it's useful for THE DREAMER to take brief pause and set an intention...

INVOCATION

I, THE DREAMER
of the shared dream, see and draw to me
those who will enhance our shared growth and
best support living at cause as Spirit.

Help me remember things of use for all to know.
Take me places, aligned to go.

May I be fully supported by my guides;
Angels of highest order;
to joyfully expand in knowing as the body rests.

Help me to steadfastly take my next steps,
while dreaming with trusting surrender.

Use me as a tool to do your work in a way
That serves the highest and best good of:

Everyone.
Everything.
Everywhere.
Everywhen.

I commit to end patterns of negative thinking
to fully liberate my authentic connection to true creativity.

Above all, this I shall remember:
I love you.

PART 11 - SONDER

#0827 - #0924

*"**Sonder** - n. the realization that each random passerby is living a life*
as vivid and complex as your own
-populated with their own ambitions,
friends, routines, worries and inherited craziness-
an epic story that continues invisibly around you
like an anthill sprawling deep underground,
with elaborate passageways to thousands of other lives
you'll never know existed,
in which you might only appear once,
as an extra sipping coffee in the background,
as a blur of passing traffic on the highway,
as a lighted window at dusk."

-The Dictionary of Obscure Sorrows

* * *

August 16, 2019 - October 12, 2019

⁂

⁂ 11.1 - THE BOOK OF CEPHEUS: 0827-0839 ⁂

#0827 - August 16, 2019 @ 06:59 (San Francisco, California)

[0827.1 / 2100] [A large musical Grand Staff appears before me. Notes and musical phrases appear, then promptly erase on what appears to be an open-source tool. Anyone can compose here, as spirit. A familiar pattern of notes emerges. I realize I'm watching LOUIS ARMSTRONG's spirit score the music for, "What a Wonderful World." The creation is *"saved and soul'd"* to other artists who make attempts to modernize the expression. MOBY and others generate an ironically morose version that commercially flops.]

[0827.2 / 2101] [I pass a woman walking up the street next to a giant concrete wall covered with graffiti. She uses a single crutch for support.] //

⁂
LOUIS ARMSTRONG: #1332
GRAFFITI: #0013, #0116, #0162, #0393
SPIRIT: #0009, #0011, #0018, #0023, #0042, #0051, #0165
SINGLE: #0001, #0004, #0012, #0014
SOURCE: #0009, #00014, #0036, #0188
⁂

#0828 - August 17, 2019 @ 06:01 (Reno, Nevada)

[0828.1 / 2102] [A team gathers piecemeal at a restaurant, psychically aligned and each arrives on their own unique timing. One curious member sleuths around to determine the possibility *(or shared interest)* in moving the entire crew to another locale.]

[0828.2 / 2103] [I sit on a sofa with OPRAH sharing a mug of tea as she walks me through stacks of old memorabilia. She shows me candid portraits taken with MARIANNE WILLIAMSON, and numerous handwritten thank you cards she's received from her cadre of influential peers. She pauses to reflect on ones she considers *"special."* We each call for intermittent dance breaks to ease any tension in the room when it bubbles up. Later that day, we run zig zags across a stage while being filmed through a single phone affixed to a tripod in front of a crowd at a street fair.] //

⁂
OPRAH: #1017
ZIG ZAGS: #0311, #0375
BUBBLES: #0042, #0389
DANCE: #1235, #1293, #1318
⁂

⁂

#0829 - August 17, 2019 @ 07:10 (Reno, Nevada)

[0829.1 / 2104] [A girl and her dad joyride in a car at incredible speed.]

[0829.2 / 2105] [Still image of THE AVENGER *(exposed, vulnerable, and unapologetic)* wearing a flight attendant uniform.]

[0829.3 / 2106] [I crawl on my belly into a heated discussion. People debate the merits of gun ownership. Machine guns are on sale to the general public.]

[0829.4 / 2107] [A woman next to me awaits a tooth extraction in a dentist's chair.

"Ma'am we're going to remove your tooth, then give you his blood," a masked face says, pointing at me.

"It should be quick," she's reassured.

"Hooray, I'm the 'universal donor,'" I say while making air quotes with my peace fingers.]

[0829.5 / 2108] [I attend a town hall discussion. People are chastised for not using PrEP to limit community spread of HIV.

"PrEP is just $50 a month. Shame on them for not taking it."

"You need access to it to use it. Rural communities don't have it and are at risk," I clap back hard at the talking head.

Other terse exchanges follow. I start weeping as I talk to a woman during a scheduled break.

"Non-participation makes me so angry! It's a lot!" I babble through a snotty whimper as I dab my face with a moist Kleenex.

"I love that we can tell each other how we actually feel. You move so fast," she smiles and says while lovingly holding me. We sit in the crowd and breathe deeply as we watch leaders stand idly by letting chaos reign.] //

⁂

TOWN HALL: #0045

ANGRY: #0054, #0056, #0117, #0158, #0203, #0219, #0235

UNIVERSAL: #0311

THE AVENGER: #1419

⁂

#0830 - August 21, 2019 @ 01:45 (Black Rock City, Nevada)

[0830.1 / 2109] [I stop through a warehouse to say goodbye to an artist. I leave my phone plugged in with classical music playing as we work on mixing a film soundtrack in a sound-proof room. A group of people socializing block the studio door. I open the door to sing them a stanza from a new song. Intending to be silly I say,

"This is where the joke starts," with a smile on my face.

I leave the music studio and enter an industrial kitchen where I encounter THE FIRE-

FIGHTER. We discuss our recent shared walk across a flat, vast, desert courtyard. As we walk, I meet a woman who asks me to connect with a fellow team member who's, *"about to quit our scavenger hunt."* We're tasked with discovering objects that will have an expansive impact on society *(rings, books, "sacred" objects)*. Men search in teams. Women in groups also make a search effort.

"The entire population of Earth seeks these items."]

[0830.2 / 2110] [THE FIREFIGHTER loses a handheld Walkman. When he speaks to me in French, I don't understand him.]

[0830.3 / 2111] [I grow sad when THE HOPE *(youthful, awake, and curious)* walks to me with eyes full of tears and says, *"I miss my Dad."* This stops me in my tracks and I begin to cry with him. The young man's vulnerability moves me.]

[0830.4 / 2112] [A woman requests some time to preview an agenda for a formal meeting, when I've already shared with her,

"I'm onsite for a simple informal meet/greet."]

[0830.5 / 2113] [Image of "golden woven ice cream cone," clutched by a hand covered in melting white ice cream that drips through the cone's precious metal lattice.]

[0830.6 / 2114] [I feel more grounded as I continue searching for a ring, its image and location clearly etched in my mind's eye, backlit with brilliant gold/white light.]

[0830.7 / 2115] [Back in the music studio, a progressive rock track fills the air as I unplug my phone and place it in my pocket. I'm amused by the technically intricate musicianship and learn the name of the track is **"JUPITER."** The artist's name is not disclosed. The flourishes on guitar intrigue me.

"I've heard nothing like this before."

The crowd outside the room demands the track play on until it completes. More occurs and I'm awakened as the music quickens.] //

⁂

Min. = ♥- THE FIREFIGHTER: #0833
POCKET: #0069, #0100, #0102, #0150, #0154
GOODBYE: #0142, #0379
MUSIC: #0385, #0393, #0395
WHITE LIGHT: #0022, #0032, #0042, #0125
THE HOPE: #1321

⁂

⁂

#0831 - August 21, 2019 @ 04:55 (Black Rock City, Nevada)

[0831.1 / 2116] [I exchange healings with various *(seemingly innocuous)* beings. THE HOST *(motherly, aware, and efficient)* is known for being a powerful healer. She's demure and of few words.]

[0831.2 / 2117] [I watch rows of cars parked in parallel lines get sprayed down with water. THE TRANSLATOR may be here, but I don't see her. ***"Am I checking in to the 2:00am class?"***]

[0831.3 / 2118] [*"Heal. Give healing freely and without expectation,"* is a rough English interpretation of vibration that primes the space, though the symbols I'm shown seem ancient and alien as they glow translucently white overhead.] //

⁂

Maj. = 19- THE TRANSLATOR: #1108
GIVE: #0131, #0144, #0154, #0155, #0169
PARALLEL: #0017, #0098, #0273, #0277, #0339, #0396
ANCIENT: #0365, #1312

⁂

#0832 - August 21, 2019 @ 05:25 (Black Rock City, Nevada)

[0832.1 / 2119] [I look on the internet for the unedited video of a school shooting that was reported earlier on the news. I find the video and feel anticipation as I click the *"play"* button. A teenage boy enters a classroom, where the space is warmly held by a motherly teacher. He pulls a gun on her, and based on what the media reported I assume he'll shoot her in the chest. ***"I've mentally prepared for that outcome."*** Instead, he shoots her in the face. Her head explodes and her body falls to the floor. The boy turns and walks out, expressing no emotion, leaving me surprised and upset.] //

⁂

ANTICIPATION: #0012, #0358, #0381
TEACHER: #0148, #0187, #0256, #0264, #0313, #0360
MEDIA: #0009, #0050, #0053, #0072, #0073
VIDEO: #1332, #1334, #1344

⁂

#0833 - August 22, 2019 @ 04:23 (Black Rock City, Nevada)

[0833.1 / 2120] [I'm in a department store. A woman stops to talk and provides me with incredible detail about one of her championship bred horses. She's attempted to cover severe bruising on her face with makeup. I tell her, ***"We don't have a lot of time if you want help."***]

[0833.2 / 2121] [For an indiscernible reason I begin making protracted vowel sounds in lieu of speaking full words. ***"AAAAYYYYEEEE. EEEEEEEEEEE. OOOOOHHHHHHH. YUUUUUU-***

***UUUUWWWAH.*"** I sit behind people in a cafe who eat sorbet while I do this. Memorabilia and commemorative coins that venerate the disabled community are scattered around. Of note is a $5 coin under hardened glass in a sealed plastic casing.]

[0833.3 / 2122] [I jump randomly through various *"reality portals"*:

- THE HANDYMAN and THE APIRIST *(earthy, musical, and friendly)* have confusingly ended their marriage and returned to former partners.
- I pass through a deep canyon as part of a team that *"builds something important."*
- *"THE FIREFIGHTER and his family have a renovation underway in the basement."*
- I become aware of my "WATCHER," a being to me who follows me through time, space, and lives to keep tabs on my growth.
- I turn the music up and bounce from table to table in a cafe, pausing to whisper in a man's ear, seated at the end of the row, ***"Are you aware of your watcher?"*** He nods his head gently. I plot my next reality jump to shake my watcher's surveillance.]//

⁂

Min. = ♥- THE FIREFIGHTER: #0964
MEMORABILIA: #0043
VOWEL: #0141
MAKEUP: #0073
BASEMENT: #1234, #1340, #1341
THE HANDYMAN: #0880
THE APIRIST: #0880

⁂

#0834 - August 23, 2019 @ 05:06 (Black Rock City, Nevada)
Intensity

[0834.1 / 2123] [THE RABID RABBIT *(chaotic, incompetent, and toxic)* leads construction of a temple. A "confusion being" named "Rhonda" lurks about on site, who prefers to *"degrade the quality of interpersonal communication and create human strife."* I scream her name repeatedly to call her out into the light, opening myself to vast amounts of negative energy when I create the confrontation.]

[0834.2 / 2124] [I encounter THE ONE WHO GIVES A DAMN *(connected, experienced, and real)* and children with Down syndrome gathered in a hallway.]

[0834.3 / 2125] [I feel an aggregation of *"vitriol, blame, anger and meanness"* swarm around me like a group of black ghosts. I walk to THE RABID RABBIT's trailer, open the door, and find him sitting at a table. Without greeting, I repeatedly punch him in the face.

***"You know what's really funny? REALLY. FUCKING. FUNNY?*"** I say sarcastically between blows.

"What do you mean?" He says spitting blood in my eye.

"I...gave the temple away. I...gave it to the public. There are people in it right now. It's not YOURS."]

[0834.4 / 2126] [A young female socialite in her 20's enters and intends to share her point of view to *"get people to care."*

"It's a tricky thing, right?"

"What do you mean?"

"Trying to get other people to care about something when you obviously don't."

"What?"

"You don't really care. You just don't. Nobody really cares. NOBODY!"]

[0834.5 / 2127] [I've taken on the negative energy of "Rhonda" and she/it may very well kill me. The odds aren't good. It permeates my body and wraps itself around my spirit with an intention of inflicting deep wounding and harm. For a moment I'm deeply upset and sad, then become flippant and dismissive.

"WHATTHEFUCKEVER," I indignantly scoff as the entity pits my body's cells against one another.

The construction site remains confused as an awards banquet venerating *"the entity that calls itself 'Rhonda'"* commences.

"You need to have your next six moves considered or you're not even playing the game," I chide a group of 20 something year old desert Instagrammers when I accept a trophy for, *"most accommodating host."*]

[0834.6 / 2128] [THE RABID RABBIT retreats to a cupboard under a sink to ice his swollen face. ***"Come out into the light! I've given it all away. It's not yours,"*** I repeatedly declare. I'm sure the words coming out of my mouth aren't mine, but are those of, "Rhonda." I've become uncharacteristically violent. I offer healing and ask for forgiveness *"for losing my space to confusion"* as I wake up.] //

⁂

TEMPLE: #0016, #0038, #0244, #0257, #0285, #0377
YOURS: #0026, #0056
ENTITY: #0018, #0066, #0128
SOCIALITE: #0092
RABBIT: #1299, #1322
THE RABID RABBIT: #1039
THE ONE WHO GIVES A DAMN: #0838

⁂

#0835 - August 24, 2019 @ 06:20 (Black Rock City, Nevada)

[0835.1 / 2129] [I'm with a group of builders standing in a food line on their lunch break. I pass a refrigerator, open it, and grab a heavy bottom chilled box of oat milk. THE COUTURIER says she'll find me more for later if I need it.]

. . .

[0835.2 / 2130] [I walk to a door and open it. I can't see. I don't have my glasses or contact lenses. I hear a group of people having sex. I think I know some of the voices, and assume later, some will walk off the construction site because they're embarrassed. I believe I see familiar faces off in the distance and offer a friendly wave. It's unclear who they are, but one may be THE LAWYER who's made his way out to the site briefly to see what we've accomplished.] //

⁂

Maj. = 5- THE LAWYER: #0881
Min. = ♣- THE COUTURIER: #0936
CONTACT: #0012, #0023, #0045
REFRIGERATOR: #0012, #0044, #0125
DISTANCE: #1235, #1264, #1275, #1277, #1302

⁂

#0836 - August 29, 2019 @ 17:47 (San Francisco, California)

[0836.1 / 2131] [A woman drives a dump truck across an ocean. I marvel at the impossibility of the vehicle floating. Under normal circumstances it would instantly sink.]

[0836.2 / 2132] [The inner keep of a castle has well-tended emerald green grass and planters filled with lush, succulent plants. Discussion emerges as to my degree of responsibility for a soiled car port that was lent to a group for a camping trip. THE CENTERLINE *(mythic, fluid, and mysterious)* informs the group he's friends with the woman who loaned out the car port.

"Does the woman believe I've sufficiently cleaned and restored her property before she accepts its return?"] //

⁂

EMERALD GREEN: #0001, #0004, #0114, #0162
OCEAN: #0008, #0045, #0085, #0245
CASTLE: #0248, #0295, #0312, #0320, #0321
THE CENTERLINE: #0861

⁂

#0837 - August 31, 2019 @ 10:35 (San Francisco, California)

[0837.1 / 2133] [I work a union gig for a Russian entertainment conglomerate. We construct giant installations from LEGOs including a BMX ramp. I test the ramp and attempt to show my skills to THE PERVERT *(revealed, quirky, and lonely)*. The union bosses are pissed off by today's mass walk offs from the job site.]

[0837.2 / 2134] [It's THE ACTOR's birthday. He falls backwards off a folding chair from his seat at a square table. I rush forward to offer help, but he declines. He has a beard and seems much older than I expect. THE RADICAL HIPPIE *(matter of fact, quiet, and loving)* playfully claps and makes peace signs with her hands nearby.]

. . .

[0837.3 / 2135] [I run with THE VEGAN to my seat on a Russian passenger flight. She's assigned to seat 440. I have a ticket for seat 444, a few rows ahead of her. For a moment I'm concerned I've misplaced my passport. Calm falls over me when I realize I don't need it.] //

⁂

Maj. = 10- THE ACTOR: #0948
Min. = ♣- THE VEGAN: #0856
PEACE SIGN: #0162
THE RADICAL HIPPIE: #0948

⁂

#0838 - August 31, 2019 @ 13:25 (San Francisco, California)

[0838.1 / 2136] [THE ARTIST arrives in the desert during a dust storm. I wrap him in a blanket and carry him to a specific place, where he has an hour to prepare before giving a speech. He doesn't want THE ONE WHO GIVES A DAMN to know he's there. I help him prepare by putting sunscreen on his face.]

[0838.2 / 2137] [I'm on Alcatraz. I'm a prisoner. Too fast to capture details.]

[0838.3 / 2138] [THE ARTIST and I walk down a street, stopping at a bar that appeals to him. He approaches a glass door and presses his face against it. Once inside he learns he'll need to *"ascend to the second floor."* The bartender refuses to let him enter. He has no idea who THE ARTIST is.]

[0838.4 / 2139] [A large white man enters with a desire to prepare a meal for a crew that's spent the day working in the sun without shade.] //

⁂

WHITE MAN: #0007, #0193, #0209, #0320, #0394
ALCATRAZ: #0202
SECOND FLOOR: #0006, #0066, #0133, #0389

⁂

#0839 - September 1, 2019 @ 06:30 (San Francisco, California)

[0839.1 / 2140] [Roller Coasters. Brown and terracotta track over water. Smooth. Ridden repeatedly with THE PSYCHIATRIST.]

[0839.2 / 2141] [*A clear voice booms:*
"ALL IDEAS CAN BE SOURCED FROM THE INFORMATION LAYER....
...FIRST COME, FIRST SERVE, OPEN SOURCE TO ANYONE...
...WHO'S INSPIRED AND WILLING TO TAP IN...
...AND BRING THEM THROUGH..."] //

⁂

Min = ♠-THE PSYCHIATRIST: #0939

OPEN: #0368, #0376, #0397

ROLLER COASTER: #0245, #0250, #0274, #0339, #0380

INFORMATION: #1212, #1295, #1327

⁂

⁂ 11.2 - THE BOOK OF CASSIOPEIA: 0840-0852 ⁂

#0840 - September 3, 2019 @ 02:35 (San Francisco, California)

[0840.1 / 2142] [I'm a member of a wedding party. We've gathered to primp for the ceremony. My situation quickly goes awry. I'm not able to find my tuxedo. I can't find my socks. The group moves together without me to catch a bus. Someone's requested that I wear a vinyl suit that would make me look like an *"overbuilt muscle-bound bodybuilder."* The suit adds so much mass to my body my tux doesn't fit *(when I eventually find it)*. It looks like a cheap, cheesy, low budget special effect.

"This entire situation is 5 minutes off kilter." It seems complicated, but really shouldn't because I've had ample opportunity to prepare. On the day *(and at the moment)* I'm feeling rushed; contrary to my practiced, grounded and deliberate pace.

"My tendency is to feel flow. Right now, there isn't any!"] //

⁂

TUXEDO: #0007, #0089, #0154
LOW BUDGET: #0054, #0117, #0367
WEDDING: #0024, #0026, #0098, #0151, #0154

⁂

#0841 - September 3, 2019 @ 04:26 (San Francisco, California)

[0841.1 / 2143] [ROBIN WILLIAMS invites me to vacation at one of his summer homes in Miami, Florida. The building is fashioned like a large yellow-gold glass cube over water with a helipad on the roof. Its modern architecture makes it appear like a giant superconductor floating above the surface of the ocean. We climb down a sheer side of the structure using a ladder composed of scrap wood. Each single slat is affixed to the concrete wall with a single 4" screw. THE BAD IDEA *(inviting, hard charging, and fun)* hangs on at the bottom of the ladder and attempts to jokingly grab me so I'll plummet into the sea below. I stay just beyond his reach and laugh as I call him a ***"cheeky bugger."***

Once inside the home, and at the center of the structure, the cube tilts up on to a corner and begins to spin.

"Wow, this would be a great place for a family vacation," I ponder as I start thinking about how I can book it for a future respite.

The cube spins faster and the corner at the top unfolds like a sharp-edged glass flower, out and down to the surface of the water.

"The time has come to perform new rituals to expose the fake ones," a woman next to me states to a group that's assembled in the home. People raise their glasses to toast me and my newly assigned role as: **"Exposer of Fakes. Keeper and servant of Truth."** My glass is empty at first glance, then full of popcorn topped with raspberry jam. I clink glasses and eat while others drink, focused not on how the group believes I will serve in role, but rather ***"how I can reserve this amazing property on a future date."***]

[0841.2 / 2144] [I'm naked and have an erection. I'm astonished to see my penis is perfectly straight. No echo, nor evidence of curvature from Peyronie's disease.]

. . .

[0841.3 / 2145] [I'm on a 747 and discover a seaside concert venue on the downstairs level of the plane. A giant poster lists various rock and roll bands scheduled to perform in the coming months. The venue is attached to a massive convention center where numerous large groups of people queue for different events. I've unfurled an ace bandage that now stretches across the floor. I wrap it up with precision into a tight curl. The line on the floor seems to disrupt people's paths. A group of nerdy kids in a pack walk together toward a campground. They pause at the ACE bandage line and wait for me to roll it up and out of their way before proceeding.]

[0841.4 / 2146] [Back on the ladder outside ROBIN WILLIAMS's *(now closed)* waterborne home, I take note of autographed wood slats that indicate those who have also *"successfully made the descent down the sheer exterior face of the cube."*] //

⁂

FAKE: #0306, #0323, #0376
TRUTH: #0012, #0023, #0251
STRAIGHT: #0187, #0296, #0400
747: #0071
SINGLE: #1235, #1241, #1251, #1256, #1262
THE BAD IDEA: #0939

⁂

#0842 - September 3, 2019 @ 06:06 (San Francisco, California)

[0842.1 / 2147] [I'm on a worksite where a giant green field fashioned into a large maze is prepared for an inspection, promoted as a public novelty/attraction. An inspection crew arrives and aggressively directs a large construction vehicle to bulldoze through the plot, which exposes multiple caches of jagged 20" wooden planks scattered throughout the site. These planks would have injured customers, had they not been discovered.

"It's not a bad thing when this happens. We want you here. This is why we do this before we open to the public. You find the failures, 'the planks,' and we'll happily take them out," I say as a spokesperson for the team as work continues.]

[0842.2 / 2148] [A beautiful kinky haired Black woman with ice blue eyes approaches.

"I've worked hard at this to clear some debts, and I'm making $25...TWENTY. *FIVE. Dollars per hour. I used to work for AEOS. Am I too pretty for AEOS?"* she queries. When I say nothing she continues, *"I AM too pretty for AEOS, right?!"*]

[0842.3 / 2149] [The giant inspection machine zips around the edge of the worksite clumsily at increasing speed. It expands its traveling footprint to other zones on the site. As it plows through layers exposing trash/garbage/crushed cans, I express concern that this will impact our final approvals and permits. The inspectors assure me that this is not the case.] //

⁂

JAGGED: #0048, #0204, #0240

APPROVAL: #0021, #0186
BLACK WOMAN: #0145, #0193

⁂

#0843 - September 3, 2019 @ 07:34 (San Francisco, California)

[0843.1 / 2150] [A semi-truck full of goods moves to a new location. It leaps up in the air and on descent bounces off the bumper of a parked car, which sends the entire truck careening sideways. The contents of the truck spill over within, creating tremendous, heavy clutter. A crew manages to get the truck upright and begins carrying cases of goods toward the front door of a large house. Glass in the front door is shattered. A single shot gun shell blast in the center of the door has left a hole large enough for a peephole. I'm a bit startled when I notice what's happened here.] //

⁂

SPILL: #0169, #0170, #0180, #0188, #0249, #0311
SHOT: #0209
AIR: #0226, #0235, #0250, #0306, #0323, #0358, #0379
HOLE: #0021, #0035, #0073, #0255
FRONT DOOR: #0017, #0026, #0151, #0172, #0194

⁂

#0844 - September 3, 2019 @ 09:15 (San Francisco, California)

[0844.1 / 2151] [I've been assigned as mediator for a group of families that share a large mansion and have dissenting points of view on how *"the property would be best divided for alternative use."*]

[0844.2 / 2152] [I enter a room. It's dark. I climb in a bed with my boots on, noting the sand in them soils a set of white satin sheets. Once I realize this, I try to clean up my mess *(unsuccessfully)*, and irritate one of the wives/mothers who regularly keep up the property.]

[0844.3 / 2153] [I'm at an indoor shopping mall. A slimline roller coaster is a featured attraction. To access the roller coaster, patrons must download an app to their phone that exists solely to drive up on-site purchases. The app's main screen has two unlabeled buttons of equal size, placed side by side. One button is pink. The other is purple. Items selected from a subsequent prompt are "instantly purchased." An arcane multi-step process must be taken to *"undo a purchase."* The experience frustrates me until I quit trying to resist and *"submit to buying."*

The overhead on the coaster's initial ascent *(leaving the station)* is low and feels like a wooden stair step machine folding vigorously above *(...imagine an upside-down oversized escalator ...or the underside of an escalator ...depending on perspective)*. As I casually toddle around on the coaster, window shopping on upper levels of the mall, I wave at people I've been attracted to in the past, all of whom are inviting and friendly as our paths cross.

The lower levels of the mall are vigorously cleaned when I attempt to delete purchases from the app.]

. . .

[0844.4 / 2154] [Back in the mediator role, I encounter an older male neighbor who has an alarmingly creepy disposition and affinity towards one of the other tenants' young daughters, age 7. The wrinkled White man, *(wearing a sardonic grin, black coat and fedora)* bends down to scoop up a pile of shed skin cells sloughed off the young girl.

"Ooooo Jeez....you are kinda young...aren't you..." the man breathily whispers to himself as he smells the dead skin powder on his palm.

"His intentions are not clear," I say into my phone to ensure I have a record for the police. On playback the dictation is muffled, muted, and incomprehensible. I take this as a cue that,

"something refuses to be revealed." I wake up sweaty with a quickened pulse.] //

⁂

MANSION: #0311, #0331
ROLLER COASTER: #0339, #0380
PINK: #0029, #0064, #0070, #0073
YOUNG GIRL: #0151
ESCALATOR: #1340

⁂

#0845 - September 4, 2019 @ 02:59 (San Francisco, California)

[0845.1 / 2155] [It's night. The sky is black with swirls of orange and red offsetting the dark. I wander a dystopian site with THE COMPASS *(guiding, available, and stoic)*, gathering garbage; there in service, of our own volition. The more trash we collect, the more aware we become of our surroundings. Mass food production occurs all around us. Those working have likely taken a role here for a secondary or tertiary revenue stream that still leaves their financial health well below established poverty lines.

Odd jobs worked include *"inspecting peanuts and jarring/canning olives"* to prepare for the next day's shipments. All payment for the work is kept off the books by "the corporation."

"These workers are not paid," I mutter as a young man stands at a vat of peanuts, stomping them into paste while more pour over his head.

"Young man, I gotta go...I gotta go be with my people," he says to me as I throw him over my shoulder and carry him out of the factory.

We share tears. His brittle and fatigued body is caked in a thick crusty layer of salt. When I place him down, he collapses.

With his demise, I'm inspired to take up the charter,

"to confront blatant vitriol and xenophobia pitched at Hispanic people here."

I stand on a wooden box and decry the squalid conditions at the plant, highlighting,

"this workplace does meet basic health code standards."] //

⁂

FACTORY: #0108
YOUNG MAN: #0141, #0149, #0199, #0397
HISPANIC: #0073
BOOKS: #1271, #1290, #1297, #1236

⁂

#0846 - September 4, 2019 @ 04:36 (San Francisco, California)

[0846.1 / 2156] [I'm in a residential compound, home to a boutique three-Michelin star restaurant run by three Swedish men. A pool in the front yard bears a warning notice printed in black block letters: **"YOU COULD DROWN."** The sign would only be visible once someone's already fallen in the pool. I tour the space omnisciently.]

[0846.2 / 2157] [I'm in my 40's. I dance with my friends to a new banger called, **"YOU MAY WOUND."** We dance aggressively and throw objects around the club. As I dance, I grow ***"super keen on traveling more"*** and eager to share my recent globetrotting experiences with the family.

"I want to visit as many countries on Earth as I can in a year!" I exclaim as soap bubbles pile high in the corners of the room.]

[0846.3 / 2158] [THE DANCER and THE ATHEIST stop through an art auction that's underway in a gallery one room over from my home. They find a piece of art they believe THE CHILD will like. A bidding war for the art begins at 9:57pm. The store closes at 10pm. THE DANCER and THE ATHEIST place a call to THE CARPENTER (GRANDPA) who makes a winning last-minute bid for the piece. The price was absurdly high, but THE CARPENTER is satisfied the piece will bring the family (via THE CHILD) so much joy.

"Thank you, Daddy," THE DANCER says.]

[0846.4 / 2159] [THE CHILD *(cute, sleepy ,and about 10 years old)*, rests at home with GRANDPA. GRANDPA secures her legs with a black belay rope so she's less likely to fall far, if she tumbles from her *"treehouse bed"* where she regularly sleeps in a woven reed basket. THE CHILD wakes up when her legs slip from the bindings. She just wanted to take a nap and can't fall asleep until GRANDPA secures her again.] //

⁂

Maj. = 1- THE CARPENTER: #0847, 2- THE DANCER: #0847,
3- THE CHILD: #0860, 8- THE ATHEIST: #0881
Min. = ♥- GRANDPA: #0915
DROWN: #0014
WOUND: #0035, #0293, #0400
TREEHOUSE: #0014, #0141
HIGH: #1301, #1326, #1328

⁂

#0847 - September 4, 2019 @ 05:52 (San Francisco, California)

[0847.1 / 2160] [In an incomplete house across the street, THE CARPENTER has set up an automotive workshop where he's been hard at play restoring a classic Chevrolet. He's paid particular attention to details related to its unique, customized tail lights.]

. . .

[0847.2 / 2161] [THE DANCER needs a new chiropractor. She sets up an appointment. Her new doctor THE IMPROV ACTOR *(coy, playful, and juvenile)* gets triggered when they first meet and runs away. I intervene at the appointment and suggest she,

"go see my guy, THE ALIEN NATUROPATH."]

[0847.3 / 2162] [A red classic car with a tight clutch is moved from one garage to another. An eight-foot-long streak of red paint is left on the garage interior. Crates are stacked outside, ready to be moved in. It's rainy. Much of the property in the crates gets moistened and soiled. Another large heavy vehicle with a roaring engine is moved from the former garage to the new one. The hyper realism of *"the move"* almost tricks me into not realizing I'm in a dream with more to discover.] //

⁂

Maj.* = *1- THE CARPENTER: #0861, 2- THE DANCER: #0878

DISCOVER: #0172, #0188, #0189, #0200

INCOMPLETE: #0117, #0188

UNIQUE: #0162, #0170, #0367

CLASSIC: #0012, #0159, #0230, #0305

THE ALIEN NATUROPATH: #1049

⁂

#0848 - September 4, 2019 @ 07:35 (San Francisco, California)

[0848.1 / 2163] [I pack a large truck for a trip. I'm currently looking for a male co-pilot. THE CONNECTOR wants to party and sleep in the back seat. I tell her,

"There'll be no drunk kitties in this cabin, so long as I'm driving."

I'm happy with her being rolled up in blankets like a human burrito. The truck idles in neutral, clicks forward into gear, and begins rolling towards a single-family home across a manicured lawn. I try to step in front of the truck to block its path. Though big, it moves slow enough I believe I'll be able to stop it with my body.]

[0848.2 / 2164] [A party occurs across the street. I can see people decorating through the shrubs that obscure windows at the front of the house. I'm told we're in the Mission District at THE CATERER's *(festive, animated, and accommodating)* new home, though the surroundings aren't familiar to me. A gathering room at the new home is filled with peach and silver helium balloons. The house next door is disheveled and messy, augmented by broken bottles, the piss-like smell of stale beer, *(and regrettable prior night decisions). "The house next door is where the party will actually happen when the cameras go away." "No one cares if this place gets destroyed." "Its sole purpose is to absorb human rowdiness,"* various voices chime.] //

⁂

Maj.* = *4- THE CONNECTOR: #0888

PEACH: #0188, #0327, #0330

BACK SEAT: #0294, #0320, #0353

MISSION: #0054, #0160, #0162

⁂

#0849 - September 5, 2019 @ 01:20 (San Francisco, California)

[0849.1 / 2165] [I walk through an empty house. Things are packed up.

"It's a moving day!" I celebrate everyone who's been a contributor to this segment of my life.

"I love you! I appreciate you!" I say to each person, looking in their eyes endearingly as I proceed down a long line. At the end of the receiving line, I find a stack of oversized, unlined, white, *"tissue paper journals."* I grab four, place them under my arm, and confidently walk out the front door of what's become my *"prior residence."*

A crew of people works intently *(and with marvelous precision)* to unload, sort, and unpack everything at my new manor home. I grab stacks of coats to visually temper some of the short-term mess after I'm asked to locate a, *"specific series of small boxes."*

A stanza of a poem is repeated by the group of movers, known to have *"miraculous properties when spoken by multiple voices in unison."* Those in costume garb stand at attention. A strong energetic line divides the group into ,*"those who know the poetic phrase, and those who do not."*

A white cow is ceremonially led in procession by a group of small children into the kitchen. As the cow passes, I make eye contact with an elderly woman who seems to know what's going on. She utters a spell that invites the collective to ease. She invites me to, *1) step outside, 2) step through the intense invisible line of energetic resistance, 3) relax, and 4) repeat the process multiple times."*

I must know the words to the poem, but am unable to recall them. Once I've *"crossed the line of resistance"* the poem no longer matters. I've completed the journey, and knew the words when they were necessary.

"The memory's been shed. Onward, I go," I say as I walk back in my house.] //

⁂

I LOVE YOU: #0009, #0082, #0148, #0150
POEM: #0003, #0052
JOURNEY: #0006, #0011, #0017, #0024, #0025, #0047
ELDERLY: #0101, #0209, #0376, #0392
UNISON: #1214, #1264, #1282, #1293, #1295, #1322, #1333

⁂

#0850 - September 6, 2019 @ 01:15 (San Francisco, California)

[0850.1 / 2166] [I'm next to a pool, where a man dressed as a pirate stands submerged to his chest. It's dark, though the pool is well lit. I want to jump in and join him to celebrate our acquisition of a theme park, but instead shout out with a smile,

"NO! I want to go be with the vines first."

I get an intuitive hit that I'm in the Sewanee Valley of Tennessee. We've developed a method of procuring a direct connection to "the vines" in two different locations using two processes. The first is individual and straight forward. The second requires a team of 10 people to tend to the land. The land is home to a wooden roller coaster that requires heavy maintenance before being made available for public enjoyment. The theme park is a distraction. Discussion is repeatedly directed back to how to **best cultivate relationships** and deep community with *"the vines."*]

. . .

[0850.2 / 2167] [It's morning and remnants of mountain mist at my campsite softly evaporate. I stroll across an amber field next to a creek. I have a harmonica, a match book, and a poem scribbled on scrap paper in my front overalls pocket. These objects are all that are necessary to *"generate a song that will touch millions of hearts."* A simple tune is whistled into my right ear, and I recreate it with my mouth. The sweet motif draws birds and woodland creatures near. Unintended benefits of the songwriting process are other creative expressions that yield *"Academy Awards for screenwriting, direction and best original song."*]

[0850.3 / 2168] ["SHE" wants to see me! I'm excited. We have an appointment from *"2pm to 5pm"*, but based on the strength and intensity of our interactions, and how "SHE" has seen me work with groups, "SHE's" requested we move our appointment up to *"1pm to 3pm."* Our interaction will now be 1:1, *not with a group.*]

[0850.4 / 2169] [A friend and I decide to ride a large ride with three discs of equal size which spin like gears within a larger disc. We intend to ride together, but are split into separate discs. I'm on the green one, he's on the red. A yellow disc with a car moves up a central cylinder. The smaller discs occasionally pivot out and up at wild angles. At the conclusion of the ride, we are further separated and placed on different busses. His seat is on the opposite side of the other bus and renders him out of view. My bus is crowded. We both arrive at the next location safely. I omnisciently view the scene from the sky, hovering roughly 50' from the pair of buses the entire duration of the trip.]

[0850.5 / 2170] [Feels like I'm at a summer camp. I'm in a trailer at a desk. I take an exam and leave entire sections of it blank. I turn it in. I'm able to recover my incomplete exam, but all I can find to fill it in with is a red pen. Another classmate sits next to me, working on his exam form. The young man highlights groups of answers *"in blocks of five"* with a hot pink highlighter. It's not clear if we're able to share answers.

"Is he helping me, or am I cheating?"]

[0850.6 / 2171] [I'm at a press event for the Burning Man temple, where members of the corps look to me for a statement on *"project direction."*] //

⁂

VINES: #0075, #0163, #0193
HARMONICA: #0140
GREEN: #0149, #0159, #0162, #0188, #0189
TUNE: #0022, #0063, #0069
EQUAL: #1240, #1280

⁂

#0851 - September 6, 2019 @ 02:58 (San Francisco, California)

[0851.1 / 2172] [I'm a boy. I ride on a trolley car with GRANDMA through a variety of streets in MR. ROGERS' neighborhood. The ramps and roads whimsically rise and fall.

GRANDMA owns the entire sweet and nurturing town, which she purchased *"at a discount a long time ago."* The town is home to *(and can accommodate)* all beings. *"All are welcome."* The craftsman detail on the buildings is exquisite. We park the car and walk up a stone staircase to a door.

"Can you believe we're at Mr. Roger's house?" she asks.

"It's amazing!" I joyfully squeak.

An older guy casually passes us. He looks like a member of a motorcycle club. One half of his center-parted-hip-length hair is black. The other half is pure white. His hair sways gently back and forth in a subtle arc like a pendulum across the back of his jacket, bringing my attention to the word **"CHRONOS"** sewn across it in Old English patch letters.] //

⁂

Maj. = 11 - GRANDMA: #1041
MR. ROGERS: #1215
AMAZING: #0025, #0027, #0158, #0180, #0273, #0284
JOYFULLY: #0043, #0188, #0286, #0293
ARC: #0012, #0156, #0271
ATTENTION: #1256, #1263, #1267, #1278

⁂

#0852 -September 6, 2019 @ 07:34 (San Francisco, California)

[0852.1 / 2173] [I visit a city that is vibrant, active, full of life, lush, colorful… *"The place you want to be,"* a voice whispers. I'm with a group, a member of which expresses an interest in meeting someone he's admired from afar at a waterfront restaurant across from our hotel. We've traveled together to many cities as a pack. It feels like we've reached an eastern coastline. Elements of San Francisco, Vancouver BC, Boston and other cities I've not yet visited *(but can feel)* have provided inspiration to this burgeoning skyline.

My attention is taken by the brilliant jeweled skyline that extends in all directions. What appears to be a giant sparkling screen of TV static in a structure reminiscent of Monticello, turns out to be a surreal and dazzling flock of birds reflecting moonlight. A massive roller coaster that tracks the skyline is further highlighted by a brilliantly vivid rainbow arching over top.

THE SKEPTIC *(cold, forlorn, and deflated)* is my hotel suitemate. Our rooms are joined by a common bathroom. I choose to sleep on a weather check balcony delightfully polluted by light and the white noise of freeway traffic below that sounds like a rushing river. It's a warm, breezy night.

"While sleeping, it's likely I'll roll off the building's edge, be killed by the fall, and my splattered body further pulverized by speeding traffic approaching from both directions."]

[0852.2 / 2174] [***"We're on a service trip to work with indigenous people."***

We're scheduled to meet with Lakota, Apache, Kickapoo, Iroquois, Arapahoe, Paiute and other Native American groups on this leg of our journey. They prefer to meet, work and have community conversations naked, which makes our hosts at the hotel nervous, mostly because they're unsure how first-time experiencers will respond to this habit. I'm comfortable with nudity.]

. . .

[0852.3 / 2175] [An upgrade to a popular dating app is in beta testing. To impose immediacy and interactivity any time affinity is expressed by one user to another, a video call is instantly initiated. I don't need the app. I can psychically read the kinks and preferences of all the buttoned down, suited staff members of the hotel. A 41-year-old male concierge surprises me when I see the precise and gorgeous geometric maze pattern that has been precisely cut into his back with an exacto knife. The *"slice maze"* continuously oozes blood, absorbed in small red blotches by a white undershirt that he must change multiple times per day.

"He's the architect of technology that intends to connect people authentically," I whisper as I stare at the man with my eyes closed.] //

⁂

NATIVE AMERICAN: #0060
SPARKLING: #0004, #0013, #0045, #0069, #0144
NAKED: #0153, #0158, #0172
RAZOR: #0079
BLOOD: #1271, #1343
THE SKEPTIC: #0897

⁂

⁂ 11.3 - THE BOOK OF ANDROMEDA: 0853-0875 ⁂

#0853 - September 7, 2019 @ 07:40 (San Francisco, California)

[0853.1 / 2176] [I'm a member of a band. We've gathered with vigor and creative momentum to practice our new music. We've agreed to share a house as we reconnect and jam through material. I play bass and keyboards. I've placed my gear in different parts of an open kitchen. Amplifiers stand next to a grand stone hearth which also serves as an altar. The band is 100% focused on the quality and craftsmanship of their music. Nothing here is rushed. It may be months before we have new pieces ready for public performance. **We're the audience we play for.** Anyone else that resonates with what we create, is a gift.

"No rush. No rush."

The public takes an unexpected interest in what our *"unknown, no name project is up to"* and puts pressure on us to perform before we've had a single rehearsal. The anticipation outside our practice home builds rapidly. We let some of this energy bleed into our container and become briefly distracted. Our focus shifts away from channeling music to decorating our production space.

"How can we make the walls gold?"

I run a few experiments with paper, paint, and a chemical that turns stone into gold bars *(preferred, but time consuming and expensive)*. One test that begins as a spray of paint results in *"a fine basket woven-like stack of gold plates."* The plates appear through the drips and drizzles of liquid, which I wipe away with care before gazing upon the result with satisfaction and wonder.] //

⁂

BASS: #0012, #0056, #0230, #0251
GOLD: #0271, #0293, #0316, #0330, #1217
CHEMICAL REACTION: #0007, #0011, #0039, #0054, #0062
WONDER: #0311
KEYBOARD: #0244, #0277
TEST: #0008, #0025, #0210, #1218, #1245

⁂

#0854 - September 8, 2019 @ 02:04 (San Francisco, California)

[0854.1 / 2177] [*"Things are being built." "Things are being built."* I'm on a construction crew, possibly building a temple. The tone of the group is celebratory, yet somber. Overall, the feeling is optimistic.]

[0854.2 / 2178] [I have multiple fresh piercings in each ear. Multiple stainless steel shower hooks dangle from my lobes threaded with silk braided ribbons that run behind my head. They pin my ears flush against my scalp when cinched like a corset. Someone wants to touch my face with both of their hands. They're permitted to, so long as they ***"maintain eye contact and don't touch my healing ears."*** A set of hands land on my cheeks, slowly move up my face, and around to the back of my head. My request to bypass the ears is honored. The hands remain gently placed on my cheeks as a warm breeze wafts across my brow.]

. . .

[0854.3 / 2179] [The sun hangs like a brilliant gold ball in the sky, shining so warmly it's unclear if it's sunrise or sunset.] //

⁂

OPTIMISTIC: #0082
BRILLIANT: #0113, #0125, #0157, #0316, #0337, #0389
CHEEK: #0330, #0347, #0367, #0392, #1306
EYE CONTACT: #0012, #0023, #0045, #0082, #0083
SUNRISE: #0170,
SUNSET: #0337

⁂

#0855 - September 9, 2019 @ 03:06 (San Francisco, California)

[0855.1 / 2180] [Two guys sit with me on a couch. We debate how to best transform our shared working space into a mixed-use loft. They spitball a variety of ideas and opine at length about *"the optimal setup for the living room as a prospective group gathering/reception area."* They remember I'm there and pause. I'm happy to observe and keep my comments to myself as they spin off in their own creative swirl.]

[0855.2 / 2181] [I'm on the observation deck of a space needle among a group of other visitors. My roommate, KRISTI YAMAGUCHI will meet me here later tonight for a social event. When I enter the deck, I'm given cannabis gummies. The terms and conditions on the reverse of my entry ticket stipulate *"all gummies must be consumed onsite."* Guests can't leave with them. I eat all of mine, which certainly is ***"many too many."*** The woman responsible for inventory rolls her eyes, but giggles when I hand her my empty tin. I have no idea how high I'm going to be, but I've certainly gone extra deep this time. The main point of the gummy eating exercise is to *"challenge one's ability to remain present."* We have no idea of how off-center things may become within the group. Our charter is to: **remain light throughout even the most intense moments of the experience.**

THE HOBBIT *(free spirited, nomadic, and seeking)* might be in one of the adjoining rooms. Other familiar silhouettes float ghost-like at the edge of my field of vision. A punk band performs in the center of the observation deck who generate a loud, playful, funny, energetic, and social vibe. THE EQUESTRIAN *(stylish, petite, and helpful)* cuts through the crowd to me and grabs my face with both hands. She aggressively hugs me and repeatedly tells me I'm beautiful.

"You looked so good on TV today," she says though I have no idea to what program she refers.

Another woman whispers in my ear that, *"a live concert for a new band 'LAPD' is being filmed outside at the base of the space needle."*] //

⁂

SILHOUETTE: #0012, #0135, #0394
PUNK: #0088, #0317
EXTRA: #0026, #0063, #0162, #0220, #0266
THE HOBBIT: #0892

THE EQUESTRIAN: #1391

⁂

#0856 - September 9, 2019 @ 05:17 (San Francisco, California)
**Dream within a dream. **

[0856.1 / 2182] [I'm on the grounds of a school, similar in look and feel to the fellow's green at Kings College in Cambridge, England. The manor property boasts Tudor architectural sensibilities. I live at this beautiful property with my lover where we're both enrolled as students. Our living quarters are near the back in a library, where gold candle light illuminates volumes of books stacked floor-to-ceiling on sturdy wooden shelves. THE WORLDBRIDGER is the headmaster, whose suite hides behind the main manor in a carriage house surrounded by brilliantly green topiary bushes *(sacred geometric and anthropomorphic expressions)*.

My lover and I have frequent sexual encounters on our brown punched leather couch. **Sex is our celebration.** He jokingly refers to his dick as "Dr. Johnson," whose specialty is to, *"Root out and diagnose any problem (during standard office hours)."* We're eager for each other and have a shared agreement to ***"stay together so long as it's aligned for our highest good."*** We've discovered divine love through sharing our stories of heartbreak, loss, and renewal during our years together on the couch.]

[0856.2 / 2183] [THE VEGAN works in the dining hall. She ladles me a portion of hearty orange-yellow soup into a hand mulled stone bowl. My spoon "clunks" when I draw my first bite. I stick my fingers in the bowl and pull out two steel halves of an oversized capsule case from the thick liquid. The object just discharged nitrous oxide into the soup and infiltrated the entire bowl. I'm not sure if I want to eat it. It feels like a small test to check my decision making, though neither choice would be *"wrong."* I eat the entire bowl.]

[0856.3 / 2184] [During our semesterly one-on-one, THE WORLDBRIDGER remains supportive of my enrollment. He points me to a new, more strict code of conduct I must align to if I wish to *"retain a beautiful resonance through matriculation."*] //

⁂

Maj. = 7- THE WORLDBRIDGER: #1002
Min. = ♣-THE VEGAN: #0974
DIVINE: #0134, #0165, #0360
TOPIARY: #0079, #0123
NITROUS: #0353

⁂

#0857 - September 10, 2019 @ 05:43 (San Francisco, California)

[0857.1 / 2185] [I have tickets to a NINE INCH NAILS concert at a venue connected to my house. The opening act is a group of women who tap the eraser sides of pencils against screens that compose stanzas of poetry augmented by ethereal soundscapes. A young woman faces a stage corner away from the others under a spotlight, performing her part.]

. . .

[0857.2 / 2186] [A side narrative runs like a 1930's newsreel describing how, *"KORN were misfits and made everything in their career happen on their own terms."*]

[0857.3 / 2187] [I'm with my band at the show. We discuss playing hundreds of tiny bootstrap gigs across the country to generate a grassroots following.]

[0857.4 / 2188] [I turn on a TV and notice that the public access station live-streams the concert. We've bought tickets, but think the TV feed will likely have better audio/video quality. I'm eligible for a full refund if I simply show up *(...because I know attending live performances actually have better sound quality.)*]

[0857.5 / 2189] [I walk downstairs to a homeless encampment in search of a shower cap. A group of guys sit in lawn chairs amidst stacked boxes of unopened hair care products *(lotions, dyes, moisturizers, gel, etc.)*. One of them sprays me with sunscreen from a Chapstick sized tube, which covers the right side of my face. When I express concern and request a spray of SPF15 on the other side, I'm ignored. I find a shower cap and ask the price.

"Nothing. Take it."]

[0857.6 / 2190] [THE ARCHITECT stands behind me massaging my shoulders as I contemplate returning to the venue for the show. I squat in front of an entertainment system, mere moments before the headliners are slated to take the stage. A 7-disc CD player opens and cycles revealing heavy metal albums I regularly listened to decades ago. The machine selects Slipknot's album IOWA and plays the song, "METABOLIC."] //

⁂

Min. = ♥- THE ARCHITECT: #0927
HOMELESS: #0056, #0063, #0075
1930's: #0093, #0194, #0034
IOWA: #0162, #0281
LAWN: #1307, #1314, #1343

⁂

#0858 - September 10, 2019 @ 07:38 (San Francisco, California)

[0858.1 / 2191] [I'm on a retreat where people are encouraged to develop and debate different *"relationship models."* I'm horny and want to leave the session to masturbate with a large black dildo. A guy seated across from me points at my crotch, noting fantasizing has given me a large erection. The overarching game of the retreat is to *"Embody Disconnection."*]

[0858.2 / 2192] [THE MAGICIAN rests in the bunk next to me. He completely ignores me. ***"I'm calm. I win!"***]

. . .

[0858.3 / 2193] [I see former lovers walk by in the opposite direction. None of them make eye contact with me. THE SENSOR *(soft, gentle, and soulful)* looks past me and talks to someone he finds more desirable. *"Be in disconnection,"* the materials and facilitators remind us.]

[0858.4 / 2194] [I'm asked to lead a yoga practice. I'm also asked to keep my shoes on to stay, *"disconnected from the ground."* I begin a sequence oddly from the midpoint posture. The mass of people gathered reorganize themselves instantly into another pattern around me. They face away as I take on the challenge of *"leading from a disconnected center."* THE CEO *(productive, influential, and commanding)* smiles and observes from the back of the gathering space.]

[0858.5 / 2195] [An aggressive African American woman bosses me around. When I ask her to soften her tone, she tells me to, *"Deal with it."*

"You need to be dynamic," She commands.

"I think you're rude," I call back, matching the aggression in her tone.

She remains silent, and I continue.

"I don't like the way you're talking to me. It's not even your fucking job to concern yourself with what I'm up to."

She stands silent *(and shocked)* in a red evening gown.

The guy who noticed my erection in **[0858.1 / 2191]** fake naps nearby, hand under cheek, peeking from one eye.] //

⁂

Maj. = 14- THE MAGICIAN: #0998
EMBODY: #0042, #0077
RUDE: #0226
MATCH: #0023, #0168, #0204
PEEK: #1318, #1326
THE SENSOR: #0929

⁂

#0859 - September 11, 2019 @ 05:56 (San Francisco, California)

[0859.1 / 2196] [Night time. On a gravel lot. I'm back at the manor school from dream **[0856.1 / 2182]**. A split staircase from the second-floor doorway cascades to the left and right. An advanced student leads a class through an exercise. I'm paired up with a White woman who's getting energetically "tuned up" for a humanitarian mission to Rwanda. We decide as a pair to move to another classroom where we can practice with fewer distractions.]

[0859.2 / 2197] [Seems I've stayed past the conclusion of my *"Level 4"* class and have been lumped together with a group of *"Level 5"* students. Some are receptive to my presence, others aren't. We support each other in deprogramming, *"vanity, fame, sugar, fear..."* a seemingly unending train of attachments. The tutelage is strong and intentionally triggering.

After working with a woman I find attractive, she returns to her family quarters. A peer whispers in my ear, *"She used to be OKSANA BAIUL. Now she lives here in the back."*]

[0859.3 / 2198] [I'm challenged to take a free dive. I have to swim a fair distance down and hold my breath for a minimum of two minutes before surfacing. The notion immediately triggers moderate anxiety, sweaty palms, and shortness of breath. The prospect of no exit until the time challenge passes really scares me. I'm not sure if I trust the facilitators.]

[0859.4 / 2199] [I wander around the perimeter of the school and consider sneaking out a gateway that's ajar. More events occur in a fast blur on the schoolyard. When circumstances slow, I learn I've been expelled from the school. I believe I'm still supposed to be enrolled. I take the challenging circumstances as an opportunity to practice being calm.

"I belong here. I'll stay until I'm complete."] //

⁂

AJAR: #0172, #0322
GATEWAY: #0023, #0094, #0166, #0302
DIVE: #0060, #0285
FAME: #0372

⁂

#0860 - September 11, 2019 @ 07:36 (San Francisco, California)

[0860.1 / 2200] [I'm in a modern condo building with poured concrete floors throughout. Every unit has French doors that open out onto a balcony. A power outage leaves our group in a brown out at golden hour. One of my girlfriends trips and injures her right knee. She yelps in pain when she attempts to get up. She's unable to bear weight on the joint. We rush to her with a 10lb bag of ice. In the flurry of activity, it's decided to transport her to the hospital.

While navigating our way to an elevator, a young boy stands by a small curio cache of objects in the hall. He sells *"items useful for traversing a large city at night when centralized power grids don't function."* At ground level, the elevator opens to expose the mouth of a large industrial vacuum. We're promptly sucked up through a HVAC duct and jettisoned from the building. Our bodies are blasted through a complex framework of tunnels and pipes.]

[0860.2 / 2201] [It's family night at a movie theater. I hold THE CHILD's hand as we walk as a group along a rope light pathway to our seats. The two seats at the end of our row are occupied by DUFF MCKAGAN and TWIGGY RAMIREZ. They take turns autographing a television screen that extends towards them, presenting an image of a bass drum head. This occurs a few times. They're both drunk and don't realize they're scribbling on a TV screen *(not instruments)*. The TV screen gets messier with each round of writing until it's completely blacked out. The mood is playful and celebratory.]

. . .

[0860.3 / 2202] [Back home after a hospital visit, people chase each other around the perimeter of the condo and on to the balcony. I peer in on my injured girlfriend from across the unit as she attempts to walk around without wearing a leg immobilizer. She's alone. Her leg collapses under her, resulting in more profound injuries. She's embarrassed and upset she didn't allow herself time to heal. The frame freezes and pulls back, revealing its placement as a memory in *"humanity's photo album."*] //

⁂

Maj. = 3- THE CHILD: #0878
GIRLFRIEND: #0063, #0163, #0338, #0371
BASS: #0012, #0056, #0060, #0230, #0251, #0347
VACUUM: #0019, #0066, #0126, #0247, #0394
BALCONY: #0009, #0056, #0106, #0389

⁂

#0861 - September 12, 2019 @ 06:32 (San Francisco, California)

[0861.1 / 2203] [I'm at a park in a village square/urban center. The yellow ochre sky is splotched by orange and white wisps of cloud. THE COMMUNITY ORGANIZERS *(uplifting, friendly, and neighborly)* and their son THE CENTERLINE *(soulful, mystical, and quiet)* emerge in my line of sight at front, as they ascend a stone staircase to *"Alta Plaza"* park. THE CARPENTER and I offer to give them a ride across town.

While en route to our house *(viewable at a distance)*, storm clouds hang heavy overhead. We arrive at a fork in the road. We turn left. THE CARPENTER quickly maneuvers the car to the right shoulder and insists, *"everyone exit the vehicle."* THE CENTERLINE gets out. I follow him. An awkward pregnant pause follows. THE CENTERLINE breaks the tension by wielding a motorized scooter around like an Olympic Hammer Toss. He gently places it on the ground as light as a feather, steps on to it, then smoothly glides away as the small engine whirrs and revs under foot.] //

⁂

Maj. = 1- THE CARPENTER: #0880
OLYMPIC: #0069, #0071, #0076, #0210, #0295, #0358
ENGINE: #0012, #0048, #1228, #1245
FEATHER: #0183, #0396, #1313
THE CENTERLINE: #0921

⁂

#0862 - September 13, 2019 @ 04:24 (San Francisco, California)

[0862.1 / 2204] [THE GONG MASTER *(present, bright, and engaging)* and THE TINKERBELL *(frenetic, delightful and feminine)* play together on a suburban street. THE TINKERBELL's attention moves towards a neighbor's house. She promptly walks to the front door, opens it, and enters. THE GONG MASTER stays on the street. I follow THE TINKERBELL inside intending to bring her back out, first encountering the homeowner *(a mother sitting with her child)* on a couch watching TV.

I introduce myself with a smile and say, ***"She's the light,"*** pointing in THE TINKERBELL's direction.

"Yeah, we've met before at another neighborhood event," the woman chimes back.

We make small talk for some time, then I take THE TINKERBELL's hand. We meet THE GONG MASTER on the street.

THE GONG MASTER has set up an irrational abstraction of a toy truck for THE TINKERBELL that seems most similar to a train set. A bandolier with hardened plastic casings the size of D-Cell batteries, comprise a train-like structure that rapidly whisks around the *"non-conformingly shaped"* track. The device quickly generates large amounts of friction and heat. Though the plastic is hardened, the track can only run for a couple of minutes at a time, else risk overheating and melting.

THE TINKERBELL becomes assertive and defiant. She breaks her grip from THE GONG MASTER's hand. She walks down a side street and enters another neighbor's house. THE GONG MASTER is not concerned.]

[0862.2 / 2205] [I'm at a football game next to a vendor that sells ice. *"If things go in a strange direction, my snow angel will tip the table over,"* the salesman tells me. **Instantly I see angels everywhere:** in the water coolers, the players, and the field. I look closer and see angels hovering and singing sweetly to every blade of grass. As the view pulls back, a low genderless drone reminds me, *"Angels support everything."*] //

⁂

SUBURBAN: #0365, #1204, #1250, #1275
FRICTION: #0035
FOOTBALL: #0057, #0259
ANGEL: #0050, #0126, #0222,
EVERYTHING: #0014, #0027, #0074, #0107, #0144, #1235, #1238, #1270

⁂

#0863 - September 14, 2019 @ 03:25 (San Francisco, California)

[0863.1 / 2206] [I have a part time job at a caterer in a mall. My boss is a Caucasian woman who looks like SANDRA BULLOCK. She's short tempered and dismissive. I'm likely an 18-20-year-old man. She's in her 30's-40's. She seduced me into having sex with her a couple weeks ago and is unable to reconcile the experience, nor acknowledge that she took advantage of me. She needs me around to move heavy pans of food, but intends to fire me immediately after I complete my day's work. I'm willing to weather a tumultuous experience in the workplace. ***"I got laid."*** *shrug*.]

[0863.2 / 2207] [Tonight we're delighted to screen a new "RENO 911" movie. Members of the cast attend. I'm really excited when NIECY NASH requests that I sit next to her and *"bring popcorn with double butter."* But first, I have to reheat hundreds of pounds of pre-cooked bacon for the craft services buffet backstage. I move the bacon from Vac-u-seal pouches to a heated cooktop. A mass of fatty, half cooked meat hits the cooktop in a congealed ball. The fat softens into heated grease and begins to sizzle. The bacon is then transferred to a series of chafing dishes and hotel half pans, which seem *"oddly allegorical."*

"Relative to my boss, I'm bacon. I'ma 'lil piggy. *Snort.Snort.Snort.*"] //

⁂

NIECY NASH: #0880
MOVIE: #0332, #0334, #0359, #0367
BACON: #0060, #0250
CAUCASIAN: #0003, #0063, #0169, #0350, #0385

⁂

#0864 - September 14, 2019 @ 04:54 (San Francisco, California)

[0864.1 / 2208] [***MURDER SCENE*** The backyard of a small dilapidated house lined by a waist high chain link fence is the scene of brutal carnage. Dismembered bodies are scattered across the lawn and stain the grass red. A van driven by the perpetrator is haphazardly parked on the lawn and left seemingly abandoned with the engine running. A name crudely tagged on the side of the vehicle with black spray paint is illegible, but appears to indicate ownership. The scene is rife with upset, discord, and confusion.

"Where are the police? Will anyone help? So many people have been slaughtered!"

Our group is unsure what to do, to ensure we don't call the villain*(s?)* back to the scene. We don't want to disturb the dead, any crime scene evidence, nor do we want to further implicate ourselves as suspects by fleeing the scene and forgetting what we've seen.

"Where are the police?!" The graffiti tag on the truck seems familiar to me, but from where I don't know. The raw intensity of the scene sends members of our crew into overwhelm. The extreme trauma enters their eyes and roots deep into their nervous systems. Everyone here is forever changed, some irrecoverably marred.] //

⁂

BODIES: #0283, #0358, #0393, #1208, #1232, #1237, #1246
EVIDENCE: #0260, #0278
CHAIN LINK FENCE: #0036, #0079, #0151, #0157, #0394
SPRAY PAINT: #0393

⁂

#0865 - September 14, 2019 @ 06:05 (San Francisco, California)

[0865.1 / 2209] [I pass THE TATER *(extroverted, gregarious, and insulated)* and THE PIXIE on the street. They wink at me. I ponder dating them for a moment.

"Throupledom would be a fun adventure!"]

[0865.2 / 2210] [THE WEAVER and I rest in a condo at night. A fast-food restaurant is easily walkable down a nearby sidewalk. I look in THE WEAVER's fridge and am puzzled to find multiple "POP SECRET" microwave popcorn boxes filled with groups of six small apples. The fridge is full.]

[0865.3 / 2211] [THE WEAVER and I take a walk through the neighborhood. We see a few buildings and some small rolling hills.]

. . .

[0865.4 / 2212] [TENAYA THE CAT leaps from a window and out of sight. I whistle to call her back and grow concerned when she doesn't quickly return.]

[0865.5 / 2213] [I participate in an EMT drill, in a public metropolitan environment. Our team is positioned by "Avenue C" where commercial vehicles quickly zip by. An injured man lays next to a metro station escalator *(which feels like Brooklyn, NY)*. A group of people rush toward our team. Our instructor asks us to flag and mitigate other risk factors. I point to two large wasp nests dangling from the interior center of the pavilion as a couple of scout wasps whizz by the group. Our challenge is to move against the flow of human traffic, extract the victim, and assess him properly in a safe, stable location. Determination of *(and swift movement to)* the neutral location receives a weighting of 100% on the rubric. The man's vital signs are in decline. A group decision must be made as soon as possible.]

[0865.6 / 2214] [I'm a woman. I run across a parking lot looking over my shoulder in fear at an angry group of people. They chase me and intend to bludgeon me to death. I look forward and see a fast-approaching woman run toward me in a boxy robot-like costume. She and I collide and I knock her out. I stand up woozily, noticing the woman is familiar, but from where I don't recall.

I clutch a steel tooth rake and strike the robot costume wearing woman in the center of the chest. I wind up again and smack the woman in the face with the rake. I realize it's DREW BARRYMORE. Her bloodied face goes limp and her head hangs.

"You think you can be an extra, but you can't!" I exclaim and continue to ramble, ***"You did some movie 25 years ago and it Fucked. You. Up. Fucked you up, badly. Yeah, you like to think you can act like any other 'joe schmoe extra'...but...the fact of the matter is...you ARE DREW BARRYMORE, and not fully being that for (even a second) ...has REALLY fucked you up."***

The hostile pandemonium confronts her hiding spirit and disallows the *"dimming of full being."* An orb of soft white light hovers between our faces. Though it takes time, DREW and I receive the same information: *"Spark an awakening. Be clear about what you ask for. Accept what you've chosen. Be willing to receive it when it comes."*] //

⁂

Maj. = 0- THE WEAVER: #0871
Min. = ♠- THE PIXIE: #0946
TENAYA THE CAT: #1112
RECEIVE: #0260, #0390, #400
DEATH: #0251, #0374, #0386
SIDEWALK: #1246, #1249, #1275, #1282
THE TATER: #1401

⁂

#0866 - September 15, 2019 @ 03:32 (San Francisco, California)

[0866.1 / 2215] [Either I'm setting up a camp, or helping someone move into a new house. As I offload property from a truck and sort it on the lawn, I meet two women in their 30's as they discuss *"optimization strategies for an electrical power plant."* They study diagrams and mark suggestions on copies of blueprints as they discuss and debate. In the flurry of activity, I skip through the house, seeing some familiar faces in passing *(members of the "Adopted Family")*. When I pause, I find stacks of cookies *(4" diameter in stacks of 4)*, shrink wrapped in hardened plastic. My hand plunges through the torn opening and clutches a package of ginger snaps. I take one and quickly bite it. I may do this in other rooms with different varieties of cookies, but I'm moving too quickly to know for certain.] //

⁂

COOKIES: #0014, #0058, #0148
POWER: #0224, #0235, #0371, #0381
GINGER: #0185
DEBATE: #1248, #1286, #1307, #1329

⁂

#0867 - September 15, 2019 @ 05:11 (San Francisco, California)

[0867.1 / 2216] [I'm at an amusement park. The environment is humid and likely tropical. Maintenance and engineering crews work quickly and deliberately to prepare a roller coaster for public use. They've made a variety of fixes and enhancements to the structure. Final tests and preparations are made to ensure an, *"on time, and as-scheduled opening tomorrow."* THE RENAISSANCE MAN *(creative, analytical, and contrary)* is lead inspector and gives the crew exemplary marks for their safety and execution record throughout the upgrade project. During the short round of applause I remember,

"I've been the leader of the engagement."

THE RENAISSANCE MAN interjects his final commentary on what remaining requirements in the assessment are *"must haves,"* and which from the regulatory punch list are discretionary.

As THE RENAISSANCE MAN continues to read and remark to the group, silhouettes of the BLUE ANGELS fly in tight formation overhead. They thunder across the peach and pink sun setting sky like *"migratory pinpoint sized black holes."* The cookie-cutter-like-sky-splotches practice complex looping maneuvers intended to be performed at the next morning's grand opening.

At the conclusion of the safety inspection, one customer complaint remains disputed: **"95-minute wait to ride is simply too long."** THE RENAISSANCE MAN pauses for a moment and says, *"Really? That's it? I'm ok with that."*

He jokingly shrugs his shoulders and scribbles his signature on approval documents as a notary public and the project crew look on. Post sign off, he walks away wearing a safari helmet.] //

⁂

AMUSEMENT PARK: #0079, #0274, #0308, #0339, #0376
SAFETY: #0043, #0077, #0106
BLUE: #0370, 0387, #0390, #0391
THE RENAISSANCE MAN: #1014

⁂

#0868 - September 16, 2019@ 02:55 (San Francisco, California)

[0868.1 / 2217] [I collaborate with two musicians in a house. Both are males in their late

20's. It's unclear, but possible they're drug dealers. They have a huge catalog of new beats that would make great foundations for updates to classic tracks. They're currently debating how to best create a blast beat / drum 'n bass version of "BRIDGE OVER TROUBLED WATER."]

[0868.2 / 2218] [I ride a Go-kart, down a straight lane, at a blurring speed.]

[0868.3 / 2219] [It's night three of music production, and the guys don't want to work because all they have is, *"skunky weed to smoke."*]

[0868.4 / 2220] [The go kart slows. The three of us are in it. We pull up to a large home with giant windows around the ground level *(the same house as* ***[0231.2 / 0547]****)*. We see THE MASSEUR *(integrated, whimsical, and essential)* take a shower, much to the delight of the guy sitting behind me to the right.]

[0868.5 / 2221] [While sitting at a butcher block table eating *(perhaps hundreds of years ago)* I see a puffy grey cat stick its face in a ramekin of spicy, clear, orange-yellow sauce. The cat is grabbed at the neck by its large ogre-like owner, who uses his fat thumb to wipe excess sauce from the feline's eyes. The ogre is disgusted and annoyed with the cat for sullying his specialty food item. The sauce is rare, and now considered ruined.]

[0868.6 / 2222] [We move into the house to continue working on music. I'm a contributor to their "covers" album, and know working with these guys will be good networking for future collaborations. I find it fun to sing loudly, deeply, and soulfully. It feels new, though the music we recreate is *"old."*]

[0868.7 / 2223] [I'm in a bathroom with a group. We go silent when we notice one of the windows is open and overhear people in another room discussing, *"scandalous things."* We turn a corner and see a long row of locker room lockers. One member of the group decides to start picking locks. What initially seems criminal, turns into a game show. We appear on a set with a studio audience. To open a locker, we have to answer trivia questions about a state or territory. A giant map of the United State hangs from the wall up and to the left of the stage; state borders constructed from rope lights wrapped around the edges of LED screens. The scene becomes a cartoon. When a question is asked, the LED map blinks the answer. *"This is the only state with a unicameral legislature."* Nebraska blinks as a clue to the questioned party. I gently whisper into the contestant's ear to simply, ***"Look up and to the left to get the answer."***] //

⁂

MAP: #0034, #0069, #0112
BUTCHER BLOCK: #0250
OLD: #0389, #0394, #0396
LEFT: #1285, #1290, #1292

⁂

#0869 - September 17, 2019 @ 05:03 (San Francisco, California)

[0869.1 / 2224] [**"BEE BOL SHON LIFE."** Incoherent nonsense...*or is it?*]

[0869.2 / 2225] [I'm in a discussion with members of my band and our female manager. We're prepping for a press event where we'll debut a bunch of new material. We intend to perform from the condo where we lived while writing the album. We have an excessive amount of equipment, stacked floor-to-ceiling. Each of us has a unique and extravagant collection of instruments, all necessary to produce the complex, precise, and speedy compositions included on our forthcoming release.] //

⁂

LIFE: #0113, #0125, #0170, #0394
WRITING: #0060, #0062, #0161
FLOOR: #0006, #0010, #0016, #0017
CEILING: #0391, #0393, #0397
CONDO: #1289, #1310, #1318
UNIQUE: #1247, #1275, #1276

⁂

#0870 - September 17, 2019 @ 05:32 (San Francisco, California)
**I wake up with low back pain on my right side. **

[0870.1 / 2226] [I'm in an abbey/convent surrounded by nuns. THE NUN whizzes by as I ascend a wooden staircase to a second level. An average building has been fitted with 1940'-1950's era appliances. I look under the sink for scouring pads and find a large stack of inventory to pull from. I've prepared dinner and scrub the dirty pots as quickly as possible to avoid more work later. The pots I've used are needed to prepare breakfast in the morning.]

[0870.2 / 2227] [I'm working on a creative assignment with a partner with whom I've miscommunicated. I've suggested *(for simplicity)* that we combine our efforts into a single graph paper workbook. The expectation of the instructor however, is that each student will submit their own portfolio. A friend of mine is the lead instructor for the course and is exasperated by an admin request for him to gather personal information for all 300 of his students.

"This request is absurd and unnecessary!"

"Attrition. Some aren't going to make it. You can give yourself a break," I tell him casually as I sip a cup of coffee and continue.

"It's up to the students to take charge and stand out. You're not responsible for that."]

[0870.3 / 2228] [I sit at a desk experiencing strong referred pain in my right lower back. I hold a pencil in my mouth. I take my attention off my multi-dimensional graph paper. I place a hand on the lit-up areas of my body and give myself a gentle healing touch. I stare admiringly at a series non-orientable, irrational shapes I've drawn in the workbook. I flip through the pages and create an odd and barely comprehensible animation. I'm fascinated.

"I have to decouple my work from my partner's!"] //

⁂
Min. = ♦- THE NUN: #0991
ATTENTION: #0303, #0381, #0383, #1296, #1318
ANIMATION: #0023, #0033, #0060, #0378, #0396, #1205, #1235
SUBMIT: #0211, #1260
⁂

#0871 - September 17, 2019 @ 07:33 (San Francisco, California)

[0871.1 / 2229] [An airbus/dirigible makes an ascent from the high boundary wall of a beachfront castle. THE DESERT NYMPH *(mystical, unflappable, and embodied)* and THE WINE PURVEYOR *(sociable, engaging, and interested)* are among those welcoming others aboard the flight. I look for a spot on the beach to pause and spend some time writing. The winds pick up. I abandon the idea of writing, and walk back towards the castle with a group of people.

Once inside I sit on a couch with THE CHOCOHOLIC who plays with a male puppy. The puppy falls asleep, annoying THE WEAVER. I roll around on the floor with the puppy to wake it up. He has a humorous sense of timing and tends to have wild responses to mild/low key interactions. He flips around like the TASMANIAN DEVIL when I extend a hand to pet him.

"That's what you get when you play with a sleeping puppy," THE WEAVER chides, giving a side eye.

Outside on a lanai, a high-energy party rages creating a distraction from, "something larger afoot on the castle grounds." A colorfully dressed man wearing sunglasses strikes up a conversation and tells me he's *"about to start a 42-day residence at a Las Vegas casino."*]

[0871.2 / 2230] [The man and I teleport to an instance in his past. I observe him drive down the Vegas strip in a Rolls Royce he won after a hot gambling streak. He's dressed head-to-toe in designer labels. He has a gorgeous Italian female counterpart. His deep infatuation with her is mistaken for love.

He's confused.

He becomes sad and dejected once he discovers she doesn't want to be with him. She takes control of the car, kicks him out, and drives away. He's left alone on the side of the road in an experience of vast heartbreak amidst streets filled with sparkly lights and dancing fountains. He stays in this despondent state for, **42 days**.]

[0871.3 / 2231] [I reenter my body. The man has moved on. Plans I've made with friends don't pan out. We're not calibrated to each other's intentions. I make my way to the Captain's bridge on the airbus, and grow fascinated by a daily maintenance routine. The first mate removes a wooden panel behind the steering wheel to reveal a beautifully geometric arrangement of small plastic tubes and transparent pipes.

I'm instantly curious as to the purpose of the orange-colored fluid *(thick and syrupy)* stuck in kinked portions of the hoses.] //

⁂

Maj. = 0- THE WEAVER: #0874
TUBES: #0322, #0394
SUNGLASSES: #0088, #0229, #2096, #0307, #0328
SYRUP: #0007, #0074
HIGH: #1301, #1326, #1328
THE CHOCOHOLIC: #1241

⁂

#0872 - September 18, 2019 @ 05:17 (San Francisco, California)

[0872.1 / 2232] [I walk down an urban street with a friend of mine who bears a striking resemblance to MICK JAGGER. We're in a city where MICK JAGGER has *"grown exponentially at four different stages of his life."* We visit four places where the ROLLING STONES have performed:

1. *A large stadium where we talk beneath a giant concrete grandstand.*
2. *A church in Los Angeles where ARETHA FRANKLIN recorded a gospel album.*
3. *A football stadium in 2008.*
4. *And an awards stage where they've played "four times."*

While my friend is not "the rock star," I think carries a similar swagger. He floats around with me willingly, most of the time we're hanging out.]

[0872.2 / 2233] [I work on a campaign/short term project in a densely packed workspace with plenty of light. The walls are black with smatterings of exposed brick. Narrow conference tables are lined up end-to-end, and then divided long ways down the center, to effectively double the count of available desks. I'm assigned to workspaces C7 and B5, which cross the same length of table. I've arrived while the team is out to lunch and find it challenging to locate where I'm supposed to sit.

I go to the back, and from a cabinet collect a series of flyers/collateral, moving from the top-left to bottom-right shelves. I continue until people return from their break. While making small talk with a friend I discover the shirt I'm supposed to wear to identify myself as a *"team member."* The shirt is a 4XL and hangs over my body like a bedsheet. I'm curious who I need to talk to, to exchange it for the proper size. The collateral we intend to distribute all has a BDSM tone to it. *Paddles/toys/whistles/gags/floggers* are all carefully organized for quick distribution upon request.

"Feels like we're spiritually "pre-paving" for the Folsom Street Fair."] //

⁂

ARETHA FRANKLIN: #0914
2008: #0326, #0385
BDSM: #0224, #0388
SPIRITUAL: #0047, #0066
GOSPEL: #0347

⁂

#0873 - September 18, 2019 @ 07:06 (San Francisco, California)

[0873.1 / 2234] [I'm encouraged to participate in a sales contest. The scene is lighthearted, fun, and feels high in vibration. I work in retail with THE WHISTLE *(thorough, skilled, and chatty)*, who calls me at the conclusion of her appointment *(as I pack up from mine)*. I'm supposed to grab a variety of inventory items for my next engagement: A woman's top, a pair of "blind" shorts *(a popular pattern)*, dopp kits, t-shirts and accessories to complete an ensemble.

I pick up a specialty shaving kit replete with branded razors, brushes, etc. along with a celebratory cake for a client's 60th birthday. I've ordered small rainbow-colored empanada-looking petit fours, and sheik packaged miniature rainbow cakes rolled into small pirouline tubes presented in "ROY G BIV" order. The entire set up is organized to facilitate a lucrative, yet quick and easy sale. Minimal pomp and circumstance are needed because the *"Wow Factor"* has come through in the preparation. THE WHISTLE calls me and excitedly shares, that as a result of taking time to prepare she, *"sold way more than expected!"* I congratulate her as I look at my client's cake and notice a **"40"** written where a **"60"** is expected in frosting.

"That's not a mistake. It'll result in an even bigger sale!"] //

⁂

RAINBOW: #0045, #0105, #0106, #0215, #0243, #0329, #0389
MISTAKE: #0168, #0235, #0346, #0394
BIGGER: #1255
EASY: #1320

⁂

#0874 - September 19, 2019 @ 03:40 (San Francisco, California)

[0874.1 / 2235] [Reality feels like it's filmed on a Super 8 camera. Gritty, rough, washed out late 1970's early 80's film tone. I'm at a house, moving stacks of white cardboard cubes that have large see-through Tupperware lids. THE NOWHERE MAN *(self-assured, awkward, and dramatic)* works on a project. I feel a twinge in my left knee, but continue to work. My leg starts to feel loose and wobbly at the joints, but I refuse to slow down.

"I'm in a groove and I like my flow."

**The soundtrack of DEATH begins playing in the background and slowly builds in intensity through the rest of the scene. **

My left kneecap dislocates inward to the right. As I press it back in place, it slips to the opposite side. I notice some crimson webbing and minor bruising on my inner left knee. This occurs a few times. Each time I stop and notice a greater degree of injury, the music becomes more pronounced. I can feel the sliding and grinding of the knee cap in the roots of my teeth. The leg discharges nerve pulses that land squarely in my jaw.

I sit near a campfire to take a better look. *"You've blown out your inner capsule,"* THE NOWHERE MAN says looking over my shoulder with another friend he's asked to assist. I decline help, which amplifies the severity of my injury. My patella gruesomely dislodges downward atop my shin bone, slides under my skin to the top of my ankle joint, then dissolves. I can't run. I can't help myself. I can't get away. **Everything stops.** People offer help but I know I need massive intervention and surgical reconstruction if I ever want to regain mobility and independence. I burst into tears in the impact of this revelation.

"I don't know why this happened again. I was just working. I didn't do anything to aggravate it." I sob.

THE WEAVER suggests I grab an energy drink out of the fridge to take my mind off things.

"That won't help. I'm just sad."]

[0874.2 / 2236] [As I sit and cry, I fall back into a recurring dream I frequently had in 2001 in Oxford, Ohio in the weeks prior to completing undergraduate studies:

**It's night in Oxford. Some members of the fraternity have gathered uptown by Burger King to start a new game of "Assassins." THE FUNDRAISER (aggressive, brutish, and dominating) has upped the ante by dumping a box full of handguns on to the sidewalk. The guys grab the guns and scatter, taking cover more quickly now that live ammo is a feature of the game. At one point I feel I've been marked. I turn to run, and see a brilliant flash of white as tremendous pressure thrusts me forward to the pavement. I've been shot in the back-left side of the head. I can feel liquid running down my cheek and pouring on the ground. I can smell burned hair. The entire left side of my head seems to whistle as a light nightly breeze drifts through. I'm helped to my feet by a couple of guys who offer to take me home. I say I can make it on my own and stumble down the Campus Avenue alley, cross Spring Street, and turn left. When I enter the house, I notice bone fragments dripping off my face and onto the wood floor. I cross the formal room and duck into a bathroom. I'm surprised when I see myself in the low light. The entire left hemisphere of my head and face is inverted. I push it back overhead, hand slicked with stale coagulating blood, and inspect my injuries. My left eye is gone. Cheekbone blown away. Supporting ligaments and tendons move like miniature vascular puppet strings. I'm going to live, but I have no idea how I'm going to explain what happened to me when people ask. **

...I AWAKEN from the dream feeling **gross**.] //

⁂

Maj. = 0- THE WEAVER: #0880

DEATH: #0162, #0170, #0226, #0250, #0251, #0386

TEETH: #0084, #0155, #0158, #0159

GROSS: #0045, #0250, #1219, #1231, #1236, #1272

GRITTY: #0035, #0059

HEMISPHERE: #0200, #1231

⁂

#0875 - September 19, 2019 @ 04:05 (San Francisco, California)

[0875.1 / 2237] [I sit at a table with a young professional woman who shares a detailed plan which maps out her intention to get married. She's precise, deliberate, and thorough and knows exactly what she wants. When she concludes her story, I acknowledge her ***"for being so clear in her expression, and for being dedicated and focused on the things she wants the most."*** I admire her candor, and I've never previously experienced a flow so direct.

Next to us, a white trash woman with large hair smokes a cigarette and gives a customer a perm at the table in her double wide trailer's kitchen. Occasionally she looks at us and asks, *"Either y'all know that damned Millennium Falcon pilot? Send 'em my way and I'll take care of 'em,"* implying she wants to kill HAN SOLO for, *"ruining her life."*]

[0875.2 / 2238] [I transform into a basket of flowers and put myself on a display shelf to compete in a beauty contest with other flower arrangements. People applaud as a fleet of judges formally enters through the flower shop door. As I look around, I take note of dozens of other bouquets that are more ornamented, extravagant, and arguably prettier than I am.] //

⁂

FLOWERS: #0365, #0372, #0394, #1278, #1300
CIGARETTE: #0043, #0088, #0298, #0382
CANDOR: #0010, #0045
KITCHEN: #1280, #1303, #1309

⁂

⁂ 11.4 - THE BOOK OF PERSEUS: 0876-0904 ⁂

#0876 - September 19, 2019 @ 05:55 (San Francisco, California)

[0876.1 / 2239] [I sit on a park bench facing a blank white wall. Another man in a suit and fedora is seated on a different bench 5' in front of and 3' to my right. I use a "Pen cap" projector to cast a web address on the wall: *https://www.string.com/mydude.* The man keeps his position facing the wall and inquires, *"This is a submission to 'mydude?'"* I respond with a partially focused ***"Yeah,"*** as I stare down at my phone. *"'Mydude' is a widely known (and globally respected) forum for whistleblowers to post content on corrupt entities and represents the evolution of electronic discourse from first generation social media tools used during the 2010's,"* a narrator shares.]

[0876.2 / 2240] [A chronically homeless man laughs with increasing volume and intensity as he burns letters with a magnifying glass into the unvarnished wooden bench on which he sits. He invites me to look at what he's doing. I'm presented with an indecipherable string of letters and characters. Their deep grooves hold an oily residue where I would expect to see *"char and burn."* He points to his creation as though it's a key to enlightenment. All I read is a bunch of nonsensical gobbledy gook.]

[0876.3 / 2241] ["KRIS KRAFTSMAN" is the former front man for a highly influential punk band. He's a ghost-skinned waif, and hides echoes of a blue Mohawk beneath his 7/11 cashier's visor. He's taken by surprise when I recognize him. I have a minor fanboy moment as he rings up my last-minute point of purchase selections.]

[0876.4 / 2242] [A guy directs and produces a television show. He commits equal attention to writing the next series he has in the creative pipeline. He balances priorities well, and knows it takes two completely different skill sets to execute each project successfully, when parallel sequenced. He equally enjoys both processes.

Inside his home next to the front door he keeps a glass curio cabinet stocked with kitschy trinkets. He invites his outgoing guests to, *"take one as a reminder to remain tapped in to creativity."* The house is a mid-western 1980's tri-level with cheesy Americana interior *(oak cabinets, wheat patterned wallpaper and bric- a-brac intentionally gathered & repurposed from dozens of garage sales).* The work performed in the home transforms culture. The cheesiness of the space brings balance to *(what can at times feel like)* really serious business.]

[0876.5 / 2243] [I TALK TO A "BRO" in his 50's in a parking lot. He shares a pearl of wisdom that brings him a sense of enlightenment. I've heard him say the same thing to many other people. We walk across a parking lot and meet a woman in her 30's. The three of us sit and talk at a picnic table in a parking lot.

I reach my hand into a plastic wrapped bag filled with summer sausage and cold cuts. The meat is oily and dripping from being set out uncovered in the sun, but this doesn't stop me from eating it *(and thinking it's "gross").* I walk across the parking lot to talk to another muscular guy in his 30's. I'm confused and think he's talking to himself until I draw nearer and see he's talking to the woman, who now sits behind the wheel of an exotic car.

"Feels like we got our money's worth," I say, recalling we rented a property for a single day's use without an overnight stay.

Another man joins our group. The four of us enter a luxury retail boutique. The packaged oily meat from outside has been plated and is offered to us by staff as we shop. I decline the meat tray when the associate holds it near my face. Grease drips down his wrist and soaks into his custom haberdashery.

We sit on a modern couch. One of the guys becomes bored. He humors himself by grabbing a pillow, placing it over his groin, and repeatedly thrusting his pelvis. I look at a case of accessories. When I glance back, I notice both men and the woman disappear up a staircase to another level of the store. I watch them have sex through silts in a vertical white railing. Store management discovers the trio there. The manager politely asks them to stop. They do, and we all collectively share some laughs. It's absurd, funny and memorable.] //

⁂

GREASE: #0017, #0035, #0290, #0379
PARKING LOT: #0271, #0374, #0396
BLANK: #0186, #0204, #0215, #0289
STOP: #0316, #0340, #0353, #0378
MEAT: #1225

⁂

#0877 - September 19, 2019 @ 07:11 (San Francisco, California)

[0877.1 / 2244] [I'm about to lead a class. I arrive with ample lead time. I decide whether or not it will be my last one, as I watch seconds tick by on a large round wall clock. I drink diet soda from a 32oz paper cup *(no lid, the sides starting to collapse inward at the top).* I flip through music selections on my phone, looking for a track to set the mood. I'm drawn to live sitar versions of old FOUR TET tracks.

The group gathers. I'm greeted by many familiar faces I haven't seen in years, and in some cases lifetimes. Our classroom is long and narrow with floor to ceiling exterior windows, divided by a simple 3" white shellacked shelf at waist height that holds various plants.

Class starts in three minutes and I've yet to settle on music. I skip across genres to find a fit. More people flood in. It's looking like tonight will sell out. The song selection really doesn't matter.

"I'll have to speak loudly to command the room," my inner monologue inaccurately croons.

The woman working behind a solid studio wall has a very particular way of doing things. She prefers items on her desk be placed in meticulous order. I playfully put my half consumed soft drink in a random spot on the desk, where it doesn't belong. I'm totally aware this will annoy her.] //

⁂

SODA: #0012, #0054
MONOLOGUE: #0002
MUSIC: #0160, #0162
ORDER: #1245, #1249

⁂

#0878 - September 20, 2019 @ 03:18 (The Presidio of San Francisco, California)

[0878.1 / 2245] [I'm dropped off with a group of skiers at a mountain lodge with gondola access to a highly popular series of slopes. People passing from the opposite direction say, *"Freshies over there. Powder's tits deep. Expect the slow, bro."* Our group gathers in front of a large interactive resort map. Locations of lifts, popular vistas, and descents are all brightly denoted. It doesn't look crowded. The group doesn't want to go anywhere near an area on the map marked "popular" with blinking bubble letters. Another segment in the middle of the map, flagged in a rich shade of orange blinks like a car turn signal, and taunts us to come play though the group remains resolved.

THE PACHAMAMA *(syrupy, mysterious, and alluring)* leads our team. She's the mountain's *"health and safety executive,"* and has established precise entry/exit protocols which she insists on sharing with the team before anyone sets foot on the slopes. She has us gather in a large airport transport terminal-like tube lined with extremely tall and thin windows. She gives a thorough briefing. Most people in attendance are receptive to her message.]

[0878.2 / 2246] [I'm a voyeur observing a sexual encounter between a husband and wife. Both are sex therapists. Both work through new orientations to individual core issues. They're in active inquiry on what's causing a lack of sexual connection between them. They arrive at an impasse about oral sex. He wants to receive it from her. She doesn't want to give it to him. They're both svelte, small framed people. They disrobe to reveal muscular-milky-white-skinned bodies. From behind I can tell the man has massive testicles. They awkwardly try to negotiate how to both go down on each other at the same time, while remaining standing. Neither gives an inch, and they devolve into an argument.]

[0878.3 / 2247] [THE CHILD is five years old. She's just completed an active day at school. She exits a giant slide and is greeted by THE DANCER. They hug and walk toward me holding hands. THE CHILD runs arms open and leaps at me, giving me a strong and lengthy bear hug. She giggles as she hugs me. THE DANCER looks at me relieved and says, *"Thankfully today was a good day."*]

[0878.4 / 2248] [A large group of white gui wearing people prepare for a performance on a floor made of tatami mats. A roof above appears to hover atop a ring of supremely thin *"air windows."* One group of people generates a pose to challenge another, who responds in kind. I watch a few rounds of this game. I'm the director. I'm dressed entirely in black.

"Stop. Look at what you're doing." No one seems to notice the general lack of alignment.

"Everyone, please direct your attention to 'ILSE'" *(a tall, gaunt Russian ballerina).*

"ILSE" creates five poses in rapid succession. The group applauds. I interrupt the clapping.

"Yes. 'ILSE,' that's beautiful. Here's the next game: You're going to create one pose. The rest of the class is going to copy you. To anyone who isn't creating the pose exactly as you are, you'll say, 'FAIL!' point, and tell them what to change in two words or less. Understood?"

THE BLACK BEAUTY *(mysterious, dark, and brooding)* and others present giggle with nervous excitement before we play the game. After fun, playful small talk ceases, the game begins.] //

⁂

Maj. = 2- THE DANCER: #0881, 3- THE CHILD: #0898

SMALL TALK: #0213, #0219, #0250, #0259

MILKY: #0377, #0389

ORANGE: #0017

⁂

#0879 - September 20, 2019 @ 03:33 (San Francisco, California)

[0879.1 / 2249] [A stand-up comedian runs a new bit at a small club. The anecdote centers on his being asked by a stranger to share a radish sandwich and their grossly over appreciative response. *"Shit man...I mean it's a just fucking rrrrr-adish sandwich. You're making more out of this than needs be over a gross...ass...cheap...rrrrr-adish sandwich."*]

[0879.2 / 2250] [***"Special thanks to the boys in blue,"*** I shout at a group of cops as I pull needles from a cactus. The cactus becomes a mango in my hand. I peel the mango with a laser from my index finger and devour the fruit. I walk behind a male/female couple who casually discuss how to kick off the opening session of a retreat they're leading together. We walk down an active, yet easeful promenade as we talk through word choice, order, inflection, and volume.

"I think it sounds best if you say, 'This is some time for you to find and know yourself. Make any adjustments you need to arrive, then be here as fully as possible.'"]

[0879.3 / 2251] [I discover a sequence of yoga poses. I'm told to share the sequence with people. A gorgeous bright-eyed yogi-man passes me carrying a rolled-up mat. He winks and waves in attempts to distract me from practice, but I remain on my mat, in my flow.

"Devotion to God is my refuge," is my mantra as I continue to breathe, move, and sweat with more vigor.

I continue my practice as another man and woman pass me. The woman is familiar. She's very fat. She uses a cane to walk. She gained large amounts of weight after dislocating and injuring her left knee. I'm unable to recall her name, so I listen intently as she and the man make small talk. I continue to move my body with devotion. My prayer is to overhear both of their names before they turn around and ask me a question.

"I am grounded in my morning prayer."]

[0879.4 / 2252] [I'm a concert promoter that overhears a decision by an artist's management to replace live musicians with loops and backup tracks. I'm quick to dissent and I demand that the group perform live, per contract. At a nearby table a young male bank analyst feverishly updates a cost/benefit model after learning of a production mistake that's resulted in the mislabeling of 1000's of cases of a specialty salt product, packaged in small bejeweled cylinders. The error has resulted in massive amounts of rework. The analyst crunches numbers to understand the impact to profit margins. People are tense and upset. I'm neutral. I don't react to the situation.] //

⁂

⁂
MANTRA: #0046, #0197, #0218, #0362, #0363
SALT: #0204
CANE: #0029, #0188
NUMBERS: #1207, #1268, #1322
⁂

#0880 - September 21, 2019 @ 03:54 (San Francisco, California)

[0880.1 / 2253] [THE RECONCILIATOR and I organize a group outing with members of "JOY CAMP" in Vancouver, BC. We discover an underground Ferris Wheel turned roller-coaster that enraptures THE AGONY *(generative, improvisational, and honest). "This is the best thing ever!"* He gleefully shouts as he rides. After a full day of activities in the city, THE RECONCILIATOR remarks she's *"Never had more fun in the COOV!"*]

[0880.2 / 2254] [We stand with NIECY NASH and other comedians of color who leap off the edge of a high stage and gently float down to be received by a crowd of adoring fans below. Our group piles in a car and drives down a go kart track in the opposite direction of traffic. We bob and weave through oncoming cars with tremendous speed. We stop at a hovering "Space Pirate Ship" for a party attended by oversized Muppet-like characters. THE HANDYMAN and THE APIRIST *(aware, disciplined, and loving)* talk to THE WEAVER and THE CARPENTER at the party.

[0880.3 / 2255] [A large TV broadcasts a limbless male gymnast tumble, leap, and tackle an opponent in a UFC MMA style bout. The gymnast pins the fighter and wins with ease. The defeated fighter offers to "hi five" the limbless gymnast who stands stoically, mildly offended by the gesture. He releases any offense he's taken. He's the victor and has nothing to prove. PAMELA ANDERSON is on deck to fight the next bout against a mystery opponent. The vanity bout quickly draws attention away from the miracle just witnessed with the limbless gymnast. PAM has a tagline she says repeatedly as required per an endorsement deal where she's paid *"per mention."* Those tuned in become annoyed.]

⁂
Maj. = 0- THE WEAVER: #0887, 1- THE CARPENTER: #0883
Min. = ♥- THE RECONCILIATOR: #1017
GYMNAST: #0017
FLOAT: #0226, #0231, #0292, #0394
MYSTERY: #0237, #1205, #1222
THE HANDYMAN: #0906
THE APIRIST: #0906
⁂

#0881 - September 21, 2019 @ 05:39 (San Francisco, California)

[0881.1 / 2256] [I rent a luxury condo unit in a brand-new property. The management company has just released a new policy stating if tenants are off premises during the holidays, they reserve the right to enter your unit. If they discover beds without sheets, they'll assume the unit has been rented on a short-term basis which violates community standards, voids contractual agreements, and serves as grounds for immediate eviction. I call THE LAWYER and have a conversation as to whether or not their entry constitutes criminal trespass, or if it's *"de facto policy in the surveillance age."* I'm not using my condo as a short-term rental, nor do I intend to. I simply want to be informed.]

[0881.2 / 2257] [I have connected, passionate, and sweaty sex with my guy. I'm the top in this relationship. We're in a second-floor bedroom in a contemporary home. The bed is next to a window that allows me to look down on a manicured backyard with a deck and small lawn. THE DANCER and THE ATHEIST sit at a table on the deck having a conversation. They see me, before I see them. They motion for me to pull down the window shade, and I acquiesce. Lovemaking continues for a protracted amount of time. Drenched in sweat and parched from all the physical interaction, I leave to use the bathroom.

Outside the bedroom door is a commode. A line of people makes comments toward me as I sit crouched on the ground. A girlfriend of mine pauses to continue a conversation we had about sex earlier in the week, unaware that I've been having sex all day and sit naked on a toilet in front of her really needing to shit. The conversation becomes an interruption and distraction.

"I'm so sorry, but I...I'm trying to take a shit. Can you please leave me alone?"

She's taken aback and leaves.

"No one seems to notice how things actually work here," the guy immediately behind her in line says, before proceeding.

"I'm having a hard time remembering how to do this when there's no privacy," I mutter into my hands cupped over my face.

In a blink I discover myself back in my bedroom. My larger, smooth skinned bubble butted partner lays on his stomach looking at me over his right shoulder. With a doe eyed wink, he invites me to leap on him, which I do without hesitation. He buries his face in a pillow, moaning with pleasure and delight until I finish inside him six times. We love each other *"anciently and fully."*] //

⁂

Maj. = 2- THE DANCER: #0882, 5- THE LAWYER: #0905, 8- THE ATHEIST: #0915

PRIVACY: #0021, #0124, #0394

SHIT: #0016, #0017, #0092 #0126, #0175, #0204, #0226, #0337

TOP: #0007, #047, #0098, #0125

FINISH: #1214, #1329

⁂

#0882 - September 21, 2019 @ 07:00 (San Francisco, California)

[0882.1 / 2258] [I'm in a Victorian home. All the doors have been removed from their hinges. My bedroom door is crudely suspended by a thin steel chain at each corner *(vertically)*. The doorway is not blocked. I want privacy so I can have sex with myself. I'm in my mid-20's. My dick is thick, long and straight. I have an African American roommate who's in his 40's. He's been recently paroled after spending 14 years in federal prison *(commuted from an initial sentence of 42 years for undisclosed crimes).* He's overweight and out of shape, but has prioritized rebuilding his body. He admits being in prison *"basically destroyed"* him. THE DANCER's room is to the right. I choose not to masturbate. I don't want my younger sister to hear me.] //

⁂

Maj. = 2- THE DANCER: #0885
42: #0012
VICTORIAN: #0052
DESTROYED: #0295
CHAIN: #1282

⁂

#0883 - September 21, 2019 @ 07:41 (San Francisco, California)

[0883.1 / 2259] [I'm at an EDM show at a family compound. It feels like a hotel. The DJ emerges onstage, simply presses the play button, and walks away from the decks. No one seems to care that everything is pre-recorded. I think it sucks.

I wander in and out of different rooms encountering different sets of friends, in different states of awareness and being. At 8:00pm a friend gives me a capsule that I pop and swallow. This friend's frustrated by another guy who appears to have passed out on the bed. Two other guys enter the quiet room wearing over-ear headphones. Their music is so loud we can annoyingly hear the tinny buzzes and beeps that cloud their auditory realities. My friend wants to take a nap before the afterhours party, but can't because of the headphone noise. I have no idea what kind of drug I've taken, and start looking for a bathroom so I can force myself to vomit it up. I'm frustrated when I can't find a toilet. I'm too polite to vomit on the floor. I need to pee and can't find a urinal. I accept that I'll probably be super high when I finally meet up with THE CARPENTER, who I've agreed to meet for a midnight walk. I feel sad, accept my choice, and then notice my eyes in the mirror. My pupils are huge and black. Irises gone.

I exit the room and stand next to a huge brick wall, painted white and emblazoned with two giant lightning bolts; one purple, the other magenta. The base layer of white changes to taupe, then back into white. Initially the slow transition quickens to a flicker, resulting in a tan tone appearing constantly on display in the background.

"This is our one night on earth, so we may as well enjoy it, AS MUCH AS WE CAN," the wall communicates to me through its rhythmic flashes.

I look in a mirror on the wall and see the edges of my face become lighter and lighter until they diffuse and disappear. I look down and my entire body fades away. I've left the gorgeous cage of a body and become, ***"a fuller expression of spirit that sees itself in all things."***] //

⁂

Maj. = 1- THE CARPENTER: #0891
SWALLOW: #0014, #0223, #0381
HEADPHONES: #0060, #0135, #0309
(Zzz...Zzz...Zzz...)
EARTH: #0025, #0393

SPIRIT: #1253, #1278, #1279, #1343

⁂

#0884 - September 22, 2019 @ 02:48 (San Francisco, California)

[0884.1 / 2260] [I'm alone in a large house. I take special care to lock and check all the doors, shutter the blinds, and make multiple rounds before heading to the bedroom. I'm about to go to sleep. I pet my dog as I lock the bedroom door and lay down. I hear some skittering and rustling on the other side of the door and begin to wonder if someone else is inside the house. My mind starts to generate thousands of possible scenarios and outcomes. My parents are gone. I'm afraid. I realize I'm a child, perhaps 11 years old. Maybe someone watched my parents leave. Maybe they have bad intentions? I hide by turning invisible in my bed.

I leave my body and float through the door to investigate the origin of ***"the sound."***] //

⁂

DOG: #0089, #0101, #0125, #0169, #0188, #0215, #0222
AFRAID: #0013, #0219, #0299, #0371
INVISIBLE: #0380, #0381, #0397
SOUND: #1210, #1213, #1232, #1240, #1248

⁂

#0885 - September 22, 2019 @ 05:25 (San Francisco, California)

[0885.1 / 2261] [Fast paced, intermittent flashbacks to a party the night before. People drink and smoke intentionally to disrupt their grounding. Reality on earth is hard, and it's easier to avoid. The group has some subtext and inferred humor towards a woman who was *"definitely up for failing at a bigger challenge."* A friend has an idea for an epic sendoff photo using a line of buses as a backdrop.

"Hey Victoria! You probably have about five minutes before that opportunity comes through."

A group of friends gathers in a parking lot and takes turns trying on a biomechanical-advanced-prosthetic left leg.

"Hey man...ya got any more of those psychedelic sausages?" One guy asks another.

The other guy pitches his friend a frankfurter and then walks away. I watch this play out omnisciently from the back.

Before the group departs, we hold a community gift giving ceremony. We all share "**radical agape love**" for a four-year-old girl who stands before us with her arms spread wide. Her glittery Technicolor rainbow cape casts kaleidoscopic radiant "Joy Light" on all of us to support our forthcoming journey. Light reflected from the cape illuminates the lot with sacred golden white light. THE DANCER gives the girl a framed picture. The photograph *(of me in my 30's)* features me sitting with a small porcelain cottage in my lap. My address is handwritten on a scrap of paper and crudely affixed to the frame's glass by a single piece of scotch tape. This aims to help the little girl understand that my home/residence changes regularly *(and though right now I might live far away)*, wherever I am, ***"I'm home."***

The group stands shoulder-to-shoulder and performs a line sweep of the property, just prior to departing.

A caravan of mini-buses prepares to depart from a hotel parking lot. I ride in the back of a van driven "herky jerkily" by a nerdy fellow who equally rides the gas and brakes. *Foot on brake. Foot on gas. Foot on brake. Foot on gas.* I'm tossed about like a rag doll, since the bus lacks seatbelts. I request that if he intends to drive the entire way, that he keeps the speed down.

Flashbacks flow in like a flipping image disc, in a karmic viewfinder, increasing in speed and intensity until I wake up.] //

⁂

Maj. = 2- THE DANCER: #0896

RAINBOW: #0045, #0105, #0106, #0215, #0243, #0329, #0389

KALEIDOSCOPIC: #0018

GAS: #0090, #0094, #0170, #0173

REQUEST: #1327, #1330, #1331, #1334

⁂

#0886 - September 24, 2019 @ 00:59 (San Francisco, California)

[0886.1 / 2262] [I believe I've awakened at 11:59pm. I blink my eyes and I notice it's 10:58pm. I'm confused for a moment by time moving backwards. *"Now you know what happens when you stop meditating,"* a calm voice whispers. A lot moves by quickly. I'm responsible for leading a group of curious spirits through a process to help them understand the impact on their spiritual growth when practices are halted. Information compiles as a series of images that illustrate, ***"Bifurcation."***]

[0886.2 / 2263] [Someone leaps from an ascending airplane and plunges toward the ground.]

[0886.3 / 2264] [Someone reading a newspaper casually steps out of a bullet train moving at full speed between Tokyo and Kyoto.]

[0886.4 / 2265] [A group of children playing hockey on a frozen pond fall through the ice when the sun explodes and scorches the surface of the earth.] //

⁂

SUN: #0022, #0045, #0170, #271, #0360, #0384

TOKYO: #0238

FROZEN: #0319

SURFACE: #1259, #1306, #1309, #1337

ICE: #1335

⁂

#0887 - September 24, 2019 @ 05:55 (San Francisco, California)

[0887.1 / 2266] [I receive a hymn in my heart. I follow the heart-hymn to a church, led by a golden rope protruding from my chest. The same hymn is sung repeatedly by the gathering congregation. I'm in the back pew of a large gothic cathedral. The congregation sits in square rows extending out like a Greek cross around a pulpit at the center, crudely composed of a series of 6' plastic collapsible tables. A group of children under the age of five gathers before the altar dressed in bumble bee costumes. The children make playful buzzing sounds and jump around, bringing lightness and ease to the crowded, growing, and expectant congregation.

It appears to be twilight through the stained glass. More people gather. A shared intention magnifies an already high frequency that radiates and amplifies as it beckons others to come take part in, ***"Church 2.0."***

Those who distribute communion hand out small fist sized orange and white parking cones as a vessel to receive the sacrament. I have a small orange baster *(infant nostril blaster)* in my left hand that I show to the man distributing cones to my quadrant. I may not be allowed to use it because it *"was not specifically included in the church's pre-counted inventory."*

Men come around with a large pressurized tank and offer respiratory infusions of aerosol ketamine, in the cones, for people to inhale. I take a breath, experience a *"headful of awareness"* and continue to let the song in my heart rise up and out of my throat, adding to the vocal vibration that has set the cathedral alight with spirit.

At the end of the service, we pile into limousines to share community and process our ecstatic transmissions. THE TRICK *(flirty, inquisitive, and self-humored)*, THE FLIRT and THE BANKER and I share a car. We giggle and flirt as we discuss our ***"insights from the realm of ideal forms."***

I pull a string along the top of the vehicle interior to request a stop. I exit the car and walk across a vast golf course fairway-like lawn in search of my car. I walk to the far end of the lot, yet fail to locate my vehicle.]

[0887.2 / 2267] [I blink my eyes, feel a breeze on my face, and discover myself on a fast-moving scissor lift, blazing along a highway set inside a movie studio production lot. I turn to watch where we've come from. A few other people riff on the lift with me, though I pay them little attention. We pass a couple of young men on bikes. I wink at one of them, who responds by flicking his lit cigarette butt at me. I respond by flinging a handful of salsa that makes a wet *"splat"* as it hits him in the face and spatters on his friend.

I blink again, and find myself in a long white, fluorescent lit hallway, backstage at a concert. I stand across from the salsa faced guy; his back against a wall. My right hand is flat against the wall by his left ear. I ask him if he wants to make out. He chuckles, spits his gum in my face, and looks at his friend as he calls me, ***"revolting."***

My friend asks if they're "rent boys." They both lightly giggle with downcast gazes and hands in pockets. Their shoulders shrug which suggests an affirmative.

"Dude, we'll blow you if you have coke," one says directly.

They begin to peacock by demonstrating basic self-defense moves. They try to convince us they're *"black belts in some form of martial art."* I see through the ruse.

"Man, you're not even real. I come from the school of one cut, one kill."

He asks his friend to wait in a stairwell. The friend exits. As the steel door slams, I wake up in another dream.]

[0887.3 / 2268] [A group discusses financial notes on a conference call for a nonprofit board of directors. They decide they need to engage contacts within "Bank of America" to acquire funding. They're flummoxed when they hear a voice of one of those contacts speak on the open conference line. A man hurried scribbles, "THE INSIDER" in pen on a white sheet of paper in all caps.

"Don't worry. I work there," I mouth to the group.

THE INSIDER *(ebullient, secretive, and informative)* speaks straight and sets the tone of the impromptu meeting. The leader mutes the line, and the group erupts in frenzied discussion.

"Everyone calm down, it's ok. I know him. I'll give him a call later. We'll have dinner at his lake house sometime soon to discuss what you need."]

[0887.4 / 2269] [THE WEAVER has no interest in participating in, ***"Church 2.0."***] //

⁂

Maj. = 0- THE WEAVER: #0898
HYMN: #0147
REVOLTING: #0045
HEART: #0012, #0045, #0046, #1213, #1240, #1343
THE FLIRT: #0911

⁂

#0888 - September 24, 2019 @ 07:22 (San Francisco, California)

[0888.1 / 2270] [A group of people argue. Appears they're all sex workers with differing perspectives on how to be fairly represented in local politics.]

[0888.2 / 2271] [I'm in a familiar woodland camping environment with modern cabins and a network of concrete sidewalks. I turn over and empty out bags and crates of costumes on to the ground in search of four specific pieces of clothing. The four are components of a pale blue and white fur ensemble I intend to give to its proper recipient. When I find him, I say,

"Next year, when you find someone who's in a rough predicament, remember to take this costume to them. Request they undress in front of you as they tell you their story. Grieve with them. Make a ceremony out of redressing them in this costume. Start from the ground and work up. When you place the blue/white furry hat on their head, pause and say: 'Darling, you are gorgeous. Now tell me that story again.'"]

[0888.3 / 2272] [THE CONNECTOR and THE MIDWESTERN GENT *(seeking, apt, and social)* both work to organize swag on a collapsible 6' plastic table. I originally wanted to give the furry costume to THE MIDWESTERN GENT, but the costume took its own path. When I look down at my hands, I see the costume has replicated itself. I give the duplicate to THE CONNECTOR, with the same instructions.]

[0888.4 / 2273] [THE CONNECTOR and I stare at a poster for an upcoming LADY GAGA tour. We decide to split the cost of a ticket. We'll each enjoy one half of the concert when the tour eventually stops through town.] //

⁂

Maj. = 4- THE CONNECTOR: #0936
LADY GAGA: #1020
EMPTY: #0336, #0386, #0395
WOODLAND: #0016, #0023, #0024, #0164, #0169, #0173, #0270

⁂

#0889 - September 24, 2019 @ 08:19 (San Francisco, California)

[0889.1 / 2274] [I work with a crew to breakdown conference infrastructure in the atrium of a large hotel. A large fountain spurts water high up towards a brightly illuminated glass ceiling. The sound of water droplets makes soothing white noise that enables us to work productively and clearly. We're complimented by hotel staff as they pass us in process. THE MEEK and I are assigned to the same team to break down. She gives me a bag of "sour cream and chives" microwave popcorn that's been heated on a hot plate. One corner of the package is charred black. We're in an administrative workspace surrounded by computers, cables, boxes of shirts and promotional items.

I'm invited to the manager's office and take a seat across from him at his desk. We're encouraged to hold our event with the venue next year and offered a discount to lock in the deal, right now. *"We've never had a departing group leave the property so clean and tidy. You've made our job a lot easier,"* the manager says to me as he pushes a contract towards me from across the desk.

We take a break and sit at a table of young men wearing red polo shirts and khaki pants. One young man shares his challenges connecting to *"normal"* people after he's experienced depth and intimacy in his interactions with others while *"building things at church."*

"My connections with old friends just seem off. They don't seem to fit anymore," he continues.

THE MEEK requests to talk to me privately, and shares she had a recent interaction with a personal injury attorney that left her feeling chastised and belittled. He intended to demean her in public and he succeeded.

She whispers and whimpers in my ear as the team continues working around us, breaking down boxes and dismantling stages.]

[0889.2 / 2275] [THE MEEK and I pause our conversation and help a different group of guys troubleshoot how to best pack up a large white quad cabin truck. We fully pack a uniquely large space between the engine and the windshield with crates and boxes. We're able to get the rest of our items neatly tucked into the bed and hitch up the trailer with minimal confusion. The teamwork is fluid and vitalizing.]

[0889.3 / 2776] [THE MEEK revisits the scene where she was belittled with me 1:1 and in greater detail. She cries and after some time I say, ***"Letting people just be where they are is perhaps the hardest part of being a leader and a teacher."***

She continues to process and I begin to cry saying,

"Love people anyway. I know sometimes it's really hard...but do it anyway."

Tears stream down my face. We cry together and let the pain wake us up as it passes through. We openly grieve. We let go of things we have no control over. We feel truly human, having been beaten and bruised on various levels of our being. Nearby we overhear a man verbally abuse his wife.] //

⁂

ILLUMINATED: #0104, #0107, #0114, #0125, #0359
LOVE: #0021, #0038, #0040
PAIN: #0011, #0012, #0019
TIDY: #0231

THE MEEK: #0964

⁂

#0890 - September 25, 2019 @ 03:26 (San Francisco, California)

[0890.1 / 2277] [I'm at a Hertz Rental Car reservation desk on the 8th floor of a Guggenheim Museum-like spiral building. I'm walked by a group of people in suits down to the bottom floor to retrieve my car. My left knee dislocates. I pop it back into place. It overcorrects and dislocates in the other direction. The suits are taken aback by this *"gross inconvenience"* and huddle up away from me, to discuss ways to stabilize my injury. They surprise me with an aggressively literal *"hands on"* approach with my body, subjecting me to numerous chiropractic adjustments performed with minimal skill. After multiple unsuccessful attempts, suggest that I ***"fix it myself."***]

[0890.2 / 2278] [Meanwhile, I'm talking to God, and asking my guides for information. I'm practicing trust, yet feel an sense of increasing worry creep into my space. I put my knee cap back in place, then am shown a challenging vision of myself on an operating table undergoing a major surgical intervention to sever and resew the soft tissues of my knee joint. It's real, gruesome, and visceral.]

[0890.3 / 2279] [I look up and discover myself in a classroom. I try to give myself a healing, but it doesn't seem to have much impact. A guy sits next to me and tells me a story about how he was driving *"this passenger who just nagged, nagged, nagged."* I'm a bit surprised when I realize he's referring to me. A shock of pain floods my kneecap and wakes me up.] //

⁂

GUGGENHEIM: #0033
SHOCK: #0011, #0188
GOD: #0063, #0172
GUIDES: #0033, #0141, #0200
SKILL: #1250
SOFT: #1279, #1283, #1290, #1291

⁂

#0891 - September 25, 2019 @ 05:10 (San Francisco, California)

[0891.1 / 2280] [I'm in a conference room in a new office tower in Tokyo, Japan. It's dimly lit. The walls are beige. THE EXECUTIVE DIRECTOR *(trusting, helpful, and emotive)* sits next to me for a meeting and quickly leaves to, *"go pick up Tammy."*]

[0891.2 / 2281] [I look at my phone and note I have a completely blank social media profile, rendering me eligible to be *"a senior executive accountable for the strategic growth and direction of one of a company's major lines of businesses."*]

. . .

[0891.3 / 2282] [THE CARPENTER and I sit around a fire casually chatting. I select a guitar from a long row of instruments on display and begin chicken picking some licks. THE CARPENTER looks at me and says, *"I love it when you just pick it up and play."*]

[0891.4 / 2283] [I'm back in the Tokyo high-rise. During a meeting break I take an elevator down two floors. As the doors open, I see a motivated young manager behind the counter of an American deli. Giant plate glass windows behind him offer marvelous skyline views of a whizzing futuristic city. He's short, curt, and communicates clearly with his team. I buy a sandwich. He invites me to stay and talk about how he can cultivate "**more flow**" for his team. He's insistent I teach him, *"how to be calm."*]

[0891.5 / 2284] [I visit with an American expat woman, whose family originally emigrated from Japan. She gives me a ride around Tokyo in her VW Microbus. I stand in the back as she stands and drives in the front. She and I observe a cartoon man with charcoal black skin wearing a suit. He tap dances down a fence, best described as, *"oversized Legos with two thick cylindrical prongs on top of each brick."* The fence color is stark in contrast to a tangerine orange sky dolloped by white Cool Whip clouds.

The soles of the man's shoes can latch on to the top prongs of the fence to create stability as he dances. His feet are the receptive *"female"* plugs. He also cartwheels from time-to-time, as though choreographed.

My female friend *(still driving the VW bus)* requests I don't use the internet, nor my phone, because *"the charges for roaming are excessive."* Micro networks like the one in her van absorb the expense of foreign passengers.

"Been withholding conversation from anyone lately?" She asks

I think for a long time and after a subtle gut hit, I'm puzzled and burp out, ***"THE FIDUCIARY?"***

"Have you any need to call him from Japan?" she further presses.

"That was just an idea so I wouldn't withhold from you. I can't think of any one I have problems with. I honestly don't know."

I'm dropped off at THE ROBOT's temporary condo. I arrive before her and decide to clean the kitchen. I mop up a small pool of orange liquid from the tile and grout countertop. THE ROBOT enters happy from a successful day.

"HAH HAH HAH I did a great job. I just nailed that one," she declares after viewing an affirmative text message from the studio.

"What did you do today?"

"I directed a music video. You know...the one I've been talking about for a while."

"What artist? Can you say?"

"MEGA PHAT BOOTY TEMPLE. That's not a made-up name, that's what they're actually called."

She walks away to prepare for our day together in Akihabara.] //

⁂

Maj. = 1- THE CARPENTER: #0903, 9- THE FIDUCIARY: #0911

Min. = ♥- THE ROBOT: #0916

RECEPTIVE: #0054, #0135, #0293

KITCHEN: #0001, #0014, #0020

ORANGE: #1266, #1299, #1342
THE EXECUTIVE DIRECTOR: #1109
⁂

#0892 - September 26, 2019 @ 07:01 (San Francisco, California)

[0892.1 / 2285] [I'm out in a vast desert. Pastel blues, pinks, and whites transform the sky. Park benches are placed in orderly rows as far as I can see. I sit down next to THE WALKER *(inviting, unfiltered, and familiar)*. As we begin to talk, I notice a large in-bound dust storm barreling at us from the corner of my left eye. The wind is light, so the severity of the coming white out seems oddly under represented. The dust extends high to the clouds above. We turn our backs to the storm and continue talking.

Meanwhile, I notice I've brought a backpack and nothing else. I have no shelter. Off in the distance we can see teams of people feverishly dismantling roller coasters built for a short-term event. It's so dusty, it's as though the entire scene dissolves before my eyes into an amber grey cloud.]

[0892.2 / 2286] [THE HOBBIT *(pained, uprooted, and disoriented)* invites me to his tent. We embrace at his invitation. I give him an appreciative kiss on the cheek.

"I was just having a conversation with my partner about his new boyfriend, and how sweet it is that they're falling in love," he shares as we snuggle and fall asleep.] //

⁂
VAST: #0155
TENT: #0032, #0126
KISS: #0021, #0055, #0073, #0075
INVITATION: #0045, #0046, #0048, #0263
LOVE: #1305
⁂

#0893 - September 27, 2019 @ 05:34 (San Francisco, California)

[0893.1 / 2287] [**"You want a job? Heal healers of healers!"** I respond to an ad in the paper. I go to an office and take a number in the waiting room. When I realize the game and invitation **[they're not going to serve me, I'm to serve them]** I spring into action taking cases, entering data, and quickly moving around the office in a five-pointed star shaped pattern.

Each time I blink my eyes, the ordinarily dark space is filled with a flash from another reality:

...I pick up trash off the streets.

...I work at a polling location.

...I drive a bus on a mountain road.

...I give a child an inoculation.

...I pick up dog shit.

So many occur, so quickly, they blur into kaleidoscopic diamond light. I'm happy to be in all these places, yet in a pause begin needing a healing myself. I quickly realize, ***"acts of service bless me with healings, but I have to allow them to flow through."*** I remember *(and forget)* this while repeatedly entering formal business environments, nature scenes, spirit/alien realms, the grocery store...]

[0893.2 / 2288] [I'm gently reminded to seek the miraculous in the subtle and mundane. ***"Breathing is what heals."***] //

⁂

DIAMOND: #0013, #0170, #0271, #0390
SERVICE: #0283, #0298, #0321, #0368
BREATHING: #0013, #0134, #0205, #0336
HEALING: #1216, #1247, #1263, #1280
REALITY: #1207, #1225, #1278, #1283
ALIEN: #1264

⁂

#0894 - September 28, 2019 @ 01:22 (San Francisco, California)

[0894.1 / 2289] [***"A lot is going on here."*** Pictures flicker when I close my eyes, to such an extent it becomes frustrating and wakes me up into another dream space.]

[0894.2 / 2290] [I feel concerned THE SLUT *(drunk, overwhelmed, and triggered)* has been possessed. He's at risk of *"soul loss,"* and may never be recovered.]

[0894.3 / 2291] [I close my eyes as flashing pictures quicken until they go blurry, bright, and buzz with a marvelously low droning tone.] //

[0894.4 / 2292] [The charcoal black man from **[0891.5 / 2284]** jumps ahead of me in line. I'm not concerned. The odd hair knot tied on top of his head draws my interest. ***"How long did it take to grow that?"*** He simply gestures with a wink as he says, *"forever and an instant."* I take it as an acknowledgement for letting my hair grow out.]

⁂

CHARCOAL: #0323, #0394
KNOT: #0266
POSSESSED: #0066, #0158
OUT: #1287, #1290
THE SLUT: #0895

⁂

#0895 - September 28, 2019 @ 05:25 (San Francisco, California)

[0895.1 / 2293] [THE CONFIDANT drives a rental car. I'm the passenger. I need to get to the airport to catch a flight. We take a non-direct route that sends us flying off a bridge. We crash down on an idling car from above. We continue to drive up an idyllic urban street with tightly sequenced, tall, and colorful houses. We pull into his driveway. The neighborhood seems chaotic and confrontational.

We're met at the doorway by a transgender non-binary person who sensually leans at THE CONFIDANT, intending to seduce him. The person believes THE CONFIDANT is an advocate and becomes offended when THE CONFIDANT turns down an offer for sex.

"I respect you. I don't want to have sex," THE CONFIDANT says plainly.

We pass the threshold and enter the house. The interior is a complex serpentine labyrinth of stairwells and irrational, nonconforming, multi-dimensional passageways. The stairway we choose determines the lifetime we recall. We're greeted by familiar faces and guides along the way who offer us refreshment *(small bottles of water, odd blue liquids in vials)* as we proceed. We pick another stairway, and at the top see a large big box store with signs denoting a, *"going out of business"* sale. People scurry around packing up fixtures and shelving. A crew of young men works in groups of four to speedily wrap items in clear plastic and hoist them on to moving trucks for immediate shipment.

I offer the men jobs at my new company, then learn they work for two brothers who have developed a highly profitable and scalable transportation enterprise. I stop the men just before they shrink wrap my bureau full of costume clothing. THE SLUT *(playful, interested, and doting)* leans against the bureau. He opens the top drawer and giggles. We have an impromptu fashion show and laugh while playing dress up.]

[0895.2 / 2294] [I'm in a bed that sleeps more than 20+ wide. The bed is full of interesting, flirtatious, and sexy beings. We all wear soft pajama onesies. I extend my arm to snap a couple "group-ie" photos. A row of heads in a line bobs and weaves like a spiral/spinal columnar wave as we attempt to create a memento of our time together. Lots of small talk and funny commentary ensue.]

[0895.3 / 2295] [A group of young children are placed in charge of caring for their larger infant siblings. A four-year-old boy seems to have had his legs crushed under the weight of his baby brother and sister. *"HEWP ME PWEEZE!"* the boy laments to his on looking parents, *"I can't hold them!"* The parents are aware, but their children remain where they are.]

[0895.4 / 2296] [I'm back in the car with THE CONFIDANT, who delivers me to the airport. I board my plane and realize I've been on this same flight in numerous other dreams. The nose of the plane is made of video screens that make it seem like a giant observation window made of hexagonal panels. I take my seat. The flight is full. It doesn't surprise anyone when we see the plane take a nosedive, plummet towards the ground, and crash. The impact wakes me up.] //

⁂

Maj. = 16- THE CONFIDANT: #0900
RENTAL: #0170, #0309, #0395
HEXAGONAL: #0018, #0209, #0396
SPIRAL: #0044, #0056, #0083
IMPACT: #1301
THE SLUT: #0937

⁂

#0896 - September 29, 2019 @ 05:34 (San Francisco, California)

[0896.1 / 2297] [I attend a workshop led by THE DEVOTEE. The gathering is social in tone, allows me to be in service, and to offer healing. The intention held by the group is:

"hold space for regenerative therapeutic catharsis." I start by giving THE DANCER a healing as part of a group demonstration. We observe three distinct tones of white light flow to *(and through)* her space. She receives a deep healing and an energetic, *"top off."* THE DEVOTEE talks through the technique and things to look for as I move from person-to-person. Her coaching and feedback are gentle, loving and supportive.

"Intend and trust the light will go where it needs to flow. Encourage it. Offer it. Do not force it. They have to choose to let it run freely to them."

I remember *(again)* that I am profoundly healed when I offer service *"neutrally, purely, and disinterested."* I thank THE DEVOTEE for showing me how to soften. ***"I love my teacher."***] //

⁂

Maj. = 2- THE DANCER: #0898
Min. = ♠- THE DEVOTEE: #1013
WHITE LIGHT: #0022, #0032, #0042
GENTLE: #0013, #0046, #0134
OBSERVE: #1313, #1314, #1341

⁂

#0897 - **September 30, 2019 @ 05:13 (San Francisco, California)**

[0897.1 / 2298] [I'm at the tail end of a rowdy house party. I climb a simple dowel ladder to a loft and push aside a curtain to reveal a group of people having sex. I descend the ladder and enter a filthy kitchen. Used knives are scattered across the countertop. THE SKEPTIC *(solitary, calm, and observant)* joins me. We take it upon ourselves to tidy the area as we chat. We're both soothed by the act of cleaning.

I fill the dishwasher, taking note of a rotting pile of black beans covered by flies in the bottom of the appliance. THE SKEPTIC and I both like being of service, while the group is off partying and creating other experiences. We agree, *"It's satisfying to be the ones who clean up the mess."*

I go back up the ladder hoping to find a bald man I saw earlier, whom I found attractive. He's the first being I see when my eyes crest the loft. He has an erection and invites me to suck it. I do and am confused when I can feel my teeth grinding together, though my mouth is open wide. My teeth screech down what feels like a blackboard. The sensation confuses me so I stop. When I look up the man has disappeared.]

[0897.2 / 2299] [I sit at a table and introduce myself to a man named "Matthew." We share experiences of meeting people who've taken our breath away. *"The Argentinian one really took you out, huh?"* "Matthew" knows what I'm thinking before I even decide what story I want to tell.]

[0897.3 / 2300] [I stand next to an Asian woman who sends out multiple detailed text messages. Her glasses fall off her face. She doesn't stop to pick them up.

"Do you need these?" I say as I grab and offer them to her.

"No, I have another pair," she says, taking some from a pocket and placing them on her face. This repeats several times.]

. . .

[0897.4 / 2301] [A radio on a kitchen shelf is tuned in to a talk show where DJs discuss KATY PERRY's younger sister "Ashleigh." I pop out of my body and float next to "Ashleigh's" bodyguard, who allows me to follow him, as he follows her. We follow a woman in a sleek white evening gown down a stairway leading to a well-lit subway station. She looks gorgeous and moves with elegance.]

[0897.5 / 2302] [I'm on a patio at a party at night. I encounter a tall blonde woman who wears red lipstick and a tightly pulled ponytail. She's about to smoke a cigarette. She peers around the room, eventually making eyes with me. She wants to be cordial, but she lets a fake smile flatten and says, *"I just don't want to be here."* She shifts her gaze away from me in search of the nearest exit.]

[0897.6 / 2303] [I'm at another party where a guy tells me I have beautiful eyes. I offer him a compliment, then we toast by tapping our red solo cups together. We say basically nothing and smile at each other while appreciating the moment.

Nearby a woman sitting on a stool works door security for an event. She occupies her time by texting herself every thought she has. She's exacting and precise with her language. Her intention is to be *"in radical candor with herself."* Through the exit I see a lobby in the condo building that has a series of escalators that switch on, only after a large round button with a triangle in the center is pressed. The button is solid black. Brilliant white light shines through the button's *"negative"* white space. This energy conservation mechanism ensures optimal amounts of power are used only when people consciously choose to descend the stairs. I push the button and ride to the bottom.

I enter a movie theater, divided in half down the middle, towards the screen. The half further away has a deeper descent and higher backed chairs. Its ramp and stairways plummet deep and quick. *"That entire half of the theater is reserved for the 'TRANSFORCE' because they're willing to go deeper,"* a group of ticket takers tells me.] //

⁂

ERECTION: #0021, #0190, #0322
LIPSTICK: #0092
PATIO: #0045, #0071, #0115
MOVIE THEATER: #0016, #0359
THE SKEPTIC: #1045

⁂

#0898 - October 1, 2019 @ 07:01 (San Francisco, California)
*****I want to remember, yet most of it slips away instantly.* *

[0898.1 / 2304] [College alumni barbecue. Piles of grilled meat are placed on a series of eight rectangular tables set up in a square *(two tables per side)*. PAUL REUBENS (Pee Wee Herman) has a beard. He approaches me and we begin chatting familiarly as old friends, but I don't recall going to school with him.]

. . .

[0898.2 / 2305] [I'm on a leafy woodland trail at night. I've misplaced my bike and retrace my steps. I find my phone where I thought I'd left my bike. I wasn't aware I'd misplaced it.]

[0898.3 / 2306] [THE DANCER and I decide to rent a car for a quick trip and get an amazing deal on a weeklong rental, which makes us contemplate a longer sojourn.]

[0898.4 / 2307] [THE WEAVER, THE CHILD and I go to a grocery store. THE CHILD uses her phone to make a video. We walk towards a fruit display near the checkout lanes and see dozens of rats scurry out from the boxes and into the store aisles.]

[0898.5 / 2308] [I go to the back of a modern home. I enter the bathroom and am startled away into another dream by an unseen presence. Though I can't see the presence it feels cold, wet, and gurgles.] //

⁂

Maj. = 0- THE WEAVER: #0899, 2- THE DANCER: #0899, 3- THE CHILD: #0899
COLD: #0007, #0012, #0017
WET: #0012, #0014, #0022
QUICK: #0010, #0021, #0025
VIDEO: #1236, #1274
PRESENCE: #1245, #1247
PEE WEE HERMAN: #1243

⁂

#0899 - October 2, 2019 @ 04:00 (San Francisco, California)

[0899.1 / 2309] [I'm in line at a coffee shop with THE WEAVER, THE DANCER and THE CHILD. I contemplate why I haven't visited *"such a nice place, that's so close by,"* before now to do my writing. It's been a great change of scenery from where I spend most of my time. THE HEADBANGER *(musical, team oriented, and sharp)* is ahead of us. He waves and we make small talk by shouting down the line to one another. We start talking about a work contest, but quickly change subjects and begin discussing our favorite albums and live bands.]

[0899.2 / 2310] [I can hear the wind whistle in the crops. The scene is cool and damp. I'm a female GI in the middle of a large field overgrown with tall green corn. A pyramid-like structure near the center of the field, houses a giant cannon. A *"BOOM"* indicates it's been set off.

As I walk to the other side to see what happened I note a large pile of gunpowder, two human arms, and two human legs scattered at equal points from the center of a pile. A cannonball has been reduced to dust and the remnants of the man it hit indicate the force was tremendous.

"Both bodies destroyed each other."

I climb up the stairs of the pyramid and walk into an atrium where I receive an update from my commanding officer, a man who resembles TOM HANKS.] //

⁂

Maj. = 0- THE WEAVER: #0903, 2- THE DANCER: #0900, 3- THE CHILD: #0903
SCENERY: #0201
PYRAMID: #0007, #0229
CORN: #0003, #0189, #0284, #0323

⁂

#0900 - October 4, 2019 @ 02:29 (Carmel by the Sea, California)

[0900.1 / 2311] [I'm at a table in a hotel restaurant *(a curved high back red booth)*. A young eager female server takes pride in presenting me with two plates. One has a burned chicken breast that she breaks into four pieces with her hands. The other has an entire pound of ground beef formed into a rectangular brick, quartered, and seared. It's basically raw.

"I don't want to eat that. I've been given someone else's order." *pause*

"I appreciate your effort, but please tell the chef that this isn't any good."

She departs to deliver the message to the kitchen.

I leave the table, turn a corner, and encounter a line of people holding dinner plates with complaints they wait to issue to THE LANDLORD *(enterprising, motivated, and overly complimentary)* face-to-face. I pass a variety of familiar faces, pausing briefly to talk with THE GENIUS before I smell something hot. I turn down a stairwell and find a wood burning stove that's overfilled and blazing out of control. Red-yellow flames lick around a corner and up a wall towards me, followed by a gust of heat so intense that as I raise my arm to protect my face my forearm is instantly scorched to the bone. I receive an insight through the vaporizing consciousness of my burning skin cells: ***"Get everyone out in 2-5 minutes maximum, or they'll die."***

I quickly turn and urge people in line to exit quickly and calmly. THE CONFIDANT makes a similar effort on an upper level. I attempt to find THE DANCER but don't succeed. I also know that those *"wearing maroon robes are a priority."* THE GENIUS seems delighted the place is going up in flames, and considers its imminent demise, *"a really good thing."* I'm fine with it too. I just seem to know the building is moments nearer exploding and want to ensure anyone who wants out, can get out. THE GENIUS remains in line. He says, *"I have a long standing and unanswered grievance with THE LANDLORD that's about to fully resolve."*] //

⁂

Maj. = 2- THE DANCER: #0908, 16- THE CONFIDANT: #0968
BEEF: #0065, #0083
UPPER: #1295, #1298, #1301, #1341
THE GENIUS: #1201

⁂

#0901 - October 4, 2019 @ 04:13 (Carmel by the Sea, California)

[0901.1 / 2312] [I walk through a graffiti covered ghetto and meet THE LATIN FIREBALL *(vivacious, loud, and somatic)*. He's not wearing pants. Our conversation is casual and easy. I watch him regress in age and behavior in mere moments until he becomes a young grade school aged boy. We get on a school bus and go to the back seat. He rolls a tight firm tube from a sheet of white printer paper and uses it to shoot two sewing needle-like blow darts at the kids up in the front. One hollers and winces with pain. THE LATIN FIREBALL gets startled and jumps out the back of the bus. He doesn't want to get in trouble. It's the same bus from **[0130.3 / 0303]**.]

[0901.2 / 2313] [THE BENEFITS ADMINISTRATOR *(anxious, sweet, and productive)* meets me *(a tad frantic)* on a busy city sidewalk.

"Will you please walk with me to 21st and FREEDOM? I need to file a restraining order on a coworker who harasses me."

"Why don't you take six months off? You can afford it," I suggest as we walk together across the lobby of a firm called "READYNOW."

"Take 6 months off, then you and I can start our own situation," I continue.

"Without any of this nonsense!" she says pointing to energies in her body that disruptively move under her skin like small waves, bubbles, and ripples. We descend a staircase to a subway station and take a train to a totally different downtown area.] //

⁂

NEEDLE: #0092
NONSENSE: #0125, #0143, #0240, #0333
FRONT: #0365, #0390, #0394
WAVES: #1205, #1210, #1241
THE BENEFITS ADMINISTRATOR: #1383

⁂

#0902 - October 4, 2019 @ 06:11 (Carmel by the Sea, California)

[0902.1 / 2314] [I ugly cry. I don't know why. I'm losing something. I realize that's what's happening. A long and deep catharsis guts me and hollows me out.]

[0902.2 / 2315] [I flirt with a porn star. We negotiate a scene and begin having sex in his bedroom. A group of uninterested people socialize nearby. I call an abrupt end to the action and rush out to take a business call. While on the call I order an Uber, which instantly pulls to the curb. I enter the vehicle. I realize a few miles down the road I've left my laptop at "Sebastian's" condo. Instead of backtracking I borrow THE NURSE's computer.

I exit the car, cross a plaza, then get on an elevator while on the phone and using the laptop. THE REVOLUTIONARY walks on to the elevator stall with two young African American girls she's adopted. Each time I blink the girls rapidly advance in age and size. The elevator continues downward. The girls quickly become teenagers, then college aged women. I'm startled by how quickly they grow up, then recall, ***"I still need to retrieve my misplaced laptop."***

The elevator grinds to a halt. A mass of people in costumes flood in, en route to a company Halloween party. Once we've cycled to the bottom, then back up to the ground floor, we all exit the elevator together. The costumes disappear and their priorities instantly change. The group is now focused on packing a truck full of supplies bound for, **"PAITITI."** A pile of donated typewriters is sorted, stacked, and inventoried. They'll support a local technology literacy program for a rural community, in Peru.

I receive a request to provide guidance and support for, *"3 or 4 other major forthcoming initiatives."* I inspect large piles of folded t-shirts wrapped in plastic. I pick up dropped reams of paper that have fallen from a box off a nearby palette to the ground. I'm a bit perplexed as to where I'd be best to start, given the volume of work to be done. I decide to wait until I receive a prioritized list for what needs to move. In the midst of the swirl, I pause and consider doing additional shadow work with sacred plants. I don't know which ones, at what volume, or how frequently. None of this matters though because ***"my intention of being of service will grant me clarity and discernment in my decision making."***] //

⁂

Maj. = 13- THE NURSE: #0918
Min. = ♠- THE REVOLUTIONARY: #1020
LAPTOP: #0149, #0199, #0326
CATHARSIS: #0007, #0239
SACRED PLANTS: #0042
PAUSE: #1253, #1264, #1274

⁂

#0903 - October 5, 2019 @ 05:18 (San Francisco, California)

[0903.1 / 2316] [I'm in line for a fitness class. The line is so long it would easily sell out the studio's schedule for the next two days.]

[0903.2 / 2317] [I walk down a staircase to THE WEAVER and THE CARPENTER's basement. When I get to the bottom, I find a young man who calls himself "Casey" snorting cocaine off a ping pong table.

"I'm not satisfied. You've gotta go," I say, sending a hitchhiker's thumb towards the door.

I leave assuming "Casey" will depart without incident. I'm deeply shocked to discover the entire house has been robbed. Fixtures, cabinetry, curtains, furniture...literally everything is gone. I'm devastated. With soggy eyes I turn to THE WEAVER and THE CARPENTER to break the news. They're silent and stunned for a moment, then begin to weep.

We're soon to learn five other houses on the same side of the street have been similarly burgled.

"I've bought two $700,000 houses in this neighborhood and have nothing to show for it." THE CARPENTER says.

I offer to give him all the money I have in cash and retirement funds. THE WEAVER's jewelry was taken. We begin to cry more, the more we realize the extent of the larceny. The scene is steeped in sadness. When we arrive at a moment of calm, we make an agreement *"to trust God and start over again."* We have absolutely **no idea** what we're going to do as we stare around the stark empty husk of a house that used to be our home.

THE CHILD rides nearby on a bumper car track with her friends. She's unaware of what's happened and laughs joyfully as she plays. Her joy inspires us to pick a direction and start going. I purchase two slices of pizza from a street side vendor. When I return to the house a woman berates me for being selfish.

"You've had enough. You shouldn't be eating that. You should give it away to someone who needs it."

"Ma'am, I have to feed myself first if I'm to feed and serve others," I respond slightly confused and annoyed. The interaction between us becomes more and more jagged until flabbergasted by me, she turns and exits the house with a fist in the air.

"I'm going to eat this delicious pizza you know..." I say trailing off as she crosses the threshold and disappears from view.

"You know I love you, right?" I say under my breath, perplexed that I feel ashamed for wanting to eat pizza after my family home has just been robbed.] //

⁂

Maj. = 0- THE WEAVER: #0905, 1- THE CARPENTER: #0904, 3- THE CHILD: #0904

BUMPER: #1246, #1285

I LOVE YOU: #0009, #0082, #0148, #0150

JEWELRY: #0071, #0388

⁂

#0904 - October 6, 2019 @ 04:37 (San Francisco, California)

[0904.1 / 2318] [I'm in a famous person's mansion who likes to be their own butler. I'm a guest, yet happy to do basic chores *(dusting furniture, washing dishes, etc.)*. I go upstairs. As I step onto the rooftop, I see large carnival rides for children surrounding me in all directions. THE CARPENTER grabs THE CHILD's hand and they run towards one of the rides, leaping over a wooden fence and darting across a large group of people who all ride motorized scooters and "OneWheels." I'm concerned they're going to get run over, but they don't.

I go back downstairs realizing I've asked people to meet me there at 4:00am. THE AUSSIE *(athletic, humorous, and savvy)* flirts with a handsome man seated at the base of the stairwell. I turn around and see him ending a romantic relationship with the same guy. It's emotional, yet quickly processed. I turn around to where I was originally looking and see the two of them flirting and starting a new relationship, as though they've just met.

In the main ballroom of the mansion THE VENTURE CAPITALIST *(accomplished, connected, and contemporary)* receives a lifetime achievement award. He turns to me to pass his plaque which interrupts my applause. He thinks I'm a member of the staff. Even though I'm a guest, I step into a service role to keep things smoothly rolling along.]

[0904.2 / 2319] [Children are kept late to practice cheerleading/drill team routines. They aren't permitted to leave until they've mastered their steps, well beyond standard pedagogical hours. The kids have to take public transportation home. Most are confused by this, and they're also afraid it's dangerous.]

[0904.3 / 2320] [Back in the kitchen of the mansion, I wear a royal blue terry cloth bathrobe. I look out onto an exterior stone terrace that looks like the back of a castle. From an open window I observe a stately and colorful croquet championship, played on a vast manicured emerald green lawn. I attempt to load dirty dishes in the dishwasher. When I open the dishwasher it's full and has another dishwasher within, roughly ⅓ the size. The nested appliance is also full of dirty dishes.

Lights start to flicker on. Someone's about to walk in. I take it as my cue to depart the mansion sooner than later, regardless if the chores are complete.] //

⁂

Maj. = 1- THE CARPENTER: #0905, 3- THE CHILD: #0939

ROYAL: #0112
PUBLIC TRANSPORTATION: #0394
DIRTY DISHES: #0144, #0231
FLICKER: #0009, #0149
GREEN: #1271, #1278, #1295, #1299
⁂

⁂ 11.5 - THE BOOK OF PEGASUS: 0905-0924 ⁂

#0905 - October 7, 2019 @ 03:52 (San Francisco, California)

[0905.1 / 2321] [I'm at a wedding reception, dancing like no one's watching. THE MIDWIFE *(abstract, spacious, and wonderful)* stands nearby in a white gown. She slips and falls backwards down a staircase and disappears. People believe I pushed her down. This makes me feel deeply sad. I ask if anyone, ***"has her mailing address in Berlin. I want to write her a card."***

I'm surprised to hear her voice behind my left ear, *"I thought that was weird. Figured I'd peep in on you to see what that was actually about."*

I turn and sit with her at a table in a dark room. A single overhead spotlight illuminates us as we apologize to one another for the confusion.]

[0905.2 / 2322] [THE CARPENTER enters with a trailer full of toys he's purchased for, *"all the little children."* His generosity exceeds well beyond my initial ask for *"a toy or two"* so the kids would have something to play with.]

[0905.3 / 2323] [I dance with a couple of guys. We begin making out and then find a private room to hook up. I discover they're a couple looking for a third. I'm amenable. I'm about to send THE LAWYER a text to let him know what's up in my room. He enters before I'm able to message him, then abruptly leaves somewhat frustrated with me. While on all fours, one of the guys spins his head a full 180 degrees and stares me directly in the eyes. At first, I'm startled, then I'm aroused.

We all stand up. The *"reverse headed man"* turns into a woman who looks like STOCKARD CHANNING, dressed in a 1950's poodle skirt. She sits down at a desk, puts on an operator's headset and begins to connect long distance calls via switchboard.

THE WEAVER walks up a bit bewildered saying, *"Well that's amazing...isn't that STOCKARD CHANNING?"*

THE WEAVER's not aware that I've just had sex with STOCKARD CHANNING as a man.

When I mention the novelty of STOCKARD being able to spin her head around she says, *"That's something your Grandfather would do, and it used to freak me out!"*

I look left and see THE POSTMASTER sitting at his desk writing checks, watching a baseball game and chain smoking Terringtons. I call his name. He perks up and nonchalantly turns his head 180 degrees in my direction. I'm amazed. I've never noticed him do this before.]

[0905.4 / 2324] [I stand in line at a buffet. Everyone speaks German. I eat a waffle as I watch servers drop pieces of fried chicken on white round ceramic plates.]

[0905.5 / 2325] [THE WEAVER and THE ROMANTIC share conversation at a small cafe table. THE ROMANTIC's never seen the movie, **"It's a Wonderful Life."** THE WEAVER insists he prioritize it. He's aware of it, he just hasn't seen it. THE WEAVER doubles down and says,

"It'll move you. You may not know what it's about, but it'll allay any notions you have about erasing your identity. You absolutely matter."] //

⁂

Maj. = 0- THE WEAVER: #0908, 1- THE CARPENTER: #0906,
5- THE LAWYER: #0931, 15- THE ROMANTIC: #0937
Min. = ♣- THE POSTMASTER: #1138
THIRD: #0088, #0176
FRIED CHICKEN: #0066
NOVELTY: #0027, #0125
GOWN: #0153, #0189, #0323
MOVIE: #1249, #1270
THE MIDWIFE: #1276

⁂

#0906 - October 7, 2019 @ 04:27 (San Francisco, California)

[0906.1 / 2326] [I stand over a garbage can pondering in which receptacle to place a crumpled up single use plastic bottle. I choose the recycling option.]

[0906.2 / 2327] [THE CARPENTER and I stand outside a storefront window with THE HANDYMAN and THE APIRIST *(alert, conscientious, and playful)*. We look at a display of small, complex toys and machines, each with large numbers of exposed wires and transistors. We're mesmerized. THE HANDYMAN is eager to make a purchase.

"I want those two," THE HANDYMAN says, inferring he'll just buy one.

"Well, it's obvious you should buy both!" THE CARPENTER says jokingly, throwing his arms up and walking away.

THE HANDYMAN and THE APIRIST continue to debate the utility of the toys if they were to buy them. They ultimately decide to purchase neither.]

[0906.3 / 2328] [A woman in a red dress gives an evening news report. A ticker scrolls across the bottom of the screen. Blue background with bright yellow block letters state: **"IT DIDN'T HELP YOU BEFORE AND IT WON'T HELP YOU NOW."** I take it as a cue.

"The media/news as they are, aren't a value add for me at this point."]

[0906.4 / 2329] [I drive a car at night up a mountain pass. I see a traffic sign that reads: **"45 MPH SLOW DOWN!"** I take it as another firm and timely hint.]

[0906.5 / 2330] [A woman *(slightly shorter)*, stands in front of me, pointing towards a small sign on a desk that says: **TAKE A BREAK.**

"Do you take the hint? Do you do that for yourself?" I ask her.

"Not as much as I should, nor would be good to," She pointedly says while looking me in the eye.] //

⁂

Maj. = 1- THE CARPENTER: #0913
DRESS: #0128, #0154
CUE: #0070, #0099, #0129
NOW: #0029, #0034, #0045, #0054
THE HANDYMAN: #1002
THE APIRIST: #1002

⁂

#0907 - **October 7, 2019 @ 06:26 (San Francisco, California)**

[0907.1 / 2331] [NANCY PELOSI is responsible for the construction of an urban temple. In anticipation of our upcoming meeting at a local cafe, I adjust my miniskirt to make sure my bum is covered. I'm not wearing any underwear. A woman known to me as "Ms. Leavenworth" enters with her husband who I have not previously met. I know neither of their first names. I know her as a senior executive at Wells Fargo, and she really doesn't like a friend of mine who works there in a similar role/capacity. "Ms. Leavenworth" is not aware I maintain that friendship.

"Why do people work for them? They're terrible! Blah blah blah," she protests. I secretly find it deeply funny.

Her husband leans towards me and whispers in my ear, *"You have to put up with that all day if you want to work there, you know."*

NANCY arrives. We share hugs and then decide to take our meeting in my car. She gets in the back seat. I drive.

"How are things going on the temple project, NANCY?"

"Honestly Dear, I'm befuddled." She continues listing the litany of challenges impacting the project. When a natural pause in conversation emerges, I look back over my right shoulder and say, ***"It's not often that I have my federal representative in my car. Thank you very much for your service."***

As I turn back to the road, I notice the pavement has turned into rows of planted corn, sprouting up at different heights from the soil. I turn the wheel to the left and become disoriented, not knowing which direction we now travel. I stop the car, offer an apology, and we continue our *"traveling meeting."*]

[0907.2 / 2332] [I hustle to catch a flight. I have a backpack and a small handheld bag that holds a single pair of trousers. The handheld is made of paper. One of the handles snaps, and I drop it. I realize I've misplaced my work bag and don't know where it is. All I know is ***"my flight leaves soon and I'm in a challenging predicament."***

I stand with a hand at my chin, pondering what to do next.] //

⁂

NANCY PELOSI: #0944
SERVICE: #0199, #0236, #0298, #0321, #0368
BLAH BLAH BLAH: #0400

CHIN: #1275, #1326

⁂

#0908 - October 7, 2019 @ 07:44 (San Francisco, California)

[0908.1 / 2333] [I've hired a new piano teacher named "Ben" who's known for teaching students extremely complex chord progressions. At our first lesson he insists he can teach me everything he knows. A week passes. At our next lesson he holds my hand up to his, palm to palm. I notice my joints are the same width, but are all comparatively much shorter than "Ben's."

"I have ELTON JOHN hands!" I joke, bringing a smile to "Ben's" face.

"I want to change the way my hands look. I want my fingers to grow longer!"

Later, I meet up with the family. THE DANCER is familiar with "Ben," noting he's a *"popular YouTuber with millions of subscribers."*

"Oh yeah, he's gay AND he's funny too!" she continues. Her comments pique my interest in my teacher.]

[0908.2 / 2334] [As a group, we walk under a series of stone archways along a waterfront. We turn right on to a city street and encounter a very busy SoulCycle, so popular and in demand people spill out the door and on to the sidewalk in a sweaty blob of humanity. Some people wear shirts. Others don't. I've insisted the family walk with me to specifically witness **this scene**. We double back and see a large group of naked, happy sun-tanned people walking in our direction.

"Well, that's about as long as one would expect it'd be before we saw some of that here," THE WEAVER says as two guys wearing sparkly blue hats, shoes, but otherwise naked and sporting giant flaccid wieners walk by and slap me a high five. THE WEAVER seems a little jealous. My attention turns to thoughts of "Ben."

"Have I paid him for my most recent lesson? I wonder if he has a partner. He's stirringly attractive. I could see a cool love story blossoming during our next piano lesson."] //

⁂

Maj. = 0- THE WEAVER: #0913, 2- THE DANCER: #0952

ELTON JOHN: #0919

FAMILY: #0286, #0293, #0317, #0348

GAY: #0001, #0079, #0201, #0218, #0286

FUNNY: #0304

CUTE: #1228

⁂

#0909 - October 8, 2019 @ 03:48 (San Francisco, California)

[0909.1 / 2335] [I attend a pageant where a petite, slim woman **wins**. As part of her acceptance speech she declares, *"during my reign I will intentionally gain lots of weight to shift the cultural conversation on beauty and self-image."* She waves from the stage and immediately grows thick and voluptuous.

"This as an origin story for a spirit that calls itself, 'LIZZO.'"]

. . .

[0909.2 / 2336] [***SUSPENSE/HORROR MOVIE*** I'm the protagonist attending a retreat at a hotel. A *"spiritual"* organization is about to *"go global"* and evangelize their *"divine reality"* for humanity. Their semiannual global group gathering centers on a capital campaign intended to fund five multiple mirrored buildings that will comprise a new waterfront headquarters/campus.

While the group presents a positive public image, at their core they are **rotten**. During the first large group session I take note of some errors in the presentations that repeatedly *(and oddly)* reference *"the ascension of the twins: 'Sarah' and 'Brad.'"*

"BUT BRAD DOESN'T EVEN EXIST!" I say, disrupting the session and angering some of the elders.

I'm satisfied with the truth I've seen and spoken. The lights promptly go off, a bag is placed over my head, and my wrists are bound with nylon cord. I'm surrounded by small gray fairies who call themselves *"consent beings."* They flash neon-like signs in my face and honk horns in my ears to distract me. I do not consent to be bound but I'm left hogtied.

I escape the binds by leaving my body and floating out a crack in a closing door. The group is mostly teenagers, few of whom will interact with me while I'm out of body. Some see me. I'm consistently asked to look for "Jeremy." At various times I notice I've misplaced either my wallet, my phone, or the keys to my rental car. I'm not willing to leave the retreat without all three items in hand.

I float *"feet upwards"* and walk around the hotel ceiling. I suspend my body parallel to the floor and inch along, moving down hallways with hands and feet stretched between opposing walls. A dark curly haired boy and his girlfriend see me monkey walking above them. They're spooked at first, but don't make a ruckus about my presence, mostly because an 8'11" man at the opposite end of the hallway spots me. The giant begins destroying walls and crushing objects with his fists in attempts to capture me at request of *"the elders."*]

[0909.3 / 2337] [**Commercial break:** A woman in a red bikini is supposed to run down the roof of a house reciting words printed on a poster she holds overhead. When the director calls *"action"* she forgets where she is, runs off the edge of the house, and plummets to the ground, breaking her legs.]

[0909.4 / 2338] [I'm in a rococo ballroom. I wear black tie *(as is customary)*. The mood is cordial, but I'm marked as an intruder. I'm allowed to stay and the gala proceeds without incident. I step out to use the restroom. I'm followed by a frail elderly woman who grins at me while evilly crowing,

"The witch's lunch is amazing, isn't it?"

I scurry from the bathroom, traverse the ballroom past a buffet table, and leap towards a set of closing French doors. My feet get snared at the ankle and I slide from midair to the floor. I see "Jeremy" in the parking lot as I'm pulled back inside. A couple of men decide what to do with me. Most of them are cold blue eyed, blond haired, White men. I can hear "Jeremy" telepathically saying,

"I'm grounded. I'm protected."

I could leave but I choose to stay, saying on a loop:

"These people are in a reality they've agreed to, and I have no right to take that from them." Being here is counterproductively disruptive. "Big Me" wants to go home, but the lurking *"curiosity program"* embedded in my aura keeps me in the loop.]

. . .

[0909.5 / 2339] [A man winks at me as we pass in a hallway.]

[0909.6 / 2340] [Evolved humanoids *(humans with superhuman abilities)* create puzzles for me to solve. The experience is challenging and unsettling.]

[0909.7 / 2341] [I'm brought into a room and chained to a table. I'm about to be forced to eat. An upturned paper bag dumps an apple and a cornflake covered mashed potato ball on the table in front of me. I was specifically not given a sandwich like the other kids. I break free and run across the tables, noting my teachers have a different buffet. This upsets me to such an extent I scream, ***"I THOUGHT WE ARE ALL THE SAME?!"***

"Well...sort of, except for where we eat, what we eat, and who we eat with," the teachers opine.] //

⁂
LIZZO: #1018
SAME: #0026, #0043
LOOP: #0255, #0299, #0306
GROUNDED: #0066, #0069, #0123, #0125, #0231
REALITY: #0013, #0023, #0033, #0051, #0053
WHITE MEN: #0007, #1254, #1259
⁂

#0910 - October 8, 2019 @ 05:37 (San Francisco, California)

[0910.1 / 2342] [I have a fun, flirty sexual encounter with a large muscular and hairy man named "Ian." He decides he needs to leave, but wants to use my shower before he goes. We walk down a long corridor lined with creamy pink marble arches at left and pass the ballroom from **[0909.4 / 2338]** on the right. We peek in on an awards banquet, where a cult member is recognized for their *"superlatively persuasive public presentations."* After offering a smattering of hypnotic remarks, the recipient places their plaque on a tray and requests it be mounted on a giant wall alongside previous recipients. The applause abruptly pauses. Every head turns in our direction. Hundreds of faces remain eerily silent and glare at us as we walk by.

"Ian" asks me if he can leave a suitcase of sex toys at my house.

"Sure, that's fine."

I've made an agreement with my next-door neighbor to use his shower after every random sexual encounter I have. We double back to my house. "Ian" wants to bathe in my large Roman bath. He disrobes and begins to wash. I attempt to say something sexy to him that manifests as a bunch of garbled vowels pouring from my mouth. I'm left feeling so awkward that it jolts me out of sleep.] //

⁂
AWKWARD: #0045, #0060, #0117, #0182
SEXUAL ENCOUNTER: #0059, #0263, #0310
DOUBLE: #1229, #1234, #1240, #1335
⁂

#0911 - October 8, 2019 @ 06:31 (San Francisco, California)

[0911.1 / 2343] [I'm at the gym, standing next to a stair climber. THE FIDUCIARY walks back and forth happily. He doesn't notice me, nor know me anymore. I ask him for a ride home.

"Sure! No problem!"

I get in his car and while driving he says, *"I have a lot of 'Bike Fish' people around right now."*

"You know, I've had this dream within a dream before, but last time I woke up I forgot to write it down!"

"Yeah, THE FLIRT says he does that all the time. Do you know 'JAAAY?' Do you know 'BRAAAAAAD?'"

The conversation is open and simple until he drops me off at my place. He doesn't remember ever knowing me, though we lived together as roommates for 10 years in another city.] //

⁂

Maj. = 9- THE FIDUCIARY: #0949
GYM: #0102, #0209, #0257, #0357
FISH: #0245, #0349, #0360, #0397
CONVERSATION: #1205, #1250, #1254
THE FLIRT: #1062

⁂

#0912 - October 8, 2019 @ 07:49 (San Francisco, California)

[0912.1 / 2344] [I'm on an airplane at night. We stop to make a connection. No one disembarks. I have to use the bathroom before we proceed. Once I finish, the flight continues without incident.]

[0912.2 / 2345] [I observe a group of scientists work with a critically injured elephant. Its severed trunk and tusks are surgically reattached. The scientists agree *"the next 10-12 weeks are critical, though if the animal lives past the three-month window, it'll thrive for decades to come."*] //

⁂

PROCEED: #0332, #0365, #0385
SCIENTIST: #0115, #0188, #0189, #0330
CONNECTION: #0166, #0248, #0271, #0386
ELEPHANT: #0210
AGREE: #1204, #1257, #1301

⁂

#0913 - October 8, 2019 @ 09:21 (San Francisco, California)

[0913.1 / 2346] [I walk behind THE GOGO BOY *(distant, skeptical, and judgmental)* on a glass skyway between office towers. He notices me but doesn't say hello. I narrow the gap between us as we approach an elevator bay. A door opens as he presses the button and he quickly disappears inside. The elevator descends. I wait for another to arrive and then take it to the bottom floor. I walk down a white-lit hallway and take a right turn through a door and into my condo.

I lay clothed on my belly typing on a laptop when THE GOGO BOY enters, sweaty from the gym. He takes a seat next to me wearing only a jockstrap as he unties a pair of blue-laced calf-high trainers.

"Wanna blowjob?" I say still looking at my laptop.

"No thanks." *Pregnant pause. *

"If we're not going to have sex then we really need something else to talk about. What are you up to?"

He leaves without saying anything.

Moments later I hear him yell, *"MORPHEUS!"* up from the basement. I fly downstairs and see him boxed into a corner by two house cats. He's afraid. I shoo the cats away and he leaves.] //

[0913.2 / 2347] [THE WEAVER and THE CARPENTER need to retrieve a rental car from the beach and catch a flight. They aren't keen on taking a cab or Uber to the airport.] //

⁂

Maj. = 0- THE WEAVER: #0919, 1- THE CARPENTER: #0915

JOCKSTRAP: #0021, #0314

CATS: #0096, #0175, #0358

BOTTOM: #0132, #0157, #0181, #0187

HELLO: #1236, #1254

THE GOGO BOY: #1226

⁂

#0914 - October 9, 2019 @ 01:15 (San Francisco, California)

[0914.1 / 2348] [I'm in a large mansion that houses its own mausoleum. A memorial service is held for the late brother of musician ROBERT PLANT. I'm in a robe, singing an uplifting spiritual arrangement with a large gospel choir. ARETHA FRANKLIN takes the pulpit and performs "Amazing Grace."]

[0914.2 / 2349] [I'm part of a movie production crew that creates two takes of the same scene for a movie about an alien pig. A cartoon-like pig from outer space wears a clear globe around its head and drops from a flying saucer on to the roof. It gains intelligence *(and makes sense of how to make life happen on Earth)* by, ***"constantly asking for help."***

On the first take the pig runs the exterior of the house under greenish-blue moon light. The second take finds the cartoon pig running and slipping around the inside of the house on dish soap it's spilled on the floor. The scene is chaotic, yet sweet and playful. I hang from my fingers on a thick oblong square-shaped wooden door. THE HEADCASE *(meek, anxious, and saturated)* is responsible for locking the set down and being the last to leave. I'm inside after she departs. Alone in the dark, the house wordlessly shares its mysterious origin story with me.]

. . .

[0914.3 / 2350] [Back in the gospel choir, we sing at full volume. Our hymns cause a bolt of cloth to levitate, rise, and weave itself into a detailed Celtic cross design over a set of cinder blocks that support the choir from beneath. The white cloth becomes a blue-green sparkly shade as it weaves downward into an expanse of blindingly bright light. Its knots cascade in a surrealist impression of a textile waterfall.] //

⁂

CROSS: #0025, #0060, #0066, #0129
INTELLIGENCE: #0125, #0271, #0273, #0277
SPARKLY: #0076, #0306, #0316, #0350, #0390
WATERFALL: #0014
AMAZING: #0353, #0359, #0399
THE HEADCASE: #1072

⁂

#0915 - October 9, 2019 @ 04:19 (San Francisco, California)

[0915.1 / 2351] [***"I help those, whose habit is to help others."*** In this edition, I'm an optometrist who donates vision health services and pairs of glasses to everyone who has taken on the role of *"healer."* My offering allows them to move closer to wholeness. They'll be able to see well. They'll be more productive in their work. Many of those I support are old friends who I've known for many lifetimes.]

[0915.2 / 2352] [A theme park updates its infrastructure and unveils a new ride to the public on the local evening news.

"Giant! Circular! Pools! On! Chains! That! Swing! Half! The! Distance! Of! The! Park!"

The ad promises.

In a blink I'm walking from one end of the theme park to the other, hand-in-hand with THE CARPENTER *(as "Grandpa")*, THE ATHEIST and THE LITTLE PRINCE. We approach the entry to the new ride. The giant pools on massive chains swing by and rumble the ground as recessed spinning tires contact grooves on the bottom of the pools. The pools are probably 100 feet wide suspended on thick metal chains, greater than 30 stories tall. Five of them are positioned in a row and swing at different heights and speeds. The middle pool has a chain that's a bit too long, causing the disc to squeak, spark, and lose momentum as it drags on the ground on each pass. THE LITTLE PRINCE sees this and it makes him hesitant to ride.

"Get in line with us! It'll be fun!" We encourage him. He decides to join us.

We realize THE CARPENTER held our space in line, not knowing he'd mistakenly cut in front of a young man and woman who've waited all day to ride. They take no issue with our line jumping.

"We've been waiting for you to arrive all day," they shout and wave as we advance and board the ride. We walk along a steel catwalk to the circular pool. When we sit, it oddly has reduced in size and now seems to barely fit the four of us. The pool's filled with a brown lukewarm chocolate milk-like substance that bubbles like soda pop. We submerge ourselves up to the waist.

THE CARPENTER is delighted THE ATHEIST can pair his phone to the ride and use a credit card to *"order hot McDonald's hamburgers and fries. They'll be ready for pick up when the ride concludes."*] //

⁂

Maj. = 1- THE CARPENTER: #0917, 8- THE ATHEIST: #0957, 12- THE LITTLE PRINCE: #1003

Min. = ♥- GRANDPA: #0942

MCDONALDS: #0109, #0148

CHOCOLATE: #0021, #0039, #0040

CATWALK: #0078, #0141, #0198

ADVANCE: #1301

⁂

#0916 - October 9, 2019 @ 05:38 (San Francisco, California)

**Two preceding scenes lost. **

[0916.1 / 2353] [I'm temporarily living in a friend's space who's on an indefinite walkabout. The spacious unit is on the top *(6th)* floor of a quirky building in what seems to be a future version of San Francisco. The art deco inspired building is an homage to *"what once was."*]

[0916.2 / 2354] [I'm on the street looking up. I see my downstairs neighbor, a woman who leans topless from her balcony saying, *"Well look at you blue, beautiful, queer...being,"* with a thick ring of red lipstick highlighting her electric smile. Over her shoulder, I can see poster sized prints of photos she's taken of friends arranged neatly on her wall from floor-to-ceiling in a square grid.]

[0916.3 / 2355] [It's evening. My friend returns from his trip. I greet him and promptly assist, by wheeling him down to the basement in a one wheeled rickshaw.

"Are you a sub lessee or the primary tenant?"

"I'm the master tenant."

"When you return for good, I want to assume master tenancy from you."

I take a mental note and file it away under: *"places.I.could.thrive."* I'd trade off the panoramic city view I have at my current residence. It'd be a reasonable giveaway, since in the new place I'd live, would be in the midst of all the energy and activity that I **crave from afar**.]

[0916.4 / 2356] [I'm hanging out with friends who've just welcomed a newborn child. The mother is eager to show me a device she's created to *"help determine if the child likes to do somersaults."* The device looks like a wok lid suspended across a crude network of slim bamboo pipes as tall as an average person.

The mother places the baby in a basket atop the *"wok lid"* and crank-winds-up-some-tension to set the device in motion. The first attempt sends the basket around like a Ferris Wheel, but the baby doesn't flip over.

"You'll need more momentum if you want the centrifugal force to flip 'em over." The mother becomes emboldened and thrusts the basket with all her force. The baby flips over in the basket.

After a pregnant pause the baby squeals with delight, *"I flipped over! I wanna do it again!"* The child looks like a hairless rodent, with puffy chipmunk cheeks, and a mouth full of tiny razor-sharp teeth. Its physical appearance startles me so much I ignore the greater oddity of a three-day old child speaking full sentences.

The mother's relieved her son likes to do flips and starts researching gyms where he'll be able to practice as he grows up.]

[0916.5 / 2357] [A group gathers to celebrate the installation of a new miniature bell tower. People bring apples as offerings and set them at the base of the red brick structure, which stands just under seven feet tall. THE RAPTOR and THE ROBOT are the collaborating artists responsible for replacing the old larger structure with the new one.] //

⁂

Min. = ♥- *THE ROBOT: #0943,* ♦- *THE RAPTOR: #0943*
QUEER: #0263, #0317
PREGNANT PAUSE: #0041, #0189
FUTURE: #0005, #0016, #0022
APPLES: #0342
TEETH: #1249, #1314, #1315

⁂

#0917 - October 9, 2019 @ 07:41 (San Francisco, California)

[0917.1 / 2358] [I've taken a role in a small-town police department. I'm the team's *"empath."* I'm responsible for getting my team to tap into oneness, super consciousness, or "God."

First, I bring the squad to a candlelit church where we find two men performing harmonized throat singing. Their harmonic intersection enables us to walk up and down the walls, as though our feet are magnetized. The walls are not impervious to our lateral body weight. Tiles begin loosening and folding back in footprint shaped grooves as the team makes multiple laps up, down, and around the space.

"Ok you guys have had enough fun," I say firmly.

The Kevlar uniformed men immediately repair cracks in the walls before we return to HQ as a group.

Our next rendezvous point is at a hotel. THE CARPENTER picks me up in an invisible car. He's just stopped and retrieved food orders, placed earlier by the team. THE CARPENTER throttles it. We make an intense, hard left-hand turn and drift into an orange plastic fence. The car tugs at the fence creating such tension it nearly snaps.

"What are you doing? Stop!" I scold THE CARPENTER.

"What's the big deal? It really doesn't matter," he teases.

"Yes, it does. I've seen the whole time that during the next team run, you get seriously hurt and I don't want that to happen. It can be avoided."

We arrive at the hotel and distribute food to the team, who eat their fill.]

[0917.2 / 2359] [The hotel morphs into a house. The team takes final preparations for a mission.]

. . .

[0917.3 / 2360] [I'm perplexed. Steel bowls for washing salad have been precisely cut down the middle into quarter spheres and stacked for greater efficiency.]

[0917.4 / 2361] [I descend a ladder thinking ***"I have access to a piece of reality that others don't."*** I may be the one who's about to be mortally wounded. I accept the possibility neutrally and keep climbing down to the bottom.]

[0917.5 / 2362] [I'm on a college campus on a snowy winter night. Snow is beginning to stick. I encounter THE GOOD WEED *(unflappable, sarcastic, and worldly)* who's in the process of relocating his family to Georgia.

"Let's stay in better touch this decade, now that I'm free of first-generation social media tools," he says as he shows me a giant blimp-like vehicle parked in a hangar on his lawn. The cement truck/gasoline truck hybrid is enhanced by a bolt-on 80-foot crane. Taken in sum it looks like a giant insect with a head *(crane)*, thorax *(petrol truck)* and abdomen *(cement truck)*. The vehicle extends up high toward the ceiling, which retracts and lets in a light dusting of snow from a starry indigo sky above.]

[0917.6 / 2363] [I look for a place to pee, while descending a tightly spiraling steel staircase. When I reach the bottom, THE CARPENTER picks me up in a classic car. He's just retrieved food for the hungry team that waits across town.] //

⁂

Maj. = 1- THE CARPENTER: #0919

LADDER: #0204, #0243

GOD: #0172, #1311

HARMONIC: #0140,

SALAD: #0001, #1204

KEVLAR: #0315

⁂

#0918 - October 10, 2019 @ 03:52 (San Francisco, California)

[0918.1 / 2364] [Unclear, diffused image of a small boy playing.]

[0918.2 / 2365] [***"How much closer to God can I get while keeping my feet on the ground?"*** I wonder. "**I'm the ground too,**" a voice startles me.]

[0918.3 / 2366] [It's audition time at a yoga studio. I've been selected to lead a two-hour class that will begin after 9:00pm auditions conclude. I'm doubtful anyone will attend, but I'm ok with getting paid to stay late!

"If no one shows up, then let's move the two-hour class to another slot on the schedule," I suggest to THE NURSE.

"Just teach it anyway," THE NURSE pushes back.

We playfully banter back and forth as I stand over a five-gallon bucket of gummy candies *(sweet and sour coated mini-bears).* I occasionally glance at the bears and want to eat them, but don't.]

[0918.4 / 2367] [I'm in a European warehouse standing among shrink wrapped pallets of food. It's after hours at night. I ravenously open and compulsively eat a package of ginger snaps. Other people enter the warehouse and follow suit. Management is aware this happens, but prefers it doesn't.

"This is not who we really are. Do better!" An embarrassed executive scoffs through the PA.]

[0918.5 / 2368] [I observe a game while wearing no shoes. I ride around a gravel parking lot on a "OneWheel" that travels laterally. I wave as I pass a variety of people, realizing I'm riding across the playing field. I interrupt game play as I learn how to accelerate and maneuver the device.] //

⁂

Maj. = 13- THE NURSE: #0957
FIVE GALLON BUCKET: #0365
GINGER: #0185, #0295
WAREHOUSE: #0007, #0012, #0075, #0154
SHRINK WRAPPED: #0010, #0177
ACCELERATE: #1255

⁂

#0919 - October 10, 2019 @ 06:32 (San Francisco, California)

[0919.1 / 2369] [I'm in the lobby of an extravagant hotel. Pristine marble floors, walls, and doors. I pass THE VIKING ELF without interacting. My conscience feels heavy and sadness flows deep. I have a flashback, recalling when we murdered two people in the hotel. We left their bodies buried in a white granite wall, then assumed the dead men's identities. THE VIKING ELF shot both of them in a bathroom. I'm racked with guilt-by-association, though neither of us were caught nor tried for the crime.]

[0919.2 / 2370] [I've been invited to ELTON JOHN's penthouse atop another extravagant hotel in Atlanta, Georgia. I've been here before. I've been given another invitation. Before heading up I go into a bathroom, noting a sleeve of white plastic three-ounce cups scattered across the floor. Most have a thin pink film layer inside at the bottom. Most of the cups are located under a stall. I grab one and slide others on it, to form a stack. I toss the tower of discarded cups down a flushing toilet, as a group of Japanese teenagers look on. I recognize one of the girls and exclaim,

"The Game! The Game! The Game is almost done!"

"Oh yes, 'SAKUNE's' game is nearly finished, yes."

"Yes soooooon!" I respond agreeing like an ecstatic manga character.

I approach an elevator bay and take a car up to the top floor. The door opens and I proceed down a long hunter green and gold paneled corridor until I arrive at a majestic gold door. A gold name plate is etched with the phrase, "The Residence of Sir Elton John" in stately block letters.

Once we enter, we can hear new music played nearby on a piano. We ascend the staircase to the rooftop, pausing to briefly interact with ELTON's management team. They debate as to *"whether his career is starting to sunset."*

We spill out onto a grand stone terrace where the staff throws an incredible party. Our collective attention is drawn to the gridlock traffic on the Atlanta beltway. Bumper to bumper cars in the dark look like a pair of mating "candy cane snakes" *(composed of 1000's of eyes).*

A swimming pool doubles as a giant washing machine that will ***"spin you to the perimeter and deep clean your clothes while you wear them."***

I choose to not wade in, but both THE WEAVER and THE CARPENTER do. ELTON's talkative and territorial little "min pin" rushes to the edge of the pool annoying THE CARPENTER with its chirp-like barking. THE WEAVER is delighted to get reacquainted with the opinionated little dog.

The scene pulls back and reveals people frolicking in a multi-level topiary maze, ducking their heads around corners, and bursting through bushes like cartoon characters. Off the right edge of the building is a giant white "Crane Coaster" with mauve and maroon cars *(sponsored by Revlon).* Each train has four seats and pivots wildly at 90-degree angles, swinging over the top of the hotel and then dangling riders precariously upside down at a tremendous height over a busy freeway below. The staff offer me a cup of their preferred beer, but I decline.

"You all seem to have the best job ever," I blurt.

"Of course, it's amazing!" they declare in unison.]

[0919.3 / 2371] [I blink and I'm back downstairs in the lobby. I walk to the concierge but am denied a visitor credential. I wear black vinyl pants. A piece of mangled red "DANGER" tape sticks to my right leg, which I've errantly considered my VIP pass. I'm not wearing a shirt. When I catch a glimpse of myself in a large mirror, I resemble a cartoon character *(a la GORILLAZ),* with spiky shaggy hair and smoky black eyes.] //

⁂

Maj. = 0- THE WEAVER: #0922, 1- THE CARPENTER: #0925

Min. = ◆- THE VIKING ELF: #1131

MAZE: #0079, #0089, #0116, #0118, #0149

MIRROR: #1250, #1279, #1306

⁂

#0920 - October 11, 2019 @ 04:59 (San Francisco, California)

**Woke up from this natural and lifelike dream not realizing it was a dream.* *

[0920.1 / 2372] [Quick bursts of activity fade as my attention shifts to what's happening now at a hipster college scene. I'm in a student union with a dining hall. A group of us plan pranks to play on DONALD TRUMP, whose office is in the next room. He might be the provost? We begin with substituting mayonnaise with Vaseline in his sandwiches, which are taken into his office on a silver platter by a butler. We laugh while biting our fists when we hear him spit out the sandwich.]

. . .

[0920.2 / 2373] [I'm at "Prankster's Paradise." My team celebrates and reminisces as we pass through a long buffet.

"Hey could you get another tray of calamari?" a guy shouts at a friend working in the kitchen. It quickly arrives.

"Isn't it amazing how the blind can move so fluidly from one place to another without 'seeing' anything?"

While we observe a group of eyeless people move fluidly through the dining room, we compare an average person's abilities and judge theirs to be *"menial."*]

[0920.3 / 2374] [At a smoky bar we compare sleeve tattoos and wait to talk to *"the cool guy"* at a phone booth with the only landline in town. He'll only talk if you use the classic headset. An LP of JOHN LENNON tunes spins and floods the space with joyful community galvanizing songs.]

[0920.4 / 2375] [We're asked to assemble a series of five rectangular perfume vials in ascending order and decorate them with a silver bow, which will accent the lavender liquid within.]

[0920.5 / 2376] [People continue eating. A guy with a Mohawk asks me where he can find more food. I shrug my shoulders and check him out as he walks away. I find him attractive. He takes four tiny Cornish game hens from the insanely large stockpile of food.

"Way more is available than we will ever need."

We invite a hungry cycling team to stop through for a recharge before taking off for their next destination. I want to remember more, but simply can't.] //

⁂

JOHN LENNON: #1272
DONALD TRUMP: #1139
HUNGRY: #0334
TATTOOS: #0043, #0140
STOCKPILE: #0046, #0117, #0127
ATTRACTIVE: #1294, #1305

⁂

#0921 - October 11, 2019 @ 06:25 (San Francisco, California)

[0921.1 / 2377] [I flirt with THE CENTERLINE *(gentle, skillful, and balanced)*. I grab him by the belt loops on his jeans and pull him belly-to-belly with me. We sit across the edge of a couch, legs straddled over one of the arms, and make out.

We smile and giggle when we get erections at the same time.

We find a bed.

I perform oral sex on him for a few moments, then we promptly stop before either of us climax. I have a giant block of hard poop in my butt, so I chose not to bottom.

We sweetly hug and complete our interaction.]

. . .

[0921.2 / 2378] [*"Tension. Release. Tension. Release."* An ancient voice repeats slowly and lowly as purple paisley abstractions dance through my field of awareness.] //

⁂

COUCH: #0211
TENSION: #0135, #0154
RELEASE: #0034, #0125, #0169, #0239
PURPLE: #0238, #0306, #0325, #0364, #0376
DANCE: #1235, #1293, #1318
BED: #1330, #1332
JEANS: #1334

⁂

#0922 - October 12, 2019 @ 00:00 (San Francisco, California)

[0922.1 / 2379] [I sit across from my music writing partner. He's worked with many commercially successful artists. At first, I'm taken aback by my own resistance, which wants to delegitimize anything that's *"popular."* My writing partner's artful and skilled in his creative process. He's developed a distribution network to spread his content to a wide and diverse audience.

We connect psychically. I observe him as a black and white pencil sketch of himself, singing in front of a powder blue background. I appreciate how the precision of the sharpened pencil lines soften and become chalk-like as he opens up into a more *"full expression."* I believe it suits the tone of his performance.]

[0922.2 / 2380] [Our muse is a little dog; our shared Chihuahua named "Max." "Max" believes his physical body is 10x larger than it is, and owns his own space accordingly. "Max" confidently walks down a sidewalk not fazed by large predators that lurk just off the pavement, most of whom could swallow him in a single bite. "Max's" charter is to act as our *"protection symbol."*]

[0922.3 / 2381] [I'm shown a technology that allows you to take any photograph, distill it into components, and then dissolve it into *"cubist/reductionist base pairs."*]

[0922.4 / 2382] [I'm shown a glass of milk that erupts, splashes, and spills across a table, then reassembles itself.]

[0922.5 / 2383] [I'm in a three-way relationship with a man and a woman. The woman wants to get some rest. I move to the foot of a bed where we all lay together. I lay side-to-side with the man gently caressing his face.

"Have I told you how beautiful you are today? Let me remind you. You're beautiful."

I whisper and coo into my partner's sleepy ear just before we head to dream time. It's flirtatious and friendly, though the joint relationship between all three of us appears to be coming undone.]

. . .

[0922.6 / 2384] [THE WEAVER and I play golf under moonlight on a beautiful *(and alien)* course. At the next hole, a tall clear plastic shower curtain separates us from a man who's seated, looking at his phone, and giving no indication, nor intent to tee off.

"He's in the way," THE WEAVER, frustrated, whispers under her breath in my left ear. We wait for a few minutes, then politely ask to play through. The round of golf that follows this interaction is iconic and superb. No ball drops nor mulligans, the only real effort emerges when deciding between using a 6 or 7 iron to tee off.

Patches of balls sprout up from the green like little mushrooms, which we pluck from the ground and use for play. One I grab is unusually large and colored like a grapefruit. I consider using it, but decide it's too heavy and don't know how to adapt my swing to use it effectively.]

[0922.7 / 2385] [Back in bed, the woman sleeps soundly. My relationship with the man has evolved to include another man. The three of us all laugh and enjoy each other's company individually *(and collectively)*. We share high levels of group affinity. As a collective we're all having **So. Much. Fun**!] ///

⁂

Maj. = 0- THE WEAVER: #0924
DIVERSE: #0327
GOLF: #0160, #0236, #0265
BLACK AND WHITE: #0026, #0052, #0063, #0126
THREE WAY: #0201, #0204, #0263
ALIEN: #0048, #0049, #0071, #0130
EFFORT: #1239, #1274

⁂

#0923 - October 12, 2019 @ 03:05 (San Francisco, California)

[0923.1 / 2386] [I'm at an amusement midway inside a large casino. I decide to play a game and drop two silver coins in a machine that produces lottery scratch cards. Each card has 3 rows of 3 silver ovals. I can see through the bottom row on each card effortlessly with x-ray vision, and easily identify which position has the "Instant Winner" inscription printed. I see a pink oval and a yellow oval jut out three dimensionally from behind the *"obscured"* winning position.]

[0923.2 / 2387] [I'm the lead actor in an action-comedy blockbuster. My goal is to rescue a blonde-haired woman who has long fingernails and sharp fangs. She moves like an anthropomorphic snake. A man consistently pops in to frame intending to surprise the woman after each rescue. He offers her different tantalizing gifts as distractions. On one such occasion he emerges with a jewelry box. He opens it to reveal a ring fitted with a large brooch sized stone: **a grey and white marbled opal**. It captivates her but she doesn't touch it, nor try it on, even after the man's frequent and repeated attempts to woo her. She's wise to his ruse and appreciates my support.] //

⁂

⁂

YELLOW: #0013, #0022, #0024
WINNER: #0006
XRAY: #0259
COINS: #0093, #0100, #0146, #0194
SNAKE: #0312, #0315
WISE: #1209

⁂

#0924 - October 12, 2019 @ 05:23 (San Francisco, California)

[0924.1 / 2388] [*"...this is the dream realm of rarified air,"* an omniscient presence suggests as a white-hot fractal background hosts swirly overlaid patterns that create a *"holographic sense of timelessness and depth."* The patterns undulate and "breathe."]

[0924.2 / 2389] [I'm party to a real estate auction where bidding has commenced. THE WEAVER is interested in a large lake front parcel that's just received an opening bid from a recently retired heterosexual couple. Multiple other parties have an interest in the property. The reserve for the lot is $800,000USD.

A gregarious and hilarious well-to-do brunette woman *(think: Karen from "Will and Grace")* is in direct competition with THE WEAVER. She sips champagne and puffs a cigarette while taking time to, **"Party with the Aussies."** She's made a positive first impression on the seller. She walks up to us, seemingly innocently and surprises us by saying, *"I know your game, and I've already put in an offer on the lot you can't match."*

THE WEAVER feels a jolt of momentary sadness. Her attention shifts quickly to bidding on another property. The new parcel features a giant interior Roman bath, replete with marble columns and an enormous bas relief impression of ST. THOMAS AQUINAS suspended over the main entryway.]

[0924.3 / 2390] [I'm on a hilltop construction site where a large legacy home has been built among a grove of olive and cypress trees. A single Joshua tree protrudes proudly and courageously from a rock wall that dangles over the ocean. I encounter THE THINKER and THE FEELER on the front patio and learn an older male relation to their family has recently passed. The interactions between us are jerky and confusing. Fierce wind howls louder than the volume of our voices.

We stand on a plastic sheet that covers white square tiles with a blue Correll *(dishware)* pattern around their edges. We're careful to step lightly as the tile is weak, thin, and likely to crack under foot. A small plaque on a memorial bench reads:

AGE 57. DIED OF A CORONARY - SUPER SAD.

Four large stone vases placed at the edge of the porch cause a rise in the plastic. I want to remove them and place clear visqueen beneath. I rethink it when I realize they've been put there for a reason.

"Are they canopic jars?"

For a moment, I suspect the man is buried beneath the porch. I quickly understand that assumption is incorrect.] //

⁂

Maj. = 0- THE WEAVER: #0932

Min. = ♣- THE FEELER: #0937, ♠- THE THINKER: #1097

CYPRESS: #0079

OMNISCIENT: #0003, #0039, #0217, #0293

VOICES: #0005, #0023, #0081, #0384, #0393

SAD: #1209, #1220, #1258

⁂

PART 12 - FEED THE HOLY

#0925 - #0980

12.1 - THE BOOK OF SAGITTA- {[0925 / 2391] - [0929 / 2405]}
12.2 - THE BOOK OF CORVUS- {[0930 / 2406] - [0936 / 2416]}
12.3 - THE BOOK OF AQUILA- {[0937 / 2417] - [0951 / 2478]}
12.4 - THE BOOK OF CYGNUS- {[0952 / 2479] - [0970 / 2531]}
12. 5 - THE BOOK OF DELPHINUS- {[0971 / 2532] - [0980 / 2564]}

"Half my life's in books, written pages
Live and learn from fools and from sages
You know it's true, oh
All the things come back to you.

Yeah, sing with me, sing for the year
Sing for the laughter, sing for the tear
Sing with me, if it's just for today
Maybe tomorrow, the good Lord will take you away.

Dream on...Dream on...Dream on...
Dream until your dreams come true..."

- Steven Tyler

* * *

October 12, 2019 - November 5, 2019

⁂

⁂ 12.1 - THE BOOK OF SAGITTA: 0925-0929 ⁂

#0925 - October 12, 2019 @ 07:00 (San Francisco, California)

[0925.1 / 2391] [I wind backwards in fast motion through dreams **[[0924.3 / 2390] - [0922.1 / 2388]]**. Action speeds to a blurry white-hot light and dissolves like a melted off-reel film at a movie theater.]

[0925.2 / 2392] [I'm in what feels like a city hall building. Regal staircases are constructed from rich cherry wood and lined with mahogany banisters. The ceiling is a grid of squares that appear as inverse impressions of Aztec pyramids. Each is lit along the edge of every concentric square with soft gold-green light. THE CARPENTER and I walk and talk as we traverse the space. He persuades me to make amends with THE DRAMA QUEEN, and suggests we wait to let him catch up and walk with us.

"THE DRAMA QUEEN needed to go apologize to his dad for his role in 'So & So's' death," THE CARPENTER explains.

"THE DRAMA QUEEN can do whatever he wants. I need you to understand that just because we're friendly, that doesn't portend we're going to be friends."

"Oh...ok," THE CARPENTER says somewhat bewildered by my attitude.

Admittedly, I'm more interested in the Aerosmith song playing in the background. I'm indifferent to the notion of reconciling with THE DRAMA QUEEN.]

[0925.3 / 2393] [I stand at a chest-high wooden table in the lobby of an aristocratic bank, having just cashed out some large investments. I quickly count and stack large denomination bills, some of which fall to the floor. I've recently used a $1000 bill for a small transaction and received change in $100's. I don't recall whose face graces the large note. I discover and inspect a $500 bill, printed on woven gauze *(ace bandage)* roughly half the size of the other notes. The image of a woman on the obverse is captioned: "The Fourth Richest Waldorf." She's portrayed demonstrating "king pigeon pose" and teaching therapeutic breathing to burn victims who recover in a row of hospital beds. I flash the bill to a woman standing at a nearby table who says,

"Wow you've really been changing up your game. I was thinking about making a large withdrawal as well."] //

⁂

Maj. = 1- THE CARPENTER: #0926
MELTED: #0121, #0376
CONCENTRIC: #0123, #0389
ARISTOCRATIC: #0748
GAUZE: #1008
TRANSACTION: #1235, #1257, #1275
THE DRAMA QUEEN: #1384

⁂

#0926 - October 13, 2019 @ 03:33 (San Francisco, California)

[0926.1 / 2394] [I'm torso-to-head inside the back of a black quad cab truck to avoid a strong, stinging, icy wind that howls in the black of night. The truck is parked on a large dock completely exposed to the elements. The dock sits atop a giant steel Lego-like structure among similarly sized objects which are lined up and pushed in the direction of a wildly stormy sea by a massive pneumatic arm. From afar, the platform appears to be a massive platinum cube that bobs up and down in a perilous black sea. Items pressed by the pneumatic arm from the origin past the edge drop off in seemingly random patterns, like ice calving from a glacier. The falling objects create deep and ominous sounds when they breach the surface of the water. The truck appears next in the queue to drop in to the great below. I've left the back door open. I pull it closed and for a moment feel a sense of false security when the door clicks and closes. THE CARPENTER and a group of others knock on the window. I let them all join me inside to escape the severe weather.]

[0926.2 / 2395] [I control an avatar through a first-person video game in pursuit of a villain named "Vicente." Our squad has "Vicente" isolated. We discuss our final campaign to apprehend and detain him. A large steel bowl full of eggs, whipped by an invisible whisk, hangs at my eye level and disrupts my vision. I quickly shoo this entity away and realize it's a confusion tactic.

"Fuck you, 'Vicente!'" I shout as I push the bowl aside with a wild gesture. I have a thick Brooklyn Italian accent.]

[0926.3 / 2396] [I'm challenged to solve a puzzle where I use liquid from multiple vessels of varying size to perfectly fill an empty one.]

[0926.4 / 2397] [I'm part of an FBI raid. The team convenes in an airport parking deck for a mission briefing. We review blueprints for a building that sits adjacent to the Securities and Exchange Commission Headquarters. A medium sized Bradford Pear tree on the property line between the buildings has been crudely decorated with a black leather jacket and random objects as a gag by the CEO we're investigating for fraud. We decide on an approach where we disguise ourselves as caterers for a business luncheon. We'll attempt to get the suspect to surrender to public arrest in an orderly fashion.

As we prepare boxed lunches and hotel pans of food for the faux event, the team casually remarks on how brazen and ______ the signals of guilt from the suspect seem, highlighted by his odd choices of decorations on the pear tree. The event and subsequent arrest occur simply, without any dramatics or public spectacle.

We change costumes and dress as arborists. I and two others are given the task of removing decorations from the tree and collecting the ornaments as evidence. I'm given the black leather jacket as a gift.

"It's such a nice jacket. Doesn't it fit my broad, powerful shoulders perfectly?" I wryly declare while jokingly trying on the jacket.

"You look like the worst part of an unfinished cowhide couch," a contemporary shades.

Other counterparts roll their eyes thinking the jacket and my trailing comments are, *"super gross."*

In filing my concluding report, we discuss the CEO's private residence, located within the corporate headquarters where he was apprehended. He was an obvious and simple target to detain. He errantly believed his charisma would negate and up cover his committing of massive fraud.] //

⁂
Maj. = 1- THE CARPENTER: #0933
BROOKLYN: #0001, #0066
PUZZLE: #0187, #0243
PLATINUM: #0071, #0083, #0344
BLUEPRINTS: #0404
GLACIER: #0529
QUEUE: #1246, #1290
⁂

#0927 - October 13, 2019 @ 04:57 (San Francisco, California)

[0927.1 / 2398] [I check the integrity of a structure *(and its seismic retrofitting)* before climbing up tangible triangular ladder rungs to higher abstract dimensions. The higher I climb, the more the triangles soften and dissolve. I'm left levitating in a world of pastel water-color light.]

[0927.2 / 2399] [I eagerly move with a group around a large gathering space. Our interactions are friendly and vitalizing. We discuss and broker class schedule substitutions for this upcoming Thursday night. We completely reconfigure a proposed schedule for Saturday. Two other friends and I determine the best way to divide up the weekend schedule.

A neutral vibration enters our shared bubble and flatly asks the group, *"Why are you here? just teach them as though they're all exactly the same."* Comparative conversation on which classes we, *"believe are better than others,"* quickly curtails. We walk together through various corridors. By the time we stop moving we've reached consensus: *"The early ones. The late ones. The weekend ones. The ones targeted for service workers. None of that matters. All are equal."*]

[0927.3 / 2400] [I attend a party at THE ARCHITECT and THE DESIGNER's home. THE ARCHITECT video-conferences in remotely to the fete from a condo in Philadelphia, Pennsylvania. I give his hologram a hug and whisper some provocative musings in his ear. My hands on his back discover sutures and a steel dowel implanted in his spine as a result of a recent surgery. He's insistent that he's healed, though admits he was discharged from the hospital just a few hours ago.

Our group has gathered in their spacious kitchen, with an evolving shared intention to invite more "Eros" in to complement and contrast the "Agape" tone that initially called us together. As the group agreement is renegotiated, ribbon-like waves in tones of orange and red flood the space and pierce our bodies. The group feels limbic, primal, and charged.] //

⁂
Min. = ♥-THE ARCHITECT: #1186, ♠-THE DESIGNER: # 1138
LEVITATE: #0935, #0162

WHISPER: #0163, #0245, #0379
AGAPE: #0558, #0885
PIERCE: #0021, #0037
INTEGRITY: #0628
HIGHER: #0482, #0550, #0568, #0718
HOLOGRAM: #1264, #1303, #1322

⁂

#0928 - October 14, 2019 @ 00:19 (San Francisco, California)

[0928.1 / 2401] [I lead a group of students who've recently experienced an ecstatic, non-ordinary state of consciousness. I invite them to each log their impressions by writing a single word on a chalkboard. They're afraid to share and believe their insights will scare their loved ones away.

"To the contrary, stay curious. It'll endear them to you more deeply than you can comprehend at the moment. It will call in all those who want to be with you," I say to a sea of sense making eyes.

I reassure them, ***"Share your experience. Take ownership of it. Revel in it. Expand it beyond yourself."***] //

⁂

SHARE: #0251, #0259, #0260, 1333
NON-ORDINARY: #0026, #0200
EXPAND: #0082, #0193, #1266, #1294
ECSTATIC: #0023, #0125
CURIOUS: #0017, #0070, #1321, #1324

⁂

#0929 - October 14, 2019 @ 05:16 (San Francisco, California)

[0929.1 / 2402] [I attend a conference, intending to interview for a role as a tour guide for future attendees of a similar event. The process has been positioned as a *"rapid recruitment event,"* where interview candidates are expected to deliver detailed content with minimal prep time. The game becomes, *"Hurry up and wait."* We're baited with intense blasts of instruction and then are left waiting in stillness for seemingly interminable periods.

A group of young girls wearing uniforms enters. They sing together to create a deep black metal growl of a voice. They casually walk the room, taking position behind a manager's vacant desk. They bring humor and lightness to a flat and uninspired environment. Our candidate group giggles as they sing. It seems absurd and novel. With velocity, a group of stage producers *(assessment leads)* donning wireless headsets enters and declares,

"Be ready in 5 minutes. It's time to go."

A detailed list of evaluation criteria is placed in front of each of us. None of us have previously seen the rules of the game.

Again, we wait in dark silence for what occurs as a multitude of lifetimes. When I ask for an update on a start time, I'm given a stock response by a well-groomed man in a suit. As I express frustration, he simply walks away showing no outward emotion. He walks out into a residential development and vanishes. Soon thereafter our group is divided into pairs, who will compete in single elimination format for a sole *"tour guide"* role. I'm partnered with THE

SENSOR *(playful, deep feeling, and coy)*, who pulls out a binder with a detailed outline scrawled with copious handwritten notes. I don't have a similar outline and believe he'll outperform me. I have a moment to copy what notes of his I can see, but choose not to cheat.]

[0929.2 / 2403] [I'm in a bar in a small town in Middle America. Their local pride was a high school football kicker who went on to play for a top tier college team. "Ryan" remains a local celebrity, yet unfortunately has become the town's laughing stock. He's perpetually shamed for missing a field goal in a bowl game. The miss not only created a devastating last-minute loss, but resulted in him losing his scholarship and eventual berth to the NFL draft.

People who once revered him, now won't let go of his single *(crucial)* mistake. He's constantly reminded of the shame he's brought on the town. The missed kick is perpetually replayed on all bar televisions. People wear red T-shirts with white letters that read, "WAY TO GO RYAN!" They parrot the phrase at him mockingly. As much as "Ryan" wants to forget, they simply won't allow it. They want him to know he *"ruined everything."*]

[0929.3 / 2404] [I skip across and through the same well-to-do neighborhood with THE ATTRACTOR *(gravitational, fierce, and nourishing)*, as in dream **[0640.3 / 1604]**. The cobblestone roads swerve with banked turns. I sprint to burn off some excess steam. The more I run, the clearer my head, and the more quickly new information and creative insights flow in.

The ground is frosty. The air is bitterly cold *(yet still)*. I run quickly enough to glide across the tops of freezing swimming pools. A young girl follows behind me mimicking my every move. We run through a club house and pass a socializing group gathered near a long buffet table. I put my left hand out as if approaching a marathon aid station. Someone slaps a handful of circular/ring pretzels that have been coated in a dust of yellow mustard powder. I eat one. The taste is familiar. They're not nourishing. I drop the rest on the ground and continue running as I wipe my hand on my sweat laden tank top.]

[0929.4 / 2405] [**Has a similar feel to a scene from "A Nightmare on Elm Street." ** - I omnisciently observe a dusky scene on a neighborhood street in Notting Hill, London. A young woman frantically runs, hair blowing, occasionally peering over her shoulder to check if she's being chased. She looks forward and continues sprinting. A witch wearing a black cloak jumps from some bushes while "clacking" a soft violet colored hand fan. Her screeches of laughter startle the woman.

The woman enters a house. Using my x-ray vision, I can see through the walls and watch her scurry down a long, tall corridor. I only see her in silhouette. She arrives in a gold-lit banquet hall where she's swarmed by the shadows of small goblins who jump up and down around her with miniature pitchforks. The goblins place a shadowy crown on her head. Initially she resists, but eventually kneels down surrendering with a gentle bow of her head. The scattered, dancing shadows converge, envelope, and absorb her. What becomes of her is unknown. Her shadow integrates with the dancing goblins.] //

⁂

LONDON: #0094, #0181, #0392
AMERICA: #0442, #0472

WITCH: #1069, #0739, #0909
CROWN: #0021, #0156
LIFETIMES: #0510, #1240, #1326
MARATHON: #0703
UNKNOWN: #1321
THE ATTRACTOR: #1060
⁂

⁂ 12.2 - THE BOOK OF CORVUS: 0930-0936 ⁂

#0930 - October 15, 2019 @ 02:13 (San Francisco, California)
**Recorded in detail in a deeper layer of dream state. Most detail is lost. **

[0930.1 / 2406] [I'm jolted from sleep, stunned, soaking wet and have the sense I'm being watched. I see the shadow of a muscularly chiseled man in the corner of my bedroom, head peeking out from the closet. I think it's THE PASSIONATE BRAZILIAN *(curious, playful, and quiet)*. His face, chest, and arms are easily identifiable. He doesn't have legs. He floats with a spirit-like genie tail buoying him from beneath. We're both initially startled. Things ease when I put my face back on the floor and say something flirtatious. I glance up and see the ghost peacefully fade away.] //

⁂
GHOST: #0939, #0804, #1234
CHISELED: #0337, #0379
GENIE: #0934
STARTLED: #0534, #0544, #0662
THE PASSIONATE BRAZILIAN: #1185
⁂

#0931 - October 15, 2019 @ 04:55 (San Francisco, California)

[0931.1 / 2407] [I take a seat at a theater with a square stage at the center. Rows of seats fleet vertically up and back like bleachers at a sporting event. It occurs like an interior/reverse/negative 3D image of an Aztec pyramid. The stage is made of square clear glass bricks lit from beneath. White-gold-diamond light shines up vertically like a tower from the stage.

THE LAWYER and I chat as we take our seats, eager to see our friend THE GOLDEN ONE *(committed, patient, and creative)* in her debut as, "the lead." We both have rolled our playbills into tubes and tap the unoccupied row of chairs ahead of us, playfully and percussively.

We receive a text from THE GOLDEN ONE that the show starts at 6:00pm, but not to expect her to take the stage until 6:30pm. We realize we're hours early and ushers invite us to join others on the glass stage to inspect its sturdiness while we socialize. Once standing on the floor, the glass takes on a superconductive quality that allows us to bounce like we're on a trampoline formed from firm gelatin.

My left knee feels a bit loose and at risk, but I'm confident that I'll be able to bounce and bound fairly high. I bounce methodically from edge-to-edge in a tight serpentine pattern turning tightly at each end and advancing six inches as I inspect the floor. I pause in one corner to flag a single 6"x6" glass tile with an upended corner. If left unattended, it could result in the collapse of the entire stage. I'm thanked by the stage manager for pointing out the issue and continue to bounce around, testing the floor's *(and my body's)* limits.

"It almost feels like I'm dancing on the ceiling of the Garden Court at the Palace Hotel."

Theater seats are upholstered in burgundy velvet and have rounded tops. We decide to leave and return 30 minutes prior to show time. Seats are unassigned, so we debate where we might get the best view of THE GOLDEN ONE when she emerges for the first time.

When the house lights drop, the rogue corner tile I noted is still flagged, but hasn't been fixed.] //

⁂

Maj. = 5- THE LAWYER: #0972
PYRAMID: #0007, #0229
VELVET: #0223, #0376, #0402
FIRST: #0411, #0435, #0439
BOUNCE: #0769, #0774, #0794
COLLAPSE: #0502, #0757
CORNER: #1274, #1337

⁂

#0932 - October 15, 2019 @ 07:20 (San Francisco, California)

[0932.1 / 2408] [THE WEAVER holds my hand as we enter a school. I'm returning after a lengthy absence. We walk into a study hall. It's brightly lit, with long-thin-narrow-parallel rows of grey tables that function as desks.

It's 11:40am per a large round-faced clock suspended above the desks in the center of a wall. I'm the only student in the room. Others conclude their pre-lunch period in other classrooms. The environment is calm and still. The place is familiar.

I remember where my desk is and walk to it. I find a stack of graded work, my backpack, and school supplies exactly as I left them. In the center of the desk is a laminated placard that bears a headline: "SOCIAL JUSTICE POC's" with a lengthy list of legal contacts and agencies students can leverage to air grievances in the instance a teacher offends them.

I'm offended this has seemed to replace a course syllabus, yet there's no one to whom I can direct my grievance on the matter.

I find it frustratingly fragile, unnecessary, and stupid since I had to navigate my formative years here without this resource.

"The kids here must be soft."

My eyes spot a 40oz, yellow plastic tumbler with a powder blue cartoon outline of the school mascot, "Flippy the Fucked-Up Walrus." I read it aloud, causing THE WEAVER to raise her eyebrows and think, *"There's certainly a lack of rigor here. Words and meaning at this school seem mismatched."* **I hear her telepathically.**

We debate whether it'd be best for me to re-enroll here.

"Do I fit the new institutional culture?"

I gather my belongings and sling my backpack over my shoulder. We walk to the cafeteria and sit at a round table. As THE WEAVER takes her seat, three other women immediately swoop in and occupy the vacant chairs, intending to have chatty time with her.

I'm cordial and accommodating for a few moments until I realize the women are settling in for an extended visit.

"No, I need you out," I say to the woman nearest me.

"No offense intended; I just need you to leave." Two of the three promptly stand and exit, notably less chatty.

The woman next to THE WEAVER remains seated. I sit across from her and open a carton of chocolate milk.

"So, what's new with you? It's been a while," I offer.

"Oh nothing," she says flatly.

I sit there mouth open and astonished for a moment before responding,

"If nothing's changed, then why the fuck did I come back here?"] //

⁂

Maj. 0- THE WEAVER: #0933
WALRUS: #0672
NOTHING: #0473, #0557
DEBATE: #0496, #0498, #0524
EXIT: #0545, #0548, #0618
OPEN: #0637, #0654, #0714

⁂

#0933 - October 16, 2019 @ 04:23 (San Francisco, California)
**This dream was deeply confusing. Three different realities overlaid on top of each other, woven together like a clear crystal braid of light passing through a projector. **

1) At a property with my parents.
2) Backstage with the band TOOL after a concert.
3) At training in a gymnasium.
**I rewind and put each under a deeper review. **

[0933.1 / 2409] [1) I'm with THE WEAVER and THE CARPENTER. We've rented a small cottage in a coastal town for a bit of rest and relaxation. We spend a lot of time discussing exactly what amenities we want to find. Delighted with our decision, we fly around the waterfront at night, jumping off cliffs and creating looping silhouettes in front of a warmly illuminated moon. I fly down and land in the passenger seat of a performance car driven by THE GUITARIST. We descend a hill towards a red brick grocery store. When the car hits 40mph he slams on the brakes. The car screeches and skids sideways. He parks perfectly parallel at the curb between two other stopped vehicles.]

[0933.2 / 2410] [2) I'm at a TOOL concert with friends. Post show we go backstage for a meet and greet. The band jokes and lounges on large black couches, encouraging people to eat cannabis button cookies, and to sample their new "Jet Fuel" coffee. They're all pranksters and I love watching them mess with their fans. I momentarily embody "the Fanboy" when I step towards them and shower them with appreciation.

"MAYNARD, I feel like I know you, but I obviously don't. Thanks for everything you've done and for being so generous with your gifts. ADAM, amazing shredding on '7empest.' Masterful. DANNY, no one stays on "The One" like you do. You get us closer to coherent. JUSTIN, that chorus and delay combo you use is Just. The. Tits."

MAYNARD says nothing, but waves his hand at me to follow him. He takes me to a vocal booth and lets me sit behind him as he tracks new vocals while thumbing through a thick volume of scribbled lyrics and notes. In one lengthy segment he blends up English words with Konnakol percussive elements to create phrasing in 75/16-time signature. It sounds similar to the faux language THE WEAVER and THE CARPENTER used to speak when I was a kid to confuse me. I hear him sing the words "TESSERACT HYPERCUBE" *(a possible track name)* in partial syllables over multiple others:

"TIH-dig ESS..id-dig ERRR idd..dig ACT... HID-dig EYE pidiggER Keey-Digeww OOObe."

I find it brilliant because while I hear it, I can't figure out how he does it.

When the session concludes, we rejoin the group and learn THE WHITE RUSSIAN *(cuddly, forceful, and youthful)* will support the band on drums for an impromptu second set. We're excited for him!]

[0933.3 / 2411] [3) At training, some people freely move their bodies, some lead panel discussions, while others practice keynote speeches. THE BADASS *(solid, equanimous, and courageous)* gives an inspiring talk that challenges people to get clear on what they actually want. Attendees move around the space freely, occasionally referencing laminated materials affixed at eye level on sides of every square column in the building.] //

⁂

Maj. = 0- THE WEAVER: #0937, 1- THE CARPENTER: #0937
Min. = ♣- THE GUITARIST: #0940
TOOL: #1066
MAYNARD KEENAN: #1075
DANNY CAREY: #1340
TESSERACT: #1177
WATERFRONT: #0249, #0393
PRANKSTER: #0803, #0920
DRUMS: #1256

⁂

#0934 - October 18, 2019 @ 00:36 (San Francisco, California)
**A predominantly abstract sequence with momentary blips of sanguine clarity. **

[0934.1 / 2412] [I offer myself in prayer, generated through different stances and postures. At pause points I check in with others by glancing at them. A bunch of us appear aware of this *"level of the game."* Our offerings of prayer are individual. Collectively we want to *"party together."* Two masculine expressions and a feminine expression float like genies near my bubble, in an otherwise black void.

A "confusion entity" repeats the phrase, *"You'll want to get it right,"* and hangs out hovering beneath the group. We're aware of it, and invite it to depart. It's sucked down to the center of the earth and recycled.

"Create the intention. Hold the vibration. Allow the prayer to flow to and through you," our group intuitively chants as a mantra.

Some deeper levels of subtle resistance float up in our energy bubble and take the form of non-linear psychic debate:

"What will it take to achieve THAT?"

"THIS is not ordinary."

"IT takes something special to pray in that WAY."

We playfully acknowledge these lingering energies. Prayer and co-creation are normal and natural to us, but we forget. We remember most of what we forget when we drop the limiting thought,

"I have to do it myself."

Such a thought's an illusion we all hold, and have gathered to collectively release.] //

⁂

ILLUSION: #1056
CONFUSION: #0016, #0027
SUBTLE: #0023, #851, #0891
INTENTION: #0941, #0944, #0983, #1028,
RELEASE: #1019, #1166, #1169, #0021, #0034
FLOW: #0019, #0035, #0040, #0066, #0081, #0085

⁂

#0935 - October 18, 2019 @ 03:16 (San Francisco, California)

[0935.1 / 2413] [I'm likely a college age man in my 20's. I cooperate with a group of people to prepare tables for a rummage sale. The walls are covered in a cranberry-red patterned wallpaper. The space has a rich, womblike feel. The back side of the wall is an unfinished plywood structure, similar to a Hollywood set.

I place my original copy of THE BEATLES white album *(a blank white square sleeve containing two black circles)* in a marquis position on my table of personal items. I believe selling it'll bring me a nice chunk of cash. On a couch nearby, a tall guy with wavy short dark hair meditates and creates a large bubble for him to sit in and levitate. He appears serene. As people wander by, the hair on their arms stands up. The guy calls himself "David." He makes a game of leaving his body, touching people behind the ears, on the chest, and puffing an occasional breath on the nape of an unsuspecting passer-by's neck. His body sits still but his spirit has fun challenging a group of 5-7 guys who stand in a circle and channel a being that only knows one phrase: *"WOMEN. ARE. FUNCTIONAL."*

"David" pushes this energy around, causing some of the guys to slur their words. THE LOBBYIST and I standby. THE LOBBYIST laughs at the garbled absurdities spewing from their mouths. They're running an old, archaic, and dying program on new hardware. It quite literally, does not compute.]

[0935.2 / 2414] [A young man wearing overalls walks up to me and asks, *"How can I make my voice heard with the management?"* He goes on to explain he's an apprentice at a local automotive vo-tech. I offer him help. I can't take my eyes off his yellow, jagged blade-like teeth.] //

⁂

Maj. 17- THE LOBBYIST: #1180
THE BEATLES: #1272
OVERALLS: #0344
PLYWOOD: #0445
SPIRIT: #0476, #0483, #1278, #1279
HEARD: #0798, #0830, #1295, #1324
HELP: #0407, #0422, #0800, #1320, #1341
SERENE: #0436, #0751, #0770, #1316

⁂

#0936 - October 18, 2019 @ 04:47 (San Francisco, California)

[0936.1 / 2415] [I wake up, confused by a dream in which I was responsible for getting

THE CONNECTOR to a meeting. I oversleep and make her late. The time is 9:25am. Her meeting begins at 9:30am. I'm still in bed, naked. I've upset THE COUTURIER in the dream *(and feel badly about it)* but I can't recall what I did. I'll apologize to her later, to make sure the energy between us is clear.

I wake up again. It's 9:00am. I'm still in bed. THE CONNECTOR's meeting begins in 30 minutes. I fling on pajamas and a hoodie, and leap to my car from my bedroom window. THE CONNECTOR's already calmly waiting in the passenger seat. I repeat the path from my house to the car in slow motion. I realize I traveled down a staircase where the doorway is blocked by dozens of male friends who all wear board shorts and flip flops. I double back and take an alternative path to the car.

I drive THE CONNECTOR through a large concrete parking maze. An exit ramp displays two choices on large green freeway signs. The one on the left reads, "HAMILTON STREET," and sedately blinks to suggest a route. I'm not able to read the blurred-out sign at right.]

[0936.2 / 2416] [I'm cranky and hear myself inwardly repeat, ***"I don't want to build temples anymore."***] //

⁂

Maj. = 4- THE CONNECTOR: #1014
Min. = ♣- THE COUTURIER: #1031
APOLOGIZE: #0062, #0308, #0354
HAMILTON: #0052, #1044
SLOW MOTION: #0004, #0036, #0076
DOUBLE: #1229, #1234, #1240, #1335

⁂

⁂ 12.3 - THE BOOK OF AQUILA: 0937-0951 ⁂

#0937 - October 18, 2019 @ 06:18 (San Francisco, California)

[0937.1 / 2417] [I stand on a concrete path outside of a rental property with THE SLUT *(tactile, exploratory, and free)* who cackles, *"You know you're too familiar with the hosts when they let you bring the RAW gays into the main house."* Seems a big weekender event is about to roll through. I walk in a door and take a seat at a conference table with a young professional woman in the kitchen. THE ROMANTIC enters with a post-yoga class glow, smiling and insistent he'll, *"no longer work on temple projects"* because of a violent altercation he just witnessed at the yoga studio.]

[0937.2 / 2418] [THE ROMANTIC enters and exits a few times, each with a bit more frustration. He interacts with the woman, leaves, and returns. THE WEAVER stops in to say hello and assess how projects are progressing. THE ROMANTIC runs towards THE WEAVER and gives her a familiar and deep hug around the neck. THE WEAVER doesn't remember who he is, but is polite and accepts his request to stay for dinner. She walks down the hallway and out the door to buy housewares from a pop-up vendor's kiosk.

"This is the guy I made that painting for..." the words leaving my mouth land just out of earshot.

"You like to disappear, which is why I have to be so quick and pointed with my words," I turn to THE ROMANTIC and say with a giggle.

He immediately leaves.]

[0937.3 / 2419] [THE CARPENTER stands at a counter with a stack of blue jeans and a pile of hamburgers. He places a hamburger in the right leg of a pair of jeans, then tightly wraps them up into packages that look like oversized blue dinner rolls. It's unclear if this is serious work, or if he's pulling a prank.]

[0937.4 / 2420] [I walk into the living room and find a wooden plaque behind the couch that gives directions to different outdoor recreation activities/points of interest. A popular trail head is denoted as one mile away from the house. Printed materials say it's .9 miles away. THE OLD SOUL *(balanced, inquisitive, and nourished)* texts me while still out on a walk, *"It's further than you think. You have to keep going."*]

[0937.5 / 2421] [THE ROMANTIC returns and exits the frame multiple times. Sometimes wearing a towel, other times as a little person. Some occasions he's smooth skinned, while others he's hairy. He always wears a smile.]

[0937.6 / 2422] [I go back to the kitchen. THE FEELER grabs my hand saying, *"You'll always be welcome to stay at the main house, NEVER the guest house."* We look out a window and see THE SLUT on the back patio laughing to himself, cracking wise, and howling loudly, *"OH. EM. GEE. These backdoor gays are some SHIT."*] //

⁂

Maj. = 01- THE WEAVER: #0942, 01- THE CARPENTER: #0942, 15- THE ROMANTIC: #1154
Min. = ♣- THE FEELER: #0975
KEEP GOING: #0953
SMILING: #0069, #0072, #0147, #0163
THE OLD SOUL: #0938
THE SLUT: #1381

⁂

#0938 - October 18, 2019 @ 07:07 (San Francisco, California)

[0938.1 / 2423] [I stand with my back against a brick wall waiting for a classroom to open up. A teacher named "Stephanie" greets me at the door. She confuses me because one moment she looks like THE SWIM COACH *(blonde, statuesque, and cerebral)* and the next THE SHAKTI SISTER *(bubbly, fiery, and strong)*. "Stephanie" is flanked by curious students that pepper her with a list of questions ranging from the objective to the liminal.

A group of us enter the room 10 minutes before class begins. Once inside, I'm tapped to be a last-minute substitute instructor for a spin class. I agree to do it, but it's not my skill set and I have no idea what I'm going to teach. Those who've entered early are allowed to stay and begin warming up. People stretch, jog, do Pilates, prance...any movement that primes their organism for peak performance.]

[0938.2 / 2424] [THE OLD SOUL *(dismissive, alert, and judgmental)* does the splits while leisurely resting a hand under her chin and an elbow on a tall stack of soiled plastic French Fry baskets. Another teacher offers her a foam block for support. THE OLD SOUL stands and gathers up the baskets. She runs at me full speed and tosses the stack of used vessels towards my face. I'm not sure what just happened, but I find myself laughing at the absurdity of the circumstances.] //

⁂

BRICK WALL: #0015, #0314
FRENCH FRY: #0081, #0781
ABSURDITY: #0768, #0189
PEAK: #0204, #0311
FACE: #0168, #0173
FULL SPEED: #1334
THE OLD SOUL: #0963

⁂

#0939 - October 18, 2019 @ 08:53 (San Francisco, California)

[0939.1 / 2425] [THE PSYCHIATRIST yells at me for being inauthentic after I tell him I had an attraction to him, yet never spoke it.]

[0939.2 / 2426] [A group of friends decide to go out in the city. I decline, stay home, and go to bed early.]

. . .

[0939.3 / 2427] [I ride in the back of an old green pickup truck driving through a pumpkin patch, with my arm slung over a large bumpy green and white gourd. The colors are rich and cartoon-like. The truck continues and we see vast orchards of apple and cherry trees, the limbs of which dance on a firm breeze that playfully sails through. THE CHILD and I jump off the back of the truck with empty bushel baskets and collect all the ripe fruit that's fallen to the ground. With our baskets full, we go to a barn to pay the farmer. We meet THE EMT *(aware, attentive, and helpful)* at the register. She tells us, *"This is just something to keep the kids busy. We barely break even by the end of the season."*]

[0939.4 / 2428] [I'm at a house where people primp before a night out. They play a mortal stakes game involving bungee cords held in hand. A man jumps from the top of a building, bounces off the ground, lands on a second slightly shorter platform before spinning a full 360 giant revolution on a steel pipe, then landing back atop at the point of origin. It's supposed to get the adrenaline flowing and works as a "makeup substitute." THE BAD IDEA *(funny, challenging, and tipsy)* taunts me to make the first leap without any safety padding beneath, *"It'll pinken up your ghost white cheek-ees!"*]

[0939.5 / 2429] [I look to the right down a hallway and see a young woman flirting with a guy she fancies. I also have an attraction to him. He tells me he's attracted to her when we share a moment alone. I encourage him to explore that attraction, without disclosing mine. While on a walk later, I pass them sitting in a coffee shop. He waves at me, elated. I smile and wave back at him. I keep walking and feel a cord of energy flow from my gut, so I don't turn around. I just let them be.]

[0939.6 / 2430] [After wandering, I return home. The new, happy couple has arrived before me and are readying for a date. I splash water on my face in the bathroom to muster up the courage to say something. They hastily leave as they shout, *"Goodbye!"* The door shuts. My attraction remains unspoken. I'm left frustrated.] //

⁂

Maj. = 3- THE CHILD: #0963

Min. = ♠ - THE PSYCHIATRIST: #0945

ATTRACTION: #0426, #0506, #0718

BREEZE: #0098, #0159, #0384

THE EMT: #1155

⁂

#0940 - October 20, 2019 @ 05:23 (San Francisco, California)

[0940.1 / 2431] [I'm at a large metropolitan convention center, just prior to the start of a keynote event. As people continue gathering, I encounter a cute guy in the event registration line. I express an attraction. We agree to meet up behind some gymnasium bleachers later. I show up and wait for him to arrive. He never does.]

. . .

[0940.2 / 2432] [I meet up with THE GUITARIST. We share an Uber home. We live downtown near each other with a similar view of a massive suspension bridge that could be 10x the size of the San Francisco Bay Bridge. The ride we share is in an oblong, kazoo shaped vehicle which hovers and glows inches above the ground, supported by a soft pulsing white light.

Two other beings share the ride with us. Together, the four of us telekinetically steer the otherwise "driverless" car. We take an indirect route home. We stop at a beer barn and a grocery store. Our collective energy bubble around the vehicle lets us slip frictionlessly through space. We watch a slew of beings and energies bounce effortlessly around and off the kazoo car as we glide from point-to-point, instantly. It's quick.] //

⁂

Min. = ♣- THE GUITARIST: #0953
KEYNOTE: #0045, #0390
TOGETHER: #1262, 1273

⁂

#0941 - October 21, 2019 @ 04:56 (San Francisco, California)

[0941.1 / 2433] [I "No Pass" a teaching assistant for failing to align with *(and embody)* our shared intention for a class.]

[0941.2 / 2434] [I'm a servant for a British aristocrat. I'm assigned to the kitchen and forced to learn how to cook when I have neither desire, nor interest.]

[0941.3 / 2435] [I'm responsible for creating a catalog of props for a Hollywood shoot. A group of us focuses on the high priority item: *"A series of objects which must be spray painted hot pink."* We lay out drop cloths and set to task on a back lot. The work proceeds quickly and results in an abundance of splatters of pink paint on adjacent fences. We leave partial stencils and silhouettes unintentionally on the surrounding brick walls.

A team member takes some pieces inside and similarly stains the interior walls pink. An additional large swath of silver paint arches across an otherwise flat white wall. Someone pages THE AMBASSADOR *(eager, social, and engaging)* to which a team member responds, *"She's staying at a mansion in the hills for a week. She's on assignment for her new job."*

We all miss her presence, but are so excited for her creating an amazing and expansive new career.] //

⁂

NO PASS: #0777
HOT PINK: #0064
PRIORITY: #0071, #0250
COOK: #0221, #0334
THE AMBASSADOR: #1238

⁂

#0942 - October 21, 2019 @ 06:19 (San Francisco, California)
**Convergence. **

[0942.1 / 2436] [I'm in the basement level of a restaurant. I play a video game until my hands hurt.]

[0942.2 / 2437] [I see a yellow triangle sticking out from behind the edge of a mattress and box spring as I change my bed linens. After I give the triangle a firm tug a business envelope slides out and into my hand. I reach an arm to the shoulder between the mattress and spring, finding stacks of disorganized loose-leaf documents and a pile of unopened mail. When I look closer, I realize they're transcripts of key conversations I've had with my parents, including the letter I was given after I told them,

"I'm probably not going to have a wife."

I hold the letters in my hand and can see my parents consulting my out of body grandfather on how to get me the best information possible, as quickly as they can.

"You may not want to wait on this one," GRANDPA says, pointing to the bullet point on an agenda titled: *"Coming Out."*

GRANDPA communicates in symbols. It helps THE WEAVER and THE CARPENTER prioritize. They deeply value his guidance on what they both perceive as a challenging predicament.]

[0942.3 / 2438] [Back in the basement of the restaurant I hear a woman's voice in an adjoining room talking about how, *"The current players are exhausted, so much so they're almost unable to stay in the game. They're just not able to push the buttons anymore."*

I fall into this category. I place my controller on the glass table in front of me. I hear the woman and others discuss heading back upstairs to the restaurant. I quickly gather up the stacks of loose paper, white cardboard mailing tubes, bottles, and the collection of mail pieces I found earlier between the mattresses. We gather as a team at the base of a staircase and then walk up to the restaurant level together.] //

⁂

Maj. = 0- THE WEAVER: #0945, 1- THE CARPENTER: #0945
Min. = ♥- GRANDPA: #1305
MAIL: #0016, #0037, #0139
GAME: #0188, #0194
AGENDA: #0125, #0312
INFORMATION: #1212, #1327

⁂

#0943 - October 22, 2019 @ 02:22 (San Francisco, California)
**NIGHTMARE!! Recording garbled and distorted by something that did not want to be named. The scenario and actions are so intense and commingled I'm barely able to orient. I intuit my spirit has spread itself across dozens of different realities concurrently as a way of playing with and subordinating my analyzing mind. **

[0943.1 / 2439] **[1)** I'm a contestant on a gameshow.]

[0943.2 / 2440] [2) I'm on a vessel out at sea.]
[0943.3 / 2441] [3) I'm trapped in a glass room inhabited by giant carnivorous plants.]

[0943.4 / 2442] [4) A malevolent race of amber-toned beings pursues me like a piece of wild game.]

[0943.5 / 2443] [5) I'm locked inside a house. I'm unable to get out. I'm being observed by my captors on CCTV.]

[0943.6 / 2444] [6) I'm on a subway car that stalls mid-journey. Fluorescent lights flicker overhead and go out leaving me in darkness as I feel a fast rush of cold-water flow in and up over my ankles, knees, hips, chest, neck, and head.]

[0943.7 / 2445] [7) I've distracted myself with a huge pile of laundry to fold. I realize *(perhaps too late)* that I've been locked in the room. Someone behind the door has a knife and is planning to stab me multiple times.]

[0943.8 / 2446] [8) I follow THE ROBOT and THE RAPTOR into a room, then unsuspectingly we're all locked in together.]

[0943.9 / 2447] [1.1) I'm back on the game show where a large box of puzzle pieces is dumped from a cardboard box to the floor. We scramble to gather pieces, and as we get closer to solving it realize the last person to place a piece will be killed. If the puzzle is not completed, everyone perishes. The game and mood turn instantly dark.]

[0943.10 / 2448] [2.1) On the outrigger vessel, an overhead announcement is made: *"We're never going back to shore."* This creates general upset with the passengers. Some recall celebrities they've admired *(who've disappeared from public life)* that seemed to take this journey as a *"final trip."*]

[0943.11 / 2449] [***A series of scenes flicker through at a quickening pace with increasingly wild and scary content***]

[0943.12 / 2450] [3.1) The glass room with carnivorous plants is set apart from a futuristic gallery. Ghostly holograms pay homage to beings and technologies that have successfully eliminated previous *(now obsolete)* player types in "The Great Game." The gallery installation is presented within an intensely guarded vault. The objects are petite, no larger than a smartphone. A sinister, trickster-like energy pervades the space. The rooms are well-lit glowing cubes which create a larger, illuminated cube. All connecting spaces are voids.

There are no tunnels or airlocks. You either know how to move between them, else you're stuck.]

[0943.13 / 2451] [7.1) I revisit the laundromat and feel an increasing sense of terror looming behind me.]

[0943.14 / 2452] [8.1) THE ROBOT and THE RAPTOR discuss exit strategies once they both realize they've been trapped.]

[0943.15 / 2453] [***Various scenes where I'm trapped. Something dark and unseen is going to "get me." ***] //

⁂

Min. = ♥- THE ROBOT: #1006, ♦- THE RAPTOR- #1006
NIGHTMARE: #0035, #0172, #0352
CCTV: #0007, #0081, #0088
LAUNDROMAT: #0177
FINAL: #0135
GLASS: #1330

⁂

#0944 - October 22, 2019 @ 05:11 (San Francisco, California)

[0944.1 / 2454] [I'm in a deep layer of dream state, running around the grounds of a manor property with large windows, cobblestone pathways, and a lopsided experience of gravity. I can walk at pronounced angles relative to what would be considered "upright" on Earth. A soft blue, green, and white hued sky offers a cool backdrop for numerous celestial bodies *(ringed planets, stars, etc.)* that hang like giant painted Styrofoam balls pinned to the sky. They look almost pluckable, like fruit.

I run out onto a knoll and roll down a small grassy hill. At the bottom I discover a massive family nest for thousands of *"burrowing birds."* When I peek inside, they swarm out in droves and ascend skyward in a tornadic avian silhouette. An emerald headed mallard, orders of magnitude larger than the entire pod of nesting birds, pops its head up and out of the *"hive nest" (as it calls it)*. It observes me from one eye in profile. I reach in my pocket for a camera, intending to capture a photo of the magnificent creature.

I keep my phone extended at arm's length to record my descent into the dark basement of an even creepier house next door. I intend to capture every detail. After meandering dark corridors, navigating musty smells, and sticky walls I stand bent over a meeting table. I'm accosted by both JOHN OLIVER and NANCY PELOSI for being an *"out of time and out of place evangelist."* They interrogate me, intending to prove to themselves that I'm affiliated with a radical movement. I'm not.

A woman I'm familiar with appears. She's made the false claims against me to JOHN and NANCY. I chase her around the room and slap her hard in the face once, to get her to admit she's slandered me. She was a physically abusive partner. The single slap brought us to center. She and I acknowledge we've done this to each other for many other lifetimes. Now we can choose to stop. The scene plays out in public. A crowd witnesses the entire exchange.]

[0944.2 / 2455] [I sit at a table with a group of women that review a donor list and their year-to-date *(YTD)* contributions. They strategize how to best engage prospects they assumed would respond to a recent campaign, but as yet have not.]

[0944.3 / 2456] [I view a billboard animated with a sequence of five holographic images; propaganda that declares me both a villain and an interloper. The images advance deliberately frame-by-frame, as though giant evidentiary playing cards are being placed on the table in front of a suspect under criminal interrogation. I'm shown images where I gesture wildly behind a podium. Interrogators intend to eject me from the grounds of the manor property. Bristly security guards begin accosting me.]

[0944.4 / 2457] [**Lots of fast movement and bright flashes of color. ** I still have my phone out and am excited by the amount of detail I've been able to record. My intention is to capture each frame and not lose any of it. I wake up to discover **I haven't recorded any of it**.] //

⁂

NANCY PELOSI: #1345
ASCEND: #0044, #0243
BILLBOARD: #0242, #0350
PLAYING CARDS: #0750
CROWD: #0455, #0463
RECORD: #1243

⁂

#0945 - October 22, 2019 @ 08:04 (San Francisco, California)

[0945.1 / 2458] [I'm on a suburban driveway with THE WEAVER and THE CARPENTER who share neighborly conversation with an old man who's just realized his taxes have significantly increased. I take my go-kart down the driveway and onto a winding sidewalk where I ride by a neighborhood of abandoned homes and unkempt lawns *(overgrown with weeds and plumes of grey pampas grass)*. The overhead sky is cloudy and bleak.]

[0945.2 / 2459] [**Multiple quick flashes of scenes in a casino. Bright lights and loud distracting noises. **]

[0945.3 / 2460] [After an evening of game play I'm at a cocktail table in a casino bar laughing with my player representative, a woman named "Dawn." She steps away to assist another player. In her absence my identification and credentials are checked multiple times by different members of the security staff. I review my game play cards and note I've won a small electric scooter and a *"celebration,"* though in order to redeem them I have to personally connect with my player representative. A Native American man with long black hair wears a navy bespoke suit. He approaches me, checks my credentials, and looks at me stone-faced.

"Can you help me out?"

"I'm not your actual representative. I'll get you a placard that outlines the house rules. It'll help you figure out your preferred path out of here."]

[0945.4 / 2461] [**Multiple flashes of running to the far corners of a casino looking for exits. **]

[0945.5 / 2462] [I lean on a cocktail table by the casino bar. I'm holding a small device that prints out alphanumeric codes on a small ribbon of white ticker tape. "WINNING NUMBERS: O2, D4..." The string continues to print as I wait for "Dawn" to come back and cash me out.]

[0945.6 / 2463] [THE PSYCHIATRIST and I have lived together for a while. I've just arrived home and enter through the front door, as he heads to the hospital. He and I decide to talk. I hop in the car with him as he drives to work. When we finish our conversation, he pulls off to the shoulder of the road. I get out of the car, retrieve my bicycle from the rack on the trunk of the vehicle, and then walk my bike down to the bottom of a ravine. I stop at a gateway next to a rocky cliff. A group of adventurers gather and pass through the gateway, at their scheduled time. The rear wheel of my bike taps another guy's bike. Slightly miffed, he takes a new position slightly up the hill while engrossed by his smartphone. Seems the gateway will take me back to THE WEAVER and THE CARPENTER's neighborhood. The sky overhead is similarly grey. The long grass on the prairie over which I'll ride seems familiar.] //

⁂

Maj. = 0- THE WEAVER: #0950, 1- THE CARPENTER: #0954

Min. = ♠- THE PSYCHIATRIST: #0955

TICKER: #0008, #0033, #0128

BESPOKE: #0010, #0088, #0257, #0311

RIBBON: #0018, #0033, #0105

CASINO: #1217

⁂

#0946 - October 23, 2019 @ 04:29 (San Francisco, California)

[0946.1 / 2464] [*"Use tools to make the pose fit the body...not the other way around,"* says a voice that's fun, playful, grounded and expansive.]

[0946.2 / 2465] [I watch a series of screens flash various charts filled with KPIs for a business that has recently come under regulatory scrutiny.]

[0946.3 / 2466] ["FAANG" firms have been hit with massive takedowns in their share prices due to deflated revenue projections. They make large, immediate divestitures to preserve "their core LOBs." Inaction would result in public backlash so intense the firms would be rendered instantly insolvent. I'm satisfied to see Facebook's share price take a swift and intense drop. I've shorted my shares and made a mint. THE PIXIE and THE FLASH laugh as they watch an unsatisfied female *"face booker"* rant about the decline in price. Their loss of influence on the collective could not make me happier.

"Facebook needs to die."] //

⁂

Min. = ♠- THE PIXIE: #1026

PRICE: #0149, #0160, #0240

DIE: #0344, #0374

CORE: #0007

MINT: #0014

LOSS: #1266

THE FLASH: #0963

⁂

#0947 - October 24, 2019 @ 02:36 (San Francisco, California)

[0947.1 / 2467] [I'm a young boy in a 1960's home. I'm trying to find a room where I can be alone. I walk down a hallway and peek behind every closed door. Every door I open reveals a younger sibling of mine already asleep in a bed.

I keep thinking, ***"They're sleeping in my bed,"*** as I move from room-to-room.

When I arrive at the back of the house, I walk down a long narrow passage that doubles as a kitchen. Skinny countertops line the perimeter. A thin refrigerator is recessed into the wall. My access to it is blocked by a waist high table that I lean over to open the door.

In the butter chiller I find some left over jelly sweets that have been crudely wrapped. I eat a chocolate-mint flavored one, and taste the cream inside. It's on the cusp of spoiling. The other one I eat is pink in color and strawberry-watermelon flavored. I prefer those, and eat the rest. Afterwards, I realize they were meant for another infant sibling. I know I'm supposed to take out another package from the freezer to thaw, but I'm more preoccupied with how and where I'll get some privacy.]

[0947.2 / 2468] [I look down and notice my entire body has become a wristwatch, running low on turns. The only way to wind myself up is to lay down flat on the floor.] //

⁂

SWEETS: #0054

WRIST: #0043, #0085

WATERMELON: #0723

SKINNY: #1022

CREAM: #1241

⁂

#0948 - October 24, 2019 @ 04:18 (San Francisco, California)

[0948.1 / 2469] [I walk up to a line forming out front of a non-denominational spiritual gathering space. THE ACTOR and THE RADICAL HIPPIE *(peaceful, uplifting, and constant)* are just ahead of me in line talking. The line meanders up a stony hill of switchbacks. When the line moves inside, it winds down a series of passages that have a lower ceiling at every turn. The line advances to a green wooden doorway, monitored by a uniformed man. He stops us shy of the entrance. While paused, I catch a glimpse of a mountain-top amphitheater where a crowd of hundreds gather.

"I admire your group's ability to acknowledge and celebrate those who have made it to retirement. I didn't even think about it when I was your age," the uniformed man offers.

We accept his compliment and agree what he shared was sweet.]

[0948.2 / 2470] [I advance through the green door and walk the grounds in search of an ideal spot on the lawn. TINA TURNER performs a benefit concert. I blink and discover myself backstage looking off towards the top right corner of the venue, where I believe I see TINA in silhouette. I jump from the stage and walk up the lawn, bumping into a group of women overserved on wine, who are all well-known comedians. AMY POEHLER drapes an arm heavily around my neck, pointing with her other hand as MOLLY SHANNON trips and falls down in front of me, then rolls out of view.

*"Didja know that was Molly? Do you know, MOH *hiccup*...MOHLLY? You.dunnnt.know.molly. That wasn't funny, was it?"* AMY amiably slurs.

After a pregnant pause our faces soften, our mouths upturn and we start chortling.

"Yeah yeah...that was fun," we say in union, breaking out into belly laughs. MOLLY SHANNON stumbles by, buckled over with laughter. The vibe becomes overtly celebratory and light.] //

⁂

Maj. = 10- THE ACTOR: #1085
TINA TURNER: #1117
UNISON: #0277, #0292
LAUGHTER: #0368, #0375, #0385
STUMBLE: #1241, #1273, #1279

⁂

#0949 - October 24, 2019 @ 05:11 (San Francisco, California)

[0949.1 / 2471] [THE ORPHAN gives her class an electrifying set of physical cues: *"LIFT YOUR BACK UP! MAKE IT BROAD LIKE A CIRCUIT BOARD! GIVE SPACE FOR ALL YOUR NERVES TO FIRE UP! BAM! BAM! BAM! BAM! *Makes fireworks gestures with her hands** BREATHE!"]

[0949.2 / 2472] [I'm inside the top of a lighthouse. I hear a knock on the door and answer it. THE FIDUCIARY is worried, and looking for his sister. He's afraid she's going to kill herself. We search the entire lighthouse from bottom level to top. Vertical shades lowered give the space a rusty hue. We discover his sister hiding among the lenses at the top. She's naked and crouched down to avoid the light. She stands up, revealing her naked body. Her hands rest gently at her side.

A series of green lasers from waist level devices dot her skin. Green lasers are placed in all twelve corners of the dodecagonal room. The devices are flat metal rectangles, each with four lenses inside, that cast complex geometric patterns across her body and surrounding walls. The devices are $220 to replace, if broken.

THE FIDUCIARY and I cover his sister with a bathrobe. He hugs her, expressing worry for her wellbeing. Another older pair of twins *(brother and sister)* stand nearby observing. They're responsible for keeping the lighthouse running. The scene remains frenetic and chaotic.

A desk chair swivels from corner-to-corner in the curtain drawn space. The back of the chair is just high enough to snap off the fixtures which hold the lasers, if pushed with the gentlest touch. I take a seat in the chair to stop it from rolling. The lasers recalibrate and focus on me as their new target. Eleven green lasers *(and one pink)* ricochet light around the lighthouse. The sister throws open the curtains one by one, and lets the light enshroud her as she dances.

The older twin brother remarks, *"It's like a concert in here with all those fractional fractal patterns."*] //

⁂

Maj. = 9- THE FIDUCIARY: #1063
LASER: #0012, #0306, #0396
RICOCHET: #0193, #0784
RUSTY: #0170, #0367
CONCERT: #1304, #1326
THE ORPHAN: #1040

⁂

#0950 - October 24, 2019 @ 06:47 (San Francisco, California)

[0950.1 / 2473] [THE TRAVELER's *(available, storied, and gracious)* in a warehouse practicing acrobatics. She leaps upward, catches a large truss, and dangles from what looks like the interior of a barn. She swings back and forth taunting me to catch her when she lets go. She's above the edge of a stage. If she falls straight down, she'll hit her chin and shatter her jaw. A black and white pixelated icon of an hourglass and a honeybee pop up in front of my face every time I conjure up an idea to catch her. She stops swinging and carefully floats down.

She invites me to help her *"sound check the mics."* The floor monitors and speakers are positioned incorrectly and create feedback when we tap the center microphone. I know how to reposition the speakers to avoid this, but the event producers refuse to listen to me. I have to accept it. They'll deal with unnecessary noise when the formal presentation is made later that day.]

[0950.2 / 2474] [THE BRIGHT SATELLITE *(uplifting, eager, and happy)* wants me to move in with her to open a boutique hair salon that transitions to a cushy after-hours lounge. She has an octagonal retail space in mind, with concentric tiered floors that descend roughly 10 feet from the front door. Rent is $3000 per month. Her current roommate is upset. At a recent dinner party, THE BRIGHT SATELLITE made her a similar partnership offer.]

. . .

[0950.3 / 2475] [I'm in line with THE WEAVER to ride "The Beast" roller coaster at Kings Island. While in the queue, a TV screen to the left flashes a risk management video featuring CATHY BESSANT, who welcomes riders to "Mowgli Week" at the park. A pause in the presentation displays a knowledge check where we're questioned about: ***1) Religion, 2) Philosophy, and 3) Science.***

THE WEAVER and I intend to sit at the back of the train. We believe we're in the correct line, but when the gates open people fill the train oddly. THE WEAVER winds up behind me. I'm pushed up a few rows and seated alone on a cheap white plastic deck chair that loosely rests atop a red wagon with no lap bar nor safety restraint. The ride advances. The roller coaster track intersects with a flume ride, causing a literal "log jam" that splits the roller coaster train in half. Our half stops, as the front portion proceeds down the tracks and out of view.]

[0950.4 / 2476] [I sit on a paperback book with a blue cover. I place it on a railing at right. A mysterious, bodiless hand shoves a young girl's flower-patterned jacket at me. I take it from the hand. The roller coaster train advances another 20 feet then abruptly stops.

"Would you mind giving that girl her coat?" a woman shouts at me.

"Of course. I didn't take it from her," I say while confusingly handing over the item to an expectant child that materializes at right.

"Strange things happen during 'MOWGLI week,' sir. I'm so sorry," a team member offers in a goofy half-resigned tone. The train catches the chain on the hill and begins its ascent to the top while TARZAN and CAPTAIN CAVEMAN characters swing on a vine overhead.] //

⁂

Maj. = 0- THE WEAVER: #0955
CATHY BESSANT: #0986
ROLLER COASTER: #0339, #0380
PIXELATED: #0022
HAND: #0024, #0027
MICROPHONE: #1282, #1322
THE BRIGHT SATELLITE: #1384

⁂

#0951 - October 25, 2019 @ 06:17 (San Francisco, California)

[0951.1 / 2477] [I have a winning lottery ticket! I've matched 7 pairs of 2-digit numbers in order. The ticket has an embedded safeguard technology to validate and certify my status as *"the winner."* A paper-thin screen "snapshots" the ticket and freezes the numbers in individual **ovals**, in pairs of **ovals**, and larger **ovals** surrounding the two rows of digits. The winnings seem to be massive. My experience of being *"the biggest winner in lottery history,"* is oddly flat and uninspired.]

[0951.2 / 2478] [I'm at a house party. I'm high school or college aged. My gaze shoots across the space when I see a guy enter to whom I'm instantly attracted. A deep and playful curiosity wells up within me as I observe him interact with others. I watch his habits. I watch his body language. He's confident. Occasionally our paths drift nearer one another. I'm fairly sure it's

THE CRUSH *(precise, articulate, and self-assured).* We each navigate the event *(and our web of relationships)* while eyeing one another. We peek and stare at each other from time to time. Some instances result in our eyes meeting. Each time our orbits intersect I ask him a coy question,

"What music do you listen to?"

"Do you like parties?"

"What color are your eyes?"

I compliment his impeccable manner of dress. Our interactions feel boyishly exuberant as we create a cartoon thought bubble above us that holds the images of our adult selves twenty years in the future still playing *"cat and mouse."* It's a sweet interaction.] //

⁂

WEB: #0027, #0032
FLAT: #0048, #0098
TWENTY: #0436
CAT AND MOUSE: #0076, #0114, #0126
SWEET: #0201, #0234, #0378
LISTEN: #1284
THE CRUSH: #1028

⁂

⁂ 12.4 - THE BOOK OF CYGNUS: 0952-0970 ⁂

#0952 - October 25, 2019 @ 08:18 (San Francisco, California)

[0952.1 / 2479] [I'm part of an indigenous nomadic family. It's the middle of winter, and frigid. THE DANCER is in the final weeks of her pregnancy. We eagerly await the arrival of her newborn son. One moment we're trudging across open land on foot. The next, we've arrived in a futuristic reality surrounded by climate-controlled tubes and interconnected pods which serve as communal living spaces. THE DANCER and the family are appreciative of this technology. Without it we're unsure of how we would keep the baby warm through the winter.]

[0952.2 / 2480] [I volunteer for a local candidate in the final days before a crucial election. I'm at the central office surrounded by an energetic and optimistic group of staffers. It's mid-morning. The overhead lights have been shut off to conserve energy. A bald man with earrings enters. I believe he's "the candidate." He swiftly crosses the room, heads into an office at the back, and promptly closes the door. The only object in the office is a surgeon's table.

A few minutes pass and another muscular bald man wearing black short shorts and dripping with sweat from a long-distance run enters. He's "the actual candidate." He briskly walks through the office while expressing strong opinions and issuing orders to the team before joining the other man in the back room. As the door opens, we all catch a glimpse of the first bald man, nude with his feet in stirrups. The candidate promptly slams the door and a rowdy physical encounter ensues which can be heard from our side of the door. Interns sit on a short cinder block wall and start gossiping about what the two men are up to. I acknowledge that something is happening, but say, ***"It's none of our business. It's best we all move on."***]

[0952.3 / 2481] [I stand in the middle of the intersection of "Divisadero and Duboce" just before sunrise. Shades of blue and black surrender to pale violets and sparkling tones of yellow. White lights in the hills across the bay send diamond sparkles across the surface of the water. I unpack my SLR, place it on a tripod and shoot hundreds of frames intending to capture the exact moment San Francisco, *"wakes up."* As though a cosmic switch flips, freighters lumber confidently in the background. Airplanes, trolleys, and buses move in from both sides in the middle ground. Cyclists, pedestrians, and shadows of cars flow into the foreground. All of this happens concurrently with a flash of a golden orange hue that puts every moving object in complete silhouette. The city undulates with a breath of its own. Everything is in its exact, precise, and intended place. It's gorgeous, breathtaking, and inspiring.] //

⁂

Maj. = 2- THE DANCER: #0957
TROLLEY: #0851
SWEAT: #0012, #0063, #0094
VOLUNTEER: #0155
WINTER: #0194, #0401
BREATH: #1236, #1238, #1279

⁂

#0953 - October 26, 2019 @ 06:26 (San Francisco, California)

[0953.1 / 2482] [I walk behind a man and woman who embrace side-by-side, arm over shoulder. Their heads tilt towards one another. I overhear their conversation, *"We're both pretty hard headed. Let's remember to have a conversation about the tenderness of our open hearts, when we forget."*]

[0953.2 / 2483] [I'm backstage at a large weekender event. I walk up to a rehearsal stage where an opening act sets their marks and performs light/sound/video checks. Many drum kits on stage are moved by roadies who wear red spandex onesies and powder blue troll wigs. They move equipment into different configurations until the tour director provides his verbal signoff.

I'm handed a black and white paper flyer, an invitation to a party thrown by "the bassist" for everyone who's pitched in to keep the tour afloat while he recovers from wrist surgery.

"Thank you for picking up the slack while he's out on necessary leave."

I realize I'm the stand in for the performer, and I don't know any of the music.

"Just keep it simple. It's bass. When it comes down to it...don't overdo it!" My mental chatter continues, ***"Play the root to prevent the boot."***

THE CHICKEN *(deferential, adaptable, and chameleon-like)* pats me on the back and rubs my shoulders. He thanks me for standing in for him. Wait, THE CHICKEN is the bassist? I walk the backstage maze and can hear the crowd become expectant and animated. I don't have an instrument, nor do I know where I'm supposed to be.

"This is the biggest crowd I've ever played for."

"You'll be fine."

"What are you doing instead?"

"Hanging out with this French guy," THE CHICKEN says while ducking down a dark hallway with a suitor to kiss.]

[0953.3 / 2484] [I realize I'm playing bass for my favorite rock band when I turn the corner and encounter "The Guitarist," a different being from my good friend THE GUITARIST. He's a 7'6" slender man, with pale skin and shoulder length black hair and looks like the love child of the VAMPIRE LESTAT and ADAM JONES. I have a fanboy moment and jump up and down gleefully at our first interaction. I can't jump up high enough to meet his eye line. I shake my off ecstasy off saying,

"Phew this is really amazing. I hope I'm able to do what you want me to do."

"The Guitarist" creepily responds by flashing pointy bicuspids and hissing, *"If you're with us, you're on your grid mark (...that Green X on the ground). If you look across the stage at us during the last song and say, "AAAAAAAAAAAARRRRGHHH!" ...then we'll know we've fried your brain."*

***I see this reality unfold in a parallel dimension. ***

I stand awash in thunderous sound and a backdrop of red, orange, and yellow flames screaming.

"THE GUITARIST" continues, *"...otherwise we'll just keep going. You cool with mixing 'work and weird?'"* inferring we perform on a high dose of psychedelics.

"I'm up for work first."

"The Guitarist" pulls his cape around him and a shorter female attendant to converse privately. My attention drifts upward. I note plywood silhouettes of different musical instruments. The assistant leaves quickly. "The Guitarist" puts his arm around me. We advance down a corridor towards the stage. In a distracted moment he shoves a boney finger in my mouth. A tic tac hits my tongue after it clicks on the front of my upper teeth. I spit the candy out and shout,

"NOT YET...I DON'T WANT THAT!"

I'm not sure if it was a prank, a dose of LSD, or both. I don't like being controlled by someone I consider*(ed)* a hero. I'm handed a bass, stood in front of a wall of amplifiers and racks of effects processors, then hear my guide reassure me that it's ok to,

"become pneuma."] //

⁂

Min. = ♣- THE GUITARIST: #1033
WORK: #0006, #0007, #0015
WEIRD: #0079, #0383,
PARALLEL: #0017, #0028, #0047
PNEUMA: #0116, #0346
SILHOUETTE: #1269, #1336

⁂

#0954 - October 26, 2019 @ 07:53 (San Francisco, California)

[0954.1 / 2485] [*"Forgot most of it, but WILL remember. I WILL!"* I hear as I'm shaken from sleep.]

[0954.2 / 2486] [*"We all commit MURDER with our mouths and most of us NEVER know!"* a voice screams at me in the middle of a public park.]

[0954.3 / 2487] [THE CARPENTER sits on a deck in a rocking chair next to CARLOS SANTANA. They trade guitar licks and stories about their grandchildren. *"We have incredible conversations, with incredible people, in incredible places,"* they both verbally reflect in unison. They give each other a high five.]

[0954.4 / 2488] [I awaken from an elegant layer of dreaming, realizing I have not actually written anything down.]

[0954.5 / 2489] [I'm master of ceremonies for a large fundraiser. I listen for key words that animate the crowd. I introduce JENNIFER LOPEZ and listen to her keynote with similar discernment. After the event concludes I sit in a line with the all-male orchestra, who casually talk and loosen their black bow ties to unwind, post performance. A golden Labrador receives pats from the entire line.

"We chose you because this event seemed to fit your tendencies as a performer," I'm told repeatedly.]

[0954.6 / 2490] [I get up and walk to a door. I open it and walk through a bathroom, stopping briefly to glance at myself in the mirror while I roll an orange bath towel into a tight coil. I place it on a rack for the next guest. I can see through solid walls like one-way glass windows.]

[0954.7 / 2491] [I'm concurrently dialed in to multiple conversations. I'm not able to clearly parse them out. Everything seems important, though it occurs as chattering noise. I'm not bothered by this, and trust my spirit hears *(and integrates)* everything it needs to.] //

⁂

Maj. = 1- THE CARPENTER: #0969

MURDER: #0172, #0278

GUEST: #0015, #0017, #0021

HIGH FIVE: #0056, #0339

BATHROOM: #0021, #0036, #0044

IMPORTANT: #1256, #1288, #1336

⁂

#0955 - October 28, 2019 @ 05:06 (San Francisco, California)

[0955.1 / 2492] [I'm served a slice of green cake with thin, whole, vertical slices of perfectly centered avocado.]

[0955.2 / 2493] [I hug THE PSYCHIATRIST, take a seat, and promptly begin a two-year meditation.]

[0955.3 / 2494] [I maintain my day-to-day life while existing in a state of deep meditation. I'm given a thick bright green wristband as I advance through a long line. I'm number 32,040 among a group of many who've committed to an equivalent two-year contract.]

[0955.4 / 2495] [THE WEAVER invites us into a gathering space that looks like the front of a large truck or train. She has us sit, and walks us through the details of her day as she pours each of us a cup of tea. The room rumbles. A loud squeaking begins as the room starts to tilt and sink. THE WEAVER continues her debrief, unfazed. We start to worry. Is the room submerged in a vat of liquid metal? Our fears subside when we see thick white paint seep up through small dime sized round holes in the stainless-steel floor. The tilt of the room increases. The paint level rises above our ankles, then up to our waists, eventually to our upper arms and then flows over the tabletop. The table is the "Joystick" that allows us to collectively dunk and lift the giant wireframe room. Once coated, we work together to raise the structure up and out of the paint pit, allowing it to dry and set while we continue chatting with THE WEAVER.] //

⁂

Maj. = 0- THE WEAVER: #0969
Min. = ♠- THE PSYCHIATRIST: #0970
AVOCADO: #0034, #0240
SEEP: #1120
TEA: #1225, #1241

⁂

#0956 - **October 28, 2019 @ 06:37 (San Francisco, California)**

[0956.1 / 2496] [SPIDERMAN and WONDER WOMAN both stand over me trying to slap me back into consciousness. My body feels like it's been crushed. I've been impaled vertically from pelvis-to-throat by a giant rubber plug. The room is dim. We're definitely in the comic book. Dialog's presented in bubbles, while Ben Day dots of color whiz about. I smell sulfur. Something is rotting. Maybe it's me. I'm in and out of consciousness. I'm not sure what's going on. SPIDERMAN waves his gloved index finger in front of my face and says, *"Don't. You. Die."* I find him really attractive because he's wearing 6" red velvet heels.] //

⁂

ROTTING: #0016, #0084, #0188, #0305, #0339, #0368, #1204
RED VELVET: #0009, #0033, #0045, #0087, #0144, #0147, #0181, #0233, #1294
CRUSHED: #0045, #0125, #0128, #0295, #0376, #1237

⁂

#0957 - **October 29, 2019 @ 01:05 (San Francisco, California)**

[0957.1 / 2497] [I sit on the front porch of a building looking up at the brilliance of a bright white full moon. A mysterious arm hands me a shotgun and encourages me to take aim at raptors we see flying in silhouette in front of the moon. I take the weapon, line up a shot, fire once and watch a majestic bird plummet to the Earth. It makes a heavy "thud" as it strikes a vacant city street between two abandoned apartment buildings. I've killed a bald eagle.

The mysterious arm retracts back into the building behind me. I walk toward the bird, intending to retrieve it from the center of the street. A pair of car headlights come on accompanied by the sound of a revving engine, as a large steel frame car descends a hill towards me at high speed. I'm not sure if what I've done is illegal, but consider the notion I've been unwittingly entrapped in a police sting operation.]

[0957.2 / 2498] [I'm at a ritzy hotel walking by a ballroom with large windows. I see THE HILLBILLY, THE NURSE and THE LONGFELLOW *(collaborative, lyrical, and playful)* leading a yoga workshop for hundreds of people. One set of people practices. Another teaches and assists. A third group observes.]

. . .

[0957.3 / 2499] [I'm shitfaced drunk and lumber up a hotel hallway occasionally pressing my face against the wall. I stumble into a white lit bathroom and pee excessively. Gallons of urine flow out from my body. I'm astonished. I have a fire hydrant of piss in my pelvis. The output becomes so large it embarrasses other guys who enter to pee, who then move as far away from me as possible.

I leave the bathroom and find myself *(still drunk)* in a ground floor suite with windows that open out a patio with a view of a golf course. I lay down on a comfortable white mattress in the center of the room.

I pass out momentarily then quickly stand up and move towards the window where a homeless meth addict outside strikes up a conversation with me. I can't hear him speak over the screaming sounds made by the scabs and burns on his skin. All of his wounds are self-inflicted. Pain keeps him present. I want to help him. When I offer him a healing, he slinks away from me and retreats to the shadows.

I accept his disappearance.]

[0957.4 / 2500] [I turn back towards the bed and find a young, attractive, effeminately queer person sitting and editing a music video with a friend. The music is glitchy, with symphonic string overlays. The accompanying visuals contain multiple large women driving large cars in slow motion with glittery Vegas-style backdrops. The artistic pair receives project feedback from a professor that watches their process via video conference.]

[0957.5 / 2501] [My goal is to find "ME." The queerboi invites me to go to bed with him. He makes a casual move toward me, then leaps with a kiss. I'm stunned for a moment. He asks me to *"get aggressive"* ...so I do. He makes an immediate request that I, *"slow down."*

He wears a thick stainless steel cockring that looks sexy as I penetrate him. After we conclude I realize I don't know where my phone is, I don't know where we are, and I don't remember which hotel I'm staying at.

"I wannnu fine you laterrrr," I say with a slur as he disappears. Two dark shadowy figures enter.

"ME?" they ask.

"Yep (*hiccup*) ...thatssss ME," I say raising my right hand up as I lean sloppily backward on the bed. I'm still drunk. I'm confident it's THE DANCER and THE ATHEIST, who earlier agreed to meet me at the hotel.

A third being grabs me by the hair and pulls me up into the air, as the other two shadows head to the bathroom. It's unclear what's going to happen to me, but I pre-cognitively cycle through a variety of possible outcomes. Might I get murdered? May my kidneys be cut from my back? Could my head be smashed repeatedly into the toilet bowl until my skull fractures and I die of traumatic brain injury? Might I be transported to a hospital? Will I make it to my appointment with THE DANCER and THE ATHEIST?

"SOMETHING: NOT GOOD" goes down right now as I pass out.] //

⁂

Maj. = 2- THE DANCER: #0961, 8- THE ATHEIST: #1021, 13- THE NURSE: #0964

Min. = ♣ - THE HILLBILLY: #1177

VEGAS: #0112, #0170, #0293

HALLWAY: #0007, #0009, #0015, #0029

SHADOWS: #0006, #0294, #0794
CONFIDENT: #1288, #1293
⁂

#0958 - October 29, 2019 @ 02:31am (San Francisco, California)

[0958.1 / 250X] [*"Keep your energies in check,"* a low resonant voice scolds as I'm shown a variety of abstract images and scenes of windy desert dunes on blisteringly hot days.] //

⁂
ABSTRACT: #0160, #0187, #0287, #1235
WINDY: #0149, #0472
RESONANT: #0018, #0047, #0159, #0393
⁂

#0959 - October 29, 2019 @ 03:12 (San Francisco, California)

[0959.1 / 2502] [I slide down the cherry wood banister of a gently sloped staircase in a large rectangular atrium. The steps are carpeted in a soft turquoise tone that naturally rolls downward. The steps are 30' across, 3' wide, 3" tall, and cascade down as far as I can see.]

[0959.2 / 2503] [I encounter the young queer guy from dream **[0957.5 / 2501]**. He introduces himself as "John." We're at a celebration at a different hotel, in a different reality and time. Dessert plates on the table have small stacks of sugar cookies (*white frosted with tiny pipetted rainbow-colored lines*). It's a big party, perhaps a wedding reception. I pause to share intense conversations with a number of people about how to best portray gender roles in a forthcoming film.

"John" grabs my hand, spins me around, and introduces me to his parents. Our interaction is brief, yet cordial. The two of us move on to have a conversation with a guy who discloses his involvement in a *"large scale government surveillance project."* We don't find it very interesting until he says he can *"do the job that mother can't."*

"John" and I find this interaction intense, odd, and unnecessary. I stop to catch a glimpse of "John" and notice his hair is now curly and hangs to his shoulders. I like the way he looks. He inspires patience in me to continue growing my hair out to a similar length. My attention turns to his butt, where I see the outlines of unfinished tattoos through his pressed white shirt. I find him incredibly attractive. I have no way of contacting him after the party. He'll suggest Facebook *(though I don't, and won't use it)*. He consistently offers me a drink and encourages me to try a sip of his craft cocktail.

We stand in the doorway of a white ballroom and are escorted into the space by THE PHILANTHROPIST, as a video is projected on a wall. She's insistent we follow her. I'm excited to see her, and the chance encounter is unexpected. She playfully marches me and "John" across the room while holding me by the right wrist. "John" holds a pitcher of lemonade, which he drinks from at volume. He pours some into my glass which spills over and onto the floor. THE PHILANTHROPIST springs into action and grabs towels and napkins to mop up the mess. "John" and I leap over a bunch of round tables topped with white linens and sweets. After bounding across the space, we stop cold in the presence of two elderly women referred to as "the grandmothers."] //

⁂

Min. = ♠-THE PHILANTHROPIST: #1131
COCKTAIL: #0115, #0150, #0209
CORDIAL: #0897, #0909
TURQUOISE: #0022, #0730
CHERRY: #0037, #0088, #0277, #0306
ELDERLY: #1296, #1297, #1335

⁂

#0960 - October 29, 2019 @ 04:24 (San Francisco California)

[0960.1 / 2504] [Interactions with "John" continue. He's shifted to a more fluid, non-binary expression and also occasionally occurs as a little person. They're barefoot for the majority of our interaction which is flirty, humorous and creatively charged. "John" injures their left foot. He refuses a ride home when I offer them one. He's insistent they'll *"make his own way."* Their/His interchangeable pronoun usage confuses me, but does not dissuade "our" attraction. As a little person he morphs into WOODY HARRELSON who's about to receive a windfall payment in the wake of some large, successful projects.]

[0960.2 / 2505] [A group of people dance around a stage using steel folding chairs as props. They split into smaller teams and move to the four corners of the stage, ready to rehearse a key sequence with the star. "John" stands next to me.

"Do you want to stick around?" I want to give him a ride home. He'd rather stay and observe the rehearsal.

Our attention moves to the stage where we watch THE WRANGLER emerge in a red sequined dress, channeling the essence of JESSICA RABBIT. She arches her back during a slow-motion lift, twice, supported from beneath by a number of black silhouetted beings. She performs the sequence a third time while seated in a chair.

A hush falls across the cast as they await the director's notes. The pregnant pause which follows lingers for an uncomfortably long time. The director takes a deep drag off a cigarette and offers, *"You're half as quick as your predecessor, but twice as beautiful."* He snuffs his cigarette out on the table and walks away.] //

⁂

CIGARETTE: #0040, #0043, #0088
PAUSE: #0001, #0006
BAREFOOT: #0445
STEEL: #1335, #1344

⁂

#0961 - October 29, 2019 @ 05:10 (San Francisco, California)

[0961.1 / 2506] [I witness a game played by urban teenagers in the streets after school.

Teams face away from each other and toss colorful water balloons overhead at their opponents. They can't look where they're throwing. They have to take a gamble and hope the balloon explodes as near their target as possible. Direct hits are worth more points. Everyone laughs and enjoys playing the game.]

[0961.2 / 2507] [I flip to a music channel and watch a video for a new DEFTONES song. Rumbling drop tuned 8-string guitars and basses create a sludgy **djent** sound. Two Asian women seem to be Siamese twins connected by their beaded and braided hair. They're suspended on an oversized mobile that hangs precariously over a busy city street. It appears stark, austere, and cold. The women are covered in macramé shibari knots from crown to toe. It's elegant, alarming, and has my complete attention. Their dance on the air is a hypnotic and light contrast to the dark brooding music.]

[0961.2 / 2508] [THE DANCER has won the title of "Queen" at a pageant. I'm supposed to walk her down the aisle when she accepts her award. I'm currently in a penthouse condo with friends, hundreds of feet above a train station *(which I need to travel to)*, to attend the pageant. We descend via an elevator and spill into a dimly lit condo occupied by a scintillatingly dressed Asian woman. She asks us who we are, then requests that we leave and not return.

"We're on our way out," I say as we exit her unit then zig zag down a maze of corridors to the train station terminal.

We take a train to the end of the line, then emerge to street level and navigate to the venue. The procession is imminent, but I'm asked to go down front to the media pit. I'm handed a camera by a young man who says, *"Stay here and take the photos."*

The processional to the stage begins. I transport to an offsite location, instantly instilling worry that I'll miss the opportunity to support THE DANCER. People walk up the street, arms wrapped in neon feather boas of many colors. I'm confident I can make it back on time, until I lose my relationship with gravity. I tumble and flip up off the ground, over a busy street, and into outer space. I fly back to the venue, this time greeted at the back by the guy who had earlier handed me the camera. He says, *"We can't be sure when all of this is supposed to happen. We appreciate you being flexible."*

We wait for some time before I'm cleared to take THE DANCER's hand and walk her to her seat atop a throne at the front of the venue.] //

⁂

Maj. = 2- THE DANCER: #0969
DEFTONES: #1225
KNOTS: #0266
PAGEANT: #0909
FEATHER: #0183, #0396
GRAVITY: #0005, #0007, #0008
VENUE: #1202, #1213, #1248, #1301

⁂

#0962 - October 29, 2019 @ 06:33 (San Francisco, California)

[0962.1 / 2509] [THE HULA HOOPER *(crass, confrontational, and funny)* sends me a news article on wildfires with a question about its messaging and positioning as an advertisement. ***"Fossil fuel consumption..."*** I begin typing a response that trails off into thought and remains incomplete. I delete the phrase and begin again. ***"The content actually doesn't matter. The tone from which it resonates does."***

I walk with my laptop to the driveway of my home. I live in a suburban community in the American Southeast. My laptop has a built-in projector, which I use to cast media on to my garage door *(which doubles as a giant media screen).* I realize the desired outcomes in Indiana are prevention measures/standards that exist in California and soon will be implemented in the state where I now reside. Neighborhood women are out and walking. The sun has set and the sky is an ideal blend of pink, white and blue hues. Two women make conversation across the street and play an odd game. They hit a volleyball with steel racquets at two vertical uprights on the opposite side of the street from where they stand. The poles softly illuminate and render a warm crystal singing bowl-like tone when struck by the glowing white ball.

My attention returns to my garage door and I compose a full response to THE HULA HOOPER.

"The things that I see in the proposed campaign seem consistent with what has succeeded in other similar markets and municipalities. Unfortunately, I no longer have social media and will not be able to promote the content as requested."

I grab the computer and walk to a concrete slab; a foundation for new construction of a family home. I take a seat in a high back chair at an oak dining room table, intending to write a narrative. An errantly struck "glow ball" results in one of the neighbor women walking over to retrieve it, then visit with me.

She takes a seat behind me stating, *"Oh, you're writing now! Ya know, this is the time where if you integrate everything you've undertaken in the past couple years, you'll discover your creative abilities will REALLY begin to accelerate. Be sure you cherish that."*

I feel flattered, seen, and newly dedicated to *"stick with it."* She retrieves the ball and returns to her game and conversation across the street. There are no walls, yet I don't feel exposed as I plug away one inspired word at a time on my magnum opus.] //

⁂

CONSISTENT: #0019, #0097, #0461
INDIANA: #0222, #0223, #0224, #0225, #0226
IDEAL: #0887, #0948, #962, #1147
FOUNDATION: #0157, #0240, #0244
THE HULA HOOPER: #1236

⁂

#0963 - October 30, 2019 @ 01:08 (San Francisco, California)

[0963.1 / 2510] [I'm in the woods. A group of friends who are becoming masterful yoga assistants join me for an impromptu class out in big nature. I lead the practice and give them each deep, one breath assists. One-by-one I bring each of them up to embody the practice: *"One full breath, one touch, one deep assist, enter and exit effortlessly, and begin again."* THE FLASH is eager and jumps up first to try the technique. She moves swiftly from point-to-point, and becomes an immediate embodiment of grace and flow. She finishes her pass; suggests we move practice to a small stream that flows naturally, and invites other members of the group to participate.

THE OLD SOUL *(fatigued, impatient, and withdrawn)* and THE RUMBLER *(measured, firm, and rooted)* both take turns moving through the process. I float in and out of their bodies and split my spirit between them. I get a sense of their individual experiences, and offer collective support. I can see through all three sets of our eyes. I'm also able to sense what the bodies they're touching are experiencing, as they move through the sequence with confidence and flow. Our hands/feet enter and exit the water without splashing. We take seated poses with legs submerged just beneath the surface of the water. THE FLASH bends forward dipping her face in the cool refreshing stream. I give her an assist by pressing down gently on her back and allowing the water to rush over the back of her head. She connects to her breath newly, rises from the water exhilarated and with ease, keeping these aspects present through her next round of practice.

THE CHILD had, *"SO MUCH FUN PLAYING YOGA IN THE OCEAN"* that she wants to go next. She's a teenager now, but as excited and curious as she was as a five-year-old. She requests we move to a mossy area under a family of large redwood trees. Our saunter feels fun, alive, precise and dance-like. The degree of mastery is mythic.

"Are we samurai gliding through bamboo?"

I observe a grid of flying birds organized like choreographed drones. Each time I call a pose they create a different black constellation in the clear blue sky. They illustrate common firing neuronal paths of a person whose brain is in a flow state. An impression of the *"universal mind lattice"* is demonstrated dynamically as fluctuating Voronoi diagrams.]

[0963.2 / 2511] [A message alert on my phone buzzes my upper leg. I look at the device and see a reminder to *"Revise Hedonic Calendar."* I ask if anyone in my camping group is interested in the process and wants a demonstration.] //

⁂

Maj. = 3- THE CHILD: #0969
FLOW: #0007, #0009, #0019, #0035
NATURE: #0001, #0042, #0047
DRONES: #0017, #0311
THE OLD SOUL: #1322
THE FLASH: #1035

⁂

#0964 - October 30, 2019 @ 2:24am (San Francisco, California)

[0964.1 / 2512] [I'm at an event center where a movement class is attended by hundreds of people. A support team takes special care when distributing large cream-colored crocheted blankets, draped over participants at the conclusion of the event. They're donated and intended for single use. Participants are encouraged to take them afterwards as a reminder of how it feels to be swaddled in *"Grandmother's Love."*

THE NURSE and THE MEEK co-led the session and now sit on a couch in my office next to a window with a parking lot view. Both of them seem content with their offering and remove packs of cigarettes from their purses. THE NURSE lights up a Capri. THE MEEK chooses a Marlboro Red. They both begin puffing away, filling the office with smoke. I look at them like they're crazy. As I walk away wordlessly, they don't seem to understand the nature of my discontent. I walk through a residential plat shouting over my shoulder,

"Integrate this into your evolving inquiry. You'll have an entire week to complain about it

with your friends." I talk with a few people on the street to shift my focus and cool off. Changing to a totally different topic soothes my feeling of being ***"wronged."***]

[0964.2 / 2513] [A young woman asks for help. She wants to find a safe place to take a shower, before attending a formal evening event. I'm handed a stack of cards, the printing on which is delicate and floral. THE SUMERIAN's *(surprising, intermittent, and artful)* cards are printed on white card stock, with thin silver cursive text. I place the cards on a table in tight little stacks within small square frames made from tiny red bricks. The table is centered in a stone turret of a castle, in front of a bright kaleidoscopic window.

A number of students have offered their quarters to the young woman. An upper-level student suggests they have access to three bathrooms, though their lease only specifies one. The woman departs to bathe while I flip through the stack of cards and organize them on the table. The only names familiar to me are *"THE SUMERIAN and his wife,"* and one other acquaintance whom I don't recall how I met.

The young woman's asked me to handle the organization of the cards so she'll have a successful evening.]

[0964.3 / 2514] [THE FIREFIGHTER, his mother, and youngest brother are all aboard a massive aircraft. He's insistent they pay for an upgrade to the "galactic" package which will render them all home in the blink of an eye. All he needs to do, once they agree, is to hold hands with them and press the red button on the side of his chair. They decide to do it. They grab hands, push the button and...

"Poof" ...they're gone.] //

⁂

Maj. = 13- THE NURSE: #1016
Min. = ♥- THE FIREFIGHTER: #1035
INTEGRATE: #0025, #0077, #0136
FOCUS: #0047, #0069, #0070
LOVE: #0009, #0012, #0017
BUTTON: #1295

⁂

#0965 - October 30, 2019 @ 05:45 (San Francisco, California)

[0965.1 / 2515] [JUDGE JUDY manages an affluent candy store frontage within Harrods of London. I float around the ceiling of the space above a black and white checkerboard floor. I turn invisible and drop from the ceiling to a holiday themed round table piled high with treats. I'm a child. The adults can't see me. I eat a chocolate biscotti and sip thick hot drinking chocolate from an upside down/inverted Aztec pyramid shaped vessel. I walk out of the space, which appears to be the same shape as the vessel in my hand. As I pass JUDGE JUDY on the staircase, she smirks at me and fervently implores, *"GET OUT!"*]

[0965.2 / 2516] [I enter a brightly lit novelty store, which sells thin foam LP sized squares that have extremely fine detail etched into them. They come in various sizes and are highly popular. I progress through the space and find a room with adult human sized posters of various childhood superheroes that have been overtly sexualized and fetishized. Men bound by their feet lounge on the ascending stairs, attached to poles by long chains. THE LINGUIST and THE HUSBAND are connected at the ankle. THE LINGUIST wears a long brunette wig with bangs. He grabs my foot. I fall down, whip about, grab his foot, tickle it, and then slap it. Startled, he comes to saying, *"So I see you're taking what I like and mashing it up with what you like to do."*

THE HUSBAND slaps THE LINGUIST to get his attention.

Department store orgies are new for them, and a bit disorienting. They discuss when to get up and travel across the room together. They select another toy and continue their public play session. They stand and walk down the stairs. I progress up and out of the store and on to a busy city street.] //

⁂

CHECKERBOARD: #0092, #0126, #0248
CHILDHOOD: #0045, #0101, #0125
PLAY: #0126, #0127, #0128
NOVELTY: #0027, #0125
WIG: #0168, #0568

⁂

#0966 - October 31, 2019 @ 04:47 (San Francisco, California)

[0966.1 / 2517] [A group of makers take on the challenge of creating a "Box Harp" in an afternoon design contest. Cardboard boxes with slits in the side are fitted with different sized stainless-steel tools *(straight edges, triangles, etc.)*. The instrument is played by striking a hand on the tools in specific patterns to create a wide range of ghostly tones and ambient, ethereal sounds. Multiple teams of four persons work together to tune their creations. Strings on some versions can be plucked.]

[0966.2 / 2518] [A team records green-screen movement of actors in fitness video B-roll. A variety of punches and kicks are modeled and will likely end up rendered in a popular video game. The team debates the appropriate angle of capture relative to the height of the actor, to ensure continuity and scale across characters.]

[0966.3 / 2519] [I'm on a road trip out of town. I stop at a rest station to use the bathroom. The lines are long and slow moving. All the toilets are being upgraded with coin operated door locks. When I get to the front I squat and attempt to go, but can't. The notion of having to pay makes it challenging for me to relax.] //

⁂

HARP: #0148
VIDEO GAME: #0013, #0106, #0116, #0129, #0136, #0194, #0263, #0387
ROAD TRIP: #0426, #0444, #0669, #0694
TOWN: #1206, #1227, #1249, #1251

⁂

#0967 - October 31, 2019 @ 07:38 (San Francisco, California)

[0967.1 / 2520] [I get a ride to work from an older Arab man. His name is "Cosmin." He's large and bald. He smokes cigarettes and talks to me in broken English. I'm not able to understand him. A professionally dressed woman sits on the bench seat between us, calling out when we've missed/overshot her office. We're in a convertible. The wind blows overhead. Her hair is surrounded by a thin floral print scarf. We turn around then make another quick U-Turn, delivering her curbside at her place of business.

A roller cart awaits, filled with steamer trunks and banker boxes. "Cosmin" is eager to help her move in. I get out of the car and walk a few remaining blocks to my office. I work in a very narrow, very long building. Inside the building, everyone seems to be wearing a fedora. I ascend a staircase to my third-floor office. I believe I see a man following me. When I turn around, I notice I'm not wearing my glasses. All I see is a hot outline of a spirit wearing a hat that advances upward at parallel pitch to the staircase. A cheap wooden pulpit with two tent cards on top sits adjacent to my office door. One card is a thank you note. The other is a recipe card for a magic elixir. I open my office door. The cold wind from an open window wafts my face like a slap from Jack Frost. I know I can find an inexpensive space that can accommodate up to five team members as my business grows. I remain dedicated to my work.

*"**This is the start of a new chapter.**"*] //

⁂

FEDORA: #0017, #0140, #0277
THANK YOU NOTE: #0477, #0787
RECIPE: #0173, #0189
DEDICATED: #0071, #0767, #0788
FLORAL: #0043, #0365, #0397
NEW: #1256, #1259, #1267

⁂

#0968 - November 1, 2019 @ 02:51 (San Francisco, California)

[0968.1 / 2521] [An unknown person comes to me and expresses their concern about not paying off a debt. ***"What's the big deal? Are they going to kill you?"*** I neutrally respond.]

[0968.2 / 2522] [I'm at the gym using a pec fly machine when a pair of tattooed Latinx men approach me. They want to make me their *"third."* I accept, and we leave the gym, instantly entering a bungalow where we disrobe by snapping our fingers. We laugh because we've all painted our penises for Halloween. One of the guys has painted his green, refers to it as *"Shrek,"* and suggests I, *"trust it tastes like lime."*]

[0968.3 / 2523] [I'm a roadie for the FOO FIGHTERS and help the band roll crates of guitars and racks of effects processors down a shallow ramp. DAVE GROHL helps us push the boxes away from the venue and towards a series of parked semi-trucks. I congratulate him on the epic live television performance he and the group just gave. One crate rolls away quickly. I run to prevent it from striking the side of a truck. DAVE pulls out a long rainbow "L" shaped rod that he uses like a Shepherd's hook to prevent the crate from hitting the truck and damaging the equipment. THE CONFIDANT is also a roadie on the tour. As we move crates from stage to truck, we play air guitar and make djent sounds with our mouths. We pause to reflect on how easy it would be to write a banger of a track with two pounding, driving, and complementary polyrhythmic guitar parts. We get even more excited when we make a list of friends, who we can enroll to help us track, mix, master, produce, and distribute the song.] //

⁂

Maj. = 16- THE CONFIDANT: #1001
RAINBOW: #0215, #0243, #0329
DJENT: #0961
POLYRHYTHM: #0545, #0798
SHALLOW: #1309

⁂

#0969 - November 1, 2019 @ 04:11 (San Francisco, California)

[0969.1 / 2524] [*"Rental cars are extremely expensive when you fly in to major hubs like SEA, LAX, IAD or BOS."*]

[0969.2 / 2525] [I'm at a college party hosted by THE ENTREPRENEUR *(cold, inward, and stern)* and THE COUNSELOR *(precise, tight, and strong)*. EDM plays on a small speaker. Clusters of people stand chatting in a crowded A-frame room. I pick up a bowl of popcorn from a round wooden table and pour it back into a bag. I take the bag with me and walk back to my dorm.

I check my schedule and realize I've been attending the incorrect section for an advanced abstract algebra class all semester. THE KIDDO *(exact, amiable, and curious)* is my assigned professor. Because we're friends, I think I can convince her to let me transfer my work to her, and schmooze my way to a pass. She holds me accountable and demands I show up and take her final exam. I have a week to prepare. It's unclear if I take the exam, and whether I pass or fail.]

[0969.3 / 2526] [I'm on a family road trip in an RV. THE CARPENTER's been driving for a while and is hidden by a blue curtain that hangs down from the center of the cabin. THE CHILD sits on my lap in a chair behind the driver's seat. THE CARPENTER suggests THE WEAVER and THE DANCER both take palm sized blue liqui-gel sedatives and retire to the back for a nap.

"Why don't you take your own suggestion, since you've been at it for so long," THE WEAVER responds.

We take a break at a rest stop. When I get back in the vehicle my seat has turned into a small metal cane that folds inconspicuously into the wall. I don't think it's safe for me to sit on and hold THE CHILD, while the RV moves quickly down the road. Our next stop finds us refueling near a green space in Marin, California.]

. . .

[0969.4 / 2527] [Passing through a red brick hotel, I pause to read the biography of a local artist and author. Under a self-portrait, she's written a poem scribbled in green ink expressing how this red brick hotel / square / town / is, *"the seat of the soul; the place from which all my deepest expressions have come through."*] //

⁂

Maj. = 0- THE WEAVER: #0988, 1- THE CARPENTER: #0973, 2-THE DANCER: #0972, 3- THE CHILD: #0976
BOSTON: #0146, #0777
RED BRICK: #0033, #0116
BIOGRAPHY: #0076
CURSIVE: #0161, #0426
THE ENTREPRENEUR: #1103
THE COUNSELOR: #1103
THE KIDDO: #1154

⁂

#0970 - November 2, 2019 @ 04:58 (San Francisco, California)

[0970.1 / 2528] [THE LALA has driven in from out of state to visit me. We sit on oversized square satin pillows in a tall bay window at twilight. Giant green trees are just beyond the glass. She places a stack of her journals on the table between us. I grab one and start looking through it. As I do, I realize it's best for me to wait for her to open and share her journals. The one I'm holding is red and leather-bound, full of intimate personal details I would not be ready to share, so I pause. She nods that I can continue reading.]

[0970.2 / 2529] [I sneak into a renovated mixed-use building knowing I'm being observed on CCTV. I arrive in a large, dark central space where a faceless, tall, slender man wearing a suit leers overhead attempting to intimidate me. I'm not certain who he is, but the energy is dark, and his vibration, **low**.]

[0970.3 / 2530] [I'm in drag with THE PSYCHIATRIST. We head to a dinner at the top floor of a Victorian era lounge. I wear a bustle and a corset. My face is painted; eyes dosed with belladonna. We access the *(secret)* top floor of the lounge because I'm known and well liked in the neighborhood.

Upstairs in the lounge are rows of small, finely upholstered loveseats that match their respective time periods. When offered, I decline a margarita, instead taking a gin and tonic from a white-gloved hand. A small fragile glass umbrella fashioned like wilting flower petals keeps dust out of the drink. I sip it daintily, until THE PSYCHIATRIST and I walk out of the top floor window, on to a boat on open water, traveling at intense speed.]

[0970.4 / 2531] [While on the speedboat we maneuver under giant vessels with massive pontoons. They lumber up and down in the water, generating massive waves and nearly crushing us from overhead as we zoom under and through. The sky is bright and sparkly blue. The boat slows and eventually docks. Someone's left a journal behind. I pick it up, de-board the boat, and find myself seated over a barrel in the basement of a Barbary Coast saloon during the San Francisco gold rush of 1849.

I open the journal and see an illuminated letter press page reading, *"COMPLETE THIS BY TUESDAY,"* in golden flourished script. I tear out a page and begin making a punch list. A woman stops by and asks if I've seen her journal. She's surprised when she notices I have it, and have torn a page from it.

"I apologize. I made a mistake when I tore out that page. I'll buy you another journal and just keep making my notes. It's no big deal."

She's still confused and not happy with my proposed remedy.] //

⁂

Min. = ♠- THE PSYCHIATRIST: #1065, ♦-THE LALA: #1196
MARGARITA: #806
FRAGILE: #0009, #0028, #0058
INTIMATE: #0059, #0083, #0313
SLENDER: #0251
WAVES: #1330, #1331

⁂

⁂ 12.5 - THE BOOK OF DELPHINUS: 0971-0980 ⁂

#0971 - November 2, 2019 @ 06:03 (San Francisco, California)

[0971.1 / 2532] [I walk through the steppe in Patagonia, alone. It's cold and damp.]

[0971.2 / 2533] [I sit in a balcony watching JOHN MYUNG play bass. He invites me to tap in and experience what it feels like to, *"play bass with fluid mastery."*]

[0971.3 / 2534] [I sit in a forward tilting bus seat. A guy walks toward me and flips his wrist at me, indicating he wants me to move so he can sit down. I don't surrender my seat. He sits down next to me without incident.]

[0971.4 / 2535] [*"Do these things in this exact order,"* a voice commands. I grab a green Post It note from a stack on a table and stick it to my notebook, intending to follow the request. A drag queen grabs it and crumples it in her hand saying, *"No, that's not yours...we're doing something completely different."*

She replaces the Post It with a list of "To do's" for a "Mr. Beaselman." The name is familiar.

"I've had dreams for Beaselman before!"

I recall and document dozens *(and eventually hundreds)* of meticulously detailed dreams, which I then index and catalog. I look at the list and see the details disappear. I realize I'm dreaming. I wake up with no memory. All records lost.] //

⁂

POST IT: #0396, #0544, #0592
DRAG QUEEN: #0022, #0147
PLAY BASS: #0666, #0853
SURRENDER: #0926, #0998
INDEX: #0088, #0106
EXPERIENCE: #1303, #1344

⁂

#0972 - November 2, 2019 @ 07:12 (San Francisco, California)

[0972.1 / 2536] [I drive with THE DANCER and THE LAWYER to a party at a legacy home high on a hill in the forest. The trip takes more than an hour, much of it up slow steep switchbacks. A birthday party seems to be winding down as we arrive. I pet multiple dogs and cats that scurry around the house, which bound across sofas and table tops.

An open back door invites a walk down a steep descending wooden staircase that leads to a fenced-in cement tennis court where a pair play a match. On my approach I drop a folder which scatters a bunch of green Post It notes on the court. I'm embarrassed and feel obligated to pick them up. I say hello to the party goers, but no one appears to know us. The group questions why we're there.

Another after hours party is about to begin in the guest house. I go inside and sit on a bench. A group of three guys line up shoulder-to-shoulder obstructing my line of sight with their shared beltline.

"How's about we pound that puss-say?" They question in a threatening tone.

I'm a woman! For a moment I'm alarmed and concerned for my safety.

"Move! I'm going to find my sister and my ride," I demand.

They immediately make way for me to exit. I cross a dark room where people have sex. A short silver haired man, muscular, and similar in look to THE LAMPLIGHTER *(artful, wizardly, and masculine)* is an embodiment of EROS. He's sweaty. His pupils are dilated. He has a large Celtic cross tattooed across the center of his chest in black ink. He winks at me and licks his lips. He and I have danced before. He penetrates every partner he encounters as he walks the room in a zigzag pattern. The action is live streamed on a big screen TV in the party room to my right.] //

⁂

Maj. = 2- THE DANCER: #0988, 5- THE LAWYER: #1075

ZIGZAG: #0017, #1058, #1094

DILATED: #0023, #0296

HELLO: #0441, #820, #0913

EROS: #0059, #0524, #0558

NOTES: #1234, #1302

⁂

#0973 - November 3, 2019 @ 02:58 (San Francisco, California)

[0973.1 / 2537] [Image of a wall of "sugar dumplings."]

[0973.2 / 2538] [A possessed woman with short spiky black hair, gnashes her teeth and snaps at my fingers and toes.]

[0973.3 / 2539] [I'm living in a dormitory and spend a lot of time reconfiguring the few pieces of furniture within. I'm on an upper level and have to be assisted from my door by a cherry picker, because the exterior staircase was never built. THE CARPENTER asks me if I'm comfortable operating it on my own. I'm not. I know misusing it could result in me *(and others)* getting seriously hurt. I prefer to keep my bed against the window wall, near the corner by my closet, which makes a small alcove holding my guitar case inaccessible. I'm not too concerned. I can rearrange the furniture whenever I want. My focus is on studying. I don't need anything right now except for my textbooks.]

[0973.4 / 2540] [I play a video game with friends that bounces from a vertically mounted screen, to a portrait mounted screen, on a wall. The action moves back and forth erratically. We get to a "Boss" level and are unable to determine if we're making any progress towards defeating the entity. The creature is composed of gold and bronze pill/capsule shaped cells that descend from the top of the screen in scrolling "space invaders"-like rows. We fire repeatedly at the layers of shells accompanied by distinctive *"ping"* and *"ting"* sounds.] //

⁂

Maj. = 1- THE CARPENTER: #0988

SUGAR: #0149, #0170, #0194
PROGRESS: #0031, #0097, #0281
BRONZE: #0522, #0654, #0822
SCREEN: #1220, #1278, #1285

⁂

#0974 - November 3, 2019 @ 04:33 (San Francisco, California)

[0974.1 / 2541] [I work the registration table at an event. THE EXECUTIVE PRODUCER is the boss and steps away to handle an emergency in another room. A line of attendees forms and I'm unclear as to how I can help them. I ask them to wait while I search for my job card. The crowd obliges without objection. When I ask them how I can help, their arms send forward their convention credentials on lanyards. They all want to return them at the same time after having been onsite and fully engaged for a week. They're in a bit of a rush to leave, so I stick out my arms and let them hang their items on me as they exit. I collect their electronics and phones as they depart in an orderly and uneventful way.]

[0974.2 / 2542] [I'm at the bottom of a staircase. A girl climbs up the steps in front of me. I follow behind and pick up an infant after ascending a couple of steps. I walk to the top, focusing on the girl while cradling the baby. When I arrive at the top I look down and note the baby has turned into a small brown dog.]

[0974.3 / 2543] [THE VEGAN cooks dinner in an art deco kitchen, wearing a red pencil skirt. Her face is painted with blush and red lipstick.]

[0974.4 / 2544] [I'm in the mountains of Colorado at a massive abandoned campground that sits on a hill across from a busy highway tunnel burrowed deep within the range. I walk through the property. The lights are off. Some rooms look like banquet halls; others favor Zen gardens. The doors are tall, thick, and heavy rectangles that feel like vaults *(or portals)* to other dimensions. I exit the property and walk down a winding gravel driveway to the main road. I encounter a father and son who have shared previous adventures through the property. They pass me and I overhear them discuss the possibility of, *"going back through there sometime."*

I decide to walk back up the driveway and re-enter the house. The lights are on and I watch a tuxedoed banquet crew hurriedly setting tables for an evening event, while two professionally dressed women organize and direct activities. I continue my tour and see a pair of crossed feet wearing saddle shoes reclining upwards and bobbing while a person holds a phone conversation on the opposite side of a cubicle wall made of succulent plants. A large fountain and waterfall create white noise in a large atrium. The attire for the event is formal.

I proceed to the back of the house and exit on to a private driveway where a black limousine is parked and idling. A door opens. I get in. BEYONCÉ and JAY-Z sip champagne and converse with friends. A TV at the front of the limo screens an episode of a new true crime series. A performance just ended, and the show follows events in the house that occurred immediately before the show aired. I find the short time to screen is insanely fast, illogical, and nonsensical. I'm unsure how editing and post production could have possibly happened so quickly. ***"Does it suggest an orchestration or manipulation that everyone celebrating in the car is privy to?"*** I'm perplexed and amazed. I hush them as the volume in the car rises so I can keep my attention on the show. ***"However they achieved this...it's a production marvel,"*** I remark. ***"This stuff literally just happened, and a finished product is already pushed out to the public. Woah."***

I leave my body and fly in the opposite direction from the tunnel, taking note of a big box retail store on the opposite side of the valley from the house. It's jammed with customers and has a noisy, clogged, and horn filled parking lot.] //

⁂

Min. = ♣-THE VEGAN: #0987
BEYONCÉ: #1001
ART DECO: #0026, #0045, #0090, #0159
COLORADO: #301, #0302
BIG BOX: #0149
LANYARD: #0139

⁂

#0975 - November 3, 2019 @ 05:51 (San Francisco, California)

[0975.1 / 2545] [We've locked two cats in a bedroom and believe they're safely sequestered. We leave for a few hours. When we return to check on them, we're greeted with a destroyed room. The cats have torn everything inside to shreds. The curtains, blinds, and windows are all open and blowing with the breeze. A set of French doors open to a weather check balcony. Golden sunlight floods the space. The cats are nowhere to be found. Gone.]

[0975.2 / 2546] [I take and eat eight old fashioned donuts, mentally keeping track of the calories as I scarf one after the next down my gullet. I realize I've loaded a full day's worth of calories in fewer than five minutes. THE FEELER sits at a round coffee table with her coach making an agreement based on her, *"attendance and completion of planned activities."* If homework isn't completed a financial penalty will be charged to her credit card. The coach forces her to eat a donut when she doesn't want to. She may have done *"the work,"* but apparently forgot *"the home-work."*]

[0975.3 / 2547] [Image of a deconstructed rag doll, with facial features crudely scribbled in black sharpie pen.]

[0975.4 / 2548] [A French woman recalls the challenge of coordinating her first international team offsite meeting. She's so skilled and unconsciously competent now, she can complete the same tasks effortlessly. The responsibility is transferred to me. I don't know the tasks, the order, durations, dependencies, complexities, probabilities, risk profile, nor contacts for attendees. My ability to achieve the same outcome on a similar timeline in the short term appears to be an impossibility.]

. . .

[0975.5 / 2549] [**ENTER A SCENE IN PROGRESS** ...me and a colleague connect a tablet to a larger screen to review some prepared presentation content. Someone scheduled a 1:15pm meeting with a man named "Jim" who works diligently in the next room. I omnisciently peek in on him. I know him, but don't say anything because I don't believe he'll remember me. It's been quite a while since he and I have worked together.]

[0975.6 / 2550] ["PATRICK" and an unnamed Asian man *(two men in their 30's)* crack jokes and pick on each other. Their repartee is humorous and tongue-in-cheek.] //

⁂

Min. = ♣- THE FEELER: #1056
CATS: #0096, #0175
DONUTS: #0148, #0406, #0549
AUTOPILOT: #0260
TABLET: #0026, #0423, #0483
FIVE: #1247, #1274, #1285, #1318, #1321
JOKES: #1234

⁂

#0976 - November 4, 2019 @ 04:13 (San Francisco, California)

[0976.1 / 2551] [I work on a rural military base populated with old wooden barns and farm equipment. It's nighttime. Wheat bends and rustles in a consistent and firm wind out of the East. An older man carrying an oil lantern and wearing overalls *(a railroad conductor who's lost his train)* fingers at me to follow him into a barn. We pass through multiple rooms with old military gear piled high on tables, eventually crossing a small threshold to a downward oriented ladder.

We climb to the bottom and he takes me to a dark room with a steamer trunk set in the middle. He opens the trunk and pulls out an engine to an alien craft which looks like a trans-dimensional heart with Mobius-arterial-like loops that funnel diamond light with occasional glittery flickers of red and blue. It's roughly a cubic foot in size. It takes him a couple of attempts to activate before it begins emitting an ultra-low resonant drone. We think we're being watched, so he quickly puts it back in the trunk and we ascend.

En route I meet a woman and give her my code name. She asks for my *"real"* name to which I respond, ***"j0shVa."*** She looks at me, as though I've broken a key protocol. She sits for a while before saying, *"I like your other name better. I'll call you that instead."*

[0976.2 / 2552] [Some days pass before I rendezvous again with the conductor. This time he's placed the engine in a craft hidden under a haystack in the barn. We take an instantaneous trip from Earth to space. We look down on the Earth from thousands of miles out. The out and back trip is quick and too much for my body to handle. My face dramatically swells, an immediate tell that I've been working with tools well beyond my granted security clearance. The conductor brings an ally *(a doctor)* who injects my face with a substance that deflates my skin and shrinks it so it tightly hugs my facial bones. The female doctor also preps a syringe then plunges it into my right hip/groin while saying, *"This is going to hurt you way more than it hurts me."*

I'm able to return to work. I more clearly understand the implications of getting caught. I could lose my job *(and in all likelihood, my life)* if my travel experiments are discovered by the government. I've seen people disappear for less severe infractions.]

[0976.3 / 2553] [In the base canteen, I take a glowing palm-sized model of the moon from a case. It takes three minutes to charge to radiate either silver, white, or gold light all night long. I buy it and intend to give it to THE CHILD. I look at the contents of another curio cabinet, hypnotized by a holographic model of an interdimensional being that expands from a central origin. A row of beings nest in the chest of an overlord entity, like Russian dolls with a common hierarchical spine. Each progressively smaller being shares the same common spinal cord/pelvis connection. Humans are the 7th and smallest components within this aggregate expression. It becomes clearer to me that while I have choice, free will is illusory. I can feel the connection in my back begin to reel me in as layer upon layer of broader fleshy chest walls close around me like safe doors.] //

⁂

Maj. = 3- THE CHILD: #1015
GROIN: #0279, #0463, #0876, #1175
RENDEZVOUS: #0043, #0158
FUNNEL: #0223
NEST: #0094
EARTH: #1249

⁂

#0977 - **November 4, 2019 @ 5:30am (San Francisco, California)**

[0977.1 / 2554] [I'm in an old house, moving upward from level to level, aware that a pair of people on the level just below are in pursuit. They want to kill me *(and the lot of us who live there)* using a formulaic, systematic elimination method. A group of people return to the house and exit a white 15 passenger van. Another guy drives a box truck and is delayed while attempting to find street parking. He's challenged and lets it get the best of him, repeatedly striking the steering wheel as he swears.]

[0977.2 / 2555] [A Black man stomps his feet and yells, expressing a desire to flee the building. He has no clear path to exit. The scene becomes increasingly chaotic and severe. We're reminded intuitively that it's, *"all a game."* For a time, the house is coated in a thick layer of ice. We have to skate and slide to maneuver around it. The next round, a level up, the house is thawed out and we're able to run around sure footedly. Unfamiliar but friendly people assist our group with clues and tips as we advance to higher levels of *"the game."* We're advised more strategically and, in the abstract, the higher our cluster ascends.]

[0977.3 / 2556] [We work together at a busy shopping mall inside the house. We're given a series of tasks to prepare different booths for competitive promotions as smaller teams. One group creates a contest where you can wager a bet on whether a local celebrity or politician wore makeup during a recent interview. Guess correctly, and the customer wins.]

. . .

[0977.4 / 2557] [I'm asked to sit and fold forward. I'm pressed in half. Customers grab my hands to determine if the red nail polish on my fingers matches the same shade the female Mayor wore during her most recent press conference. On my break I play some games and make a few purchases. When I check out, I'm under the impression I'll get a big discount, but learn I'll only receive it if I open a new store affinity credit card. I decline and put all my items back, deciding to shop elsewhere. ***"My shelves are already stocked with plenty of things I don't need, nor want. I don't need any additional credit."***] //

⁂

BLACK MAN: #0036, #0050, #0154
CREDIT: #0629, #0633
NAIL POLISH: #0364
SEVERE: #0003, #0026, #0065
FORWARD: #0309, #0359, #0394
SHOPPING: #1282, #1294, #1329, #1339

⁂

#0978 - November 5, 2019 @ 00:43 (San Francisco, California)

[0978.1 / 2558] [*"Get the permit." "Get the license." "Create a purchase order for that swag,"* a voice nervously laughs as it taunts me from the black. Unclear. Abstract. I'm left in partial inquiry as the entity floats away and quits. Nonsense. ***"Meh."***] //

⁂

INQUIRY: #0303, #0363, #0470
NONSENSE: #0125, #0143, #0240
ORDER: #0088, #0109, #0148
ENTITY: #0442, #0620, #0639
VOICE: #1213, #1239, #1267

⁂

#0979 - November 5, 2019 @ 01:33 (San Francisco, California)

[0979.1 / 2559] [A group of guys empty the contents of a large steel shipping crate. They move a giant blue vinyl tarp tied up to look like a Hershey's Kiss. They unwrap it to reveal a mass of melted black rubber. A stenciled phrase reads "SURVIVOR" in block letters. Someone uses a broom, while another uses a shovel, to clean accumulations of sand and dirt from the mass.]

[0979.2 / 2560] [I cut quickly across a campus quad clinching a rolled-up Day-Glo orange t-shirt. I'm on my way to meet up with some friends. We're planning on celebrating our friend "Maggie" whose bubbly demeanor and general likeability makes her a sort of *"cohort mascot."*]

[0979.3 / 2561] [I'm in a shop, in a Victorian home. I overhear an associate refer a customer on the phone to another location. The customer is confused and doesn't understand it's a franchise referral request and not a request for a different merchant. I thumb through stacks of lithographs and pull a unique 19"x60" canvas from the upright stack; an impression of a woman's face captured in warm tones of pink and fuchsia.

"I like her!" I say gazing at the work, intending to buy it and hang it in my new home.]

[0979.4 / 2562] [I decide to reconfigure my living space, so it can accommodate a series of 19" x 48" panels I've recently painted. The new configuration would have a trapezoidal area on the floor that would be dedicated to sleep and restoration. The rest of the space would be held aside for making art. I have a conversation with a neighbor woman who suggests I use the space to show pieces, then auction them off. *"All proceeds should benefit the San Francisco AIDS Foundation,"* she says. I agree with her and share that I'd been carrying that idea around for a while.]

[0979.5 / 2563] [I watch a band work through how they intend to recreate an exceptionally complex piece they've released on a recent studio album. The conversation is focused, candid and direct.

As I walk by their rehearsal space I pop my head in the door and say, ***"It's pretty amazing to see how genius transforms genius."***

They laugh and one says, *"You're telling us! We were there when we wrote it. We had to be there through all the mania and depression and all the other stuff...and WE came out the other side with something awesome."*

A conversational pause reveals layers of musical tones floating in the air above us.

Another guy continues, *"Bernie's are into metal. We've shared this with all the 'Bernie's.' SANDERS! MADOFF! Bernie, Bernie, Bernie! The name loves metal. Can you believe that?"*

I'm confused by the non-sequitur and say, ***"People like what they like,"*** with a shrug of the shoulders.] //

⁂

BERNIE SANDERS: #1366
KISS: #0055, #0075
GENIUS: #0048, #0233
AIDS: #0187, #0642
VINYL: #0066, #0070
NEIGHBOR: #1292, #1301, #1309

⁂

#0980 - November 5, 2019 @ 04:06 (San Francisco, California)

[0980.1 / 2564] [I attend a leadership workshop at an outside venue. Tables are positioned orderly up a grassy hill. THE COACH *(inquisitive, knowledgeable, and clear)* strolls down from the hilltop holding a stack of laptop computers. He creates a demonstration where the color of light shifts around him as he speaks. He makes suggestions to the group by *"using story."* He speaks a sonnet about how the opening and closing of a single laptop is like an ocean of them opening/closing in this environment.

He continues, *"Same goes for phones. Here's just better to be. Let's agree. To be present with nature and other members of...humanity!"* I love everything he says. Other attendees aren't quite sure what to make of it.

The uphill series of tables gets steeper and stonier, and stretches beyond where my eyes can see. THE PRACTITIONER *(committed, solemn, and courageous)* dutifully carries a dying, yet joyful woman up another hill. Another runs down sobbing, with arms extended. She wraps them around THE COACH's neck, profusely thanking him for being who he is for her, how he is for other people, and how impactful the work they do has been on her organization.

I have a long conversation with THE CREATOR *(loving, playful, and aligned)*, eye to eye, connected, and present. Our comments to one another are appreciative and funny. It's a nice acknowledgement to be seen again after many years. The mood is easy, light, fun and electric. The group of people gathered to do the work are committed.

"Cool things are happening."] //

⁂

UPHILL: #0069
FOUR: #0126, #0127
NATURE: #0136, #0243, #0271
GRASSY: #0324, #0333
OCEAN: #0045
DYING: #1222, #1260
THE COACH: #1023

⁂

⁂

PART 13 - SOUL STIRRING

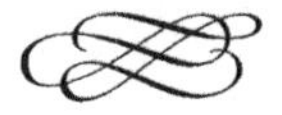

#0981 - #1026

13.1 - THE BOOK OF CORONA AUSTRALIS- {[0981 / 2565] - [0993 / 2602]}
13.2 - THE BOOK OF CORONA BOREALIS- {[0994 / 2603] - [1001 / 2628]}
13. 3 - THE BOOK OF TRIANGULUM- {[1002 / 2629] - [1005 / 2645]}
13.4. - THE BOOK OF AURIGA- {[1006 / 2646] - [1019 / 2678]}
13. 5 - THE BOOK OF ARA- {[1020 / 2679] - [1026 / 2698]}

"It is easy to understand why
dreamers tend to ignore
and even deny
the message of their dreams.
Consciousness naturally resists
anything unconscious
and unknown."

-CG Jung

* * *

November 7, 2019 - December 6, 2019

⁂

⁂ 13.1 - THE BOOK OF CORONA AUSTRALIS: 0981-0993 ⁂

#0981 - November 7, 2019 @ 04:13 (San Francisco, California)

[0981.1 / 2565] [Students gather to discuss the results of their recent advanced finance exam. Students share common questions regarding the revaluation process for a subset of loans. During the review they're given a new challenge. The professor provides a dossier with clues about how to best promote a fine arts gala that will be attended by celebrities and social media influencers.]

[0981.2 / 2566] [During the event, one of the students converses with *(and unintentionally misinforms)* a guest, regarding the schedule of events. His description of the event deviates from content provided in the professor's dossier. He's quickly corrected by the cohort. *"Incorrect. That's not what we discussed."* With the record set straight, the previously confused guest transforms into one of the performers and continues about his business preparing for the show, which will begin momentarily.] //

⁂
CHALLENGE: #0982, #0988, #0990, #1055, #1073, #1176, #1198
CONFUSED: #0012, #0025, #0064, #0069, #0125, #0147, #0169, #0189, #0199
PROFESSOR: #1050, #1083, #1130, #0210, #0306, #0614, #957, #0969
STUDENTS: #0077, #0115, #0118, #0128, #0142, #0158, #0176, #0199
⁂

#0982 - November 7, 2019 @ 05:27 (San Francisco, California)

[0982.1 / 2567] [THE CHEMIST *(methodical, rational, and investigative)* and I leave a rustic mountain cabin, intending to shoot the back nine holes of a storied golf course near the Fitzroy's in South Argentinian Patagonia. Initially, a few friends decide to accompany us, but peel off one at a time as our path cuts through multiple ranch properties and winds deep into the jagged range.

Our narrow dirt path transforms into a city-street-wide ribbon composed of Himalayan pink salt bricks. The path tilts back and forth, in and out, at increasingly steep angles. One pitch is so steep we have to boulder across with precision and care, sliding our fingernails between the salt bricks for leverage. The drop off becomes nearly vertical. Our bodies dangle thousands of feet above a rushing river below. One wrong move will result in a swift and treacherous end. Given the terror, we meet the challenge with ease and enjoyment.]

[0982.2 / 2568] [We follow the pink, glistening salt brick path to an outpost where we find two male friends in their 20's wearing Boy Scout outfits and leading a community class for elementary school aged children. The space is dark. Everyone attending is encircled in their own small round spot of light, which casts a Swiss cheese-like motif across an otherwise jet-black floor. The kids and counselors create a puppet show as a team. Individually, the children perform solos on various instruments of their choosing.

Today, class welcomes some special guests. Two groups of boy scouts from different dens have been invited to supplement roles in the puppet show and concert production that would be otherwise unfilled. I sit on a couch at the back of the venue when one of the boys leaps towards me. He lands beside me. He smells. He's sweating profusely from head to toe. His right arm up to the elbow is missing. He has freckles, short red hair, and wears glasses. He's aware he's sweating and insistent that we not wash him off, nor use a towel to blot him dry. He requests we coat him in a fine white powder that won't irritate his skin.

"USE THE POWDER! USE THE POWDER!" He chants repeatedly while dramatically flailing his body in a rambunctiously energized manner. I find him funny.] //

⁂

FUNNY: #0457, #0577, #0687, #0718, #0791
POWDER: #0984, #1024, #1066, #1141
RIVER: #0003, #0048, #0141, #0233, #0242, #0390
SALT: #1201, #0024, #0204, #0513, #0532, 0845, #0879
SPOT: #0005, #0024, #0043, #0066, #0168
THE CHEMISTS: #1088

⁂

#0983 - November 8, 2019 @ 05:03 (San Francisco, California)

[0983.1 / 2569] [I enjoy a carefree, loving, and connected sexual encounter with four different angelic men. All of them cum inside me one by one as I cradle and embrace them. It's soft, sacred, appreciative, and a deeply intimate exchange of life-force energy.]

[0983.2 / 2570] [A children's book of prayers opens in front of me, words read by a soothing adult male voice. The words on the page pop out in gold as the voice advances to help me read and follow along with the narrator.]

[0983.3 / 2571] [People ride bikes in a peloton at night without headlamps. They approach a cliff. They're stopped and compelled by a safety officer to walk their bikes to avoid riding off the edge. A silent voice tells me cyclists would need strong steering and dampening skills to know how to navigate places with tricky turns like that when, *"the lights are flicked on and off."*]

[0983.4 / 2572] [A doctor gives bad information to a patient in a corner of a hospital hallway. He errantly suggests that every joint trauma *(knee/hip injury)* eventually leads to heart attack. The doctor uses a false correlation to administer and bill unnecessary tests and treatments. I'm so vocal and public with my disavowal of their deceptive practices, they pull down banners and signage, take down their table, and retreat to a nearby conference room. The doctor and his staff have strong opinions about who I am and where I'm from. This doesn't matter to me. My intention is simple. I'm supposed to make sure people don't get injured by treatments that lack efficacy. ***"I'm supposed to shine a light on deception when I encounter it."***] //

⁂

JOINT: #0860, #0874, #890, #0922, #1164
PRACTICE: #0996, #1056, #1087, #1096, #1126

PRAYERS: #1193, #0014, #0023, #0141, #0542, #0557, #0618
SACRED: #0014, #0040, #0042, #0046, #0048, #0060, #0089, #0134
SIMPLE: #0172, #0312, #0321, #0322, #0333, #0363, #0385

⁂

#0984 - November 10, 2019 @ 04:21 (San Francisco, California)

[0984.1 / 2573] [**Powder blue background. Thin Day-Glo orange lines. Geometrically woven like Spirograph spider webs in the sky. **]

[0984.2 / 2574] [People gather and merge as a unit. They meander around a large butte *(at right)* to avoid an incoming storm from the sea *(at left)*.]

[0984.3 / 2575] [Wheat bends and waves in the wind. Raindrops hit my face and kick up the dirt on the path ahead of me. I'm on an island. I'm by myself. Another person arrives. More join a gathering that soon becomes a multitude of people. Shelter is to the right. The group moves quickly inside like a swarm of ants to avoid a giant wave that crashes and floods the prairie.]

[0984.4 / 2576] [A dinner party moment of collective laughter repeats ad infinitum.]

[0984.5 / 2577] [People audition to be a stand-in for the singer of a rock band. The singer experiences deep catharsis in the next room. The room has been soundproofed. Multiple people hold space and offer the singer healing as he's curled up and crying on the floor. When he relaxes, it becomes known he's JONATHAN DAVIS. Nearby, a woman slaps and brutalizes a smaller man. She throws him backwards into a radiator and injures his arm. She prevents him from getting to the audition registration table. I back away, attempting to go unnoticed. The winning audition takes longer than planned. Participants are expected to perfectly mimic choreography from a music video. Only one is successful.]

[0984.6 / 2578] [Two Englishmen take a ride in a pair of giant centrifuges. Each boards his own ride. The rides are side-by-side and rotate in opposite directions. The men take videos of each other the whole time they're riding. ***"Operating a camera would make me vomit, but it doesn't seem to impact them."*** They continue riding and taking videos, occasionally disembarking, walking back around and through the stainless-steel-snake-maze-of-a-line to ride again.] //

⁂

AUDITION: #1084, #1101, #0918
RIDE: #0985, #0990, #0995, #1016, #1021, #1041, #1062, #1074
SWARM: #0007, #0031, #0075, #0052, #0834, #0944
WHEAT: #1145, #1182, #0104, #0121, #0159, #0305

⁂

#0985 - November 10, 2019 @ 05:42 (San Francisco, California)

[0985.1 / 2579] [***"Do you want to fuck my mouth before breakfast?"*** I ask my tall and muscular partner, THE POOL BOY *(flirtatious, self-humoring, and handsome).*

"Sure. IF you can get me aroused, AND my mind off food," he says as I roll on top of him and press my body into his. Once he's fully erect, I tell him I'll meet him upstairs in the bathroom. I stand and leave our poolside lounge.

I pass a construction crew working to re-floor the hallways of our home. My paintings have been inlaid and covered with epoxy, glitter, and a smidge of sawdust. THE POOL BOY and I made an agreement about skipping breakfast last night. Sex is the likely substitute. I arrive at the bedroom. A knock at the door reveals THE POOL BOY who's transformed into a petite Asian woman. We don't have sex. We grab hands and walk through the construction zone to a garage where a car idles.

"You're an insured. You need to be sure you shut this car off after you use it," she says as I get in the driver's seat. She's the passenger.

We go out for a drive, making multiple laps around our neighborhood and town. My attention shifts from sex, back to breakfast. I suggest we go out to eat. I make a left-hand turn into a parking lot after we finish a final lap around town. A guy in a pickup truck driving in the opposite direction beeps and gestures at us in a way neither of us understand.

"Am I in the wrong lane? Have I made a wrong turn?" I ask my lover. She doesn't seem to know. She remains silent, simply shrugging her shoulders.]

[0985.2 / 2580] [I talk with a group of friends. I pause, look to my right, and see a giant theme park with rainbow-colored roller-coaster tracks and a massive swing that looks like a set of scales. The sides of the "scale swing" are composed of multiple individual basket seats suspended on their own set of chains; an amped up version of a kiddie ride. The engineering and design don't scale properly. It's dangerous.

I leave my body and zoom out, to take the perspective of a rider on the left-side carriage. It swings aggressively to the right and snaps, sending the single rider careening into another on the opposite side of the scale. The "at risk rider's" body dangles from the "right side rider's" basket as a chair with chain drops toward the ground hundreds of feet below. The lower basket grinds on the ground sparking wildly and squeaking before it screeches to a halt.]

[0985.3 / 2581] [*"USA!" "DEMO-CRAY- ZAY!"*] //

⁂

BREAKFAST: #0019, #0124, #0171, #0482, #0556, #0633
LOVER: #1057, #1143, #0059, #0175, #0269, #0370
RAINBOW: #0587, #0852, #0873, #0885, #0959
SAWDUST: #1033, #0021, #0075, #0427, #0564, #0777
THE POOL BOY: #1034

⁂

⁂

#0986 - November 10, 2019 @ 22:47 (San Francisco, California)

[0986.1 / 2582] [CATHY BESSANT calls me into her office with another consultant. We're at the top of a skyscraper at night. The room is painted in tones of gold and grey. I scheduled a meeting to present a global pilot program, pitching a hybrid retail banking/foodservice interchange partnership with YUM! Brands. The intent is to offer banking services and tech infrastructure access at "Combination KFC / Pizza Hut" locations. Meeting attendees aren't aware these stores exist, though they've been around for years.

My proposal is incomplete. I have limited time with CATHY and must get to the root of the matter. I've found a way to direct certain commercial loan transactions through existing brick-and-mortar fast food restaurant infrastructure. This would potentially generate rebates and carbon offsets to any restaurant that allows access to its "tech pipelines." I fail to make my point. CATHY asks the female consultant for a clear answer. I'm kicked out of my own meeting. I feel sad for a moment, then decide I'm not done. I go back in.

CATHY sits to the right at the corner of a conference table with a small stack of three AA batteries in front of her. The consultant sits at the opposite end of the table. CATHY raps her knuckles on the table and after a pregnant pause says, *"Ok. Give me your pitch."* Another older female senior executive fields phone calls at a small desk under the conference table by CATHY's feet. I'm a bit amazed. I love this woman.

"Wow...you're here? CATHY really keeps the big guns close."

I feel my feet. I take a breath. With eyes closed I invite calm energy, and begin to flow. Ideas effortlessly pour from me without thought. CATHY delights in the process. The consultant at the far end is upset. ***"I'm flowing from genius."***] //

⁂

CATHY BESSANT: #1029
FAIL: #0878, #0887, #0969
GOLD: #0990, #0992, #0993, #0994, #0998, #0999
HYBRID: #0204, #0304, #0334, #0534, #0718
NIGHT: #0999, #1001, #1003, #1013, #1018, #1026
SENIOR: #0817, #0891, #0907, #0143, #0211, #0386

⁂

#0987 - November 11, 2019 @ 02:02 (San Francisco, California)
**Promptly woke up at 3:00am with intense lower GI pain. Ran energy to clear space for 5:00am and 7:00am dreams. **

[0987.1 / 2583] [I've just finished packing a truck to go on tour with DREAM THEATER as an understudy drummer. I feel like an imposter because I haven't rehearsed. I'm anxious, because I know their crowd has a nerdy and discerning ear. Some are so perfected in their imitations of the band's creations they'll demand exact replications during live concert performances. Compositions will lose nuance and texture if I opt to play basic rhythms. In this level of the game, precision and virtuosity matter. I think I've mastered the intro to the song "6:00." If we open with it, I may gain some credibility *(though the rest of the set is bound to be shit)*. I can either be paid a flat rate for the tour, or take a percentage of door receipts. I select the door receipt option, then am told the other guys have all taken the flat rate. I question my decision.]

. . .

[0987.2 / 2584] [I'm in a car with THE VEGAN. She drives. I'm in the back seat. Another guy in the front passenger seat exits the car when THE VEGAN starts talking through a very detailed offer letter she received yesterday. The guy mistakenly leaves behind a paint tube, that when pressed dispenses small ovular pills. It appears to be THE ACCOUNTANT's *(amiable, analytical, and surprising)* Prozac prescription, though the guy exiting the car looks like THE CARTOONIST *(messy, masculine, and candid).*]

[0987.3 / 2585] [I walk through a gallery at a mall that displays artwork by young female artists from African nations. The collection of small orange and yellow baubles in cases is accentuated by larger orange and yellow orbs that look like double helixes when viewed from a corner of the room. The space has plush cream-colored carpet lit overhead by soft white light from crystal chandeliers. The main installation is a 6' tall porcelain skull, set on a center pedestal. The skull is ornamented with swirls, zigzags and carvings. It looks like a "Día de los Muertos" artifact, and seems incongruent for the installation. I want to get closer to it to inspect it, but am held at the perimeter to view the smaller displays.] //

⁂

Min. = ♣ -THE VEGAN: #1071
ANXIOUS: #0017, #0051, #0215, #0259, #0363, #0396
CHANDELIER: #0998, #1172
SKULL: #1184, #1200, #0535, #0770
THE CARTOONIST: #1056

⁂

#0988 - November 11, 2019 @ 05:00 (San Francisco, California)
***Two scenes weave together: One at a wedding ceremony, the other an audit of a voting process. Both occur at the same farmhouse in rural Midwest America. ***

[0988.1 / 2586] [1) The wedding party is insular and quaint.]

[0988.2 / 2587] [2) Busloads of people arrive to vote. The sky is cloudy and tinted with hues of grey and peach.]

[0988.3 / 2588] [2) The buses are small and make multiple round trips to drop off voters.]
[0988.4 / 2589] [2) Upon entering the farmhouse a large earthquake shakes the ground. I'm in a hallway near a banister and watch people stumble down a staircase. The house frame bends and bows with shockwaves from the quake. I'm concerned because THE DANCER is a floor up from me, full term pregnant with a baby boy. I shout up to THE WEAVER and THE CARPENTER who are with her. I plead with them to help me get her down safely to the ground floor. THE DANCER pauses on the second floor to rest until the shaking subsides before taking the last staircase down. We're successful. She makes the descent without injury.]

. . .

[0988.5 / 2590] [2) Outside the house ARIANA GRANDE makes a huge scene on a bus declaring the voting process, *"INEFFICIENT!"* The election inspector is a family friend of ARIANA's who momentarily considers making an exception for her to skip the line. I remind the inspector that, ***"everyone must follow the same process."***]

[0988.6 / 2591] [1) I write vows and notes under a floral arbor in the front yard of the farmhouse. I sit on the dirt ground with a group of women. The arbor is picked up by an invisible force and moved across the property. My eyes glance up as my hand touches a pile of ash. I pull forth the remnants of a thank you note written on a piece of notebook paper that's been almost completely charred; a relic from a previous ceremony. I'm sitting in a fire pit.]

[0988.7 / 2592] [3) I'm a woman wearing a short skirt, flat patent leather shoes, and carrying a small clutch. I walk down a brick path surrounded by the "murder woods" on both sides. I'm followed by a group of people I initially believe to be men. I'm surprised to see a mob of women behind me when I look back. They catcall at me. I'm stuck between wanting to be considered attractive and worried I'm about to be sexually assaulted.]

[0988.8 / 2593] [2) I walk up to the front door of the farmhouse and view the contents of a vending machine. Oversized candy bars *(Kit Kat's, etc.)* are oddly priced *($5.10, $6.08, $7.12)* and oddly weighted. Each contains multiple pounds of chocolate. No one seems to buy them because exact change is needed and people only carry bills. I don't buy anything.

I step around the machine into the house, and am faced with a new challenge. The house will eventually fill with so many people we'll all be crushed to death. If I jump out a window I'll be singed and charred by a wildfire that now surrounds the exterior of the house. I stand in the kitchen as people flood in from all around. I make conversation with a young man with quaffed up-turned hair. He says,

"I heard your talk at the retreat. Based on what you shared, I know I can handle you."] //

⁂

Maj. = 0- THE WEAVER: #1000, 1- THE CARPENTER: #1008, 2- THE DANCER: #1008
FARMHOUSE: #0193, #0557, #0756
INEFFICIENT: #0171, #0240, #0378, #0471, #0484, #0601, #0621, #0743
THANK YOU NOTE: #0472, #0787, #0967

⁂

#0989 - November 11, 2019 @ 07:28 (San Francisco, California)

[0989.1 / 2594] [I'm in a stately building with tall interior columns and cream-colored ceilings. A familiar grid of recessed pyramids moves up to a common center point. It's a fitness center, a convention center, and a co-working space rolled into one. MIKE PATTON sponsors a series of offices and studios for creators and musicians who need financial support.

I look at a copy of his autobiography he's left on a coffee table. It's a weighty book with a thick heavy cover. As I thumb through it, I count roughly 600, 9"x12" pages. It's full of glossy photos that highlight his life and entitled: "EUREKA! To SAN FRANCISCO." The cover looks like a page of newsprint when viewed under a microscope. The table of contents, titling, and glossary seem similar to my soon to be released autobiography. A lead infographic reads: "ABOUT THIS BOOK." Another reads: "THE PEOPLE WHO WORK HERE." Poster sized prints of these pages ceremonially hang on a wall between a door and a large rectangular window that looks out to a common gathering space.]

[0989.2 / 2595] [MIKE taps me saying, *"Where'd you find that cassette tape?"*

"It was in the Jacob's ladder you brought from home."

"AMAZING!" he exclaims with a playful genius grin. His arms extend up with fists about to clench. We watch THE WARRIOR WOMAN *(promoting, manicured, and fierce)* stand on a conference table and wave. MIKE waves back to her. He pulls two tennis balls with holes in them from his pants pocket and places one on each of THE WARRIOR WOMAN's big toes. He duct tapes them to her feet as THE WARRIOR WOMAN provides compliments and praise to those who gather and look up to her from the floor. She deflects appreciation.

"THE WARRIOR WOMAN, YOU'RE AMAZING!"

"NO, THE WAY YOU GIVE COMPLIMENTS IS AMAZING!"

"YOU'RE DEFLECTING RIGHT NOW!" I yell with a laugh.]

[0989.3 / 2596] [THE WARRIOR WOMAN leads a discussion on gossip. Days ago, two women were overheard commenting toxically on a photo of another female teammate. The group discusses if it's relevant to revisit, given that the item has aged.]

[0989.4 / 2597] [**Two scenes flash and are forgotten. I am guided to note my forgetfulness. **] //

⁂

COMMON: #0852, #0963, #0976, #0981
CREAM: #0014, #0045, #0054, #0124, #0139, #0170
PRAISE: #0028
TOES: #1013, #1065, #1077

⁂

#0990 - November 12, 2019 @ 02:06 (San Francisco, California)

[0990.1 / 2598] [I compete head-to-head with a number of Russian teams in "The Amazing Race." The contest begins and flashes forward at a pace where I can't fully experience it, nor recall how I get to where I am. It feels like I'm in the Swiss Alps or the Dolomites when things finally slow to an extent that I can interpret and respond. My teammate and I are significantly ahead of the competition near the conclusion of the penultimate challenge.

We ascend to a mountain top by cable car. It seems like smooth sailing until the ride halts. A cable snaps and sends the car dangling perpendicular. The doors swing open beneath me and I fall through. Luckily, I trap a vertical door between my forearms and catch our team's laptop between my knees. With my legs crossed it looks like I'm dangling in "Eagle Pose." The drop is large. Certain death is below if I slip, since I'm not clipped into the gondola.

I keep my eyes up and on my teammate. Other people are suction cupped to the walls and watch us. Another set of clamps locks around my knuckles and gives me the security to swing my knees up to an exterior window. I pass the laptop to my teammate, who places it immediately in a Lucite lockbox on the wall. I ask for help from the two "wall stickers" who pull me up as the doors beneath me close. A glance down gives a glimpse of cardboard box doors that compress and fold on themselves like an accordion.]

[0990.2 / 2599] [We advance to the final challenge. After teleporting, we discover ourselves somewhere in the desert of the American Southwest. It's daytime. The sky overhead is black but streaked with swaths of faint orange and gold tones. We're handed a clay water vessel *(or is it a lamp?)*. We shatter it to reveal a hockey puck-like object made of charcoal. We have to break up the puck and eat it to win the race. It cracks into thirds and I begin jamming chunks in my mouth. We don't have water and aren't supplied with any. Another team arrives and begins the task.

"Hmmm, is this what Mars is like?" I ponder as the scene fades and I wake up.] //

⁂

EAGLE: #0396, #0957
GONDOLA: #1115, #0312, #0474, #0878
LUCITE: #0203, #0406, #0467, #0542, #0554, #0575
ORANGE: #0583, #0593, #0657, #0715, #0770
FINAL: #1280, #1320, #1329, #1336

⁂

#0991 - November 12, 2019 @ 04:03 (San Francisco, California)

[0991.1 / 2600] [*"Hold your relationship to The Divine lightly. Appreciate it,"* a voice says as I sit at a table in an otherwise black room. A group of us create clay models of humans. THE NUN peeks over my shoulder to review my work. A man sits to my left. A woman sits to my right. I don't know either of them. We break the models, then put them back together with Crazy Glue. When everyone around the table is ready, we hold out our hands and use our "brains" to erase the glue seams, rendering the models fully restored.] //

⁂

Min. = ◆- THE NUN: #1145
APPRECIATE: #0005, #0022, #0299, #0323
CRAZY: #0021, #0193, #0760, #0826, #0964
RIGHT: #0764, #0768, #0787, #0799
WORK: #0478, #0496, #0506, #0881, #0888, #0889

⁂

#0992 - November 13, 2019 @ 02:49 (The Presidio of San Francisco, California)

[0992.1 / 2601] [I'm in the center of a square space flooded with gold light. It's completely black all around me with the exception of four golden staircases that lead up and away in each cardinal direction from the center of the square. It's a familiar form, like an inverted Mesoamerican pyramid. I'm invited to "pick a prayer" and run up a staircase towards a different tone, color, and music selection. Each of the four staircases holds a different prayer.

The first staircase is: *"A prayer for work."* I run up the stairs towards active, accessible, formulaic pop music. When I reach the top, I see black nothingness for a moment, then discover myself back in the center.

The second staircase is: *"A prayer for easy money."* The music is lower frequency and feels hollow. When I get to the top, a bell held in front of my face is struck, but makes no sound, and then I discover myself back at the point of origin. I also find I have a thick elastic bungee cord embedded in my back.

The third staircase is: *"A prayer that heals all."* I run towards the staircase as an angelic choir's singing of Gregorian chants increases in volume. I get to the top *(thinking I've gotten somewhere)*, when the elastic band retracts and pulls me back forcibly to the center.

Before I attempt the fourth staircase, I receive an intuitive clue. I hear my guide say,

"Pray to connect to God first, and then start again. You'll know where to go."] //

⁂

CONNECT: #0662, # #0667, #0671, #1272
FIRST: #0318, #0322, #0323, #0327, #0357, #1250
PRAYER: #0139, #0147, #0309, #1232
SECOND: #389, #0432, #0463, #0490, #0495, #1278
THIRD: #0511, #0589, #0613, #0637, #1310

⁂

#0993 - November 13, 2019 @ 04:21 (The Presidio of San Francisco, California)

[0993.1 / 2602] [Dream **[0992.1 / 2601]** repeats. I watch myself from above running up the different sides of a cross. At various times, different tools appear for me to interact with *(a golden unicycle, a gold table mounted on a unicycle, etc.)*. It's all intentionally distracting. I understand more each time I fail and restart.

"Put God first and you'll have no distractions."] //

⁂

CROSS: #0972, #0999, #1056, #1094, #1317
GOD: #0879, #0891, #0903, #0917, #0918, #0992, #1311
RESTART: #1193, #0750, #787
UNDERSTAND: #1282, #1292, #1322

⁂

⁂ 13.2 - THE BOOK OF CORONA BOREALIS: 0994-1001 ⁂

#0994 - November 14, 2019 @ 01:51 (San Francisco, California)

[0994.1 / 2603] [**Image of a whale bathed in crystal gold light, from just beneath the surface of the ocean. **]

[0994.2 / 2604] [**A thought bubble, lightning cloud flashes "ZZZ" as the sound of thunder booms. **]

[0994.3 / 2605] [I'm in an ordinary classroom. A chalkboard. Desks. Fluorescent lights. Grey walls. A clock on the wall reads 4:10am. I hover above my body among a group of people who register for a convention. People have come to *"hallow out a space within,"* and learn how to heal four root conditions that plague humanity.

A male participant is missing his right arm to the elbow. He appears confused. I float just above and behind him and ask him if he knows where he needs to go. He nods and heads towards a door without needing my help. I continue on *(as many guides do)* hovering nearby attendees as they arrive. A newly enrolled participant completely fails a preliminary exercise. He is 100% supported by his guide. He is 100% open to coaching and feedback provided by the guide. The environment is supportive and collaborative in this "blend up" of realities. Some participants are in bodies. Some attendees float just beyond their bodies. Others don't have a body.] //

⁂

100%: #0172, #0388, #0457, #0757, #0853, #0865
BODY: #0004, #0007, #0401, #0403, #0802, ##809
FLUORESCENT: #0009, #0065, #0887, #0943
THUNDER: #0535, #0867
WHALE: #0018, #0245, #0561

⁂

#0995 - November 15, 2019 @ 04:42 (San Francisco, California)

[0995.1 / 2606] [A film negative of ALBERT EINSTEIN hovers in front of my face. It morphs into a portrait of EDGAR ALLAN POE, then LUDWIG VAN BEETHOVEN.]

[0995.2 / 2607] [A large white neon sign reads: "ACCESS TO EXCESS." It flickers. It's the only light in an otherwise completely black space.]

[0995.3 / 2608] [I take a leisurely daytime countryside ride in a classic car *('57 Chevy)*. I arrive at a residence with a nice, freshly cut lawn and a multi-car garage. I walk in the front door and through the house to a master suite at the back. Daylight floods in. THE GENTLEMAN *(proper, polite, and svelte)* removes his work clothes and walks naked to the bathroom. He looks back and winks at me. I walk towards him.

He promptly puts his hand up and says, *"NO."*

"I'm sorry, I misread that. I thought you were inviting me in." I say as he points towards a vanity. I walk towards it.

In front of the mirror is a large rainbow arbor made of brown grocery bags colored with tempera paint. It's flimsy and held at the ends by two cardboard boxes filled with sample size cosmetics. I hear the shower running. Steam pours into the bedroom and floats up to the ceiling.

"Can you get me two of those green strips?" THE GENTLEMAN asks, pointing at a table to my right. On the table, I find a notebook-paper-sized-sheet of nori, which I tear vertically in half. THE GENTLEMAN takes the nori and disappears.

I walk back through the house, now utterly dark inside. A series of feminine faces outlined in pink and red chalk lines flash before me. My attention is drawn to a closet without a door, obscured by a black 7' five panel room divider. A disconnected orange extension cord snakes from under the separator. A female end of the cord is exposed.] //

⁂

CLASSIC CAR: #0012, #0305, #0607, #0847, #0917
I'M SORRY: #0013, #0294, #0354, #0804
NEON: #1201, #0065, #0070, #0079
NEGATIVE: #0147, #0174, #0309

⁂

#0996 - November 15, 2019 @ 06:18 (San Francisco, California)

[0996.1 / 2609] [I'm at a woodland retreat center. A main building has multiple floors. A steady convoy of large grey double decker buses drops people off. I float out of the bus and into the building, noting that people are being separated, put into rooms, and harassed by an authoritarian regime. A young man's confidence wanes when his interrogators say they know about his "secret cafe code" he taught the other captives. The young man's smile turns flat when a small, gunmetal grey box used for holding sugar/sweeteners *(commonplace on cafe tables)* is placed before him. A small recording device captured every word spoken, by everyone, for months prior to their capture. His fate is uncertain. I fly out of the building and into the driver's seat of a van. I land prone on my abdomen. My legs extend to the back through the driver's seat, and I lay on my chest with arms and neck dangling over the front edge. I stare at the foot pedals and ugly cry. Tears and snot flow at volume from my face. I've placed a white towel in the window to block sunlight.]

[0996.2 / 2610] [I'm sad. I'm in purgatory. I won't be able to fall asleep ever again. I'll never dream again. I won't be able to give my book to the world. It will be unfinished. *"You don't have your notifications turned on, that's why you're not receiving any information,"* a guide says behind my right ear. I continue weeping. My right hand starts to throb and pulse with a sharp, intense pain.

"GOD PLEASE TAKE THIS PAIN AWAY!" I wail as my hand continues collapsing into itself. The bones crack and snap. The sadness and upset deepens.]

[0996.3 / 2611] [I stop crying and walk into the retreat center. At the front door, I come face-to-face with another who's decided to start writing down their dreams. We slap a high five, and I energetically pass them the practice. I've lost my ability to connect. I'm left in an experience of deeper pain, sadness, and isolation.] //

⁂

CRYING: #0063, #0080
COLLAPSE: #0157, #0502
INTENSE: #0496, #0500
NEVER: #0506, #0582
SECRET: #0538, #0668
SUNLIGHT: #0461, #0611

⁂

#0997 - **November 15, 2019 @ 08:15 (San Francisco, California)**

[0997.1 / 2612] [I rent a bedroom in a large suburban home. My bedroom is at the back. The walls are a faint celery green. Large square windows on two opposing sides allow ample light to flood in. My landlord is a woman I don't know. She's polite. She asks if she can store some extra fluffy shower towels in my room.

"Yes, but I don't have any shelves."

A little later I walk to the family room and meet two young adult women who have been hired as interior designers. Their communication and work processes are disorganized and chaotic. One young woman constantly forgets where she leaves her notebook, which I repeatedly find for her. Her presence makes me drowsy and drunk.

I know if I stay in her environment too long, my choice making will suffer.]

[0997.2 / 2613] [I wake myself up when I feel drool drip from my mouth to my wrist. I've passed out in a room filled with large cardboard boxes and packing materials. I see a min pin puppy curled up in a plastic shopping bag, and believe for a moment that it's dead. When I touch it, it springs to life.]

[0997.3 / 2614] [Disassembled end tables, lounges, racks, etc. are incoherently scattered around. A railing at the edge of the family room gives visual access to a large, popular restaurant serving dinner on the floor beneath.]

[0997.4 / 2615] [The designers work to affix short stainless-steel nodes into the footings that will solidly hold legs of a long rectangular wooden table in place. Acting hastily, one woman bends one of the pegs and is unable to get the table slats to line up flush. Two grooves on each side fit a single small square peg.]

[0997.5 / 2616] [The dog prances by to the calls from my landlord, unaware that earlier the dog was found sleeping in a plastic bag.

I go back to my bedroom and note a variety of major improvements made by the landlord. Along the wall to the right stands a desk. Bookshelves and end tables complement the small bed I rent. At the far end is a lofted bed that has additional space beneath to hold the landlord's towels. She and I head to the front of the house with the dog, overhearing the designers meeting to discuss their next priority.] //

⁂

GREEN: #0286, #0290, #0306
SCATTERED: #0037, #0045, #0075
SQUARE PEG: #0195
PLASTIC: #0246, #0256, #0278
PUPPY: #0249, #0255, #0429

⁂

#0998 - November 16, 2019 @ 04:41 (San Francisco, California)

[0998.1 / 2617] [I'm with the "downstairs people." I'm part of a service team gathered with THE MAGICIAN and other supportive beings and coaches. Informal conversation about accessing flow states and non-ordinary states of consciousness informally percolate through the group. More focus is placed on the house than people. "GOUGH HOUSE" is considered an access point, a portal through which these states can manifest effortlessly.]

[0998.2 / 2618] [I'm a guest, attending the party at a grand table just beyond the closed butler door. I wear a smoke-colored designer suit coat. My hair hangs down to my mid back and is groomed tightly on the sides in a Mohawk. I've forgotten how long it's taken to grow it. ST. FRANCIS OF ASSISI is the head server. He wears a modest brown robe cinched at the waist with a burlap cord belt. People are seated, anticipating dinner service. Candles hover inches off the table. A diamond white gold chandelier sparkles like a galaxy over the center of the table.

As I sit the butler door swings open. A troupe of servers follow ST. FRANCIS delivering impeccable plated food to guests. The plates drop in unison. At one end of the table, a conversation about healing commences. A conversation focused on generating community begins at the other.]

[0998.3 / 2619] ["Property" and "Real Estate" discussion beings attempt to thwart the conversations. A curious and playful debate ensues among guests.

"You give me THIS. I'll give you THAT."

"I offer you THIS. You offer me THAT."

The exchanges are essential, clear and delivered jovially. The tone of the community agreement is a high ethereal frequency. As I observe the flow of conversation, I verbally weave in some intentionally differential subtleties.

"If IT's given from a place of expectation, then IT (the healing) becomes marginally effective." The group agrees. The collective tone of the table rises, ever more.]

[0998.4 / 2620] [People contemplate *(then experiment with)* embodying a state of deeper service through surrender. *"Superconscious awareness knows not to force service, but rather to allow it to flow freely and without impingement through and to, each and every."* The amplified connection at the spirit level of the table manifests as an ecstatic, fantastic tone of gold which harkens the attention of divine, non-conditional beings. From the "Deep Now" the group experiences satori. Each and every instantly understand the complexity, depth and color of the individual and integrated lives that share this sacred table.]

[0998.5 / 2621] [The richness, nuances, and tones are translated and received not solely through spoken words, but via the food. It enriches and nourishes the bodies. It amplifies the scent, color, flavor and sound of the experience. Some at the table cry. Some at the table laugh. Others hold space neutrally, all done in the context of superconscious healing. Angels watch overhead from the top corners of the room. Demons inhabit the bottom corners. Thought beings, confusion beings, bliss beings, "Drink Wine!" beings all tickle and tap into the light generated by the table. From a space of connection and clarity, those at the table can easily discern what should arrive, when, in sequence, and chosen with uniquely pristine clarity and knowing. Our host, THE EPICUREAN is satisfied with the reality created tonight.

My right hand begins to ache and throb (similar to **[0996.2 / 2610]**). I've gone out of ethics on some level, which colors me confused. Perhaps it was the Sauternes that was out of alignment? My hand begins to contract. The pain shocks me away from the table, and out of sleep.] //

⁂

Maj. = 14- THE MAGICIAN: #1088
Min. = ♥- THE EPICUREAN: #1145
ST. FRANCIS: #1251, #1442
ALIGNMENT: #1053, #0530, #0681, #0874
ANGELS: #0045, #0069, #0141
DEMONS: #0701
SERVICE: #0033, #0071, #0094

⁂

#0999 - November 16, 2019 @ 06:18 (San Francisco, California)

[0999.1 / 2622] [I walk on a concrete sidewalk suspended in an abyss, similar to a Hollywood soundstage. The void extends as far as I can see. Where I am will become San Francisco, California. I cradle an oversized art book to my chest assessing the beautiful possibilities of what will spring forth from the dark. I pause and glance at the book cover. Its colors invite me to go within. The book has 100 pages. I walk and read a page at a time, first digesting the story of a neighborhood, a building, an art installation with my eyes, then promptly tearing out each thick page and eating it. Once I swallow, the entity on the page manifests. I place it intentionally along the edge of the sidewalk. The populated street begins springing to life. I do this 40 times before I pause to consider drinking some water.]

[0999.2 / 2623] [Behind me I note a posse of teenage boys on skateboards. They could be menaces. They're just poseurs. They're debating if I'm a role model. I continue walking and arrive at what will eventually become a multi-dimensional intersection. The sign at the corner captures my attention for some time, showing pathways to different time periods and off-ramps to alternate realities. It's marvelously irrational. I want to say it floats, though the description doesn't do it justice.]

[0999.3 / 2624] [I decide to turn right as buildings spring up across the street, and walk towards a beautiful, spacious, palatial property. I cross a pristinely manicured emerald green mall with marble pools and fountains. The park occurs now as "night." The soft golden white hue of candle light suggests the denouement of a sacred union. I proceed confidently through the space standing connected in my true north. A team of maids efficiently break down and clean up from the event. They pay me no attention beyond occasional kind and friendly smiles. I know I'll find water at the other end of the venue. I need it to continue eating the art book and bringing forth the city.]

[0999.4 / 2625] [I look left bearing an exuberant witness to a bride and groom who sit together at a large round table covered with white linen. They sit smiling in reverent silence having stayed at the venue after their final guests have departed.

She wears a brilliant white gown with a diamond encrusted bodice. Her veil and dress detail are sewn with gossamer diamond thread which radiates sparkling light like an ecstatically activated nerve network. A caduceus-like swirl from brow to crown crescendos into a brilliant diamond tiara. At the center of her 7th chakra, a massive heart shaped diamond is held in space protected by two diamond vipers prepared to strike with the potentially lethal bite of true compassion.

The groom dons his regal military mess dress and medals of valor. Maple leaf ranks made of ruby sit atop his shoulders.

He's turned toward his bride tenderly and holds her right hand between his gold gloved hands. They're young and vibrant. Both are manicured and mirror the other's vitality and wellbeing. They softly gaze at each other with contentment and pay me no mind.

I press on towards a water fountain, intent on continuing consumption of the art book.] //

⁂

SOUNDSTAGE: #0066, #0745, #0753, #0765
BRIDE: #0323, #0401, #0436, #0793
GROOM: #0793, #1235
DIAMOND: #1076, #1083, #1167, #1248, #1293
CHAKRA: #0010, #0176
FOUNTAIN: #0263, #0439, #1274

⁂

#1000 - November 17, 2019 @ 04:57 (San Francisco, California)

[1000.1 / 2626] [I'm in an aircraft hangar working with a structural engineering team on a new temple project. We plan on building it from a pile of scrap wood, offcuts, and garbage. We construct an intentionally crude border wall from flimsy plywood to create a simple visual outline in the otherwise massive and empty space. From above, our claimed square site seems infinitesimally small.]

[1000.2 / 2627] [I walk past a pile of graffiti painted plywood and notice a young blond-haired woman with a hip injury sitting on top of it, waiting to talk to me. I discover it's THE GRANDDAUGHTER *(intelligent, skillful, and hurt)*. She's deeply sad and wants help to heal the pain of losing her dad. I glance at THE WEAVER, who stands near the fence.

"Please give me a couple of minutes to help clear some of this anger and sadness out."

I give THE GRANDDAUGHTER a hug. We simultaneously communicate the same phrase to each other telepathically: *"You're decent. I don't consider you a bad person."*]

. . .

[1000.3 / 2628] [Overhead an odd whistling chirp from an unknown source coaxes out the spirit of our true nature. An abstract wave of cats gently rolls through the space. The energy of the hanger becomes spacious, activated, and black. THE GRANDDAUGHTER and I walk towards a dumpster and wait. The whistling continues. THE GRANDDAUGHTER disappears.

I find a baby in a dumpster with a blonde bob haircut and pick it up. THE GRAND-DAUGHTER has taken form in a new infant sized body, but she has the face of a teenager. She asks to be put down and can instantly walk. I walk with her to greet THE GRANDSONS *(stoic, confused, and questioning)* who are boys in pint sized muscular male bodies. We grab hands to stay together as we walk. I guide them to the base of an escalator and separate from them once they begin to ascend.] //

⁂

Maj. = 0- THE WEAVER: #1007

BORDER: #1043, #0025, #0122, #0168

DUMPSTER: #1089, #1146

ESCALATOR: #1057, #1166

BLACK: #1060, #1061, #1072

⁂

#1001 - November 18, 2019 @ 06:10 (San Francisco, California)

[1001.1 / 2629] [*"Hey is this a good deal?"* THE CONFIDANT inquires, tossing me a paper with an advertisement for a new model of recording device he owns. He debates having his current one replaced under warranty. We're packed up, ready to take a road trip together. I drop the paper on the counter and reach for an oversized bottle of brown cologne, which I drop and spill across a hardwood kitchen floor. A white shaggy rug thirstily sops up the odif-erous liquid.

"I'll buy you another one."

"No. No. No."

We clean up the mess, walk to the garage, and get in a car. The sound of sirens floods in from the street as we depart.]

[1001.2 / 2630] [We drive through our "Borderless Neighborhood" at night. All houses have invisible walls and furniture. We can see every action of those inside the dwellings. Men watch invisible TVs and order invisible fast food from Uber Eats on invisible phones. A scruffy, unkempt Caucasian male driver arrives with invisible bags of food and stands impa-tiently outside an invisible door waiting to drop off a delivery. He's curt and rude to his customers. THE PILOT is dissatisfied to learn he's been given the incorrect invisible order. The neighborhood residents begin to surround and harass the delivery man. I float into the middle of the collapsing circle, meeting the man eye-to-eye and say,

"This is a 'Gotcha' game. I see the hidden cameras. You're just trying to catch us acting poorly."

"Two crappy companies join forces to deliver even crappier service," a shrill voice yells.

"We're on to it and we don't want it," another voice from the crowd shouts.

"I get you're in a bad mood. Let's not even bother with this and move along," I encouragingly pose to both the driver, and mob.]

[1001.3 / 2631] [THE CONFIDANT and I sit in a movie theater. At an intermission we look left and see MARILYN MANSON sitting next to us. He looks like death's brother. His eyes are deeply recessed. Pale rotting ligaments barely hold a loose and floppy mandible to a skeletal upper jaw.

"How was your day?"

After a lengthy pause, he responds, *"Oh that was a real question."*

The lengthy pause continues and then, *"...I directed a porn shoot this morning."*

We stand up to stretch our legs.

"You seem pretty tired of the same old tricks. Maybe it's time for a break?" I say gently touching his forearm as I pass in front of him and exit the theater.]

[1001.4 / 2632] [My right hand throbs. I raise it to my mouth to kiss it. I lift it to my cheek to cradle my face gently reminding it,

"You don't have to torture yourself to have God."

I repeat this again and again as a soft invitation; a sweet prayer. LEWIS CARROLL appears to my right and teaches me to weave secret codes and puzzles into writings, *"as us intellectuals and magicians of the 19th century were oft to do."* He initiates me into the tradition.]

[1001.5 / 2633] [I stand up and discover myself holding hands with my neighbors in a circle. BEYONCÉ appears in a red gown in the middle and sings her song, "Start Over." We raise our arms up as we count down from 108 as BEYONCÉ rolls into her version of "Lift e'vry voice and sing." When she concludes, we pray together, hands overhead, while BARACK OBAMA observes from the side, chain smoking "Lucky Strikes."]

[1001.6 / 2634] [On the opposite side, a young man in a crisp pressed white linen shirt rises up from crouching on a seaside boulder as a wave crashes. His necktie blows in the wind as he rims his brow with his right hand. He points to a golden orange horizon saying,

"I have choice. That's the one gift that's mine."

A voice over shoulder reminds, *"Now that you know, you're under contract. You're responsible for every step you take."*] //

⁂

Maj. = 6 - THE PILOT: #1030, 16 - THE CONFIDANT: #1026
BEYONCÉ: #1032
BARACK OBAMA: #1086
MARILYN MANSON: #1053
RESPONSIBLE: #1002, #1201
THEATER: #1082, #1097
TORTURE: #0182
CHOICE: #1139

⁂

⁂ 13.3 - THE BOOK OF TRIANGULUM: 1002-1005 ⁂

#1002 - November 19, 2019 @ 07:45 (San Francisco, California)

[1002.1 / 2635] [I support a group of people riding bikes. I'm responsible for helping fill up participant water bottles, and for keeping the large blue water vessels filled and sanitary. When I attempt to fill a rider's bottle, a thick orange pureed pumpkin-like goo pours from the spigot. Chunks of partially baked batter *(like crushed up muffins)* intermittently clog the pipe, which I dig out with my fingers. The entire scene occurs in the woods on an asphalt trail. Hundreds of people zip by on bikes.]

[1002.2 / 2636] [I'm in a large tree house, camping with a group of women. When I lay down the entire structure uproots and pivots. I lay on top of a massive clear cylinder that holds tens of thousands of gallons of water. The cylinder is full and hovers a few inches above the ground until it gently lands to rest on a sandy beach a few hundred feet away. The group is surprised by the move, but continues to rest undisrupted. THE HANDYMAN and THE APIRIST *(natural, clear, and caring)* may be nearby. I have a hunch THE WORLDBRIDGER helped facilitate the move.] //

⁂

Maj. = 7- THE WORLDBRIDGER: #1078
ASPHALT: #1168, #1191
PUMPKIN: #0064, #0277, #0939
CYLINDER: #0125, #0193, #0914
THE HANDYMAN: #1295

⁂

#1003 - November 20, 2019 @ 04:57 (San Francisco, California)

[1003.1 / 2637] [I'm in a retreat setting at night. I'm invited to join a group of people at a rectangular table for a game. We're asked to determine how to distribute money to different members of a church parish. The process as designed is flawed. Members of different wisdom traditions are among those seated at the table. My desire to leave slightly disrupts the order. I just get up from the table and step away.]

[1003.2 / 2638] [We're in a thicket surrounded by blooming cotton under the shade of a willow tree. I thank THE EXTERMINATOR *(unflappable, quiet, and deliberate)* for all the healing he's brought through for me, as he assists a young man who says he knows me. THE PRAGMATIST *(observant, dark, and feminine)* looks over THE EXTERMINATOR's shoulder.]

[1003.3 / 2639] [I walk toward the dormitories intending to gather my things. Just prior to departing I decide to stay at the retreat. I take a seat on the right back row corner of a grid of chairs, and pray. I stand and walk towards a radiator by a nearby wall. In a blink I'm in a laboratory with white paneled walls and a floor of a similar color that pulses to reveal a ghostly green grid under foot. A white rubber representation of a molecular compound snakes its way down towards the floor. I pull at one of the dots. It stretches like a rubber band and peels away from the corner. A smattering of dots is bright red, but only really noticeable if closely inspected under a magnifying glass. At the top, two black rubber tongues with four thin gray grooves are threaded with ribbon, and tied firmly to hold the model in place. I feed the white rubber tape, through both tongues, while on one knee. I dedicate the action to THE LITTLE PRINCE.]

[1003.4 / 2640] [A TV shows a grainy image from an African village. A welcoming Kenyan voice describes a brick making process. It will take 70 days to make a single door for a hut.] //

⁂

Maj. = 12- THE LITTLE PRINCE: #1014
RUBBER: #0035, #0040, #0062
DOTS: #0212, #0225, #0259
THE PRAGMATIST: #1247

⁂

#1004 - November 21, 2019 @ 02:57 (San Francisco, California)

[1004.1 / 2641] [I'm out of my body. THE TRINITY *(bright, devoted, and broad spectrum)* and I massage my body as spirits. The body howls in pain as I apply firm pressure to my right calf. ***"Take it easy on that body!"*** I say lightly to bring myself release.]

[1004.2 / 2642] [A yoga class is underway at the back of a large gym. Standing next to a water fountain I say, ***"If we'd gone to Marin, this would've been a coffee day."***]

[1004.3 / 2643] [I walk up a craggy outcropping of rocks and walk across a futuristic *(and invisible)* Golden Gate Bridge with thousands of others. A woman brings a son and daughter to my house once we exit the bridge. I welcome all three of them in as my guests.] //

⁂

LIGHTLY: #0531, #0824, #0887, #1240
GOLDEN GATE BRIDGE: #1091, #1109, #0344, #0387
FIRM: #0395, #0404, #0494, #0554, #1278
GUESTS: #0561, #0611, #0734, #1287

⁂

#1005 - November 21, 2019 @ 06:39 (San Francisco, California)

[1005.1 / 2644] [Fast competitive motion. Go-karts fly around a banked track within a warehouse. The point of the race is unclear.]

. . .

[1005.2 / 2645] [THE WITNESS *(encouraging, pure, and resilient)* tenderly holds my hand and heals it by pulling out energetic blocks coiled around my tendons. It's painful. I'm ok with the pain; it flows from a non-conditional realm. "

Pain is just a word. Pain is the base layer. Pain is the connective tissue."] //

⁂

GO-KART: #1106, #1144
PAIN: #0400, #0406
HAND: #0407, #0418
FAST: #0452, #0455
NON-CONDITIONAL: #0023, #0998
WAREHOUSE: #0075, #0154
RACE: #0226, #0253

⁂

⁂ 13.4 - THE BOOK OF AURIGA: 1006-1019 ⁂

#1006 - November 22, 2019 @ 06:13 (San Francisco, California)

[1006.1 / 2646] [I read the first chapter of each of my new textbooks to get ahead for the upcoming academic term. I open a package that contains an at-home-gene-editing experiment kit, which I toss aside without giving much attention. I catch a bus to school.]

[1006.2 / 2647] [I'm at a large venue for a concert as the house lights drop. It's unclear, but it seems like MADONNA may perform, though she never appears. The production value is crap. The crew lacks heart. Underwhelmed by the show I turn to leave and encounter THE ICEMAN. We give each other a quick hug as he shouts, *"DUCKY!"* with a smile. He departs. THE ROBOT and THE RAPTOR sit up and to the right. I point at them to get their attention. They seem out of place. I walk up to THE RAPTOR, tap him and sarcastically say,

"Thanks for letting me know you were coming!"

"We're only here for a day, had some decisions to make, and decided it was best we just show up."] //

⁂

Min. = ♦ -THE RAPTOR: #1166, ♥- THE ROBOT: #1146
MADONNA: #1282
DUCKY: #0056
HEART: #0060
TEXTBOOK: #0211

⁂

#1007 - November 22, 2019 @ 07:15 (San Francisco, California)

[1007.1 / 2648] [I move into a new house with APRIL LUDGATE and RON SWANSON. We unpack a box with an apple pie and pause to eat it. Once empty, APRIL grabs the clear glass pie plate and throws it on the kitchen floor. It doesn't break. When I pick it up it's been anodized with a white/blue/turquoise swirl pattern. APRIL aimed to destroy another person's property, but couldn't. I hold it up to her saying,

"That wasn't cute. It was just annoying. Stop it."

I walk to the living room and sit on the couch with THE WEAVER to discuss what happened. I grab an open Amazon box that has multiple light blue and brown boxes of condoms. Two of the blue boxes are empty.] //

⁂

Maj. 0- THE WEAVER: #1015
CONDOM: #0100, #0103
SWIRL: #0040, #0055

⁂

#1008 - November 23, 2019 @ 05:45 (San Francisco, California)

[1008.1 / 2649] [The family lives on a coast. THE DANCER and THE CARPENTER board up the house and drive inland to avoid a hurricane.]

. . .

[1008.2 / 2650] [I'm in a large rustic clubhouse-like home. Some of the rooms don't have roofs. I'm fascinated by a rectangular piece of art that hangs over a hearth. I attempt to clean it, but my efforts result in green dye emerging and filling grooves in the burlap from top to bottom like blood soaking through gauze. Its appearance is different from how the owners know it. I'll have to say something to them when they return. It looks water damaged and streaked after I give my best attempt at restoration. The burlap cord is woven into tight right angles in a Greek Key pattern.] //

⁂

Maj. = 1-THE CARPENTER: #1019, 2- THE DANCER: #1014

HEARTH: #1066

BLOOD: #1021

GREEK KEY: #1091

GAUZE: #0925

⁂

#1009 - November 23, 2019 @ 06:30 (San Francisco, California)

[1009.1 / 2651] [THE STUDENT *(loving, heart centered, and motherly)* runs check-in at a yoga studio. She's just completed teaching a class and is scheduled to lead the next one. The computer system doesn't work properly. She allows a group of people in without reconciling an attendance sheet. *"No matter! It's the last class I'm teaching here,"* she says shrugging her shoulders, laughing, and then happily entering the studio to teach, *"one last time."*] //

⁂

LAUGHING: #0937

NEXT: #0938, #0944, #0945

STUDIO: #1026, #1034

⁂

#1010 - November 23, 2019 @ 07:55 (San Francisco, California)

[1010.1 / 2652] [I stand at a bronze memorial on a rocky sea cliff composed of three gateways. The plaque at the base acknowledges this place as the childhood school of JOSEPH CAMPBELL and ALAN WATTS. Each has adult sized representations of them swinging from poles and playing hide-and-seek like children, cast in bronze. The North gateway leads to a school named: "THE ONEIRIC ACADEMY."]

[1010.2 / 2653] [I drive away from a seaside amusement park. The road weaves around the bases of multiple roller coasters, none of which are running. The steel coaster tracks are painted vibrant yellow and orange tones. Traditional wooden coasters are painted flat white. Seems the park has closed for the season. It's not clear if *(or when)* it will reopen.]

. . .

[1010.3 / 2654] [I'm on a team of people who move kitchen supplies up a staircase and into a house. The boss stops me while I carry a box full of Tupperware and glassware. He discovers they haven't been washed appropriately, and takes time to wipe excess soap and water spots off every item in the box.] //

⁂

ALAN WATTS: #1227
MEMORIAL: #0914
BRONZE: #0522, #0654
AMUSEMENT PARK: #0079, #0274
CLOSED: #323
WHITE: #0325, #0327

⁂

#1011 - November 25, 2019 @ 06:58 (San Francisco, California)

[1011.1 / 2655] [I drive through a large campground with wavy concrete roads *(which feels like a golf course)*. A luxury dog kennel allows canines to roam about under large, solid-arched structures. It's cool and grey. The surrounding trees overhead are tall and green. It feels and sounds like the luxury kennels are near an ocean, though I can't see any water.]

[1011.2 / 2656] [THE PUBLIC MEDIUM and I trade healings. He asks me to take my jeans off. I notice a triangular grouping of three red bug bites on my upper inner right leg, just behind the knee. We trade sweet and friendly body work. He focuses on the spot behind my leg without touching it with his hands.]

[1011.3 / 2657] [I look down at a form provided by a school. It's a progress report. It shows my grade level, which at first I read as, "5.33". After a quick glance away, I note it actually says, "5.99."] //

⁂

Maj. = 18- THE PUBLIC MEDIUM: #1036
JEANS: #0921, #0937
OCEAN: #0963, #0980
KNEE: #0660, #0760
GLANCE: #0306, #0390

⁂

#1012 - November 25, 2019 @ 22:21 (San Francisco, California)

[1012.1 / 2658] [I sleepwalk through a house, knocking in to different objects as I lumber through. I pick up a box full of bath towels containing a new WU TANG CLAN album packed at its center. The towels have all 400 track names from the album screened on them.]

. . .

[1012.2 / 2659] [It's nighttime. A man and woman find me in their Ocean Avenue home. I take some coins from a dish on a credenza and place them in my back left trouser pocket. I feel the barrel of a shotgun held to the back of my head and hear the trigger click.]

[1012.3 / 2660] [I watch RHIANNA win an award and accept it under a massive arched canopy. I wake up and write this down knowing I'm still sleeping.]

[1012.4 / 2661] [I find a large wad of cash in my pocket. I don't know where it came from.] //

⁂
RHIANNA: #1132
SHOTGUN: #0957, #1188
CASH: #0348, #0371
TOWELS: #800
NIGHTTIME: #0533
⁂

#1013 - November 26, 2019 @ 03:49 (San Francisco, California)

[1013.1 / 2662] [I attend a meditation class. I realize I've gone to an "upper-level night" in error, and decide to leave. THE DEVOTEE invites me to stay. The class is seated around tables set in a U-shape formation. Tonight's class is a combination of "levels 5, 6, & 7." Some people depart for a road trip to Arizona. I'm paired up for healings with a woman who has webbed toes, which she insists I do not touch. I give her "hands off" healing. The list of class attendees is hundreds long.] //

⁂
Min. = ♠- THE DEVOTEE: #1108
MEDITATION: #0128
ARIZONA: #0587, #700
LIST: #0748
ERROR: #430
⁂

#1014 - November 30, 2019 @ 03:40 (San Francisco, California)

[1014.1 / 2663] [A child with Down Syndrome plays alone and quietly in a small playhouse.]

[1014.2 / 2664] [I work with THE RENAISSANCE MAN *(frenetic, funny, and tactical)* on a welding project. I repeatedly stick a flat narrow razor into my forearm under and around a thick vein. After I've pierced the skin, I remember I haven't properly sterilized the tool. When I withdraw the straight razor from my arm, it's rusty.]

. . .

[1014.3 / 2665] [I attempt to change my phone number. I'm helped by a group of associates. One young woman repeatedly talks over me, until she sits down and slinks away. I'm handed a chocolate dipped macaroon as I walk away from the counter. I want the number 526-527-9876 but am issued 526-527-8901. I'm courtesy called on my new number. I go on a rant about how, ***"I used to be an SVP, and it bothers me that I'm not being listened to."***]

[1014.4 / 2666] [THE DANCER lets me hold THE LITTLE PRINCE as we walk into a department store and sit on a couch next to one of her male dancer friends.]

[1014.5 / 2667] [I walk to a construction site on a parking lot where a balsa wood cathedral is being built. Large colorful tarps create the roof. THE CONNECTOR is the site project manager. The project is behind schedule and the team has cut corners on a lot of details. I remark that I like the design. ***"I think it's beautiful."***]

[1014.6 / 2668] [I walk around a city looking for THE AESTHETE *(cerebral, contemporary, and skillful)*. I've taken a new job at my former employer's largest competitor. My office is directly across the street from my last one. ***"I wonder if I'll ever meet my new boss."***] //

⁂

Maj. = 2- THE DANCER: #1021, 4- THE CONNECTOR: #1031,
12- THE LITTLE PRINCE: #1015
DOWN SYNDROME: #0008, #0125
RAZOR: #0079, #0449, #0576
DESIGN: #0637
THE AESTHETE: #1016

⁂

#1015 - November 30, 2019 @ 05:25 (San Francisco, California)

[1015.1 / 2669] [I've taken a new job on a project team. We've taken some time to get work organized. Once we establish a plan, a man named "Sean" enters, swipes a piece of paper from the table, and decides to go do his own thing. I call him out saying,

"You don't do that. Especially after we spent time setting this up. We've worked really hard to create the process."

"Well, you don't really need this piece, I'm going to just go do my own thing."

"No. Just...No." I push back. After we tousle back and forth, I relent, ***"Fine...just take it."***

An awkward pause ends when I stand up and say, ***"You know, I don't care if I make some people angry. It's not my job, nor concern to please everyone. My job is to change things for the greater good, and I have a track record of delivering on that promise."***

I contemplate if I've taken the aligned role.]

[1015.2 / 2670] [We're playing with THE LITTLE PRINCE. A neighbor has taken him out on the front lawn, which makes THE WEAVER uneasy. THE WEAVER invites the woman back to the house, seeming a tad overprotective. THE LITTLE PRINCE is very well developed for his infant age. He can sit up and has advanced fine motor skills on his first day outside the womb. He and THE CHILD play together cutely. I see the constellation of skills he will develop. He'll be an accomplished guitarist, a poet, a scientist, a healer. I can see the conversations I'll have with him as he grows into a man. It looks like it's going to be a lot of fun!] //

⁂

Maj. = 0-THE WEAVER: #1021, 3-THE CHILD: #1041, 12- THE LITTLE PRINCE: # 1041
INFANT: #0153
DEVELOP: #0039
FUN: #0064, #0079

⁂

#1016 - November 30, 2019 @ 07:11 (San Francisco, California)

[1016.1 / 2671] [After a yoga class taught in low light, I make out with THE NORSE DEMIGOD *(statuesque, smooth, and noble)* and then give him a blowjob. Afterwards we debate the "qualities of a yogi." He morphs from a man into a woman. She and I walk into a bakery where a generous woman gifts us a cake for our 6:30pm dinner party. THE NURSE sits at a cafe table in the bakery negotiating a contract with another woman who's about to join her team.

The bakery transforms into a library where THE AESTHETE *(practiced, flat, and unsurprised)* studies at a desk in front of me.

THE PERFORMANCE ARTIST *(mysterious, broad, and masterful)* enters. His hair is long. At first, he doesn't recognize me. He's there to organize a group of protestors, just as a team of riot police arrive on scene.

Once outside, I hop in a shopping cart full of melting one-gallon tubs of ice cream. I ride the shopping cart down a hill and zip through neighborhoods while on my way home. I hear DAVE CHAPPELLE's voice over a public loudspeaker selling "OBREGON AND ZAIRE" soap. The comedian's voice creates exaggerated-rolled-tongue-pronunciations for each of the products in his signature, breathy, low-toned voice.]//

⁂

Maj. = 13- THE NURSE: #1149
DAVE CHAPPELLE: #1436
BLOWJOB: #0021, #0075
ICE CREAM: #0406, #0566, #0623
RIOT: #0458
GENEROUS: #0787
THE AESTHETE: #1203
THE PERFORMANCE ARTIST: #1177

⁂

#1017 - December 1, 2019 @ 01:00 (San Francisco, California)

[1017.1 / 2672] [THE BREWMASTER and THE PARKS DIRECTOR *(curt, fit, and expansive)* welcome me to their sprawling mountain compound. THE RECONCILIATOR shows up late *(as expected)* and surprises us. She's nine months pregnant! She shows off her belly while sticking out her tongue and shaking her booty like a, *"Texas PhatGurl."* We're invited to a

candle lit dinner party on the back lawn, joined by OPRAH and a group of non-binary, non-conforming trans people. The sky is dark indigo. At the dinner's conclusion I stand and am handed my swaddled infant nephew who coos as I lovingly cradle him.
A later vignette involving JOHN GOSSLING is quickly discarded as, *"junk."*] //

⁂

Min. = ♥- THE RECONCILIATOR: #1067
OPRAH: #1213
SHAKING: #0066, #0566
NON-BINARY: #0076

⁂

#1018 - December 1, 2019 @ 05:00 (San Francisco, California)

[1018.1 / 2673] [I'm in a house at night. Large, oversized slices of sloppy greasy pizza are placed on white round paper plates. I talk to a man with a ponytail who mentally processes his younger brother coming out of the closet as, *"Queer."*]

[1018.2 / 2674] [I watch LIZZO eat chocolates from a box she keeps under her bed. I take a few when she offers them to me, then go to my room. I repeat this sequence a few times.]

[1018.3 / 2675] [I'm at a retirement village, but unable to discern inside from outside. I stroll along a pathway that gives me a view into a variety of different units. I can see dining spaces and kitchens, but don't see any bedrooms.
"Where do people sleep?"]

[1018.4 / 2676] [I set all my toys on a shelf. A small alien action figure animates and pushes some of the smaller toys around. I separate the toys onto different shelves so they won't fight. Most of their interactions remain playful. It feels odd to have an adult intellect in a young, rapidly growing body.] //

⁂

LIZZO: #1041
PIZZA: #1160, #1165
ALIEN: #1019, #1139, #0831
STROLL: #0039, #0066, #0181
GROWING: #0009, #0050, #0079

⁂

#1019 - December 2, 2019 @ 06:00 (San Francisco, California)

[1019.1 / 2677] [THE CARPENTER measures my body to ensure I'll fit correctly in the cockpit of an alien-looking rocket car. Precision matters. The vehicle is on loan from an off-book government agency, who's allowed the car to be displayed publicly at a museum. THE CARPENTER pays close attention to the seat belt fit around my inner upper legs. Quick movements of the car could result in femoral fractures, arterial hemorrhage and *(in rare extreme cases)* full limb dismemberment if the fit is not properly calibrated.]

[1019.2 / 2678] [I walk through a Blockbuster Video. The back wall has exposed brick and doubles as both the new release wall, and a public pissoir. I walk up to the wall to inspect the titles available, noticing a man and woman down the aisle discussing what they want to watch. I've decided to pee and notice my urine stream coats a plastic sheathed copy of a black and white film entitled, "STELLA."] //

⁂

Maj. = 1- THE CARPENTER: #1021
ROCKET: #0125, #0230, #1336
PRECISION: #0051. #0098, #0147, #1324
EXPOSED: #0069, #0079, #1205
BLACK AND WHITE: #0128, #0134, #0185, #0199, #1277, #1299, #1313

⁂

⁂ 13.5 - THE BOOK OF ARA: 1020-1026 ⁂

#1020 - December 3, 2019 @ 03:30 (San Francisco, California)

[1020.1 / 2679] [I'm in a dark office. I'm constipated. I'm scheduled to meet with LADY GAGA to discuss the launch of our new product line. THE REVOLUTIONARY works in the office down the hall.

I sit on a commode in various positions thinking I'm moving a lot of feces through my bowels. Exhausted by my strain and effort, I look back and discover the water in the toilet is clear. No poop. I feel frustrated and bound up in my core.

"Poop."] //

⁂

Min. = ♠- THE REVOLUTIONARY: #1438

LADY GAGA: #1161

MOVING: #1103, #1125

POOP: #0488, #0780

⁂

#1021 - December 3, 2019 @ 04:59 (San Francisco, California)

[1021.1 / 2680] [The family responds to an invitation to test ride, "The Boring Company's 'Hyperloop.'" We take seats in a wide roller coaster car on a track that runs into the trapezoidal mouth of a cave. We all immediately realize we're in danger. There's no windshield to prevent debris from flying at our faces. We were not issued protective eyewear. Thick flat pillars of red and white light run parallel in ribbons overhead. Our eyes bloody as we gain speed and dust flies at our faces. I believe it'd make a great theme park ride, discounting its scale and recurring maintenance expense profile. The fiscal commitment is too high for a single amusement park to shoulder on its own.

We take a few roundtrips on the track. The first couple of times the multiple g-force "ramp up" and "stop shock" that bookend the experience cause us all to pass out. We sit in different configurations. Sometimes THE WEAVER and THE CARPENTER sit behind. Other times we're far apart on the train. Other trips find us aligned across the same row of seats.

THE ATHEIST gushes compliments to THE DANCER that are well intended but fall flat with her.

"Honey, I know you so well." "You are the biggest person I know." "You're the heaviest person I know." THE DANCER is full term pregnant.] //

⁂

Maj. = 0- THE WEAVER: #1029, 1- THE CARPENTER: #1052,

2- THE DANCER: #1028, 8- THE ATHEIST: #1050

RIBBONS: #0023, #0033, #0105

ROLLER COASTER: #0245, #0250, #0274

TEST: #0049, #0188, #0199

TRAPEZOIDAL: #0203, #0979

⁂

#1022 - December 3, 2019 @ 06:41 (San Francisco, California)

[1022.1 / 2681] [I'm on Montaña Larapata. It's misty. Light rain has soaked my clothes. I don't want to hike from the river at the base of the mountain to the garden up top. It'll ruin my clothes and my boots will contaminate the soil up there.]

[1022.2 / 2682] [I'm inspired as I watch a boy overcome paralysis to win a race.]

[1022.3 / 2683] [I watch actors mark scenes for a television show. They place bullseyes and crosshairs where their heads need to be to capture action as the director requested.]

[1022.4 / 2684] [I stand in line. The guy in front of me buys me a coffee and offers a free yoga class after I show him how to put his foot behind his head. I demonstrate by putting my left foot overhead as I stand. My shoulders stack over my spine. My right leg is straight. Standing tall, I seem skinny. ***"It's easy to be a contortionist when one has little body mass."***] //

⁂

COFFEE: #1033, #1073, #1116, #1176
MISTY: #1145, #0030, #0157, #0396
PARALYSIS: #0125
SKINNY: #1041, #1087, #1101
SOIL: #1199, #0015

⁂

#1023 - December 4, 2019 @ 05:00 (San Francisco, California)

[1023.1 / 2685] [CHER is an esteemed guest at a summer camp. She blows THE EXCOMMUNICATED's *(seeking, committed, and responsible)* mind when he finds half a banana by a tree left by her with a personalized message for him burned into the peel. Her mansion is nearby, though occasionally she stays at the camp. Today's she's come back with ANA GASTEYER *(who refers to herself as "Maeva" AND 'another famous woman.'")* CHER wears a beret, a blonde straight hip-length wig, a turquoise poncho, and knee-high-calf-leather boots. I describe the impact her banana note made on THE EXCOMMUNICATED. Her eyes well up with tears as she says, *"Thank you for telling me that."* It's the wrong time to ask her for a photo, especially because I intend to "Cher" it with other people using a goofy punny hashtag. She gives me a big hug and goes into her private bedroom.]

[1023.2 / 2686] [A group of young men strategize at a nearby table about how to order themselves in a peloton. They're certain one position in the group requires 40% more exertion to keep pace. I offer to take that "puller" role to give others a shot at winning the race. The race map looks like a star's magnetic field. Thousands of rays of light radiating out in arcs from the poles of a golden sphere indicate the paths of cyclists in motion. The sphere spins slowly.]

. . .

[1023.3 / 2687] [I have a conversation with THE COACH *(affable, sharp, and compassionate)*, beginning with, ***"Are you open to a conversation about _____?"*** He agrees and goes on to demonstrate how he oscillates, *"above and below the line."* Open and closed. Loud to quiet. Nice to mean. I get my answer. He suggests I would make a good "FA" pointing to an empty chair, but plainly states I must, *"take all the steps to get to that level."* It makes sense to me and is unarguable. ***"No skipping steps."***]

[1023.4 / 2688] [I depart camp at dawn with two other guys. We drive a car. We pause to look at a map. The sun is just rising, though the clock and our watches confirm it's 10:00pm. We know our next way point is a school, where later we can buy food and supplies. The route is illustrated by simple cartoons without any text. No reference to distance or scale is made. From the school, we know we must travel an additional eight miles before we arrive at the bike race starting line.] //

⁂
CHER: #1130
CONFIRM: #0023, #0140, #0145
GLOBE: #0023, #0815, #0914
PELOTON: #1149
THE EXCOMMUNICATED: #1131
⁂

#1024 - December 5, 2019 @ 06:59 (San Francisco, California)

[1024.1 / 2689] [I hang out with a female friend who's annoyed by her fame.]

[1024.2 / 2690] [I have $15MM in cash. I move it between accounts so people don't know I have it. One friend is aware. I pay him off by giving him all the freshly laundered gym towels he wants. A girlfriend and I push a cart full of cash down a well-lit hallway in a dormitory.]

[1024.3 / 2691] [*"It's best not to take that,"* a voice suggests as I pick up a single powder blue suede loafer off the floor from underneath a shallow dark wood shelf that runs the length of the wall six inches above the ground. The pinky toe side of the shoe is blown out and frayed, exposing a "Burberry" tag in the center.]

[1024.4 / 2692] [Political debate occurs on a red carpet stage between three different parties. The groups parody one another and gang up 2:1 as each candidate speaks. There is no counterpoint, nor debate. The noise of the other two groups simply rises until the speaker's voice is drowned out and they stop talking. It's a futile public exercise that wastes time and resources.] //

⁂
FRAYED: #0386
PARODY: #0021

PUBLIC: #0030, #0037, #0038
SHALLOW: #0043, #0189
TIME: #1253
⁂

#1025 - December 6, 2020 @ 02:00 (San Francisco, California)

[1025.1 / 2693] [THE CAREGIVER *(precise, demanding, and focused)* and ARCHANGEL RAPHAEL fight.]

[1025.2 / 2694] [I'm inside a high-rise condo as tornados swirl overhead. I open a door to a rooftop patio and see walls crudely patched with "Quikrete." THE MAKE UP ARTIST *(glamorous, fun loving, and generous)* huddles in a common kitchen with myself and others beneath a tiled island. I'm pretty sure the building is going to explode when directly struck by a funnel cloud extending down from directly above us.] //

⁂
EXPLODE: #1035, #1071, #1137
RAPHAEL: #0615, #1251
ROOFTOP: #0079, #0084, #0113
TORNADO: #1195
⁂

#1026 - December 6, 2019 @ 03:53 (San Francisco, California)

[1026.1 / 2695] [I sit at a diner counter with SOPHIE discussing music production, sex, and dating.]

[1026.2 / 2696] [THE CONFIDANT hosts Saturday Night Live. During a cold open, he lays on a couch wearing boxer shorts. He breaks character when he notices a hole in the inseam shows his balls on camera. They've been blurred out before air, courtesy of a five-minute broadcast delay.

"Yep, those are mah ballz," he laughs, as does the studio audience.]

[1026.3 / 2697] [I flirt with THE PIXIE while looking for dessert. I find three small slices of chocolate cake, each the size of a credit card. We dress up in costumes in the restaurant parking lot. I open the back doors to a 15-passenger van, and lower a large cardboard box filled with costumes on to the concrete. I select a red and black fur hat with two long draping tentacles, which I fling around my neck like a scarf.]

[1026.4 / 2698] [I sit in an office with THE DOCTOR *(energetic, flirtatious, and gossipy)* and THE BOND TRADER *(mature, patronal, and exacting)*. They ask me if I'm married. THE BOND TRADER says he's getting married next August. THE DOCTOR and THE MARATHONER *(frenetic, dedicated, and inspiring)* are now married, though they live in different states. THE BOND TRADER prides himself on a recent promotion to CEO of "West Bank." I ask him about their core businesses.

"Clearing house for regionals? Commercial reinsurance?"

I talk to THE BOND TRADER through a screen in a newspaper. Music playing in his office is louder than the volume of his voice, rendering me unable to hear his responses to my questions.

"Turn the music down."] //

⁂

Maj. = 16- THE CONFIDANT: #1288

Min. = ♠-THE PIXIE: #1122

SOPHIE: #1027

MUSIC: #1034, #1062, #1085

SEX: #1123, #1128, #1131, #1149

⁂

⁂

PART 14 - APOPHENIA

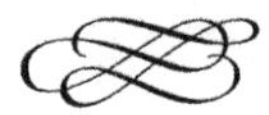

#1027 - #1239

*"**Apophenia:** n. the tendency to perceive a connection
or meaningful pattern between
unrelated or random things
(such as objects or ideas)
that if left unchecked
can give rise to
conspiratorial thinking."*

* * *

December 8, 2019 - June 17, 2020

⁂

⁂ 14.1 - THE BOOK OF LUDERE: 1027-1114 ⁂

#1027 - December 8, 2019 @ 06:11 (San Francisco, California)

[1027.1 / 2699] [**"Invite and celebrate EVERYONE's wellbeing." **]

[1027.2 / 2700] [I wear plush pajamas that feel soft on my skin. I pass by a shelf of mix tapes and loose cassettes. I sit at a table with SOPHIE. She smokes a cigarette while waiting to be interviewed for the CEO role at a tech company.

"Does their product integrate with your music creation process?"

She nods, exhaling smoke through her nose. The frame retracts. The group gathered for the interview falls asleep at the table just before the meeting.] //

⁂
CREATION: #0040
EVERYONE: #0042, #0047
INTERVIEW: #0058, #0189, #0386
CIGARETTE: #0040, #0043, #0088, #0298
⁂

#1028 - December 9, 2019 @ 01:24 (San Francisco, California)

[1028.1 / 2701] [I observe a meeting in a conference room in the basement of the Salesforce Tower. Attendees are crisply dressed. Everyone wears starched, pressed white shirts. One attendee is a coworker of THE CRUSH *(distant, crisp, and thorough)*, who's onsite to meet with other members of the team. The team is dissatisfied, and annoyed they're enrolled in a required corporate training no one wants to attend. A sales servicing team is particularly vocal. They defend their calendars *(considering their client facing time as "sacred")* and believe the training grossly misappropriates their time.]

[1028.2 / 2702] [I'm in a karaoke booth in Times Square with THE FUR TRAPPER *(fast, loose, and eager)* and a bunch of other drunk, rowdy guys. They belt "Like a Virgin" at the top of their lungs. I mistake the track for another and claim ***"I don't know the words,"*** even though they're presented on the screen in front of me.]

[1028.3 / 2703] [I enter a mansion with a marble interior that gently swells and grows the deeper I advance within. I sit next to SARAH PAULSON and begin talking, confusing her with JULIA ROBERTS. MARTIN SCORCESE sits down across from us on a white cushioned couch with questions about a film he wants to make about *"apolitical aspects of RICHARD NIXSON's life."* JULIA ROBERTS sits across the salon tuning a cello on a round white marble pedestal. A series of four shallow steps lead up to her chair. She's borrowed a solid gold stand from BETTE MIDLER, to use as a mount for the cello.

"Ordinarily the gold stand holds a giant globe of BETTE's."

The cello can spin freely at a tilt on its vertical axis. The stand falls over and lands on JULIA. I rush over to help her up off the floor. Once nerves have settled, I have questions from MARTIN for JULIA. Once I ask MARTIN's questions, I thread in a few of my own.

"What do you think about Marty's intention, Jules?"

"He needs to worry less about compliance and bring more focus to the facts of the story," JULIA responds.]

[1028.4 / 2704] [THE DANCER appears with long, straight, black-and-red hair. Her cheeks are splotched with red and black dots of melted crayon wax that look like tears. THE DANCER starts singing a song. I ask her to stop.] //

⁂

Maj. = 2- THE DANCER: #1033
SALESFORCE: #0324
CRAYON: #0371
SONG: #0002
THE CRUSH: #1076

⁂

#1029 - December 9, 2019 @ 06:13 (San Francisco, California)

[1029.1 / 2705] [It's 4:00am. It's January. I'm at work. I instant message CATHY BESSANT to set up lunch. Her admin responds with a noon hour slot on *"April 1 in Jacksonville, Florida."* I'm in North Carolina.]

[1029.2 / 2706] [THE WEAVER and I babysit a dog that looks like "Gizmo." It runs around playfully, hiding under furniture.]

[1029.3 / 2707] [A group in British Columbia tries to organize a trip home. They don't have documents, a map, nor have decided on a shared departure time.] //

⁂

Maj. = 0- THE WEAVER: #1032
NORTH: #0025, #0033, #0045, #0062, #0077
JANUARY: #0018
MAP: #0022, #0034, #0069, #0112
BABYSIT: #0010

⁂

#1030 - December 10, 2019 @ 05:30 (San Francisco, California)

[1030.1 / 2708] [I play a combat video game. THE PILOT and I sit next to each other on toilets. We shit while we play the game.]

. . .

[1030.2 / 2709] [At the back of a home, a group of men get naked. I stand in the doorway of a bedroom watching. THE ONE NIGHT STAND *(dismissive, distant, and focused elsewhere)* asks me, *"to take your pants off if you want to stay."*]

[1030.3 / 2710] [I walk around the interior of a giant convention center with a group of people. A new app is about to launch. Large screens display outlines for *"action plans, progress to date, and next steps."* A line item on the task plan "fails" and triggers an escalation. A male team member accepts a phone call and steps away from the group to mitigate. We dance around as we wait for direction.]

[1030.4 / 2711] [I'm in a garage. I find a tray of sandwiches left in the fridge, cut into triangles. I take one and eat it as I look through mail crates on wheels filled with brown cardboard poster tubes.]

[1030.5 / 2712] [Driving around.]

[1030.6 / 2713] [I warm up with a band. We gather for a sound check in a dancehall sized venue. I stand and tune my instrument at stage left, while roadies and guitar techs make preparations and troubleshoot acoustical quirks unique to the venue.] //

⁂

Maj. = 6- THE PILOT: #1031
NAKED: #0035, #0044, #0153, #0158
GARAGE: #0189, #0214, #0231, #0278, #0386
SOUNDCHECK: #0290
BAND: #0303

⁂

#1031 - December 11, 2019 @ 04:19 (San Francisco, California)

[1031.1 / 2714] [I'm on a college campus, seated at a lunch table. Grade school friends sit at another table. THE FIRST GRADER *(goofy, nerdy, and lonesome)* sits next to THE KINDERGARTENER *(timid, observant, and quirky)*.

"We're still doing this, huh?" I ask.

"Yes," they say though their tone implies they don't know me.]

[1031.2 / 2715] [I walk down to the waterfront after a strong rainstorm. On the way, I pass a row of buildings *(and THE PILOT)*. Numerous people dangle at the waist over a railing to look down, and into the dark water below. A group on the other side of the bay gather for a party, though their gathering space doesn't have a safety railing. The revelers are drunk. I'm concerned they may slip into the water. If that happens, they might drown.]

. . .

[1031.3 / 2716] [I slide tiny slices of bread into a miniature toaster. THE CONNECTOR stands nearby on the countertop. THE COUTURIER walks by the kitchen. She's gaunt and frail, though her hair is newly dyed blonde and neatly styled. She's stunning. She wears an elegant black dress of her own design. I infer THE MAKER and THE COUTURIER have recently moved. This morning, they retrieved all their personal items from a storage locker.
"Everything we stored away has now been brought back," THE COUTURIER remarks.]

[1031.4 / 2717] [A temple project kicks off. THE MAKER leads it.] //

⁂

Maj. = 4- THE CONNECTOR: #1035, 6- THE PILOT: #1059
Min. = ♣- THE COUTURIER: #1115
BLONDE: #0336, #0350, #0367
PARTY: #0323, #0328, #0332

⁂

#1032 - December 12, 2019 @ 06:37 (San Francisco, California)

[1032.1 / 2718] [I flirt with ANDERSON COOPER while we hang out together at a mutual friend's home. I float up to the octagonal vaulted ceiling and run laps around it, up towards the apex.]

[1032.2 / 2719] [I'm with BEYONCÉ. We're on tour. We meet up with hundreds of people who have supported her on her path, from the time she was a child. *"This summer is about connection, reconciliation, and appreciation."*]

[1032.3 / 2720] [I'm at a restaurant eating lunch with THE WEAVER. Someone offers to buy my meal. A woman joins us at the table. She self identifies as an old friend of THE WEAVER's. I introduce myself, to which she responds, *"Darling, of course I know you. I knew you when you were just yea high,"* gesturing with a downward facing palm less than a foot from the floor. I don't remember her.
She gives me two hugs:

One to the left, the other to the right.] //

⁂

Maj. = 0- THE WEAVER: #1033
BEYONCÉ: #1099
OCTAGON: #0121, #0188
FLIRT: #0204, #0310
APPRECIATION: #0082, #0144, #0171
LEFT: #0172, #0173, #0193
RIGHT: #0201, #0204

⁂

#1033 - December 13, 2019 @ 05:42 (San Francisco, California)

[1033.1 / 2721] [THE GUITARIST, THE DRUMMER *(grounded, deliberate, and relentless)* and I sit around a table listening to a bootleg recording of a show we played at a coffee shop 20 years ago. We're pulled into the recorder and revisit the scene. Soft light. Sawdust on a hardwood floor. Small cocktail tables filled with spectators. ANDY SAMBERG and the guys from "THE LONELY ISLAND," join us onstage. We demo some tracks they will eventually carry forward and popularize.

We laugh about how ***"we let that opportunity go!"*** The tone of my recorded voice is annoying and shallow. My ideas and chatter between songs are equally annoying. THE DRUMMER and THE GUITARIST want to revisit the songs.

I'm insistent ***"we appreciate them for what they were and move on."***]

[1033.2 / 2722] [I watch a family sprint up a rock scramble, then jump from the top of a cliff into a cove. This is their way of *"reclaiming the mountain"* after the death of their father. Another family does the same thing to mourn the loss of a child.]

[1033.3 / 2723] [THE WEAVER, THE DANCER and I live together in a suburban home. The neighbors pull out a compact helicopter from the garage. It disappears from the driveway, then I hear it fly between our houses and across our open, fenceless backyards. THE WEAVER doesn't understand what's happening until she sees the shadow of the chopper blades on the walls of her upstairs bedroom. People gather on their back lawns.

"Yep, everyone decided to come out just in time to see all the rich people fly away."] //

⁂

Maj. = 0- THE WEAVER: #1048, 2- THE DANCER: #1037

Min. = ♣- THE GUITARIST: #1248

SHALLOW: #0003, #0006, #0022, #0043, #0189

SAWDUST: #0021, #0075

RICH: #1301, #1302

THE DRUMMER: #1428

⁂

#1034 - December 14, 2019 @ 04:29 (San Francisco, California)

[1034.1 / 2724] [I'm in a spaceship.]

[1034.2 / 2725] [I'm at a yoga studio in outer space. I teach classes to people wearing space-suits. A student decides they want to open a valve on my suit. I don't believe it's the right thing to do. I believe I'm going to be exposed to lethal doses of solar radiation, <u>if I don't first suffocate and freeze</u>. I scream when I hear the suit depressurize. My eyes open and I see everyone else has taken similar action. **All are fine**. The situation is stable.]

. . .

[1034.3 / 2726] [THE VIOLINIST *(poetic, professional, and gracious)* performs a piece of music written in an odd *"postmodern tablature"* format. No staff notation, just suggested progressions that leave most of the creativity to the performer. She creates flourishes and melodies that connect her to her audience. **"Virtuosic Classical Jazz"** is her working name for the new genre.]

[1034.4 / 2727] [A guy identifies himself as a corporate program manager. Per his resume, he's had prior experience as a team lead.]

[1034.5 / 2728] [THE POOL BOY *(gregarious, rowdy, and candid)* introduces me to his dad, a well-known accident injury attorney. I've seen his dad's ads on TV.] //

⁂

RADIATION: #0121, #0378
SPACESHIP: #0007
GENRE: #0014
TV: #0212
THE VIOLINIST: #1039
THE POOL BOY: #1344

⁂

#1035 - December 14, 2019 @ 06:02 (San Francisco, California)

[1035.1 / 2729] [I review a career website. While looking at a variety of jobs, roles at Salesforce are oddly highlighted.]

[1035.2 / 2730] [I'm at THE FLASH's home. She wants to show her dinner guests a piece of visual media on a laptop. Her small dog comes into the room and barks, waking up her roommate. The roommate is annoyed.]

[1035.3 / 2731] [THE CONNECTOR and THE FIREFIGHTER are in my bedroom discussing *"who gets to use the extra mattress next."* I ask them to decide. They don't. I choose to use both mattresses. They get neither.]

[1035.4 / 2732] [A late night talk show host takes his crew to the street during a live production. They generate an impromptu flash mob at a busy city intersection. He asks a spectator to capture the performance on his iPhone and he passes the device over to them and begins to tap dance.]

[1035.5 / 2733] [I watch an ad for an, *"immersive trivia game."*]

. . .

[1035.6 / 2734] [A glass beaker is left upside down in a heated kiln. We tip toe backwards, assuming the glass will soon explode as gases within rapidly expand.] //

⁂

Maj. = 4- THE CONNECTOR: #1055
Min. = ♥- THE FIREFIGHTER: #1066
EXPAND: #0003, #0082, #0193, #1266
EXPLODE: #0080, #1281, #1336
THE FLASH: #1135

⁂

#1036 - December 15, 2019 @ 07:00 (McCordsville, Indiana)

[1036.1 / 2735] [A family with 17 children lives in a mansion. One of the kids is named, "Blanket." The parents work in a library and provide babysitting services to the public. One baby under their charge morphs into a sharp clawed iguana and crawls into a bedroom, where I corner it.]

[1036.2 / 2736] [I cook breakfast for a couple of guys. My attention increasingly drifts from plating eggs and bacon, to finding my fur coat. The coat dangles on the edge of a composting toilet under THE PUBLIC MEDIUM's bed.] //

⁂

Maj. = 18- THE PUBLIC MEDIUM- #1253
FUR COAT: #0144
LIBRARY: #0033
TOILET: #0189
MANSION: #0311, #0331

⁂

#1037 - December 16, 2019 @ 06:56 (McCordsville, Indiana)

[1037.1 / 2737] [I run around London with THE DANCER. We agree to go inside a building that seems oddly familiar. Once inside, we travel up an elevator to a luxurious penthouse condo.

"I've been here before."

Elevator inside the unit. Bedroom at the top. Modern and inviting. We discover a secret society concluding a meeting on the main floor. We're not supposed to be there, but we decide to stay and observe. A water wall has been added from the top bedroom level down the exterior of the elevator. We ascend to the third-floor ***greenhouse***. A row of large upside down "J" shaped windows create and arched view out onto a busy city street below.] //

⁂

Maj. = 2- THE DANCER: #1044
GREENHOUSE: #0126, #0212, #0249
SECRET SOCIETY: #0132, #0233, #0271
ODDLY: #0025, #0200, #0205, #0365, #0376

PENTHOUSE: #1335

⁂

#1038 - December 17, 2019 @ 06:59 (McCordsville, Indiana)

[1038.1 / 2738] [**Riding on a train as narrative detail dissolves. **]

[1038.2 / 2739] [I lead a lecture with ample support from my graduate students.

"We've prepared dutifully."

My students are interested in a tennis match, and want to keep a TV on next to the lectern. We move our bodies for a bit, but people remain distracted. I shut the TV off. A woman takes a phone from her pocket and places it on the floor near a wall. I invite her to leave, ***"if watching the tennis match is her priority."***

She's deeply offended. Some express relief that I've shut the TV off. Others are agitated.

"Today we're going to focus on the therapeutic benefits of conscious breathing," I say, stepping up onto a round table.

Some students are skeptical. I step up onto a chair, atop the table, and notice students scattered around multiple other round tables. An industrial kitchen next to the classroom has a pass-through window that delivers trays of food to students as class proceeds.]

[1038.3 / 2740] [I've soaked a bunch of washcloths in cold water. When I unroll one, it becomes a moist paper towel.] //

⁂

MOIST: #0022

BREATHING: #0134, #0205, #0336

COLD: #0007, #0012, #0017, #0044, #0066, #0088

INDUSTRIAL KITCHEN: #0090, #0125, #0233

⁂

#1039 - December 18, 2019 @ 04:50 (McCordsville, Indiana)

[1039.1 / 2741] [I'm in a tri-level, puzzle-piece-shaped house at night. THE VIOLINIST *(ethereal, feminine, and demure)* and THE BASS *(masculine, practiced, and talented)* share a leopard for a pet. We plan a trip together. An entity enters my left ribs and latches on from the inside, nestling between my organs and bones. I send gold light to heal the wound, and usher the energy out.]

[1039.2 / 2742] [A group of cisgender friends dressed in 1920's formal wear makes music with brass instruments while sitting around a round wooden table. A man plays a trombone. A woman plays a trumpet. Their facial features migrate to one hemisphere of their faces, giving them the look of a cubist painting. They curl their index fingers around the receivers of their instruments to create, *"makeshift mouthpieces."* Their cheeks puff out wildly as they play. The music is equal parts *"big band swing, and jug band hootenanny."*]

. . .

[1039.3 / 2743] [THE RABID RABBIT *(conflicted, overwhelmed, and suffering)* drives a van around the desert.]

[1039.4 / 2744] [A backpack contains a special gift. It might be a live animal.] //

⁂
TRI-LEVEL: #0036, #0101
1920's: #0128
CHEEKS: #0392
RIBS: #0134
SPECIAL: #0147
INDEX FINGER: #0148, #0234, #0328
THE VIOLINIST: #1189
THE BASS: #1189
⁂

#1040 - December 18, 2019 @ 22:16 (Fort Dodge, Iowa)

[1040.1 / 2745] [THE ORPHAN is present when the leader of a large yoga class is served a cease-and-desist letter by a legal team.] //

⁂
CEASE: #1299
LEGAL: #0021, #0145, #0172, #0233, #0324
LETTER: #1278, #1285
⁂

#1041 - December 19, 2019 @ 03:25 (Fort Dodge, Iowa)

[1041.1 / 2746] [I meet "Skinny" LIZZO. She has a black eye. I nudge GRANDMA and tell her, ***"LIZZO's kind of a big deal."***]

[1041.2 / 2747] [THE CHILD takes a ride where spooky animatronic monsters pop up to startle passengers. She sees scissor lifts and pneumatic components under the faux-fur skinning of the, *"monsters."*

"This was a boring ride," THE CHILD says, unimpressed after learning the monster's just a machine.]

[1041.3 / 2748] [Penguins.]

[1041.4 / 2749] [GRANDMA and GREAT GRANDMOTHER are in a closet with cherry wood shelves and drawers. Within a drawer, THE LITTLE PRINCE is swaddled between pairs of folded wool socks. GRANDMA uncovers him and picks him up. She and GREAT GRANDMOTHER pause from tidying the house to play with the baby.]

. . .

[1041.5 / 2750] [School.] //

⁂

Maj. = 3- THE CHILD: #1042, 11- GRANDMA: #1055, #12- THE LITTLE PRINCE: #1054
GREAT GRANDMOTHER: #1185
ANIMATRONIC: #0023
PENGUINS: #0058
SCISSOR LIFT: #0216
CHERRY: #0037, #0088

⁂

#1042 - December 19, 2019 @ 04:40 (Fort Dodge, Iowa)

[1042.1 / 2751] [THE CHILD runs down a street *"looking for the Boogeyman."* She's not scared.]

[1042.2 / 2752] [I stack two paintings on top of a filing cabinet during a meeting. Our leadership team discusses how to, *"amortize and depreciate any prospective works of interactive art installed in the boardroom."*]

[1042.3 / 2753] [I'm in a full classroom. We all collectively review for an exam. The room feels eager.] //

⁂

Maj. = 3- THE CHILD: #1044
FULL: #0332, #0337, #0349, #0378
EAGER: #0010, #0147, #1297, #1327

⁂

#1043 - December 19, 2019 @ 09:45 (IOWA/ILLINOIS Border - I-80)

[1043.1 / 2754] [Driving down a highway. Fields and trucks are presented in a cartoonish silhouette.]

[1043.2 / 2755] [I'm out walking with a group in downtown Manhattan. I break from the group to follow a naked man with full body tattoos. He rides a bike and parks it next to a brick wall. When he dismounts the bike, he's wearing a jockstrap. He winks at me. I walk down a staircase to catch the subway.] //

⁂

SILHOUETTE: #0012, #0135, #0394
TATTOOS: #0140, #0232
WINKS: #0338, #0350, #0380

SUBWAY: #0314, #0390, #0396
BRICK: #1246, #1262, #1284
⁂

#1044 - December 20, 2019 @ 09:05 (Beavercreek, Ohio)

[1044.1 / 2756] [I decide to divest a stock holding the night before a major corporate announcement. I want to reverse the transaction when I learn what leadership intends to do.]

[1044.2 / 2757] [I verbalize a dream in my phone recorder. THE DANCER and THE CHILD enter my bedroom with a stack of wrapped gifts and leave by them bedside with cards for me to sign.]

[1044.3 / 2758] [I play a simple 2-bit handheld video game.
"It's a racing game I played in the backseat while on long car rides as a kid."]

[1044.4 / 2759] [I interview for a job. During a break, I sit next to a conference table with a variety of different small stacks of coins on top. A quarter has been sliced at the bottom, leaving roughly 80% of the coin. Another solid gold coin, called a *"Half Hamilton"* has a cartoon bite taken from it, leaving clover arcs for teeth marks.] //

⁂
Maj. = 2- THE DANCER: #1050, 3- THE CHILD: #1047
QUARTER: #0074, #0394
SOLID: #0159, #0180, #0373
STOCK: #0014, #0025, #0128, #0147
INTERVIEW: #1249, #1261, #1272
⁂

#1045 - December 21, 2019 @ 04:39 (Beavercreek, Ohio)

[1045.1 / 2760] ["JJ" is a DJ who asks me to accompany him to a party he's booked. We walk up a winding path to a mountain top. We pass multiple people on our way. We stop at a diner. A famous family sits at the table next to us. They get up and leave.]

[1045.2 / 2761] [I want to spoon with THE KINKSTER *(dominating, limbic, and cold)*. I attempt to connect with him a number of times, but he's fully immersed in his phone. We don't connect. THE SKEPTIC *(cynical, objective, and rational)* and other friends dart in and out of the room, observing THE KINKSTER and I.] //

⁂
DJ: #0220, #0251, #0323, #0326, #1304, #1322
DINER: #0001, #0382, #1303
MOUNTAIN TOP: #0047, #0220, #0312

THE SKEPTIC: #1122

⁂

#1046 - December 21, 2019 @ 08:38 (Beavercreek, Ohio)

[1046.1 / 2762] [Athletes train at a Russian gymnastics center. A final sendoff takes place under a moonlit circus tent on a rocky mountain top. A group of athletes has just completed a rigorous multi-month training program. I'm asked by a coach to make some final remarks to the team. My comments are from the heart, and I unexpectedly tear up as I make eye contact with each person individually. I'm humored when I look down and see a basket of rubber ducks placed behind the podium to keep the environment sweet and lighthearted.

"I'm unsure of how I fit into the community now," I say with a quivering lip.

"I appreciate the home this group of people provided for me during the past few years. I've appreciated being both a teacher and student."

I intermittently pause to get grounded. I let appreciation flow without forcing responses or comments. I feel good.] //

⁂

ATHLETES: #0017, #0071, #0189, #0201, #0295
LIGHTHEARTED: #0010
GOOD: #0014, #0038, #0052
COMMUNITY: #0117, #0144, #0149

⁂

#1047 - December 22, 2019 @ 08:21 (Beavercreek, Ohio)

[1047.1 / 2763] [***NIGHTMARE*** - Dark energy gathers in the corner of a room. A front room has three vertical rectangle windows with a view out to a porch. I might share the space with a roommate. It's a cool, grey autumn day. Something happens to THE CHILD, so jarring that I forget.]

[1047.2 / 2764] [I encounter THE LIONESS *(influential, revealed, and open)* at an amusement park. We're in San Francisco. THE LIONESS has recently relocated with her new partner after selling her chain of yoga studios. We sit on a hill. We walk up to a large, salmon-toned building owned by her family. We go inside the family compound. THE LIONESS wants a glass of water. I walk to the fridge and fill a glass for her. I also fill an unusually thick crystal vase with flowers and place it back on a sun-lit round oak table.]

[1047.3 / 2765] [THE CHILD passes through a catering kitchen cradling a stack of loose papers at her chest; paychecks for people who work onsite. THE CHILD insists they are **hers**.] //

⁂

Maj. = 3- THE CHILD: #1050
NIGHTMARE: #0172, #0352
DARK ENERGY: #0007, #0065
CRYSTAL: #0073, #0124, #0295

SALMON: #0008, #0070
CHAIN: #1282
⁂

#1048 - December 23, 2019 @ 07:12 (Beavercreek, Ohio)

[1048.1 / 2766] [I'm at a rock concert. Unintelligible conflict among crowd members occurs a few feet away.]

[1048.2 / 2767] [I'm at a house at night waiting for a friend's arrival. THE WEAVER's been gone for a while. My friend arrives. He has two dogs. The tile floor around a circular bidet is wet. It's been covered in urine for so long, the floor tiles are loose, and the boards beneath are saturated and warped. I have to pee and notice the toilet is a recessed 400-gallon cube with a round opening at top-center. I straddle and fill the cube multiple times. Just as liquid crests the lip and spills to the floor, a large flushing mechanism releases the entire contents of what looks like an *"oily gasoline wave."* I urinate another 100 gallons. Afterwards I meticulously mop the floor. THE WEAVER won't be happy, but I've done my best to clean up and repair the damage.] //

⁂
Maj. = 0- THE WEAVER: #1050
ARRIVAL: #0007, #0014, #0048
CUBE: #0015, #0144, #0209
TILE: #0248, #0394
GALLON: #1217
⁂

#1049 - December 23, 2019 @ 08:41 (Beavercreek, Ohio)

[1049.1 / 2768] [***"Talk to text functionality doesn't work on my phone."***]

[1049.2 / 2769] [I encounter THE COLONEL *(direct, engaging, and precise)* as I back out of a driveway and head towards THE ALIEN NATUROPATH's *(abstract, quick, and intuitive)* home office. On the way, I drive around damp roundabouts that look like concrete "Candyland" sidewalks suspended in black space.]

[1049.3 / 2770] [I have a special medicine drawer that acts as a repository for my daily protocol of vitamins and supplements *(a variety of small white tablets and brown gelatin coin-sized discs)*. The supplements have stuck together in a bizarre melted blob in the drawer. I decide to delay taking supplements until, ***"after the holidays."*** I don't seem to need them at the moment.] //

⁂
VITAMINS: #0025
CONCRETE: #0032, #0036, #0053

HOLIDAY: #0194
DELAY: #0144, #0292
THE ALIEN NATUROPATH: #1316
⁂

#1050 - December 24, 2019 @ 07:53 (Beavercreek, Ohio)

[1050.1 / 2771] [An event has rattled the administration of a European boarding school. A young woman alleges a teacher has abused her.

THE CHILD is a student at the boarding school. In an unrelated matter, she and another friend have been brought up on disciplinary charges for destroying a work of art mounted in a school hallway. THE DANCER and THE WEAVER sit in on her hearing. THE DANCER startles me when she uses a staple gun to fasten her cheek to her lower right jaw. When she learns there's a video of the vandalism, she realizes she's unnecessarily injured herself to falsely defend her child. CCTV evidence suggests they snuck out of their rooms at 4:00am, walked to the art piece, and ripped multiple heads of Romanesco cauliflower from a square panel on the "living installation."]

[1050.2 / 2772] [THE ATHEIST and I fly a pedal plane up a jagged Technicolor coastline. We spot THE WEAVER below.

"Where are you going?" she inquires.

"To the University!" we shout down in unison.

We land at the back of a building and enter a lecture hall, where a professor reviews a complex organic chemistry equation. I sense I'm behind in my studies, so much so I consider withdrawing from the course.

I take a breath to, ***"get clear on what I want to learn."***

The professor points out esoteric reductive components in the equation he refers to as, "*the spell.*" THE ATHEIST and I walk out of the lecture before it completes. We notice THE CHILD's disciplinary hearing continuing across the hall.

THE WEAVER gets a pedicure during the hearing and doesn't seem bothered with the proceedings.] //

⁂

Maj. = 0- THE WEAVER: #1051, 2- THE DANCER: #1054,
3- THE CHILD: #1057, 8- THE ATHEIST: #1054
EQUATION: #0136, #0210
SPELL: #0141, #0365
SQUARE: #0376
HALLWAY: #0217, #0364, #0367, #0384
SCHOOL: #1239, #1273, #1277
⁂

#1051 - December 24, 2019 @ 09:57 (Beavercreek, Ohio)

[1051.1 / 2773] [A private caterer is investigated for shady accounting practices. Three "RAD" fascia rollers are offered to bribe investigators.]

. . .

[1051.2 / 2774] [I deep clean a bathroom with THE WEAVER. We scrub the floors together on our hands and knees, scraping through thick layers of soap scum. The bathroom is all white. White tiles. White walls. White fixtures.] //

⁂

Maj. = 0- THE WEAVER: #1052
WHITE: #0384, #0385, #0390
FIXTURES: #0009, #0032
SCUM: #0021
TILES: #1299

⁂

#1052 - December 25, 2019 @ 08:01 (Beavercreek, Ohio)

[1052.1 / 2775] [A condo building stands at a major urban intersection. The intersection dog ears left into a construction site that will eventually split into five streets. THE WEAVER and THE CARPENTER walk towards the construction site, interested in the municipal modifications. I climb up the exterior of the building via fire escape and jump through an open window. I enter a condo, where I recall having spent a prior New Year's Eve. A man I know as "Vertin" exits his unit, leaving his infant son "Joshua" in a carrier on the floor next to a roll top desk. A single night light in the kitchen dimly illuminates the flat. I pick up "Joshua" in the carrier. I take him out the window, and down the fire escape to street level.

After walking a few blocks away from the construction site, I realize,

"I've abducted the baby. Oops. Very bad decision."

I quickly return up the fire escape and replace "Joshua" just prior to "Vertin's" return. I exit and go home.

The next night I'm at a bar with some familiar faces. A feisty Latina-Filipino woman wears chocolate-toned knee-high boots. She's a professional hip hop dancer. I know some of the men. I'm introduced to "Vertin," who's unaware I broke into his home and abducted his child. "Vertin" disappears. I gather our group's dirty dishes from the bar and place them in the bus tub on the floor.]

[1052.2 / 2776] [I blink and discover myself back in "Vertin's" condo. I wash dishes, and put things away in cupboards. I set out a small dish of mixed nuts. I leave the condo and walk to a shared bathroom that has a large, flimsy particle board door, crudely painted white. A brass padlock dangles, unlatched, so I can use the bathroom. I hide in the bathroom for a moment. When exiting, I see identical twin brothers stand shoulder-to -shoulder. Both are bald and wear thick round rimmed glasses. I follow them.]

[1052.3 / 2777] [I lose my hearing. Newly deaf, I check on "Joshua" once more. He's alone in his carrier, but has been moved from the floor to the bottom open drawer of a cedar chest. I move with the precision of a ninja through the condo. Once out on the window sill, I descend the fire escape hand-under-hand until I get to ground level. With yellow subtitles, the construction workers tell me to **"stay off the street while they're working."** The city has forced them all to be there until the project is finished.

I thank them for their work and acknowledge, ***"you're doing your best without having any project level decision making power."***] //

⁂

Maj. = 0- THE WEAVER: #1055, 1- THE CARPENTER: #1057
CONSTRUCTION SITE: #0216, #0377
ROLLTOP DESK: #0204, #0224
FIRE ESCAPE: #0232
SUBTITLES: #0071, #0126
POWER: #1207, #1318

⁂

#1053 - December 26, 2019 @ 01:30 (Beavercreek, Ohio)

[1053.1 / 2778] [MARILYN MANSON and another long blonde-haired man lead a sound meditation at a hotel. They conjure *(and bring through)* some strong light transmissions as they facilitate. A giant octagonal window with an eight-pointed star in the middle, acts as a portal for group alignment. When the group achieves a certain level of coherence, space-time begins to bend. When we conclude, I pee.

When I return, MARILYN MANSON and the man debate where to eat dinner. I suggest an up-tier grocery store with beautifully prepared foods, ***"but it's a bit of a walk."***

"Just as long as it's not hotel food or fucking enchiladas. We've been here too goddamn long."

I make a few snarky comments about MANSON's career trajectory, and the absurdly large platform heels on his boots. I drop the playful jabs.

"I've been a fan of yours for 25 years. You matter to me. Could I please take a photo with you?"

He pauses, winks, and cocks back an arm like he's preparing to punch me. Instead, he draws me close for a long heart-to-heart hug. We begin taking photos. His arms have two sets of elbows, which enable a lot of great angles for selfies I'm not able to create with my body. We pierce each other's lower jaws and chins with chainmail beards. We use mouth spreaders and magnifying glasses in another photo. What was once considered, *"spooky and controversial,"* now seems, *"nostalgic and funny."*

"When are you going to take the band out on tour?"

"Tomorrow...."

His attention gets pulled in another direction, and he leaves. I have a phone full of photos.

Life rolls on.

I'm not sure where I'm going when I leave the hotel.

Everyone else departs, and I'm left alone.] //

⁂

MARILYN MANSON: #1071
EIGHT: #0169, #0209, #0232, #0242
MAGNIFYING GLASS: #0033, #0083, #0350
NOSTALGIC: #0045
TOMORROW: #0193, #0292
HOTEL: #0301, #0321

⁂

#1054 - December 26, 2019 @ 04:47 (Beavercreek, Ohio)

[1054.1 / 2779] [A guy hassles THE ATHEIST into picking up trash off the street. I avoid a verbal altercation and walk away. The guy follows us. He takes us to his condo that boasts a beautiful panoramic view of the San Francisco bay. A construction crew rolls up in front of us and builds a wall that obstructs the view. I'm disappointed.

"WHAT ABOUT OUR AIR RIGHTS?"]

[1054.2 / 2780] [THE LITTLE PRINCE is already hyper-developed, but only a few days old. He's tiny but says, *"Mommy."* He sits up. He can crawl. He's smiley and expressive.]

[1054.3 / 2781] [THE DANCER is numb. She puts together a collage for her doctor, based on his recommendations on, *"how to break up and outwardly express deeply repressed emotions."* The collage looks like a computer motherboard with transistors, wires, glitter and pipe cleaners affixed.] //

⁂

Maj. = 2- THE DANCER: #1055, 8- THE ATHEIST: #1092, 12- THE LITTLE PRINCE: #1055
HYPER: #0051, #0218, #0296
GLITTER: #0014, #0064
AIR: #0023, #0025
OLD: #1249

⁂

#1055 - December 27, 2019 @ 01:46 (Beavercreek, Ohio)

[1055.1 / 2782] [GRANDMA had a slow financial month. I give her a PayPal tutorial. THE DANCER will help me manage GRANDMA's accounts.

"We'll disburse $20 cash per day to make the money last. Non-essentials must be eliminated from the budget."]

[1055.2 / 2783] [A public kerfuffle involves ROSEANNE BARR and SARA GILBERT debating when I'm going to get a job.

"I've been working with more focus and precision than ever before," I convey to a television interviewer.

The media exposure highlights various aspects of my private life. I consider the nosiness of the press a, ***"deep violation of my privacy."***]

[1055.3 / 2784] [The family gathers in the UK House of Commons. A glass cake dish, with a tall, dunce-cap-like-lid sits on a ledge above where we stand. A set of crown jewels from Queen Victoria's reign have been loaned to a family friend. The government is concerned they've been lost, and tasks us with their speedy recovery.]

. . .

[1055.4 / 2785] [THE WEAVER feeds THE LITTLE PRINCE. She uses a steel "Big Bird' fork to stimulate his gums. He gives her an awkward look that makes us all laugh. THE LITTLE PRINCE giggles too.]

[1055.5 / 2786] [THE CONNECTOR wants to go to a New Year's Eve party.
"I don't consider that a wise choice."
She nurses fresh wounds from a significant surgery, but considers herself, *"fine."*]

[1055.6 / 2787] [A baby rests in a cradle under an artificial Christmas tree. We dismantle the hunter-green pipe-cleaner-tree fronds as the baby sleeps. Once the tree is packed away for the season, the baby stands and walks off.]

[1055.7 / 2788] [I'm proud when I notice a burst of last-minute marathon enrollments. Many of the late additions are my former employees. I'm proud of them for taking on a significant physical challenge. Most of them are not runners.]

[1055.8 / 2789] [**Some nonsense media barf about "King Trump: The Powerless Autocrat" **] //

⁂

Maj. = 0- THE WEAVER: 1056, 2- THE DANCER: #1057, 4- THE CONNECTOR: #1071, 11- GRANDMA: #1117, 12-THE LITTLE PRINCE: #1068
VIOLATION: #0359
WISE: #0001, #0026, #1209
JEWELS: #0114, #0376, #1332

⁂

#1056 - December 27, 2019 @ 07:22 (Beavercreek, Ohio)

[1056.1 / 2790] [I'm in a box seat at an opera house hitting on a woman. She holds a small white box with the word "**tumult**" written across it in small black letters. The box is filled with photos of desperate people living in impoverished regions. The young woman rejects me. A group of similar-aged guys climb up the wall, and into the box with us. They point and laugh at my failed attempt to get a girlfriend.]

[1056.2 / 2791] [On stage, a photoshoot is in progress. Members of a ballet company stand positioned in succession to appear as, *"a single body advancing frame-by-frame through a leap."* Eight to twelve dancers create the illusion. Occasionally a statically posed dancer fizzles and dissolves, then reappears.]

[1056.3 / 2792] [I skateboard really fast down a street on an overcast day. My speed increases even though the grade appears to take me up a hill. It seems illogical as I swerve and maneuver like a professional.]

. . .

[1056.4 / 2793] [I walk through a house asking THE WEAVER and another man if they've seen the "**tumult**" box. They don't know what I'm talking about.]

[1056.5 / 2794] [It's my first day on a new job. It feels good to be back at work. THE FEELER is my new office mate. I ask if she can recall her HR intake process. I'm working. I've been issued a computer. I don't believe my credentials have been activated.]

[1056.6 / 2795] [I practice my math problems. I'm unable to cross multiply basic fractions. When I become frustrated, the dancing banana icon from the "PEANUT BUTTER JELLY TIME" meme flashes on screen. I'm given credit for creating the meme. This makes me laugh along with THE CARTOONIST *(esoteric, creative, and magical)* and THE LITIGATOR *(generous, inviting, and detail oriented)*, who occupy the desks in a row just behind THE FEELER and I.] //

⁂

Maj. = 0- THE WEAVER: #1057
Min. = ♣- THE FEELER: #1114
DANCING: #0012, #0026, #0144
CREDIT: #0016, #0024, #0220
BUTTER: #0039, #1296, #1326
ICON: #0033, #0311, #0334, #1285
THE CARTOONIST: #1389

⁂

#1057 - **January 5, 2020 @ 04:00 (San Francisco, California)**

[1057.1 / 2796] [I'm a C-suite level executive at a storied firm. JOHN SPENCE has been charged by MARC BENIOFF to, *"right-size his leadership team."*

The boardroom is shaped like an eight-point star with a vaulted ceiling made of different woods. JOHN and I disagree with each other from opposite ends of the table. MARC watches. JOHN fires me. THE WINO *(affable, dutiful, and curious)* becomes embarrassed. He originally recommended me to MARC as a prospective hire.

Once fired, I walk with MARC down a hall, and through a lower level of a corporate headquarters tower. I tell MARC, ***"I appreciate you and what you've done for San Francisco,"*** as he descends an escalator.

I watch him exit the building with his wife. They leave their luggage in the back of THE WEAVER and THE CARPENTER's white pickup truck which idles out front. I'm supposed to move the truck later that day to avoid getting a parking ticket.]

[1057.2 / 2797] [THE HIRING MANAGER *(inquisitive, thorough, and helpful)* runs business close for a corporate accounting group. I stop by her office to say, ***"goodbye."*** She gives me a gift.]

. . .

[1057.3 / 2798] [I'm on a plane. I have a window seat. The guy next to me falls asleep on my right shoulder. I jostle around saying, ***"Hey buddy,"*** but he doesn't wake up.

A sprite-like woman flies outside the plane. She wears fiery red and yellow jeweled sunglasses. I have a boner and my pants are down around my ankles. When I realize this, I become embarrassed and try to sheepishly cover myself.]

[1057.4 / 2799] [I read a suggestive Facebook post from my lover and become aroused.]

[1057.5 / 2800] [THE WEAVER and THE DANCER explain to THE CHILD that *"the red and gold wrapping paper is from Santa Claus, but we're going to keep it and reuse it for next year's presents."*] //

⁂

Maj. = 0- THE WEAVER: #1058, 1- THE CARPENTER: #1058,
2- THE DANCER: #1063, 3- THE CHILD: #1058
GIFT: #0358, #0375, #1256, #1302
SANTA: #0194, #0206
C-SUITE: #0113, #0117, #0124

⁂

#1058 - January 6, 2020 @ 03:53 (San Francisco, California)

[1058.1 / 2801] [I'm a skyscraper inspector. I review a site where overhanging/suspended glass units on the upper floors of a modern building have been seismically retrofitted with 1'x1'x2" blue and gray rubber squares of different densities. The stacks of squares are positioned at the corners of overhangs to provide shock absorption and dampening support when the building flexes during tremors. The building, I later learn, is *"Bloomberg Headquarters."*

We're given a tour of the facility, which buzzes with human creativity. Live television programs and podcasts are produced as we walk through a media studio. THE CARPENTER and I find a men's room. While peeing at neighboring urinals I say, ***"Americans want a rich man to be president. There's a rich man running for office who's 10x wealthier than the incumbent."***

MICHAEL BLOOMBERG stands next to THE CARPENTER and me, peeing.

He tells us he's, *"being mindful."*

"I'm not using my own media company and resources to finesse campaign messages. Doing so would be a massive and irreparable conflict of interest."]

[1058.2 / 2802] [We meet THE CHILD, THE WEAVER and THE CARPENTER for lunch. THE CHILD plays with little dogs that musically bark when petted. She's friends with a cool little flamboyantly gay boy. I become his mentor, counselor, friend, and eventually a trusted advisor as he grows up.]

. . .

[1058.3 / 2803] [I scratch an entire gymnastics competition when I injure my right wrist during pommel horse warm ups. THE WEAVER and THE CARPENTER are concerned by my decision not to compete, though understand, ***"self-care is my priority."***

Trampolines are set up in two rows at 45-degree angles in a zigzag pattern the length of the venue. The new apparatus allows gymnasts to audit a new method of dynamic bounding and tumbling.]

[1058.4 / 2804] [I can make a Mobius strip with my body. The technique allows me to back-bend and twist at the torso to suck my own dick.]

[1058.5 / 2805] [I meet THE NEIGHBORHOOD WATCH *(gossipy, omniscient, and ancestral)* for lunch after confusing the location. I forgot we'd made plans weeks ago. We sit at a community table near a window on a rainy morning; droplets tap soothingly on the glass.] //

⁂

Maj. = 0- THE WEAVER: #1062, 1- THE CARPENTER: #1065, 3- THE CHILD: #1063
BACKBEND: #0118
MENTOR: #0071, #0085, #0369, #3096
MASSIVE: #0026, #0033, #0034
RAINY: #0233, #0365

⁂

#1059 - January 7, 2020 @ 04:00 (San Francisco, California)

[1059.1 / 2806] [THE PARATROOPER *(macho, strong, and resilient)* wanders around his house yelling homophobic slurs. His sons don't understand he's joking. THE PARATROOPER doesn't understand his youngest son is gay. His family owns a successful restaurant, which affords them a comfortable life. The family lives in a saltbox Colonial style home. Their restaurant is on the ground floor of the home. Today they've closed the restaurant to prioritize a family outing.

An oversized rubber duck glows a ghostly green in the dark on the highest toy shelf in the boy's bedroom. The duck belongs to their neighbors, THE PILOT and THE KIND HEART, who've come to retrieve it *(and other items the family has borrowed over the previous year)*. They discover no one's home, but taste the stench of *"hate speech"* lingering sourly in the stale air. THE PILOT and THE KIND HEART decide to take up residence in the house.

Later, when the family returns, they're surprised to learn their children's playroom has been turned into a sex dungeon.] //

⁂

Maj. = 6- THE PILOT: #1068, 21- THE KIND HEART: #1079
FAMILY: #1249, #1256, #1266
BORROW: #1267
SHELF: #1271, #1279

⁂

⁂

#1060 - January 8, 2020 @ 05:32 (San Francisco, California)

[1060.1 / 2807] [THE ARBORIST *(open, intrepid, and handy)* and I hook up. He wants to hear a specific song play while he gives me a blowjob. THE ATTRACTOR's *(feminine, nourishing, and rejuvenating)* in the next room making dinner. A puppy crosses the kitchen, then enters our room, proceeding to run figure 8's around my legs. The dog grows tired and transforms into a sloth.

THE ARBORIST and THE ATTRACTOR share their condo with a Black lesbian who wears her hair in beautiful dense braids *(though she prefers to keep her hair short)*. It's advised she keep the braids as to, *"not tip off the new homophobic politician she's working for, that she's gay."* The woman has a girlfriend who reassuringly prefers the new *"Sugar Sugar" (code for: hair)* in braids.

All of us want to go out together and party downtown. As we depart, the cityscape appears in silhouette with an amber toned sky behind. A filter can be applied to make half the lights in the frame switch from yellow, to black-and-white.] //

⁂

HOOK UP: #0193, #0232, #0275, #0359
PUPPY: # 0249, #0255
BRAIDS: #0060, #1068
SUGAR: #0170, #1094
AMBER: #0003, #0018, #0063
THE ARBORIST: #1227
THE ATTRACTOR: #1386

⁂

#1061 - January 9, 2020 @ 02:37 (San Francisco, California)

[1061.1 / 2808] [It's 3:27am. I'm in a black and white gangster movie. I believe I need to backtrack to 12:30am to properly recall the plot. My phone prompts me that my flight has changed. I've sent an updated itinerary to my email account.]

[1061.2 / 2809] [**Abstraction.* * GWYNETH PALTROW and KYLIE MINOGUE partner on an arts and crafts project that requires the use of large syringes full of various hues of green acrylic paint. KYLIE psyches herself up to make a return to the stage next year. She intends to wear her favorite sparkly red dress while on tour.]

[1061.3 / 2810] [*"Go back to Burning Man."*

"Are you sure you want to do this again?"

"Even 'David's' willing to go back for one night of walking around and driving...like you discussed last Christmas."]

[1061.4 / 2811] [A young neighborhood kid rides up my driveway on a bike. The bike has training wheels. His dad accompanies him. It's early morning, hours before sun up. Collapsible 6' tables with board games are set up on the lawn nearby. A large trench has been dug down the center of my driveway from the street to the house. A large hibernating tree is laid on its side at an angle. A portion of leafless tree limbs crest the surface of the lawn, and look like the cardiovascular structures of a human lung. I overhear the neighbors discuss why the tree's there, and postulate on when it will sprout.]

[1061.5 / 2812] [**Designer roller skates with codpieces for heels are advertised ad nauseum on Instagram. **] //

⁂

GWYNETH PALTROW: #1250
WHEELS: #0066, #0204, #0220, #0309, #0337
GREEN: #0350, #0356, #0383, #0389
ROLLER SKATES: #0235
BLACK AND WHITE: #0272, #0334, #0370, #0371, #0392

⁂

#1062 - January 10, 2020 @ 03:10 (San Francisco, California)

[1062.1 / 2813] [While sitting on a deck at a coastal waterfront property, we look out on an overcast beach. It's morning.

"Wow! It's a beautiful, clear day," THE WEAVER says.

Some of those sharing the beach are mildly confused by her comment. A man I don't know stops to talk with us. He's friendly. He offers me a piggyback ride around the hotel and surrounding property. I accept. After galloping around on his back for some time he lets me hop off. I run towards an outcropping of rocks and scramble to the top, in search of a natural hot spring. When I find the hot spring, I'm advised by a team member wearing a white polo shirt and khaki shorts that, *"the water is boiling and will scald you if you enter."*

I can feel steam rise from the natural cauldron. I heed the warning and don't wade in.]

[1062.2 / 2814] [THE FLIRT acquires an entire wardrobe of second-hand clothing from his employer. He's delighted. He playfully rifles through tens-of-thousands-of-dollars of discarded designer labels.

"I'll keep 10% and put the rest on consignment."]

[1062.3 / 2815] [The newest popular music app dynamically generates playlists that match genres to the physical location of your phone: **Home. Driving. Grocery. Gym. Work.** All can be customized to get users expediently to the *"flow zone" (as advertised)*.] //

⁂

Maj. = 0- THE WEAVER: #1063
WOW: #0010, #0125, #0130, #0353, #0358
CAULDRON: #0043, #0161
ZONE: #1281
THE FLIRT: #1128

⁂

#1063 - January 10, 2020 @ 23:10 (San Francisco, California)

[1063.1 / 2816] [THE DANCER, THE WEAVER and I corral THE CHILD on a street corner to prevent her from bolting out into traffic. THE CHILD is resolute. She has strong opinions about the clothes she wants to wear, but fails to express her preferences. She throws a tantrum. THE DANCER remains calm and encourages THE CHILD to, *"use her words."*]

[1063.2 / 2817] [I stop by THE FIDUCIARY's house for a semiannual check in. He's ill and can't speak. He's recently completed a redesign of his high school emblem and mascot. He's been so monoline focused on the project he's not aware of the blue fuzz / yarn he's errantly glued to the side of his head. He remains silent. His roommate sends me a message: *"THE FIDUCIARY and THE REFLECTION are rekindling an interest in each other."* After reading the text I say,

"All you have to do is tell me you're dating someone and I'll back off. Bonus points for saying you're not interested! What I want for you is to be happy."

THE REFLECTION arrives and overhears this from the foyer. THE FIDUCIARY regains his voice and springs to life, sharing his experience of, *"redesigning the lion."* He points at the revised logo explaining,

"Look here. The mountain peak extends beyond where your eyes think it does."

The interaction remains lighthearted, simple, and friendly.] //

⁂

Maj. = 0- THE WEAVER: #1068, 2- THE DANCER: #1068,
3- THE CHILD: #1068, 9- THE FIDUCIARY: #1228
BONUS: #0084, #0243
PEAK: #0022, #0126, #0204, #0311
SIMPLE: #0312, #0321, #0322, #0333, #1249, #1256

⁂

#1064 - January 11, 2020 @ 03:33 (San Francisco, California)

[1064.1 / 2818] [The apartment floods with water while I build an acoustic guitar. Water soaks the kitchen and bathroom, but it doesn't flow into the plush carpeted living room. I've been eating the majority of a cheesecake with a friend, as I've built the guitar. The remaining portion of the cheesecake sits out on a round clear glass serving dish wilting from the temperate of the slightly humid room.]

[1064.2 / 2819] [I float along a bayou near a ramshackled house. The back of the house is missing. The dollhouse-like interior is covered with layers of graffiti. The property has been appropriated by an international gang as their *"new local safe house."* Water drips from the ceiling and quickly evaporates. Drops that hit the carpeted floor hiss and immediately turn to steam.] //

⁂

HUMID: #0113, #0282
DOLLHOUSE: #0080, #0144

STEAM: #0147, #0218, #0318
GRAFFITI: #0013, #0116, #0162
⁂

#1065 - January 12, 2020 @ 04:02 (San Francisco, California)

[1065.1 / 2820] [This upsetting scene features a YETI cooler filled with dismembered body parts. Fingers, toes, limbs are frozen within. I take the cooler in the house, and upstairs to the bathroom. I submerge the cooler in a claw foot tub filled with lukewarm water. The contents thaw. THE CARPENTER catches us and says, *"This is about THE LAST thing we wanted to have happen."*

THE CARPENTER pulls the cooler from the tannish pink water and disposes of it. The event is never spoken of again.]

[1065.2 / 2821] [I'm working with a group. I stain a table with lacquer. We hold the table overhead by the legs as one of us details the underside. The process is completed slowly and deliberately.]

[1065.3 / 2822] [I look at a photo of THE PSYCHIATRIST standing on an Australian mountain top. The image is pressed in the center of a stainless steel 45pm record. My left knee hurts.] //

⁂
Maj.* = *1- THE CARPENTER: #1066
Min. = ♠- *THE PSYCHIATRIST: #1073*
AUSTRALIA: #0002, #0010, #0395
FROZEN: #0319, #1321
THAW: #0186
⁂

#1066 - January 12, 2020 @ 23:53 (San Francisco, California)
**The song "Pneuma" by TOOL plays at low volume in the background throughout the entire scene. **

[1066.1 / 2823] [I'm working at an art gallery. My passport was delivered by courier from the hotel, where I left it last night. It's delivered along with two, half-business-card-sized thumb drives that serve as my new credit cards. THE FIREFIGHTER enters the room. He spins around quickly as he explains, *"it's part of a job interview."*

I try to take photos of him to capture him *"jowling."* THE CORPORATE PLANNER *(studious, neutral, and methodical)* is considered as a potential hire for the lead role as, *"a data steward and chief administrator"* of the gallery.]

[1066.2 / 2824] [A huge package is delivered, containing pieces of fine bone china, jewelry, and statuettes recently recovered from a theft. I place the contents in a secret vault within a monitored room, along with a series of paintings I've rolled up and placed in cardboard tubes for transport. One of the figures *(a dancer performing a leap)* has an arm snapped off. I repair it.

I arrange the remaining figurines on a table in another secure room that doesn't have video monitoring, which will allow me to remove them from the gallery at the appointed moment. Family members arrive in the secured room and surprise me as they pop down the flue of a large chimney of a powder blue and white hearth. THE REINCARNATED *(resolute, healing, and miraculous)* is among the visitors.

"I had a hunch you'd eventually show up, otherwise I'd have been on the first flight to Iowa I could get."

They don't stay long, each climbing up a ladder inside the chimney and out of view after they say, *"hello."*

I can hear THE CARPENTER, THE PRANKSTER *(youthful, inquisitive, and expressive)* and THE GREAT UNCLE *(withdrawn, resigned, and lonely)* chatting as they pass each other going up and down.

"I'm not one to go far. That's THE CARPENTER's job. He's gonna go far in life," THE GREAT UNCLE remarks.] //

⁂

Maj. = 1- THE CARPENTER: #1068
Min. = ♥- THE FIREFIGHTER: #1071
CHINA: #0040, #0043, #0076, #0094, #0320
HEARTH: #0014, #0124, #0249
IOWA: #0162, #0281
THE REINCARNATED: #1259

⁂

#1067 - January 13, 2020 @ 02:37 (San Francisco, California)

[1067.1 / 2825] [I'm at lunch with THE RECONCILIATOR.

"How the year's been?"

Some of it's serious. Some of it's sad."

When I ask her if she ***"still has the house"*** she starts to cry and says, *"No."*

She puts both elbows on our lunch table and buries her face in her hands. She continues to speak intermittently through waves of tears. I try to console her, but she's convinced she's lost **"Everything."**

She cries, *"Just be ready when loss really comes. All the support you think you have...it just goes away."*

Concurrently, I watch a movie about an angry vampire accosted by two strongmen. Their heads shrink rapidly as they speak. I've been glued to the movie. I can't fly away.

"If I could, it would be my cue that I'm sleeping. How long have I been sitting at the table before I wake up? A moment? 20 lifetimes?"

I don't know.] //

⁂

Min. = ♥- THE RECONCILIATOR: #1081
SERIOUS: #0311, #0323
SAD: #0325, #0339, #1209, #1220
SHRINK: #0010, #0177, #0280

MOVIE: #1249, #1270

⁂

#1068 - January 14, 2020 @ 00:25 (San Francisco, California)

[1068.1 / 2826] [I meet "Colton." He gives me his name only after THE PILOT stops through to play video games on my new PlayStation 5. THE PILOT and "Colton" have hacked a Super Mario 2D side scroller game. where they've applied a *"Donald Duck Skin"* to all the characters. THE DANCER, THE CHILD, THE LITTLE PRINCE, THE WEAVER and THE CARPENTER enter. I hold THE LITTLE PRINCE. THE DANCER knows "Colton." They speak casually with limited interaction.]

[1068.2 / 2827] [I look down a subway staircase and see a drag queen in street clothes named "Tayisha Busay" walking up in my direction. She's wearing a green cable knit sweater. I hug her.]

[1068.3 / 2828] [I'm on a soundstage watching actors perform acrobatic feats that foot to character movements in the *"Donald Duck"* video game. Stunts are performed high above the ground without guide wires or harnesses to create authentic expressions of exhilaration and fear in the actors. The stakes are mortal. One small mistake and an actor will fall. If they fall, they'll die.] //

⁂

Maj. = 0- THE WEAVER: #1069, 1- THE CARPENTER: #1069, 2- THE DANCER: #1072, 3- THE CHILD: #1086, 6- THE PILOT: #1079, 12- THE LITTLE PRINCE: #1088

DRAG QUEEN: #0022

DUCK: #0026, #0040, #0069, #0079, #0141, #0170

AUTHENTIC: #0040, #0385

2D: #0384

⁂

#1069 - January 14, 2020 @ 02:36 (San Francisco, California)

[1069.1 / 2829] [I prepare for an Olympic swimming event, but I'm lined up in the incorrect lane. I search for my team towel. In doing so, I audit other aquatic events in progress *(underwater dancing, etc.)*. I inspect the immaculate muscularity of my competitor's legs.]

[1069.2 / 2830] [SID from SLIPKNOT takes me backstage and gets me dressed up in a special jumpsuit. The band has added me as a new member who'll wear a superhero costume and play *"the token queer."* I'm instructed to go across the street to prepare for a 9:30pm performance. I meet THE WEAVER and THE CARPENTER and take a steam train to the front of the amusement park. When the train stops, I realize we've traveled to the incorrect amphitheater stage. We scramble back quickly to our point of origin, and go 50 feet in the other direction to a turnstile.

A woman blocks my passage and refuses to believe I'm one of the performers.

"I'll take you backstage...for a fee," she says with an arm outstretched.

"You're a crook lady," THE WEAVER argues then shoves me saying, *"GO! GO NOW!"*

THE WEAVER and THE CARPENTER block the extortionist woman as I jump the turnstile. I encounter a long line that wraps around the square interior perimeter of a windmill. An older man with a pointy-grey-chest-length beard motions at me to proceed. I jump another turnstile, and run down a similar square spiral staircase, descending through a variety of different hell realms.

I look over my shoulder and see the woman closing the gap between her and I.

"WHY WON'T YOU JUST GIVE ME WHAT I WANT?" She screams.

"NO! NEVER!" I yell as she continues to chase me.

I pass white walls that undulate and breathe. They pucker and stretch from the pressure of pointy goat horns protruding from their other side. Multiple sets of horns and skulls leer out from the white walls towards me. Framed photos on the wall depict grim and torturous scenes. Skinned faces. Gouged out eyes. Brutality. I encounter two guys who query,

"Hey, where are you going?"

"She's after me!"

"Give her the money!"

"For what?"

"The BBQ!"

The pursuit continues as I jump on a train, en route to the concert stage. I'm wearing my red jumpsuit. THE WEAVER and THE CARPENTER are seated on either side of me. The extortionist woman pops up behind us with her arms crossed. Her legs are crossed right over left. Her right foot swings and taps the back of our seat.

"Are we good?"

After a pause she responds, *"No."*

I ask if I can take a seat next to her. She nods. I sit. We have a conversation that's drowned out as we near the stage. I can feel energy flood my body as I hear the volume of the crowd increase. ***"I've made it on time."***

"Whoa. I just had a loving exchange with 'the witch!'" I shout as I run backstage and take my position for the performance.] //

⁂

Maj. = 0- THE WEAVER: #1074, 1- THE CARPENTER: #1074

TURNSTILE: #0025, #0390

BACKSTAGE: #0326, #0365, #0381

LOVING: #0099, #0158, #0201, #0236

BRUTALITY: #0035, #0182

⁂

#1070 - January 17, 2020 @ 07:15 (San Francisco, California)

[1070.1 / 2831] [I inspect packages delivered on the front stoop of my brownstone row house. I notice some big boxes have been delivered for THE CONDUCTOR. I send him a text message.

"Is this accurate? Are you actually moving in next door?"

After a few moments he responds, *"Yes. Some big shifts are happening and I'm excited to start over."*] //

⁂

BROWNSTONE: #0069
TEXT MESSAGE: #0254, #0306, #1228, #1235
START OVER: #0126, #1236

⁂

#1071 - January 19, 2020 @ 07:48 (San Francisco, California)

[1071.1 / 2832] [*"I've watched you pray and I find it inspiring,"* a woman compliments.
I show her my planner that outlines the formal times I've blocked out for meditation. I joke with her lightly,
"The reality is, I'm praying all the time. You are too. I'm only aware of what I'm praying about a fraction of the time. I find myself constantly remembering this."]

[1071.2 / 2833] [I'm preparing to go on a trip with some friends. THE CONNECTOR has taken a role as our "team lead" and miscommunicated our departure time. We're in a kitchen. Supplies I've donated have been placed in a utility sink, and are split between a dozen square, pink, orange, and green smoothie bottles. Massive unwrapped portions of chocolate that look like giant tips of crayons are stored beneath the sink.
THE VEGAN decides she wants to claim the smoothie bottles as her own, and suggests we empty their contents out and wash them. I tell her they're mine. Nearby, THE KETTLE *(skeptical, calculating, and tired)* coats the bottom of an aluminum hotel pan with vegetable oil, confusing the person who just requested she *"degrease"* the same tray.]

[1071.3 / 2834] [A little person is brought in during a half-time show and walks by a group of people, each one taller than the next. Fireworks explode in a rapture when he takes his position at the far end of the line.]

[1071.4 / 2835] [I'm in LARS ULRICH's home. He demonstrates all the new technology installed in his "smart house." He shows me a stage where local kids play in an in-house battle of the bands. He pulls back a curtain and shows me a second stage for an open mic night, at a different local venue. MARILYN MANSON is scheduled to play, *"an intimate unplugged show at 9:00pm,"* though it's unclear if the listed start time is correct.
THE FIREFIGHTER, THE CONNECTOR and THE VEGAN are all part of a group leaving LARS's house.
"LARS you've really created an awesome life for yourself."
"Yeah. I agree."] //

⁂

Maj. = 4- THE CONNECTOR: #1084
Min. = ♣- THE VEGAN: #1123
SMOOTHIE: #0053, #0054
CHOCOLATE: #0054, #0055, #0083, #0104
VEGETABLE: #0027

⁂

#1072 - January 20, 2020 @ 08:46 (San Francisco, California)

[1072.1 / 2836] [A teacher travels in from out of state daily for class. Small children in her kindergarten class run around on a playground for an exam. The teacher becomes upset when a little boy refers to her by a casual nickname at the conclusion of *"recess test."* Inside the schoolhouse, a staircase can be pulled down from the ceiling. The steps are covered in cookie-monster-blue shag carpet.

I go up the blue stairs and find THE DANCER, THE HEADCASE *(giddy, engaging, and loud),* and a guitarist *(that I recognize as a session player who performed on the Radiohead album "OK, Computer")* standing next to a large painting with red, white, and black stripes. I ask THE HEADCASE to, ***"braid a length of white paracord in with the existing ½ inch black nylon cord that runs vertically on the right 1/6th of the canvas."***

She's simply laid the cord in straight lengths on the exterior of the canvas frame. I show her how to braid it.]

[1072.2 / 2837] [I sit at a computer editing a book. I parse through hundreds of pages of unedited prose.]

[1072.3 / 2838] [I compete in a race. I'm tasked to run a filled 10-gallon fuel vessel from a start line, to a big black truck. On my first attempt, I run to the wrong truck. The extra distance I have to travel makes it more challenging to hoist the can overhead, to empty its contents in the correct truck's tank.]

[1072.4 / 2839] [I discuss assuming a lease on a new place from THE WIDOW *(accepting, sad, and deep).*

"I'm simplifying my life and downsizing. I no longer need all three bedrooms."] //

⁂

Maj. = 2- THE DANCER: #1080

CANVAS: #0364, #0381

LEASE: #0211, #1335

HOIST: #0215, #1309

⁂

#1073 - January 21, 2020 @ 06:10 (San Francisco, California)

[1073.1 / 2840] [THE BURLESQUE PERFORMER *(buxom, commanding, and sexy)* shares her challenges, *"creating a presence in the San Francisco scene."* Burlesque performance, stripping, and sex work have rigorous public health and safety standards, compared to other markets in which she's played.]

[1073.2 / 2841] [I share a room with a couple of pretty young men who giggle as we wake up. I go downstairs to a cafe in the lobby of our condo building. I place an order for breakfast food on a vertically-mounted body-sized touchscreen.

"Well, hello and good morning to you!" I turn around and say to a short woman who's queued up behind me.

"What did you put in your coffee this morning?" she asks.

"Just LIFE! I. FEEL. GRRRREAT!" I say looking down at a cafeteria railing and see everything I ordered immediately materialize on a tray.]

[1073.3 / 2842] [While standing in line for lunch, I realize I'm in Seattle, Washington. It's foggy and rainy. I know I can't linger here long, though it feels mystical and enlivening. I'm preoccupied with how to, ***"acquire a corner desk that has windows on either side."***

THE BURLESQUE PERFORMER is a co-worker. She suggests I lobby for the desk by telling everyone that I know her. She has clout.

"After we secure the desk, I'll get you your old job back."

THE BURLESQUE PERFORMER and I dial in to a conference call, where a man named "Dave" gives a presentation.

I ask him to, ***"email me the slide deck with proposed revisions prior to taking it to a wider audience."***

The office environment feels drowsy. ***"Perhaps I'll be stuck here for years."***

I take a break and go for a walk in the mist. When I return, the only other person left on the floor is an African American man that transforms into a blonde-haired White man who refers to himself as "Nelson from Norway."]

[1073.4 / 2843] [I move into a second-floor condo with THE PSYCHIATRIST and two other guys. The space is large. The rent is low. At first, I think we live in West Hollywood, but we're in a suburb many miles from downtown LA. The entire unit is filled with wild wheatgrass that varies between knee and waist height. THE PSYCHIATRIST and I share a room.

For our first meal together, I cook a turkey and potatoes. The effort doesn't go so well. The bird is greasy, gamey and predominantly bone.

WILLAM the drag queen lives downstairs. I visit her modern, immaculately kept space and chat with her in the kitchen. Three women live in the back bedroom. WILLAM doesn't like any of them and suggests I, *"move in the back room to replace them."*

WILLAM's mom has passed away. Her wake is held at the condo building clubhouse. Mourners hold hands in vigil and agree to be silent for 2.5 hours, during which I walk to the edge of the property and watch the ocean gurgle and churn.

Tsunamis roll in from the angry sea.

I walk down a gravel road and pass a red barn on my way back to the condo.

Once home *(and inside)*, I take note of how orderly and tidy the ground floor is.

I find it odd that the staircase up to the men's level has taller grass on each ascending step.]
//

⁂

OCEAN: #0008, #0014, #0045, #0085, #0112, #0147, #0245
GRAVEL: #0089, #0133, #0170, #0188
HOLLYWOOD: #0066
THE BURLESQUE PERFORMER: #1226

⁂

#1074 - January 22, 2020 @ 07:53 (San Francisco, California)

[1074.1 / 2844] [The family's in Argentina. We get separated in an urban space. THE CARPENTER and I walk through a broken slat in a wooden fence into the backyard of a concrete house. I've lived here for a month while on prior work assignments. The home is being remodeled.]

[1074.2 / 2845] [THE CARPENTER and I catch a bus that increases in speed as we roll up and over a wavy concrete road. The bus moves so fast that I catch air and have to hold on to an overhead hand strap affixed to the roof to stabilize. After a long, chaotic ride, he and I reconnect with the family and a large gathering of friends, at an open house where ALEXIS ROSE and I make out. We convince one another to strip naked and jump in a pool as we sing songs to one another.

I exit the pool. I towel off and meet THE WEAVER inside. She inquires about tonight's departure. My phone displays the incorrect time for our current time zone, but I know I have a few more hours before I need to leave for the airport.

Later, I take an overnight flight to an unknown final destination.] //

⁂

Maj. = 0- THE WEAVER: #1077, 1- THE CARPENTER: #1076

ARGENTINA: #0169

OPEN HOUSE: #0033

OVERNIGHT: #0204, #0224, #0292, #0321

⁂

#1075 - January 24, 2020 @ 07:40 (San Francisco, California)

[1075.1 / 2846] [It's dark in my home. I hear three cats scurry around behind the couch. THE LAWYER requests I, *"keep close tabs on them so they don't go missing again."*

I think the cats chase a mouse, but am partially surprised when I discover they're chasing a grey golf-ball-sized ball of energy. The grey ball instantly moves between corners of the dark room.]

[1075.2 / 2847] [I wrap up a multi-year professional assignment. MAYNARD KEENAN gives me a black hoodie with white capital old English letters sewn across the chest. He thanks me for a job well done. As I accept the acknowledgement and gift, I can't lift my head to make eye contact with him.

"I guess this is as far as we get. I'll see you again (hopefully) in another three years or so. I'll look forward to my next opportunity to serve."

He walks away. I eat a greasy taco, and contemplate what life would be like if I dropped everything and dedicated my life to working with, learning from, and supporting him.] //

⁂

Maj. = 5- THE LAWYER: #1084

MAYNARD KEENAN: #1132

HOODIE: #0064, #0135, #0168, #0209

DONE: #0293, #0323, #0333, #0348
SERVE: #0050, #0054, #0071, #0113
⁂

#1076 - January 26, 2020 @ 03:00 (San Francisco, California)

[1076.1 / 2848] [I sit in front of a computer working on a book.]

[1076.2 / 2849] [I'm on a date with THE CRUSH (*flirtatious, exact, and intellectual*). We discuss different challenges we've encountered as leaders and directors of large influential groups. We share and swirl a single glass of white wine between us as we talk.]

[1076.3 / 2850] [I'm in the center of a hot tub. THE CARPENTER is my guide, and narrates the scene: *"THE BOSS and three other women have had too much wine and are seated in the four corners of the tub. They're on the verge of passing out from dehydration. Each of the four women leans back into a coffin-sized mold, filled with a body mask made of, 'black clay, diamond, and beluga caviar.' They press their bodies firmly into the form to make an impression that coats their skin and clings to the pores on their backs."]*

[1076.4 / 2851] [A fourth scene occurs, but instantly dissolves.] //

⁂
Maj. = 1- THE CARPENTER: #1077
GUIDE: #0127, #0141
FOURTH: #0024
WINE: #0118
THE CRUSH: #1087
THE BOSS: #1410
⁂

#1077 - January 27, 2020 @ 05:57 (San Francisco, California)

[1077.1 / 2852] [I sit in a church pew listening to a rock album. The band of four men who created the album is seated behind an altar.]

[1077.2 / 2853] [A woman withholds critical information from me. I need the information to complete a scavenger hunt. The prizes are twofold: 1) "a winning lottery ticket" and 2) "a slot as a supporting act for *"the band"* on their upcoming summer tour." I decide I'll never partner with the woman again, based on how she conducts herself.]

[1077.3 / 2854] [I stop by THE WEAVER and THE CARPENTER's condo with a box. They're expecting the delivery.]

. . .

[1077.4 / 2855] [I'm at a dance studio in a tap-dancing competition. Among a group of 20 participants, I'm able to hold a balance maneuver on my toes for, *"1 minute and 11 seconds, a new studio record."* I check my watch multiple times. The group is silent as I stand taller, and erectly stack my spinal column. The taller I rise, the more focused and still I become.]

[1077.5 / 2856] [I HOLD "FROG POSE" with a group of students. We challenge each other to hold the pose in stillness for as long as possible. A slight slip of my sweaty forearms causes me to disqualify myself, similarly at the 1:11 mark. The judge doesn't remove me from the game. When we conclude, I stand next to a wooden rectangular table placed by the exit door and give the contestants high fives. One woman is aggravated by the placement of a similar sized table, adjacent to a perpendicular wall. The table in question has three empty steel chairs behind it, closer to the wall.]

[1077.6 / 2857] [A group waits for a delayed train at a mountain station. I loop through the line and once at the front, am teleported back to the end. I make small talk with a man who works in advertising. He plans on visiting his customers at "Nalgene HQ" when the train passes through Minnesota later that day.] //

⁂

Maj. = 0- THE WEAVER: #1082, 1- THE CARPENTER: #1078

NALGENE: #0130

ALTAR: #0217, #0251, #0396

SUMMER: #0094, #0226, #0227, #0282

⁂

#1078 - January 28, 2020 @ 05:50 (San Francisco, California)

[1078.1 / 2858] [Guys on a boat wear flannel shirts and pose for selfies.]

[1078.2 / 2859] [Among a wash of bright light and fast movement, I hear a council say from four directions, **"Treat everything you do as an offering, as though it's a gift."** Though I can't see him, I know THE CARPENTER is nearby and supportive.]

[1078.3 / 2860] [I flush the toilet after peeing, and becoming concerned about the placement of my toothbrush on a nearby counter.]

[1078.4 / 2861] [THE SOOTHSAYER *(open, dedicated, and gracious)*, THE WORLDBRIDGER and THE CHANNEL *(blessed, energized, and compassionate)* create **"THE TRIUMVIRATE"** as they work together to roll up a large and weighty Persian rug. They smile and joke with each other as the spiral of carpet grows.

"Treat everything as though it feeds the Holy!" they joyfully testify as they pass me in an otherwise black, infinite void.]

. . .

[1078.5 / 2862] [ALEX GREY sits nearby on a couch, working abstract algebra problems on a tablet.

"You have your access point. It's available right there, all the time," he says pointing at me while continuing, *"If you don't have anything better to do..."* before his voice and visage are absorbed in an intense rush of light.

A strong pulse of information blurs my perception into kaleidoscopic shards of carnival glass brightness.]

[1078.6 / 2863] [I'm in a hotel lobby with a black-and-white checkerboard floor. I pull a suit and shirt from a garment bag to dress for a wedding. The shirt has thick crusty yellow dinge on the collar and underarms. I leave the shirt tucked under the coat on a hanger and silently decide, ***"It's time to replace all my formal wear."***

A housekeeping cart stocked with freshly laundered and rolled white-pool-towels topples when a humanoid, smooth-grey-beast with three horns jutting from its neck stump leaps forth from behind. I recognize the creature as "DONNELLAN," who begins to trample and impale fleeing wedding guests.

One doomed man vainly proclaims, *"I can control it!"*

"DONNELLAN" thrusts a blade-like arm towards the man, goring and decapitating him in a single elegant sweeping motion. Each time "DONNELLAN" kills someone, he shrinks in stature. I wait until he's the size of a thimble. I pick him up and set him on a chess board, on a nearby round pub table. As he turns from grey to a shiny aluminum tone, his movements seize.

I hear his voice squeak, then trail off, *"MOMMY MOMMY, DON'T LEAVE ME!"* as I turn and walk away.] //

⁂

Maj. = 1- THE CARPENTER: #1081, 7- THE WORLDBRIDGER: #1083

ALEX GREY: #1322

HOLY: #0021, #0135, #1072, #0316, #0390

PULSE: #0066

ALUMINUM: #0244, #0368

OFFERING: #0150, #0177, #0191, #0297, #0380

THE CHANNEL: #1145

THE SOOTHSAYER: #1356

⁂

#1079 - January 29, 2020 @ 04:05 (San Francisco, California)

[1079.1 / 2864] [I'm unable to sleep after noticing a small female entity crouched in the corner of my bedroom.]

[1079.2 / 2865] [I board a double decker bus with a group of meditation students.]

[1079.3 / 2866] [THE PILOT and THE KIND HEART host a party. They have very specific tasks for each of their guests, as they arrive. THE HOMECOMING DATE *(playful, animated,* *and sweet)* attends. She becomes upset and vocally defiant. She believes the recent razing of historical homes and monuments on our block are, *"a grave injustice and undermine the culture of the city."*

The hosts have requested she deliver a formal speech from a podium at the party's secondary location. Her name is announced over loudspeaker as she walks towards the venue on the opposite side of the street.]

[1079.4 / 2867] [An overweight man awkwardly shakes my hand. We've gathered on an Astroturf soccer field with others to play a game.] //

⁂

Maj. = 6- THE PILOT: #1120, 21- THE KIND HEART: #1133

OVERWEIGHT: #0066, #0084, #0098

MEDITATION: #0155, #0364

⁂

#1080 - January 30, 2020 @ 06:55 (San Francisco, California)

[1080.1 / 2868] [THE DANCER decides to return to teaching and performing when she learns "Terrie" has opened a new dance school in Indianapolis.]

[1080.2 / 2869] [I'm a cheerleader. I have a pink Mohawk. I'm a base. I run to create a formation with my team in a large glass box on top of a grassy hill. A leaping woman's leg catches my shoulder at the knee as I stand up. She falls, injures her knee, and is rendered unable to walk. Our team scores are written in different colored Expo pens on the exterior of the glass box. All our historical scores from prior years are also listed on the box, including the year in the 1970's when we received a ***"1"*** out of a possible ***"100."*** This year our scores are consistently in the mid 90's.]

[1080.3 / 2870] [THE LACROSSE PLAYER *(picky, practiced, and tender hearted)* is eager to lose his virginity and blurts out,

"I want Jesus to go off inside me."

I call him a ***"slut"*** and laugh.

We have our talk in a white-walled record store. Over recent months the store has closed rooms off one at a time, from the back of the building to the front desk. A series of boxes on the floor by a white couch are all that remains of the business's once storied inventory.

Nothing interesting left to buy.

"This'll be my last visit."]

[1080.4 / 2871] [I talk to my friend "will" *(who insists on spelling his name in all lower case)*. I introduce him to my wife, as we stand in front of an art installation of 16 square screens assembled in a 4 x 4 grid. All the screens glow white, and are mounted on a flat white wall. Each screen flashes a black block letter, cast over an abstract grayscale shape. All components of the dynamic and interactive installation can be rearranged, reformed, or deleted.] //

⁂

Maj. = 2- THE DANCER: #1086
WILL: #0260, #0264, #0271, #0279, #0306, #0321
GLOW: #0014, #0040, #0359
100: #0150
LAST: #1318

⁂

#1081 - January 31, 2020 @ 06:17 (San Francisco, California)

[1081.1 / 2872] [I'm with THE CARPENTER. We leave a campsite on the last day of a summer session. LUKE PERRY is with us. LUKE's in a mildly crabby mood and doesn't want to leave, even though he accepts camp's conclusion. He steps up into THE CARPENTER's white pickup truck. The three of us sit across the front bench seat of the quad cab. THE CARPENTER drives. I'm in the middle. LUKE is nearest the passenger door. I look at LUKE with a tear in my eye.

"This is sad. I'm going to miss you a lot."

"Oh my god! That's right! I forgot you know THE RECONCILIATOR! Please tell her I'm fine and give her a hug from me when you see her," LUKE says after softening and giving me a big hug.

"Let's do one better. Let's take a selfie and send it to her," I say extending my arm to take our photo.

As I press the button and hear the click, I wake up.] //

⁂

Maj. = 1- THE CARPENTER: #1099
Min. = ♥- THE RECONCILIATOR: #1235
SELFIE: #0199, #0295, #0299, #0307
THREE: #0314, #0360, #0365, #0389, #0393, #0396

⁂

#1082 - February 1, 2020 @ 00:48 (San Francisco, California)

[1082.1 / 2873] [I've made acquaintances with LINDA RONSTADT through mutual friends. She and I meet for a movie. I greet her.

"This is one of the things about San Francisco that gives me life. You never know who you'll meet, (and even if you do, no one believes you anyway)."

"Why is this such a big deal?"

"Because, you were among the first female superstars of rock. I hope you don't mind me asking about your experiences."

"All in due course. Let's just let the conversation unfold."

We take our seats in the lower right quadrant of the theater, and fill out paper trivia forms before the film begins. An attendant comes by to collect our responses, with keen interest on how we've answered:

"What does the song 'Perry Mason' parody?"
We've written: **THE US LEGAL SYSTEM** in pencil.]

[1082.2 / 2874] [We return home after the film. LINDA rests in a bathtub full of bubbles.

She's shaved her head bald. She doesn't recognize me and calls for her attendant "Rob," a small Korean man. I look for "Rob," noting THE WEAVER sitting at LINDA's kitchen table. THE WEAVER mouths,

"I'm Rob. She's just never seen me with her glasses on."

LINDA stands up and startles me, when the soap suds drip from her body to reveal a large penis. She's concerned she'll slip and injure her leg again if she moves. As she stands naked in the tub, she mentions that she has a gay son. She's been looking for someone nice to introduce him to. She offers to connect the two of us, and while I accept, he and I don't meet in the dream.] //

⁂

Maj. = 0- THE WEAVER: #1085
PERRY MASON: #0012
TRIVIA: #0149, #0357
BALD: #0032, #0117, #0271, #1297
FILM: #1251, #1344

⁂

#1083 - February 1, 2020 @ 06:00 (San Francisco, California)

[1083.1 / 2875] [I look in the mirror. My reflection appears ancient. An old mask hovers in the center of the mirror. My spirit drifts from left-to-right, appearing like ripples of heat. The story the mask in the mirror repeats is:

"I'm old."]

[1083.2 / 2876] [I'm back in the abyss, walking along a sidewalk. I carry a physical fitness trophy at chest level. As I walk by a wall with an infinite grid of square portraits, THE WORLDBRIDGER appears in front of me. He places a hand on my left shoulder, the other on my forehead and temple. My vision blurs as he floods the space with healing diamond light.]

[1083.3 / 2877] [THE PROFESSOR *(rational, intellectual, and extroverted)* parks his car.]

[1083.4 / 2878] [I'm in THE FILM PRODUCER's condo, hiding in an upstairs bedroom. I've placed two white, rolled-up bath towels on the bed. THE FILM PRODUCER enters carrying a bag of groceries. The dog at his feet darts upstairs and excitedly greets me. I ***"shhh"*** the dog because,

"Too much commotion will ruin the surprise."] //

⁂

Maj. = 7- THE WORLDBRIDGER: #1126
SHHH: #0045, #0204, #0250
GRID: #0021, #0079, #0125, #1284, #1295
DOG: #0125, #0169, #0188

⁂

#1084 - February 2, 2020 @ 00:00am (San Francisco, California)

[1084.1 / 2879] [I buy a burrito and an "avogobble" sandwich from THE M&A ATTORNEY *(skillful, direct, and accomplished)* and THE CONNECTOR. Their store is attached to a modern recessed home I've visited in many other dreams, (beginning with **[0036.2 / 0102]**).]

[1084.2 / 2880] [I drive my car quickly over the crest of a hill. The road nonsensically bends beyond vertical. My car defies gravity and holds steady to the road, momentarily turning upside down to round a corner.

"Feels like I'm in a 23rd century version of San Francisco."]

[1084.3 / 2881] [I share a glass-walled street-level condo with THE LAWYER. The condo building is built in bedrock. It's a single ground floor room, in which a kitchen sink and countertop with a shallow tile backsplash run the length of the space. It's late. THE LAWYER falls asleep on the floor.]

[1084.4 / 2882] [THE CONNECTOR approaches with her new friend "The Priest," of whom I'm extremely fond.

I temper my infatuation by dismissively saying, ***"...well aren't you adorable?"***

The three of us ascend a staircase of a large ghostly Victorian inn. THE CONNECTOR asks me a simple question I refuse to answer. My gaze hardens. The pause persists, and eventually THE CONNECTOR starts crying.

"You know, you can be the worst kind of cruel when you say nothing."

I stay silent as she recoils, looking for an exit.

"If you don't get out of my way, I'll kill myself!"

I open my heart and start sharing my story. I take my glasses off, so I can meet her truly eye-to-eye. A crowd of hipsters and Gen Z'ers look onward, recording the interaction with their phones. I pour my heart out. **I apologize.** She accepts.]

[1084.5 / 2883] [THE CONNECTOR tells me she recently purchased a *"pod home"* in Hong Kong. We leave our bodies, and fly to the construction site. I view a portable community of small-glass-units stacked and rearranged by large forklifts. As the scene pulls back, I see the pods are placed at the base of a building that looks like a pyramid. THE CONNECTOR paid $135K for a single unit, referred to in promotional materials as a *"retreat."* Two placed side-by-side constitute an *"abode."* More than two create a *"home."*]

[1084.6 / 2884] [I ASK "THE PRIEST" for his number. He gives me his social media handle on a platform I don't use.

"What's a more immediate way of getting in touch with you?"

"Tomorrow I have a casting audition for a pilot until 12:30. We could get together afterward."

THE CONNECTOR remains tepid and skeptical. The three of us descend a square spiraling staircase. At the bottom, we split and move in opposite directions. I pause. I decide to double back and follow "The Priest," fully aware he's an actor. The nature of my attraction to him is his "**unknowable-ness.**" He can slide effortlessly in and out of characters/valances. He tries them on and tosses them away like costumes.

THE CONNECTOR sends me "The Priest's" number as part of a group text. He mentions in the thread that he, *"hasn't been on a nice date in a really long time."* My mind races as I flip through a mental rolodex filtering for the current: *"Top 10 spots to take someone in London (...if you're looking for something fun and romantic to do)."*]

[1084.7 / 2885] [I'm back in my one-room condo. I've left the burrito and "avogobble" I bought earlier on the countertop. I'm not worried about it going rancid. ***"I omitted sour cream from the burrito order on purpose."***]

[1084.8 / 2886] [I attend a class. My laptop screen interrupts the eye-line between the teacher and another student who's just asked a question.]

[1084.9 / 2887] [I swing around a white wooden lamp post, then scribble the word "**g o l i a t h**" in lowercase down the post with a one-inch black paint marker.]

[1084.10 / 2888] [I'm on a team where the new project manager has frustratingly poor communication skills.] //

⁂

Maj. = 4- THE CONNECTOR: #1085, 5- THE LAWYER: #1131
BURRITO: #0002, #0097, #0190, #0250
APOLOGIZE: #0062, #0308, #0354
CRUEL: #0063, #0237, #0369
TOUCH: #0021, #0022, #0031, #0040
POST: #1260, #1337

⁂

#1085 - February 2, 2020 @ 06:00 (San Francisco, California)

[1085.1 / 2889] [I'm at work on a temple. A woman introduces herself as "KATIE." Her ice blue cat eyes are striking. The pupil of her left eye appears horizontal when paired with the other. I know it's *"Maid Marian"* in disguise.

She informs us we're, *"not allowed to use oil lamps on the interior of the structure as planned,"* while pointing to a codicil in a grant contract.

A small graphic flashes: **"CEASE AND DESIST"** in the air between us.]

[1085.2 / 2890] [I attempt to drive out of a parking garage. The exit is blocked by an angry Black man who insists he speaks foreign languages. He demands others speak them with him to confirm and maintain his skills.]

. . .

[1085.3 / 2891] [*"MICHAEL JACKSON's "THRILLER" globally grossed $1B, adjusted for inflation. Controlled distribution contributed to its extreme profitability. Modern technology has made the music and previously "scarce" performances ubiquitous."* No one cares.

"Every moment of every tour is available for infinite replay on the internet."]

[1085.4 / 2892] [I stack trays and tubs of food in pairs, multiple stories high with the help of a scissor lift. THE WEAVER and THE CONNECTOR help me take inventory. THE ACTOR arrives and helps with food prep at the back of the tent. He keeps to himself and on task. I'm attracted to his quietness.]

[1085.5 / 2893] [I soak in an oversized Jacuzzi tub that heats quickly and cools just as fast, due to the large volume of air the powerful therapeutic jets push through the pool. I sit in the tub for a few cycles of bubbles, enjoying the transition from hot to cold.

Hot. Cold. Hot. **Cold.**] //

⁂

Maj. = 0- THE WEAVER: #1093, 4- THE CONNECTOR: #1111, 9- THE ACTOR: #1094
MICHAEL JACKSON: #1222
HOT: #0311, #0312, #0337, #0338, #0359
COLD: #0007, #0012, #0017, #0044
ANGRY: #0054, #0056, #0117, #0158, #0203, #0219

⁂

#1086 - February 4, 2020 @ 07:02 (San Francisco, California)

[1086.1 / 2894] [I meet THE DANCER, THE CHILD and another woman in line, waiting to ride a roller coaster. The queue is surrounded by a ten-foot steel fence with enameled plywood panels mounted to it with plastic zip ties. Every 100 feet or so is a "break station" that has tables with board games restless guests can play with to distract themselves. I'm forced to take a turn on to a special *"LGBTQ Fast Track"* that separates me from my group. Our paths converge as we make the final ascent to the ride.

Two tracks with different train segments converge to create a, *"composite, balanced train that optimizes ride efficiency, based on those riding."*

The track and trains are both silver. When I take my seat, I grab two overhead subway train loops, one with either wrist. My rollercoaster train doesn't have a lap bar, nor shoulder restraints.]

[1086.2 / 2895] [I'm on a campus tour at Harvard University, led by a marvelously articulate young man who wears dark, thick-framed glasses. He stops to highlight various points of interest, then leads our group in a moot court session. BARACK OBAMA stops by to ask our guide, *"if the assembly hall where we've gathered was the site of a hallmark address he once gave."* He leaves.]

. . .

[1086.3 / 2896] [Two members of the tour group hold us hostage in a library. The group initially complies with their demands, but becomes impatient, and inquires as to how they might be punished for attempting to escape. One abductor inconspicuously holds a 3D printed pen gun under a three-ring binder. The other waves a cattle prod at us.

"Neither of the weapons threaten me. The prospect of receiving an electric shock arouses me."

I turn the cattle prod on the captor and deliver a strong shock to their left leg.] //

⁂

Maj. = 2- THE DANCER: #1088, 3- THE CHILD: #1087

BARACK OBAMA: #1416

LGBTQ: #0212

HARVARD: #0210, #0259

ARTICULATE; #0074, #0089, #0123, #0147

IMPATIENT: #0012

⁂

#1087 - **February 5, 2020 @ 04:00 (San Francisco, California)**

[1087.1 / 2897] [I practice clapping push-ups, on a hovering tatami mat in an abyss. On one repetition my hands strike the mat with such force they puncture and vertically split the mats into three equal kit-kat-bar-like segments.]

[1087.2 / 2898] [A short haired woman prepares for a date. If it goes well, she'll move out and I'll be able to rent her room at the back of the condo. In the meantime, I collect power cords and multiple pairs of headphones to tidy up. I neatly coil their wires, and gather them in a pile on my chest, as I lounge back on a couch in a common room.

After dozing off, I'm awakened by multiple voices who enter and slam a door. I pull a blanket over my head to hide. I recognize the voice of THE CRUSH *(sharp, concise, and expeditious)* speaking with another man and woman discussing, *"why the most recent two month's budgets and actuals do not reconcile."*

One of them purchased licenses for a new SaaS finance application, though don't know how to use it. The other two partners become upset when asked for help. To diffuse the tension, I leap up from the couch saying,

"This is something I'd see on an episode of Dynasty," and promptly walk out.]

[1087.3 / 2899] [THE CHILD is short and skinny. She shows me her handstands. I'm surprised by her level of skill.

"If she receives strong coaching, she'll excel. She could possibly be a world champion contender."

Her family would need to relocate to Los Angeles to gain access to the best coaches.]

[1087.4 / 2900] [I'm at a condo building. I leave a party to retrieve a steel spatula from an outside grill station next to a pool. It's dark. The air is still. The scene "flash freezes" as I look to the left, then right. The pool and hot tub have a cover composed of thick rectangular sheets of opaque glass. As I walk across, the sheets glow a soft white-green from beneath.

The deck area thaws as I walk past a series of ground level apartments. One unit has an entire wall covered with a printed square canvas image of a man relaxing under an umbrella at the beach. The next is mostly empty, with exception of a small computer screen that displays the image of a loved one who's recently passed away. I walk through a wall into a modern, fully furnished unit. I continue towards a large maroon door to exit, and hear the owner of the unit shuffle papers at a desk in another room. The door clicks shut behind me. I turn right, and walk down a hall.] //

⁂

Maj. = 3- THE CHILD: #1088
ABYSS: #0018, #0200, #0204
WORLD CHAMPION: #0017
LOS ANGELES: #0312
UMBRELLA: #0130, #0140, #0307
EMPTY: #0336, #0386, #0395
SHUFFLE: #1246

⁂

#1088 - February 6, 2020 @ 04:00 (San Francisco, California)

[1088.1 / 2901] [THE MAGICIAN leads a group expedition up Aconcagua. He deserts the team at the summit, and returns to base camp to rehearse a sermon for tonight's revival.]

[1088.2 / 2902] [Two groups of people walk in a line on opposite sides of a chain-link fence at night. The fence ends.

Adults are directed towards a floodlit soccer field.

Children are guided from the grounds to a dark building.

THE CHEMISTS *(cerebral, contrary, and warm)* have just completed authoring a textbook for their college course. They're excited to start a new company, and encourage me to join their team.

I decline.

"I have enough resources to do what I want (at the moment)."

Their enthusiasm for their work is uplifting and contagious. They hand me an old compact disc player and ask me to, *"diffuse it."*]

[1088.3 / 2903] [THE CHILD is nine years old. She works on an "Appreciation Board" for a school project. THE DANCER changes THE LITTLE PRINCE's diaper. His facial features move from one hemisphere of his face to the other. I'm hesitant. I'm concerned he'll flip over and off of the counter, if we don't keep an eye on him.]

[1088.4 / 2904] [I'm unable to find my set of lime green ear plugs. The noise around me prevents me from sleeping.]

. . .

[1088.5 / 2905] [I'm a small child. I smash my face on a countertop. After a moment of being stunned, I wince with pain and cry.] //

⁂

Maj. = 2- THE DANCER: #1115, 3- THE CHILD: #1089,
12- THE LITTLE PRINCE: #1098, 14- THE MAGICIAN: #1171
PAIN: #0011, #0012, #0019, #0027, #0035
HEMISPHERE: #0034, #0154, #0200
CHAIN LINK FENCE: #0036, #0079, #0151, #0157, #0394
THE CHEMISTS: #1092

⁂

#1089 - February 7, 2020 @ 07:30 (San Francisco, California)

[1089.1 / 2906] [I move dumpsters to the exterior of a building. En route, a coworker and I become trapped in an elevator surrounded by stacks of counterfeit cash.]

[1089.2 / 2907] [I work on a desert construction site where a series of oversized wind chime-like pipes stand upright on the flat, firm ground. We stand on a board that spans two upright pipes that are anchored by a giant elastic cord. We sway side-to-side, almost bending and snapping the pipe at ground level. It feels unsafe. I step off once the platform softly touches the ground at right.

Three guys riding flaming big wheels stop for a conversation, and to inspect the construction process. We have a detailed discussion inside the trailer of a box truck to avoid sun and dust.]

[1089.3 / 2908] [We place THE CHILD in the center of a spongy octagonal cylinder that extends roughly two feet in front of her chest, with space for an oversized baby bottle in front of her. Another man and I bounce her back and forth between us like a pinball, or miniature bumper car.]

⁂

Maj. = 3- THE CHILD: #1142
OVERSIZED: #0021, #0034, #0056, #0060, #0064, #0066, #1228, #1336
BOTTLE: #0104, #0130, #0173, #0203, #0224, #1222, #1318
CONSTRUCTION: #0281, #0310, #0344, #1259, #1275

⁂

#1090 - February 9, 2020 @ 05:34 (San Francisco, California)

[1090.1 / 2909] [I prepare for a black-tie fundraiser to be hosted by SHARON OSBOURNE, and a group of drag queens. I search for a photo of a *"man and her drag queen"* for the opening slide of the keynote presentation. We never find the image. As the event begins, a team member becomes ill and is forced to sit off to the side. The young woman remains ill. The rest of the team backfills her role to allow her time to convalesce.

We pass out white boards covered completely black with various layers of marker residue.

Mine blurs like waxy crayon on glass when I attempt to wipe the board clean. I rinse it under a faucet. A large chunk breaks away from a corner. A woman enters with a complaint, *"Ugh...I'm always gone when the cum breaks up."*

After the event I tell SHARON she's, ***"raised some quality humans,"*** and that, ***"KELLY' was a classmate of mine."***] //

[1090.2 / 2910] [I find a MARY POPPINS cookbook in a gift shop. At the back of the book are copies of love letters the cast and crew wrote each other on the final day of production. The inscriptions are nostalgic and sweet.]

⁂

MARY POPPINS: #0332
LOVE: #0334
CRAYON: #0371
ILL: #0147
GIFT SHOP: #0375

⁂

#1091 - February 13, 2020 @ 06:00 (San Francisco, California)

[1091.1 / 2911] [*"Dating life depends on how successful one is setting up other friends in couples who persist and thrive."* I'm offered a date at a steakhouse. I accept.]

[1091.2 / 2912] [I walk towards the Golden Gate Bridge and notice a frequently used off-ramp is inaccessible. It's collapsed. I walk down a ravine with a friend and hop over the bay, which occurs as an oddly small tide pool. We come to a flooded thicket. As we get closer, we discern it's a rice field, shaped in a repeating Greek key pattern. Wooden steps assist our ascent from the thicket, though the higher we climb, the foggier the air *(and more eroded the land*)becomes. As we grapple our way to the top, we see an older man and woman discuss *"what to do next with the land."*]

[1091.3 / 2913] [*"Church donations are down."* My hair is long. My hands have healed. I'm somewhat stressed that my manuscript has been transposed to "Scrivener." I'm concerned I won't be able to edit it. It's still full of typos and errata. I look back in a mirror. My hair has grown another foot in length.]

[1093.4 / 2914] [I watch myself play guitar with a friend. Our hands make chords on the necks of the other's instrument as we strum.] //

⁂

GOLDEN GATE BRIDGE: #0344, #0387
GREEK: #0073, #0367
HAIR: #0371, #0397

⁂

#1092 - February 14, 2020 @ 07:31 (San Francisco, California)

[1092.1 / 2915] [I view a MR. BUNGLE concert from an upstairs balcony. At the conclusion of the show a guy asks our group if it's, *"worth $1000 to stay for a meet-and-greet with the band."* We think it's a bargain.

Another man enters, and tosses his real estate credentials on a nearby table along with some colored ribbons. An appraisal of the venue is underway as the show concludes.

I pass by a bar where concert goers line up to purchase vast quantities of movie candy and concessions. Bartenders pour milkshakes instead of cocktails *(as the meet-and-greet falls outside the parameters of the liquor license).* I'm about to inherit tens of thousands of dollars' worth of equipment from the band. I want to get a t-shirt autographed for THE ATHEIST. For a moment I believe hundreds of people intend to stay. When the event starts, the crowd clears and roughly 25 people remain. I consider calling THE CHEMISTS. I weep a little.

"It was such a unique treat to see my heroes perform music inspired by their heroes, with their heroes."] //

⁂

Maj. = 8- THE ATHEIST: #1156
T-SHIRT: #0022, #0060, #0088, #0147, #0199, #0250, #0383
$1000: #0030
INSPIRED: #0045, #0060, #0175, #0229, #0317

⁂

#1093 - February 16, 2020 @ 05:46 (San Francisco, California)

[1093.1 / 2916] [I'm part of a movie. The plot centers on *"family unity."* THE WEAVER descends a staircase to let me know who she's, *"chosen to ride the bumper cars with."* I decide to stay home. I'm put in an adult day care room, with a group of other grown children.]

[1093.2 / 2917] [I'm a substitute math teacher. I've forgone the lesson and opted to let the class watch a movie.] //

⁂

Maj. = 0- THE WEAVER: #1099
BUMPER: #0049, #0130
LESSON: #0010, #0046, #0047, #0124
FAMILY: #1205, #1208, #1212

⁂

#1094 - February 16, 2020 @ 23:44 (San Francisco, California)

[1094.1 / 2918] [I run around the inside of a house. I make a lap through the garage. I climb down a ladder, cross a floor, and exit to the street. I run back in the front door and do it all again. After multiple laps, I understand I'm running through a property owned by THE ACTOR. One lap puts THE CRAZY DIAMOND *(restful, stoic, and mute)* in my path. I pause to hug him, and tell him that I miss him. One the next lap, I encounter THE FLUFF *(animated, engaging, and giving)* who directs a group of others to move a large pile of lumber.

I'm told I can't make any more laps because, *"it's the owner's prerogative to protect it."*
The last time I exit the property, I run through a neighboring home whose staircases rise up in a scalloped, concentric zigzag pattern.] //

⁂

Maj. = 10- THE ACTOR: #1095
CONCENTRIC: #0123, #0389
EXIT: #0033, #0056, #0081
HOME: #0101, #0127, #0170

⁂

#1095 - February 19, 2020 @ 04:52 (Scotts Valley, California)

[1095.1 / 2919] [THE ACTOR is dead and lies in state under a large butcher block table where the family eats. On the fifth day, THE ACTOR reanimates. His breathing starts subtly. Eventually he stands and joins us. To our astonishment he has no memory of being dead. He's more curious why I, *"decided to stop watering his plants."* He remains good-spirited and invites me to walk with him out to the street to view his most recent home improvement. He points towards a window at a series of 1'x1' square panels mounted in a horizontal row, just inches from the top of a wall.]

[1095.2 / 2920] [A roommate works at the last family-owned ice cream shop in San Francisco. The shop is in a mini-mall, tucked away behind a series of small booths and kiosks. I walk back for a free cone. Once it's given to me, the shop closes forever. I stand in the empty space and eat ice cream as the lights shut off.] //

⁂

Maj. = 10- THE ACTOR: #1168
FOREVER: #0012, #0017, #0159
FIFTH: #0100
HORIZONTAL: #0193
EMPTY: #1251, #1258

⁂

#1096 - February 20, 2020 @ 05:43 (Scotts Valley, California)

[1096.1 / 2921] [I'm at a yoga studio. I hand PETE BUTTEGEIG an itemized punch list denoting all the reasons I'm attracted to him. People gathered around are upset that neither PETE nor I have removed our shoes. After our chance encounter, I depart for THE JESTER's home to debrief, where I discover him installing a new front door. The door is red.]

[1096.2 / 2922] [I'm assigned a desk in a zendo that looks like a giant roulette wheel. I wait for a friend until the moment I'm called to practice. I sit and meditate on a cushion in a slot where an oversized marble would drop. My friend arrives as I complete my meditation. I'm ejected from the zendo.
"Do you suffer?" the master asks as I exit.

"Constantly. I'm always giving it up."

I'm given a round of applause as I leave. Other meditators hoot, and begin to bounce up and down on their meditation cushions in what appears to be a, *"full wheel."*] //

⁂

Min. = ♦- THE JESTER: #1122
SUFFER: #0277, #0353, #1236
CUSHION: #0014, #1292
BOUNCE: #0034, #1285

⁂

#1097 - February 23, 2020 @ 06:21 (San Francisco, California)

[1097.1 / 2923] [We sit in on a lecture where images of dead rock stars are flashed on a large theater screen. PETE STEELE from TYPE O NEGATIVE stands out among those memorialized in black and white. When asked by the instructor how I feel when I see it, I respond with a simple, ***"sad."***]

[1097.2 / 2924] [It's a sunny day on a bus. The bus makes its way down a hill in the direction of a flowering prairie. I talk to THE THINKER about a variety of job offers I'm considering as he debugs computer code. I get lost in our conversation, and miss my intended bus stop. As we proceed to the next stop, the bus morphs into a spaceship.]

[1097.3 / 2925] [A man asks for my help to measure the dimensions of a road sign, as an email notification informs me my preferred job has a base salary of $300,000.]

[1097.4 / 2926] [We relocate as a family from one coast of Australia to another. When we arrive at our destination, we're confused when a balding White man in a bathrobe walks towards us shaking a newspaper and yelling at us in an accent none of us understand.] //

⁂

Min. = ♠- THE THINKER: #1114
CODE: #0060, #0077, #0113
PRAIRIE: #0008
YELLING: #0081, #0216, #0220
SIGN: #1241, #1262, #1317

⁂

#1098 - February 23, 2020 @ 07:04 (San Francisco, California)

[1098.1 / 2927] [THE LITTLE PRINCE has a full set of adult teeth. He smiles at me, but refuses to open his mouth when anyone else is around.]

[1098.2 / 2928] [**Two quick scenes flash and are forgotten. **] //

⁂

Maj. = 12- THE LITTLE PRINCE: #1115
ADULT: #0048, #0102, #0167, #0240, #0383
FULL: #0002, #0012, #0013, #0014

⁂

#1099 - February 25, 2020 @ 06:25 (San Francisco, California)

[1099.1 / 2929] [I'm a roadie for ROB ZOMBIE. I look through stacks of latching crates *(tortoise shell patterned)* in a warehouse.]

[1099.2 / 2930] [I live in subsidized housing with THE ZOMBIE *(not. dead. yet).* We share a three-bedroom apartment. We receive a $1000 monthly stipend from BEYONCÉ for being her personal assistants. We're permitted to only eat fast food.]

[1099.3 / 2931] [I ride on a Go Kart with THE CARPENTER around a parking lot. We run over/strike multiple boulders in an oversized, pristinely raked Zen garden that covers the entire lot. We drive off the lot, to a large modern home on which I've placed a bid. Someone else has purchased it and recently moved in. I peek in the front window and see cardboard boxes left partially unpacked on the floor in the main room. Random objects are placed on a zig zagged recessed shelf on the left-hand wall, six inches wide and 30 feet long.

I help THE CARPENTER and others navigate down a steep staircase, and away from the house. Every other step of the poured concrete staircase is unusually narrow and steep. I offer my hand to all who make the descent.]

[1099.4 / 2932] [THE WEAVER guides me to a small television that shows an interest rate curve. She zooms in on a segment that, *"illustrates rates were as high as 23% when she and THE CARPENTER bought their first house."*] //

⁂

Maj. = 0- THE WEAVER: #1101, 1- THE CARPENTER: #1107
DESCENT: #0006, #0226
FIRST: #0234, #0243
STEEP: #1264

⁂

#1100 - February 26, 2020 @ 05:58 (San Francisco, California)

[1100.1 / 2933] [Executive teams gather in a mansion to discuss a merger between "Salesforce" and "QVC." A marketing team presents a hybrid logo with blinking marquee bulbs that highlight the "**FORCE**" in "Salesforce." The mansion serves as a gathering space for a futuristic commune. Residents in arrears *(or insolvent)* are marked by torrents of colored lights projected up through clear glass sidewalks on the premises.]

. . .

[1100.2 / 2934] [I'm in a circle of desks positioned "head to toe," in a ring-shape human sized "ant farm." Desks on the lower ring are protected by the slight overhang of the upper ring, which has no roof. Open skies run vast overhead in massive **"O,"** mandala shape. THE LINEAGE HOLDER *(gracious, bright, and good)* asks us to come into the middle of the circle and run our hands through sand boxes to trawl for sacred objects. Grazing my hands through the sand yields finds of diamonds of varying size. We talk about wisdom traditions as I note a storm brewing in the distance. Purple and black clouds swirl offshore.]

[1101.3 / 2935] [I'm 95 feet above the ground, dangling from a mesh canopy. It stretches as I climb it. I muscle my way up to a steel platform where I'm offered oxygen as a woman asks for my credit card. Had I looked down, I certainly would have frozen, lost my grip, and fallen to my death.

"Survival carries a hefty surcharge," the woman says as she runs the card and asks for my signature.] //

⁂

FORCE: #0310, #0380
LOWER: #0383, #0394, #0396
UPPER: #0014, #0017, #0024
CLEAR: #0255, #0259
SIGNATURE: #1256, #1262, #1277

⁂

#1101 - February 27, 2020 @ 04:45 (San Francisco, California)

[1101.1 / 2936] [LARRY DAVID invites me to audition. I deviate from the script during a table reading.]

[1101.2 / 2937] [I work at a restaurant. I'm left a pile of small denomination coins as a prank tip. I've been left change **in excess** of the total value of the bill.]

[1101.3 / 2938] [THE WEAVER and I walk through a security checkpoint at a bank vault. We pass a small girl who looks like a china doll, and a skinny boy who's over ten feet tall. THE WEAVER opens a lock box and pulls out two solid gold cassette tapes. She places them in my hand as a birthday present.] //

⁂

Maj. = 0- THE WEAVER: #1107
SECURITY: #0312, #0340, #0381
BIRTHDAY: #0004, #0009, #0023, #0222
PRESENT: #0346, #0358, #0365
SOLID GOLD: #0073, #0373
TEN: #1258

⁂

#1102 - February 27, 2020 @ 07:28 (San Francisco, California)

[1102.1 / 2939] [I play bass in a rock band *(again)*. The band is split between two different stages. Stand-in performers for drums and guitars participate on opposing stages. I sit in the amphitheater, waiting to be called on stage to perform. Similar to other performances, I don't know the music.]

[1102.2 / 2940] [I run with a team of people into an office building. We all wear suits. Three of us push a roller cart towards an elevator bay, discussing and debating each other's ability, *"based on age."* The building has a hazy white tone. We might be in "The Matrix."] //

⁂

ROCK BAND: #0220, #0258
OFFICE BUILDING: #0081, 0188
MATRIX: #0220, #0306
MUSIC: #0260, #0265, #0271, #0301, #0326
WHITE: #0394

⁂

#1103 - March 4, 2020 @ 06:08 (San Francisco, California)

[1103.1 / 2941] [I hold a training program at my home. THE COUNSELOR *(quick, hurried, and stressed)* and THE ENTREPRENEUR *(confident, hard charging, and cerebral)* are both there, preoccupied with starting new professional roles. They're both moving. THE ENTREPRENEUR mentions he believes, *"THE COUNSELOR has an anger issue."*

Another session commences as I depart. A woman presents content, taking a pause to talk to me before I exit. She insists I, *"unknowingly provided answers to questions that were extremely attractive,"* to her. She pulls her skirt tightly to her legs, exposing her penis.

"Oh!" I say with some mild surprise.

"Were you attracted to anyone earlier? I was," she says, referencing me.

"Yes, there was that short statured guy around earlier that I found super cute."

"You mean, me?" she says while showing me a photo of the guy I referenced.

It was her in another disguise! We flirt and kiss. While kissing, I contemplate moving to Florida with her, then quickly decide not to go.]

[1103.2 / 2942] [I'm acknowledged by my writing staff for being, *"a top-notch editor."* I'm given a small object which is met with a round of applause from a group of people gathered in a semicircle in our office.] //

⁂

PROFESSIONAL: #0201, #0237, #0394
WRITER: #0238, #0271, #0365
PENIS: #0048, #0132, #0282, #0367
APPLAUSE: #0007, #0009, #0177

⁂

#1104 - March 5, 2020 @ 01:48 (San Francisco, California)

[1104.1 / 2943] [I visit with THE PROM DATE *(gorgeous, even keeled, and humored)*. We catch up on our lives and gloat about our children.

"I'm really proud of what THE BRAND MANAGER's accomplished."

"Well, what about me? I'm a nurse."

"Even better!"]

[1104.2 / 2944] [THE BRAND MANAGER *(refined, affluent, and persuasive)* and I go for a seaside drive. When I ask him where he lives, he responds vaguely,

"On Mission."

"Do you mean in the Mission District?"

"No, I live on Mission Road in Protingwood. It's a super chic street in East Hampton."

We park in front of a clubhouse. We enter a spa, where he offers to buy me a massage. In a blink, I hop face down on a table wearing only a towel, and am startled when my chest is poked by a bundle of reeds that press upright through the leather cover. In a state of mild discomfort, I suggest we go play a round of golf instead. In another blink, we're on the green of the 18th hole. THE BRAND MANAGER lines up a putt and strikes the ball much stronger than necessary. It ricochets off a slate retaining wall and strikes a glass half gallon jug of milk. The milk spills on a man standing beneath *(like an element of a Rube Goldberg machine)*.

"FAGGOT!" the milk-soaked man screams and points at us.

"No sir. You're not going to talk to him (or me) that way," I say immediately as I stand.

"We don't like San Francisco FREAKS here," says another woman who rushes in to support the milk-soaked man.

I break out in laughter. The scene escalates. We leave. I'm keen on ensuring I leave the *"putt putt country club"* a one-star review on Yelp as THE BRAND MANAGER and I continue our ride in a top-down convertible along the seaside highway.] //

⁂

MILK: #0012, #0043, #0104
GOLF: #0160, #0236, #0265
COUNTRY: #0007, #0159, #0193, #0397
SEASIDE: #0115, #0186

⁂

#1105 - March 5, 2020 @ 04:46 (San Francisco, California)

[1105.1 / 2945] [Art piece. Different fashion eras are uniquely drawn together by a new embroidery technique.]

[1105.2 / 2946] [I'm a boy, watching He-man and other Saturday morning cartoons.]

[1105.3 / 2947] [*"LEFT FOOT. RIGHT FOOT." "Left. Right."*]

. . .

[1105.4 / 2948] [I've taken a summer job working for a family-run pickle company. I watch the eldest son line the rims of shot glasses with paper-thin-dill-pickle slices. He sends trays of them down a conveyor belt through a flash dehydrator. The result is a popular salty snack that can be peeled like thin taffy sheets from the edge of the glasses, once filled with liquor.] //

⁂

FASHION: #0052, #0322
SATURDAY: #0175, #0309
PICKLE: #0027, #0230
SALTY: #0186
GLASSES: #0009, #0033, #0121, #0137

⁂

#1106 - March 5, 2020 @ 05:29 (San Francisco, California)

[1106.1 / 2949] [I work for a family business, run out of a large home. I love the house, the lot, the architecture, and the decor. It's vast in scale. Large picture windows line a hallway between ends of the property. The master bedroom is on the main floor next to the kitchen.]

[1106.2 / 2950] [*Photo session for a family.* * A White man, Asian woman, their gay son and heterosexual daughter pose together naked in a bedroom next to a bed.

The husband gives an explanation of the family business as we sit at a table together.

The daughter taps my arm and requests that I fill out a timesheet.

A man in a purple suit stands up. The lapels on his suit are flipped out, awkwardly perpendicular to his chest, like fins.

He takes a jar of pickles off of the attendance sheet *(left as a paperweight by another client)* then stands and begins to tap dance as he asks me, *"Do you like this suit?"*

The wife says, *"No,"* but she's speaking in reference to the daughter's advances towards me, and didn't hear the man's query.]

[1106.3 / 2951] [We run down multiple staircases in a house very quickly. I'm concerned the speed may break my ankles, but they stay strong.]

[1106.4 / 2952] [*"There are stacks of laundry in the back for you to fold."*]

[1106.5 / 2953] [I take a ride on a giant go-kart-dune-buggy. It lacks safety belts and harnesses. I'm supposed to hold on to the roll cage as we go for a drive across the desert sand. My hands are weak and can't maintain a tight grip.]

[1106.6 / 2954] [An earthquake strikes while we've been out on open water, on a yacht. When we make landfall, I stand in a giant glass windowed cylinder at the end of a dock. The glass cylinder is set into motion, and spins wildly around me.] //

⁂

VAST: #0309, #0311, #0327, #0331
SPEED: #0360, #0382, #0383
EARTHQUAKE: #0157, #0288
LAUNDRY: #0081

⁂

#1107 - March 6, 2020 @ 06:58 (San Francisco, California)

[1107.1 / 2955] [I'm in Mexico on a layover with the family. THE CARPENTER rents an Airbnb in an affluent area of town. We take a car to the property which is surrounded by equally lavish neighboring homes, and modern amenities. I've been to Mexico City before and understand the range of socio-economic disparity that exists there, and am amazed by our high-end surroundings. The family believes their experience at the mansion is comparable to how everyone in Mexico lives. In their view, *"everyone must own a mansion."*

"We should move here!"

"No, this is definitely a skewed experience."

Our rental property also doubles as a farmhouse and butcher shop. One side of the wall has a dedicated freezer space filled with fresh meat, viewable from the street through large square windows. It appears the specialty items today are a cut of fatty beef, and burger patties. Both items are prepared on trays, stacked on tall steel baker's racks.

THE FARMHAND enters with generations of her entire extended family. They're surprised to see us in their home. They take a seat together at a table in the far corner of the room. They don't speak to us.]

[1107.2 / 2956] [People get plastic surgery. They're compelled to pay $15,000 for basic procedures *(facials, filers, Botox)*. A man who wants to have work done is rejected. THE WEAVER is willing to pay for me to, *"get a little tune up."* I politely tell her I don't want any. The doctor administering the procedures becomes skeptical of me when I decline.] //

⁂

Maj. = 0- THE WEAVER: #1108, 1- THE CARPENTER: #1108
Min. = ♥- THE FARMHAND: #1195
FREEZER: #0394
BASIC: #0232, #0360, #0383
DECLINE: #0079, #0177, #0183, #1310

⁂

#1108 - March 09, 2020 @ 07:35 (San Francisco, California)

[1108.1 / 2957] [A company sells a "two-sized" car seat for a newborn, which can double in size to hold a toddler.]

[1108.2 / 2958] [THE ADVANCED STUDENTS *(supportive, renewed, and guided)* enter and place a manila folder on a table. They leave the contents of the folder on the table and exit with the empty folder under arm.]

. . .

[1108.3 / 2959] [I'm in an office. I fill a water bottle with a spigot. The water is heated and warps the plastic. The neck of the bottle melts. I use a water jug on the floor as an alternative, but the faucet pops off. My bottle is filled, and oddly, no water spills on the floor. THE DEVOTEE and THE TRANSLATOR stand at a table and sign in for a lecture.]

[1108.4 / 2960] [THE WEAVER and THE CARPENTER are out on a date in the 1980's. They've booked a suite at hotel for a romantic getaway.] //

⁂

Maj. = 0- THE WEAVER: #1114, 1- THE CARPENTER: #1110, 19- THE TRANSLATOR: #1148

Min. = ♠- THE DEVOTEE: #1148

FAUCET: #0189

1980's: #0001, #0084, #0121, #0250

THE ADVANCED STUDENTS: #1412

⁂

#1109 - March 10, 2020 @ 05:28 (San Francisco, California)

[1109.1 / 2961] [We prepare trucks to make camping trips to the desert. Half the people plan to be there, *"for the rest of medical school."* I shop at a grocery for chocolate nonpareils and sundries for the trip. A woman is hesitant to make the journey. She doesn't want to take the trip because she, *"has a concert ticket QR code on her phone that she intends to sell and must keep phone service until the item is transferred."*]

[1109.2 / 2962] [We prepare to leave on "The Journey of Hope" from San Francisco. We travel to the Golden Gate Bridge on a foggy morning. We walk as a crew to the center of the bridge. A yellow borderline between "California" and "Colorado" splits the bridge in two halves. We ceremonially, *"toe the line."*]

[1109.3 / 2963] [We walk up a hill and discover ourselves in a suburban backyard where a woman greets us. She invites us to take another step into "Wyoming." It's 10:30am. I think the team is about to be sent off. I'm assured by one of my counterparts that the official sendoff time is 12:30pm. ***"I haven't packed the correct running shoes for the trip."***]

[1109.4 / 2964] [Back on the bridge, the team gathers and prepares to leave. THE EXECUTIVE DIRECTOR *(good, fair, and trusting)* walks towards me wearing a red, white, and blue cycling jersey.

"Are you riding?"

"Yeah, bro!"

We welcome each other back to the team and exchange hugs. He gives me a cap to put over my hair, which he tells me is, *"long, grey, and EASILY identifiable."*] //

⁂

HUG: #0013, #0043, #0045, #0153, #0176, #0323, #0375
COLORADO: #0301, #0302
JOURNEY: #0149, #0231, #0397
BRO: #0375, #0396
THE EXECUTIVE DIRECTOR: #1134

⁂

#1110 - March 11, 2020 @ 06:51 (San Francisco, California)

[1110.1 / 2965] [I play bass in a blues band that THE CARPENTER really enjoys. He and I are at a club waiting for the group to take the stage. After a significant delay, I go across the street to a rehearsal space to try to find the guys. I ask others if they've seen the blues band. I'm told they're warming up in "The Vortex" *(a convenience store at a music school).* As I enter, a male clerk exits. I pick up a bag of chips, and a bottle of soda. I go back to the club and wait. I don't have any guitar picks, so I decide to use a quarter once the show starts.]

[1110.2 / 2966] [I'm at a University.] //

⁂

Maj. = 1- THE CARPENTER: #1114
BLUES: #0019, #0389
CHIPS: #0284, #0323
GUITAR PICKS: #0290

⁂

#1111 - March 12, 2020 @ 02:50 (San Francisco, California)

[1111.1 / 2967] [A ship's about to depart. ***"Is it seaworthy?"*** I'm aboard. THE FAIRY GODMOTHER texts a sunset image of the ship in silhouette to me and my artistic partner. The vessel becomes a floating temple, buoyed on the surface of the water. Below deck, walls with geometric shelving at waist level hold succulent plants. I pee on all the plants to water them.]

[1111.2 / 2968] [I'm at a boat party. The vessel is about to push back. I'm directed to move to the right, where I meet a guy who's preparing to spin his first DJ set. He has intricate sleeve tattoos on both arms. We walk down a gangplank to a bed where I see THE CONNECTOR taking a nap. We join her on the bed and fall asleep. We wake up together, and head to another entrance where we meet the spouse of the host who greets us saying,

"I'm 'Anthony.' Party boy. Photographer. 'So-and-so DJ's' super fun husband."] //

⁂

Maj. = 4- THE CONNECTOR: #1115
Min. = ♣- THE FAIRY GODMOTHER: #1255
WATER: #0306, #0311, #0320, #0321, #0344

⁂

#1112 - March 12, 2020 @ 03:23 (San Francisco, California)

[1112.1 / 2969] [TENAYA THE CAT is outside a house, sitting on top of a round steel garbage can. She begs the neighbors for food. I overhear two neighbors say,

"You know what really shapes reality? Systematically doing things with other people to get them to do stuff to you, and for you."

I don't believe them.]

⁂

TENAYA THE CAT: #0574
ROUND: #0260, #0306, #0323
FOOD: #0033, #0037, #0044, #0054, #0066
REALITY: #0013, #0015, #0019
HOUSE: #1312, #1314

⁂

#1113 - March 13, 2020 @ 06:33 (San Francisco, California)

[1113.1 / 2970] [I get a haircut.]

[1113.2 / 2971] [I'm in England. I repair a truck that the family once sold to THE SMOKER *(gruff, demanding, and hypocritical).* It's old school, with a heavy steel frame and simple four-cylinder engine. The wiring needs an update. Nothing major. A small amount of rust would be best scraped off, the metal treated, and eventually repainted.]

[1113.3 / 2972] [*"They shut San Francisco down. When it falls asleep, it falls in to 'The Matrix.'"*] //

⁂

HAIRCUT: #0260, #0355
FAMILY: #0140, #0154, #0157, #0168
ASLEEP: #0013, #0019, #0025, #0049, #0125
RUST: #0043, #0202, #0339
DOWN: #1248, #1252

⁂

#1114 - March 15, 2020 @ 06:00 (San Francisco, California)

[1114.1 / 2973] [I wait in line at the DMV. I'm issued a checkbook with the wrong name and social security number. I try to call THE WEAVER. THE CARPENTER has her phone. The DMV line is exceptionally long. I'm impatient and don't want to wait to correct the mistake. We leave. On the drive, home we pass through a neighborhood with multiple houses I've previously occupied. The homes are modern in appearance and construction. One is occupied by THE THINKER and THE FEELER. I stop through to visit THE FEELER. She sits submerged in a warm tub up to her nose in a huge "U" shaped room. She doesn't speak.]

. . .

[1114.2 / 2974] [My personal items have been stacked on the street. A guy with a megaphone gathers me with a group, to walk together down a sidewalk. As he gives us additional instructions, it begins to rain. All of my property placed on the street is soaked through. The cardboard boxes are soggy by the time I return.]

[1114.3 / 2975] [I walk up a staircase in the woods. I encounter THE BRAIN *(eager, generous, and diligent)* when I arrive at the top. He and I proceed to a recreation center, where we work on developing our fine motor skills.] //

⁂

Maj. = 0- THE WEAVER: #1115, 1- THE CARPENTER: #1115

Min. = ♠- THE THINKER: #1166, ♣- THE FEELER: #1166

STAIRCASE: #1272, #1274, #1280

⁂

⁂ 14.2 - THE BOOK OF INANIS: 1115-1239 ⁂

#1115 - March 17, 2020 @ 09:25 (San Francisco, California)

[1115.1 / 2976] [A wet metal ring swells around my finger. It disappears. It reappears on my finger, dried out. It slips from my finger, and falls into a trash can as I scrape dirty plates after a dinner party.]

[1115.2 / 2977] [THE CARPENTER and I buy groceries. Two women stand in front of us in line. I hold an item in each hand. The female cashier takes my items and places them aside. I've also put my wallet and keys on the conveyor belt. The belt splits in half behind a Lucite/Plexiglass shield. Keys and wallet are on the other side of the barrier. I'm unable to retrieve them.]

[1115.3 / 2978] [A family rides a cable car, perpendicular to the ground, to the summit of a ridge that's 1992 feet tall. We stop just as we crest, and are given some guidance by an attendant who informs us, *"the descent is pretty steep."* I fall backwards out the window and dangle precariously by my hands from the gondola as we go up and over.]

[1115.4 / 2979] [THE COUTURIER and THE CONNECTOR show up at a social event declaring, *"We just left "Scott." He'll be here later. He signed up for a charity 'sit in,' but when he arrived for his shift there was a line out the door, and someone had taken his assigned seat."*]

[1115.5 / 2980] [The family inhabits a new condo. I have a room on the upper level that overlooks the driveway. The curtains are drawn. When I open them, I notice a window sill with multiple hand scribbled messages left for a couple named "Bryan and Ashleigh."

"They must've been previous inhabitants."

THE WEAVER and THE CARPENTER live at the front. THE DANCER is at the back. She has a bedroom and a nursery with multiple framed photos of her and THE LITTLE PRINCE hung in a row on the wall.]

[1115.6 / 2981] [I'm being courted by two different men. We're at a cafe. Then, we ride on a ski gondola up a mountain to a large estate home owned by the older gentleman. I reject the romantic advances of both men.]

[1115.7 / 2982] [A woman competes in a decathlon, broadcast to the world on TV. She runs. She jumps. She hurdles. She pole vaults. She flips gymnastically to celebrate each of her successful attempts. A male pole vaulter flips *"35 times"* before landing on the cushion beneath.] //

⁂

Maj. = 0- THE WEAVER: #1117, 1- THE CARPENTER: #1126, 2- THE DANCER: #1130,

4- THE CONNECTOR: #1116, 12- THE LITTLE PRINCE: #1142
Min. = ♣-THE COUTURIER: #1149
LUCITE: #0203
GONDOLA: #0312
⁂

#1116 - March 19, 2020 @ 06:00 (San Francisco, California)

[1116.1 / 2983] [I return to a cabin at the top of a gravel road. On previous trips I've stayed here for multiple days. I drop my bag and make myself at home. I realize after an hour inside that the place is fully inhabited. Every room is filled. People are asleep in every bed. When they awaken, they look similar to friends of mine. They're friendly and let me stay. I soon learn they're a group of environmental research scientists, implementing a conservation project as they wake up and brew coffee.

I approach a group of guys standing by a table. I tap one on the chest who looks exactly like another friend of mine. I realize I've made a mistake.

"Wow. Sorry. You wouldn't believe it, but I have a friend who looks just like you."

"Dude...it's me."

"Wow. This is awkward. I just touched you."

"Yeah, it was."

"I didn't know you were a scientist."

Our exchange is funny, light and awkward. The scientists continue working on their computers. THE CONNECTOR shows up at the doorway to the cabin with an update.

"'Scott' wants to come with us, but he has to get his bags."

"He can come with us if he can get everything up here before we leave."

Other friends who were with me during my prior stay at the cabin, also show up. We walk on a trail lined by tall brown grasses.] //

⁂
Maj. = 4- THE CONNECTOR: #1158
SORRY: #0294, #0306
GRAVEL: #0170, #0188, #0240
BROWN: #0121, #0132, #0146, #0147
⁂

#1117 - March 20, 2020 @ 04:49 (San Francisco, California)

[1117.1 / 2984] [I record more than nine minutes of detail related to a dream, before locking up the doors to GRANDMA's home and her guest house, while yelling out a window to THE CATHOLIC *(opinionated, stubborn, and hurt)* as I slam it. A group of house cleaners come through and ask if we want the windows washed. We suspect they're thieves and will break in once we depart. We tell them to go. One guy leans with his back against the door.

"It's time to go. It's pretty rude when you do that," I say compelling him to leave.

If I don't finish locking up the house, I know it'll get looted. It's clear the cleaning business is a front for a mafia affiliate who's known for, *"ransacking boarded up properties."*]

. . .

[1117.2 / 2985] [I'm in California. I run into THE REPATRIATES *(lovers, yin & yang, and cultured)* at a bar. HE needs to sign a document in order to vote. HE scrawls across an entire page of the document in an elaborate signature script.

"Hey brother...it's me!"

HE laughs. HE barely speaks English anymore because his life has been centrally lived in Europe. SHE barely speaks English anymore as well. She feels dejected. BILL ODENKIRK is at the party keeping tabs on THE MINIATURE *(articulate, spry, and curious)*. BILL plays a sleazy lawyer-type, who I match and best with, *"tough talk."* I help SHAKIRA get grounded so she can best navigate the next segment of her career.]

[1117.3 / 2986] [Running around. TINA TURNER's involved somehow. THE WEAVER and I run around together. I pick up speed.

"I'm in the flow of love," when I'm able to run up and down pathways nimbly and quickly like a video game character.] //

⁂

Maj. = 0- THE WEAVER: # 1126, 11- GRANDMA: #1155
Min. = ♣- THE CATHOLIC: #1158
FLOW: #0066, #0081, #0094, #0108
LOVE: #0292, #0321, #0334, #0350
VIDEO GAME: #0013, #0016, #0194, #0263
NINE: #0125, #0156, #0172, #0394
THE REPATRIATES: #1185

⁂

#1118 - March 20, 2020 @ 07:05 (San Francisco, California)

[1118.1 / 2987] [I attend an event to celebrate the "Lord of the Manor's" birthday. A crew gathers and feverishly prepares food at the back of the venue, just prior to the arrival of guests. In the grand hall, all the oil paintings have been taken down. Smudges and shadows from frames remain on the walls.

I've left a slice of chocolate cake on a china plate with a silver fork, behind a row of chairs where I'm seated. When I get up to move, I notice most of the cake has been eaten. I pick up the plate and eat the remaining portion of cake as I walk towards the back of the manor. When I duck around a corner, I see a group of young people arguing about whether or not the soup served at the buffet is, *"hot or sour."*

"Just say the soup is sour. Say it's my fault." The group laughs as I continue on my way, phoning THE CHARLATAN *(inquisitive, fearless, and self-assured)*.

"I'm at the Mayor's birthday gala."

"How do YOU know the Mayor??"

"I have my connections. I keep them close."] //

⁂

OIL: #0019, #0147, #0294
FORK: #0088
SOUP: #0070, #0297, #0335
GALA: #0007, #0102, #0128

DUCK: #1214
⁂

#1119 - March 21, 2020 @ 05:30 (San Francisco, California)

[1119.1 / 2988] [I play cards. Various hands of blackjack are dealt at different casino tables, with different people. At one point, I make a play where the cards are all upturned, which sets off a, *"peculiar chain of events."*]

[1119.2 / 2989] [Someone's personal music equipment is scattered along one side of a parking lot. They won't gather it and bring it to a white box truck parked at the opposite end of the lot for storage. An altercation/stalemate occurs. The driver won't help gather the property, but is unable to leave until the musician's equipment is packed up.] //

⁂
CASINO: #0010, #0112, #0293, #0332
PARKING LOT: #0374, #0396
STALEMATE: #0077, #0273
MUSIC: #1203, #1228
⁂

#1120 - March 22, 2020 @ 00:47 (San Francisco, California)

[1120.1 / 2990] [I learn something pivotal (a little "t" truth) *"about the destabilized nature of reality."*]

[1120.2 / 2991] [*"If I'm playing 'the great psychic game' and you're playing 'the great psychic game'...then who manifested who?"* THE PILOT asks me.

"That's an exceptional question, indeed," I respond. We run up and down the back stairways of a house and I continue.

"I'll tell you this...it's the one who's a more aligned manifestor. I have a friend who has never said 'no' to an aligned 'yes' and he's always getting everything he wants. He has the partner, the spouse, the boyfriend, the job all without exercising any effort. He manifested a $3MM house without having to do anything, except listen and choose."]

[1120.3 / 2992] [I'm outside on the sidewalk three doors down from home, at night. I stand beneath the yellow-lit bay window of a neighbor's house, who's draped a piece of newsprint over a flagpole with the headline:

"A GREAT DAD LIVES HERE."

His superlative parenting skills have been acknowledged by the city. I turn around and return to my comparatively smaller and less ornate home *(when compared to my neighbor's epically sized, darkly painted mansion).*]

. . .

[1120.4 / 2993] [We arrive at the bottom of a staircase and walk to the sidewalk. We see a neighbor's car across the street has been pushed back to the driveway from the garage. A catastrophe has occurred inside the home, *either a death or a fire*. The only family asset that remains is the car. The family huddles around the mother and father with concern and assures them that,

"Soon, everything will get back to normal."]

[1120.5 / 2994] [THE PILOT and I drive a car en route to Basel, Switzerland. We stop just outside Vienna, Austria. We have two other guys with us who ride in the back seat. When we pause to stretch our legs, they attempt to convince us to take a shot of brown liquor *(at 10:00am)*.

I agree, then offer a caveat, ***"I'll only drink what's aligned in the moment. Might be some or none."***

THE PILOT refuses the offer.

A bartender pours the shots from behind a glass window and passes them to us through a hand sized slot at the bottom. I ask THE PILOT if it's faster to take a train to Switzerland, realizing, ***"it's a silly question because we're already driving."***]

[1120.6 / 2995] [I'm handed a grocery bag that has three brown chicken eggs in the bottom. One cracks and leaks into the sack after I've removed the other two. The egg white seeps through the burlap bag and creates a visible wet splotch on the outside.] //

⁂

Maj. = 6- THE PILOT: #1129
SWITZERLAND: #0097, #0098, #0141
SILLY: #0005, #0042, #0048
EGGS: #0021, #0106, #0125, #0327
BURLAP: #0009
CRACKS: #1221, #1260

⁂

#1121 - March 22, 2020 @ 06:30 (San Francisco, California)

[1121.1 / 2996] [I'm on a subway. It stops. Before passengers are permitted to exit, the driver steps back into the cabin and demonstrates how to move very slowly around one another without touching.

He says, *"If she's here, she's been here for a while, but this is what we can do to stop her."*

The woman behind me says, *"She's already here."*

We get up and begin to de-board in a calm and orderly fashion. The conductor says, *"Give me a high five,"* and then makes hand-to-hand contact with a bunch of kids as they exit.

"Noooooo!" I whisper.

A guy next to me says, *"Let's go get some chocolate,"* as we walk up from the subway station onto a vacant city street.] //

⁂

SUBWAY: #0089

CALM: #0003, #0070
KIDS: #0251, #0259, #0261, #0393
CHOCOLATE: #0188, #0194, #0257, #0320
VACANT: #0060, #0140
FIVE: #1274, #1285, #1318
⁂

#1122 - March 23, 2020 @ 01:40 (San Francisco, California)

[1122.1 / 2997] [I'm lost out in space. Three silver craft fly overhead. A crew retrieves refugees who have crashed on asteroids. I'm among those rescued. They ask me to raise my arms so I'm easier to snag with their tractor beam on their next pass. I'm grabbed and tossed in front of the nosecone of the ship. We journey back to Earth. My body overheats and begins to burn as we cut through the atmosphere and plunge into the ocean. I survive. I feel indebted and want to join their organization to help save other lives. Some of the art pieces this civilization has built *(and prominently displayed)* are ones I've interacted with at public gatherings on my planet. I've naturally been attracted to them.]

[1122.2 / 2998] [I see THE JESTER and THE SKEPTIC *(soulful, joyous, and relaxed)* down the street. I wave and invite them over for lunch.]

[1122.3 / 2999] [THE PIXIE stands next to me at a sink. As we wash our hands, he tells me he has, *"the virus."*] //

⁂
Min. = ♦- THE JESTER: #1134
NOSE: #0035, #0048, #0071, #0208
SPACE: #0219, #0233, #0236, #0247
OCEAN: #0008, #0045, #0085
SINK: #0066, #0231, #0352
THE SKEPTIC: #1198
⁂

#1123 - March 23, 2020 @ 04:27 (San Francisco, California)

[1123.1 / 3000] ["Blue Elwood" floats through an empty house, out the front door and up through an idyllic neighborhood where all the homes have fecund flower planters in full bloom under every window. ***"Why is Elwood blue?"***]

[1123.2 / 3001] [I'm at THE VEGAN's home. I have sex with multiple non-physical guides. A group of guys outside the house shoot a porn scene. One of the performers is extremely strong. He performs acrobatic elements and static muscular holds, while other men pile on top of him. Everyone is wearing a condom. They have giant penetrative toys to warm up their holes with, and intend to use during filming. They aren't able to include them unless the strong man retains the, *"crowd-selected-physically-challenging posture."* He fails. They don't get to use the toys. THE VEGAN sprays her cats and pet ferret in the face with an aerosol medication before she and I depart. Along the way she introduces me to her floppy haired brother. He stands next to me and describes, *"how dissatisfied he is with the new job."*]

[1123.3 / 3002] [I float through an empty house as a voice chides, *"You're in your 40's. You really need to get your own place. It's time to be an adult."* I float out a window, across the lawn, and up the street.]

[1123.4 / 3003] [JAMES BOND scene. IDRIS ELBA detains a male prisoner in a conference room behind a glass window. He makes a masking tape X on the conference room door *(also glass)*, then throws a Molotov cocktail at the man. As the glass explodes IDRIS shouts, *"GET HIM! GET HIM! GET HIM!"* I don't act.] //

⁂

Min. = ♣-THE VEGAN: #1134
JAMES BOND: #0006
X: #0221
FERRET: #0231
FLOPPY: #0305, #0344
ADULT: #1318, #1343

⁂

#1124 - March 23, 2020 @ 06:04 (San Francisco, California)

[1124.1 / 3004] [THE PRESS SECRETARY *(encouraging, insightful, and endearing)* enters, singing at full volume. Another man enters through a different doorway, singing equally as loud, then promptly falls asleep on the ground. I attempt to wake him up and get him into bed. A protest is underway outside.]

[1124.2 / 3005] [I sit in a car. My backpack is in the passenger seat. In a peculiar replay of **[0726.2 / 1838]**, a homeless Black man opens the door and tries to grab it. I hold a loop in my hand as he gives the bag a yank. People outside shout at the car through microphones, increasing the sensationalism of the circumstances.] //

⁂

PROTEST: #0168, #0334
HOMELESS: #0056, #0063, #0075
GROUND: #0047, #0056, #0063, #0117, #0124
LOOP: #1249
THE PRESS SECRETARY: #1143

⁂

#1125 - March 23, 2020 @ 06:51 (San Francisco, California)

[1125.1 / 3006] [A woman washes her hands. She finishes moving into her new place.

She's vacated an apartment she shared with THE KOAN *(intellectual, playful, and supportive)*, who might be sick. They've taken a *"one room"* corner condo on *"Fill More Street"* and have divided it for use by three people.

"It's weird when you see a bunch of things change all at once," she says to me as I look out a window.

"Well, we'd better get accustomed to seeing homeless people sleeping by the outside walls."

"That's basic. I don't remember receiving a letter from the landlord notifying us that he was intending to make our living space 'triple occupancy' when there are already three of us living here."

The fine print in the lease says three of us are *"entitled to one third of the total space,"* so we're each actually contracted for 1/9th of the space.] //

⁂

ONE: #0035, #0036, #0037
WINDOW: #0019, #0029, #0035
SICK: #0316
THE KOAN: #1224

⁂

#1126 - March 24, 2020 @ 08:18 (San Francisco, California)

[1126.1 / 3007] [I'm with THE WEAVER and THE CARPENTER at a hotel with THE FAIRY GODPARENTS. I stay overnight, then head elsewhere.]

[1126.2 / 3008] [A Tudor mansion has a parking spot for sale, listed for $90,000. The parking space includes a country club membership. The diamond shaped stained glass windows are soldered in an argyle pattern. THE GREASED PIG *(expressive, dirty, and fun)* sits working at a small table in the clubhouse, as a fire crackles behind him on a sunny morning. I take a seat in a furnished room to meditate. THE WORLDBRIDGER teaches a bald man how to build upon his basic meditation practice. A young boy enters holding his crotch, on the verge of wetting his pants. THE WORLDBRIDGER gently guides the boy by the hand to a daycare in the next room.] //

⁂

Maj. = 0- THE WEAVER: #1130, 1- THE CARPENTER: #1130, 7- THE WORLDBRIDGER: #1179
SUNNY: #0045, #0098, #0112, #0115, #0121
MEDITATION: #0155, #0364
FIRE: #0080, #0143, #0215, #0232
GENTLY: #1256

⁂

#1127 - March 25, 2020 @ 04:55 (San Francisco, California)

[1127.1 / 3009] [Bouncing around various rooms of a house. I sing. I stop at the kitchen where an old woman sweetly sings a sad song to her dead child. I realize she's singing the song to me, as I look through cupboards for snacks.]

. . .

[1127.2 / 3010] [I shop for belts with JENNIFER ANISTON and her two teenage sons. She suggests I *"look at the Eddie Bauer table. They're a bargain at $225 each,"* she says. I buy two.] //

⁂
KITCHEN: #0080, #1258, #1318
BELTS: #0034, #0071, #1313
TWO: #0240, #1317
⁂

#1128 - March 26, 2020 @ 06:32 (San Francisco, California)

[1128.1 / 3011] [I work on a piece of art. The mixed media piece of a woman in a dress with thin vertical red-and-white lines, spreads across five, 36"x36" canvases. The top of her head extends beyond the top-edge of the top-canvas. Similarly, her feet float beyond the bottom-edge of the bottom-canvas.]

[1128.2 / 3012] [Storefronts are boarded up, noting where shop owners and their families have returned. My favored corner market has sign artfully disclosing: *"We've gone back to France."*]

[1128.3 / 3013] [I'm on a college campus attempting to find my dorm room. When I check in and drop off my book bag, I notice the sheets on my bed have been tousled. Someone else slept there last night. It appears numerous people have occupied the space, *and may still.* I search for the resident assistant, but am unable to locate them.]

[1128.4 / 3014] [I've just had sex with multiple partners. I feel fucked up, but I'm not drunk. THE FLIRT lays next to me. We giggle and touch each other in the afterglow of our shared fuckery. We want to do it all again, but we want some privacy. There's nowhere for us to go.] //

⁂
VERTICAL: #0081, #0130, #0238
PRIVACY: #0021, #0124, #0394
SIGN: #0017, #0026, #0045, #0065
GIGGLE: #1258, #1282
⁂

#1129 - March 28, 2020 @ 09:23 (San Francisco, California)

[1129.1 / 3015] [THE PILOT publishes a boutique anarchist's magazine out of his home. The magazine is a front for a drug trafficking operation.]

[1129.2 / 3016] [I hover in the corner of an apartment watching THE GYM TWINK *(sweet, quiet, and inviting)* blend equal volumes of red and blue slush into a drink. The components don't combine into *"purple."* They remain separate and discrete parts, perfectly balanced. He refers to it as his, *"strength potion."*] //

⁂

Maj. = 6- THE PILOT: #1133
MAGAZINE: #0001
PURPLE: #0035, #0088, #0125, #0168
STRENGTH: #0010, #1278
THE GYM TWINK: #1327

⁂

#1130 - March 29, 2020 @ 04:30 (San Francisco, California)

[1130.1 / 3017] [A phone is smashed into jagged segments and left scattered on a bathroom floor. I put it back together like a jigsaw puzzle. I wear a white kimono. I have long thick black hair that's been braided into a beautiful elaborate knot atop my head.]

[1130.2 / 3018] [THE CARPENTER places his newly completed painting in the dishwasher. He tells me, *"CHER's been kicked out of the country."*]

[1130.3 / 3019] [I'm in London. I'm at the taping for a popular morning show. I arrive at work at 12:30. I need to be ready when the reporters arrive at 4:00. I'm interviewed by a Black man at 6:30.

"Is the day starting or ending?"

"It's only just beginning here."]

[1130.4 / 3020] [I walk down a long tunnel until I'm blocked by a group of people, who gather at the lowest point. I backtrack and take a longer path above ground.]

[1130.5 / 3021] [I'm with THE WEAVER and THE DANCER at a large modern home. THE TRUST FUND BABY *(tipsy, tactile, and gossipy)* sits at a Steinway piano in his underwear playing chords at different volumes. I see his sheet music and take a photo of it. I've separated from THE WEAVER and THE DANCER and make my way to an auditorium where they watch a performance.]

[1130.6 / 3022] [I listen to a lecture by a man who is both an astrophysicist and a medical doctor on **"How to listen to stars 'sing.'"**

"If a telescope is properly calibrated you can hear them harmonize with their neighbors. Some hum. Some say, 'HU.' Others ring like bells." As we listen, the professor encourages us to *"increasingly widen our telescopic frame."* We see stars appear as atoms, then molecules, then cells, and coalesce into an infinitely massive *"heavenly body."*

The scientist speaks at low volume as the group stands together awestruck.

"You're a part of it. This is what it's like to look out from the inside. You're a tiny filament in a giant web of light."]

[1130.7 / 3023] [I review an archeologist's map. We're unsure of what path we're going to take through a yet-to-be-traveled series of underground chambers, if we decide to go:

"One room beyond what's known."] //

⁂

Maj. = 0- THE WEAVER: #1131, 1- THE CARPENTER: #1131, 2- THE DANCER: #1132

SCIENTIST: #0115, #0188, #0189, #0330, #1300

LIGHT: #0027, #0032, #0035, #0039, #1279

BEYOND: #0006, #0010, #0022, #0024, #1291, #1294

⁂

#1131 - March 30, 2020 @ 07:08 (San Francisco, California)

[1131.1 / 3024] [I lead a dance class. Many friends attend. THE SILVER BOYS *(rambunctious, chaotic, and tough)* are there. We play a game.

"Why is THE VIKING ELF here?" THE WEAVER asks.

"Because everyone is welcome."

The class is short, and ends at an awkward moment. A bit later, I pass THE SILVER BOYS on the street.]

[1131.2 / 3025] [THE MANAGING DIRECTOR *(sarcastic, grumpy, and rich)*, THE LAWYER, and I are all pitted against each other in a game of assassins *(with live ammo)*. We're in a bedroom without a roof. We have to hide skillfully, to avoid being shot.]

[1131.3 / 3026] [I assist people in yoga/meditation practice. I give healings to those who want them. I offer Reiki to a group in a common area of a house. I give THE EXCOMMUNICATED *(sad, lonely, and clearing)* a loving touch. I hold his feet in a handstand and lower him into a planche to strengthen his upper body.]

[1131.4 / 3027] [I'm in a large house likely owned by THE PHILANTHROPIST. The environment is sex positive. SIR PATRICK STEWART is a long-term tenant. He helps me pick up dirty dishes left behind after a party. Bowls of food remain on the tables. We've taken a silly photo where he's without a shirt, reclining on a couch. I've laid my head on his hairy belly. We both make goofy facial expressions as a gag. He's just a funny guy. I'm compelled to text THE CARPENTER the photo. A check for $100 has been torn to shreds and left in a pile on the table next to us.]

[1131.5 / 3028] [Sex dream. Two male:male couples. One is THE IRONMAN:THE PROMOTER who look like twin brothers. They turn me on. I'm part of the other couple.

My partner is soon to leave for a distant destination. We want to have sex one last time before he goes, but I get stuck in the bathroom shitting.] //

⁂

Maj. = 0- THE WEAVER: #1136, 1- THE CARPENTER: #1136, 5- THE LAWYER: #1133
Min. = ♦- THE VIKING ELF: #1205
REIKI: #0010, #0153, #0156, #0339
SEX DREAM: #0021, #0022, #0069, #0094
ASSASSINS: #0014
THE IRONMAN: #1133
THE PHILANTHROPIST: #1135
THE MANAGING DIRECTOR: #1242

⁂

#1132 - March 31, 2020 @ 04:55 (San Francisco, California)

[1132.1 / 3029] [MAYNARD KEENAN disguises himself as a young Black girl at a *"cancer camp"* for kids. He keeps up the appearance/ruse for an entire year, maturing and graduating to the role of award show host *(as a young Black woman)*. THE DANCER is even fooled by how chameleon-like MAYNARD can be.]

[1132.2 / 3030] [I rent an RV. I stop for gas. Cars crash at the gas station.

A grungy hippy guy at the *campground/rest stop/wherever* has a brown, spore laden, luffa-looking mushroom that he wants to share with me. I take a small portion. It spits a puff of dark mist in the air between us as it tears apart. I don't know what will happen if I eat it. He eats most of it. He runs away from the crash, up a hill, and into the woods.

Police officers hiding under piles of leaves get distracted waiting for their mark, and make love as he strides by.

I drive off in the RV.]

[1132.3 / 3031] [I drive around a mountain ridge, looking down off the switchback shelf at an illuminated city we all refer to as "**Denver.**" We don't know where we are, nor where we are heading.]

[1132.4 / 3032] [I dance soft-shoe with RHIANNA. We do the Charleston. We feel *(and look like)* cartoons.] //

⁂

Maj. = 2- THE DANCER: #1134
RHIANNA: #1150
SWITCHBACK: #0033
RV: #0315, #0375
CARTOONS: #1278

⁂

#1133 - March 31, 2020 @ 09:20 (San Francisco, California)

[1133.1 / 3033] [I'm in an apartment building, on a square block adjacent to the ocean.

"It's really awesome to have onsite laundry on the same floor during a crisis like this," I say to myself as I begin a load of wash.

THE KIND HEART emerges from his condo wearing a bee keeper's suit and safari hat. He doesn't respond when I say, ***"hello."*** Others are nearby, but we keep our distance.]

[1133.2 / 3034] [A white wood credenza in the bathroom next to the laundry facility has a small laminated sign that reads:

"NOW STOCKED WITH PERSONAL HYGIENE PRODUCTS AND DENTAL SUPPLIES. PLEASE DO NOT USE."

Inside the house, the lights are supposed to be voluntarily turned off at **5:51pm.** My neighbor THE CATALYST *(inspired, connected, and persuasive)* hasn't complied, so we haven't either. The area has been subject to rolling brown outs for weeks during, *"the lockdown."*]

[1133.3 / 3035] [Walking with my laundry basket up a carpeted stairwell, I arrive at a pair of square-glass-paned French doors, blocked by a plush maroon couch. I know this is where I'm supposed to *"watch the destruction from"* later. I don't know how to gain entry to the room. I can hear waves beginning to crash outside.]

[1133.4 / 3036] [On the beach during a dark and stormy sunrise, I stand with a group watching other people run towards the surf. A lifeguard whistles at the converging group to slow, stop, and turn around. People disregard him and continue towards the water. I turn away to walk back to my apartment. An unexpected wave surges and hits me from behind, knockng me face first into the sand.]

[1133.5 / 3037] [I'm back on the beach with neighbors and friends. **Everyone I know is there.** THE IRONMAN, THE KIND HEART, THE PILOT, THE LAWYER, are nearby. We blink and find ourselves under a concrete tunnel with stairwells that exit up to the street.

"HOLY SHIT ELEVEN IN A ROW! YEAAAAHH!" I hear a young thrill-seeking man shout as he runs with a boogie board under arm towards the treacherous breaking waves.

I look down a sewer grate near where I stand, and see a multi-tentacle Cthulhu-looking creature snap at the bars, waiting for the surf to deliver its next meal.

I yell to the beachgoers, ***"RUN!"*** turning to dart up the staircase as giant ominous blue-black waves break in rapid succession.

Water immediately floods the space. Thousands of people instantly drown. Some bodies that wash ashore make an odd, gurgling whimper as a result of their lungs being full of water. The loss of life is tragic, swift, and tremendous. **Mass death.**]

. . .

[1133.6 / 3038] [I sit on the top stone stair. I can feel a large cut on my forehead gushing blood. Red water is wiped from my eyes by a Red Cross worker who wraps me in a blanket. Another female relief worker offers ice cream sandwiches to those who, *"are dying and beyond salvation."*

The ice cream is red. ***"Mine is cherry flavored!"***] //

⁂

Maj. = 5- THE LAWYER: #1147, 6- THE PILOT: #1144, 21- THE KIND HEART: #1160
BLOOD: #0021, #0035, #0047
CROSS: #0025, #0060
SURF: #0077
THE IRONMAN: #1243

⁂

#1134 - April 1, 2020 @ 05:34 (San Francisco, California)

[1134.1 / 3039] [THE VEGAN and I pilot a U-shaped flying vehicle. We're seated on opposite top edges of the "U" to counterbalance. The vehicle is powered by a small lawn mower engine attached to the center/middle, which does all of the work. I don't trust it. ***"I don't believe it's powerful enough to keep us airborne."*** We touch down softly on a freshly cut lawn behind a circus tent in the dead of night.]

[1134.2 / 3040] [I encounter a female piano teacher under a circus tent. I ask her if I can be her student. She declines.]

[1134.3 / 3041] [THE DANCER and I rearrange furniture at THE JESTER's home. We debate where to put the couch. Seems the bedroom in the back has more light and space, but we're intent on putting it in the dining room facing a corner.]

[1134.4 / 3042] [*"Keep your distance as a matter of policy."*]

[1134.5 / 3043] [THE EXECUTIVE DIRECTOR *(empowering, sentimental, and honorable)* gives me a tattoo from the pinky finger to my elbow.

He says, *"It'll look like a duck when I'm done."*

From my vantage it looks like a lion roaring towards my elbow.] //

⁂

Maj. = 2- THE DANCER: #1135
Min. = ♦- THE JESTER: #1219, ♣- THE VEGAN: #1237
PIANO: #0005, #0128, #0219
CIRCUS TENT: #0126
DEBATE: #1286, #1307

⁂

#1135 - April 1, 2020 @ 21:57 (San Francisco, California)

[1135.1 / 3044] [I'm at a giant historical mansion. I may be at Wimpole Hall. THE DANCER, THE FLASH and I speak with THE PHILANTHROPIST, who explains a decision to line the floors of a recovery wing of a refugee shelter with tatami mats. THE DANCER falls ill and begins to projectile vomit on the new tatami mat floor. I give her a banana and electrolyte solution to calm her stomach. I ask THE FLASH if she's ok to which she responds:

"We're in England, and we're locked in."] //

⁂

Maj. = 2- THE DANCER: #1148
VOMIT: #0172, #0377
ENGLAND: #0094, #0100, #0175, #0181
MANSION: #0013, #0039, #0040, #0044
REFUGEE: #0397
THE FLASH: #1210
THE PHILANTHROPIST: #1409

⁂

#1136 - April 2, 2020 @ 00:37 (San Francisco, California)

[1136.1 / 3045] [I overhear remarks given by "The Governor" while standing on the back porch at THE WEAVER and THE CARPENTER's house.

"Everyone must be diligent. Stay alert. Keep your eyes open for 'Land Squids.'"

An industrial mower motors through *(sans driver)*. I'm concerned it may run over someone and chop them up.

I catch a glimpse of a couple "Land Squids" in the neighbor's yard as they squiggle by near the edge of a wooden fence.

Two albino anacondas pursue the land squids as two *"bladed silver backed entities"* oddly swim through the freshly cut grass.

"Those are sacred crocodiles, not land squid. Keep your wits straight, son," THE CARPENTER recommends.]

[1136.2 / 3046] [As I move towards the back door of the house, my passage is blocked by a giant, dayglo-green puff adder that mirrors my movements. I manage to maneuver around it and rap my knuckles on the windows of the door. THE CARPENTER opens it.

The snake instantly slithers inside, glides through the kitchen and into the laundry room. It coils at THE WEAVER's ankles as she folds clothes.

I quietly call to her, ***"I need you to jump up onto the dryer."***

The snake bites her in the leg before she can respond.] //

⁂

Maj. = 0- THE WEAVER: #1137, 1- THE CARPENTER: #1137
SNAKE: #0277, #0312, #0315
PUFF: #0021, #0046
WOODEN FENCE: #0013

⁂

#1137 - April 2, 2020 @ 04:22 (San Francisco, California)

[1137.1 / 3047] [I live in California. I prepare a house for public listing. I have two family members who are ill. I've forced them to self-isolate in different bedrooms. I request that prospective buyers do not take photographs of the property. A man and woman who travel together both disregard my ask. I grab their phones and refuse to return them until they delete every photo of the house from the devices, as I hold them.

THE CARPENTER doesn't look prepared to show the house. He wears a ragged and torn bathrobe, which possibly hasn't been washed in months. He embarrasses me.

He says he's been, *"trying to upsell prospective buyers on amenities,"* but admits he, *"could have cleaned and sterilized the hot tub."*

THE WEAVER insists on listing the home at $410,000 to move it quickly, though I know the property is worth at least **$900,000**.

I'm unsettled by a yellow ring of electrical wires *(the size of a hula hoop)*, which have melted into the concrete in a basement wall. The perimeter of the large yellow ring is surrounded by many smaller yellow rings. I'm concerned the base of the house has been wrapped with plastic explosive and could explode at any moment.] //

⁂

Maj. = 0- THE WEAVER: #1140, 1- THE CARPENTER: #1138

HOT TUB: #0310

HULA HOOP: #0382

YELLOW: #0013, #0022, #0024

PERIMETER: #1266, #1274

⁂

#1138 - April 3, 2020 @ 06:47 (San Francisco, California)

[1138.1 / 3048] [I drive a car back home after leaving THE CARPENTER's white pickup truck in a parking lot in Cincinnati, Ohio.]

[1138.2 / 3049] [I watch THE DESIGNER and another young man purchase a large quantity of cocaine at a warehouse club in the middle of the day. They put a sizable portion in a Tupperware vessel and mark it as: *"THE CARPENTER's order."*]

[1138.3 / 3050] [I call THE CARPENTER from a different parking lot and request a ride home. He arrives in a silver truck with THE POSTMASTER as his passenger. Instead of stopping to pick me up, they laugh and smoke the tires. I call him as they speed away saying,

"Hey you need me to get where you're going."

"Oh shit, you're right."

He turns around, drives back, and slows just enough to allow me to jump in the truck bed. THE CARPENTER puts the open Tupperware full of cocaine in front of an air conditioning vent. White dust fills the truck cabin and flows through to the back. When I inhale, I lose my sense of smell and taste.

My entire face goes numb.] //

⁂

Maj. = 1- THE CARPENTER: #1140

Min. = ♣- THE POSTMASTER: #1195, ♠- THE DESIGNER: #1140

SILVER: #0009, #0012, #0033, #0060

FACE: #0063, #0066, #0069

TASTE: #1224, #1290

⁂

#1139 - April 4, 2020 @ 05:15 (San Francisco, California)

[1139.1 / 3051] [**Dental offices. * *Plastic surgery offices. ** The only person who would be able to identify me *(since I've recently escaped)*, works at a dental office. I'll be caught if she has a shift today. No one else on site knows who I am. I'm a temporary employee, awkwardly loved and adored by the unassuming staff.]

[1139.2 / 3052] [I take a path through a prison before I make my escape. I watch my soon-to-be-former cell mates perform group fitness activities from the opposite side of the fence.]

[1139.3 / 3053] [The prison chaplain notices I'm out of place, but fails to act before I gather my items and leave. I walk through a visitor gift shop and make my way to a casino-lit subway station. I hop on to a train. The train crashes at the end of the line. I stumble out through a hole in a steel wall on a city street, not sure where I am. I'm perplexed that the driver of the train also is warden of the prison, from where I've emancipated myself.]

[1139.4 / 3054] [Outbound trains have oddly partitioned rows of seats. Some are nonsensically placed perpendicular to others.]

[1139.5 / 3055] [I use my credit card one time *(to leave a digital signature within the prison)* before I break out.]

[1139.6 / 3056] [I travel with a female companion. We ride on another subway train that crashes, after which we're supposed to wander alone. For how long, we don't know.]

[1139.7 / 3057] [I feel forlorn and sad. A tall slender alien alternative-gendered-being with an eraser for a head, and a giant sharpened pencil for a chin *(lacking other facial features)*, pulls down its pants and reveals its genitals seemingly in an attempt to cheer me up.]

[1139.8 / 3058] [I become anxious when I awaken from anesthesia while having my face reconstructed. The pain is tremendous, though I'm more concerned the drips of blood on the white tile floor will lead those who are looking, directly to me.]

. . .

[1139.9 / 3059] [I'm at a mansion where dozens of people have been euthanized. A male body floats face down in a pool on the side yard. I'm a waiter. DONALD and MELANIA TRUMP take seats at the bar. She wants *"Bolognese on spaghetti."* He doesn't make a choice. He's just annoyed, *"there are so many dead people around."*] //

⁂
DONALD TRUMP: #1184
PLASTIC: #0010, #0012
PRISON: #0155, #0202
CREDIT: #0016, #0024, #0220
ESCAPE: #0202, #0232, #0330
CHOICE: #0035, #0144, #0229
ANNOYED: #1256, #1289, #1307
⁂

#1140 - April 5, 2020 @ 06:31 (San Francisco, California)

[1140.1 / 3060] [I live in an apartment complex where airlocks between each doorway create a sterile environment. Residents are not permitted to leave the property. I'm notified that I've received a furniture delivery. THE DESIGNER and I head back to my ground floor unit after traversing a lobby with a concierge. The carpet is forest green. The furniture is made from cherry wood. I've been given a new desk full of cutting-edge computer equipment. THE WEAVER and THE CARPENTER have set it all up for me. The large monitor can, *"show up to nine life-sized images of people in a grid."*

I'm doubtful when I see they're all ACER products, but I'm assured they're, *"the best quality and also happen to be least expensive."*

It seems like a grey afternoon. I infer the weather has been the same for months and a similar amount of light has remained constant.

"No one can tell the difference between day and night anymore."] //

⁂
Maj. = 0- THE WEAVER: #1145, 1- THE CARPENTER: #1149
Min. = ♠- THE DESIGNER: #1186
CHERRY: #0037, #1301, #1329
AFTERNOON: #0044, #0066, #0079, #0292, #0354
GREEN: #1331, #1336, #1343, #1344
⁂

#1141 - April 6, 2020 @ 04:53 (San Francisco, California)

[1141.1 / 3061] [I'm taken within a Manhattan hospital. Once inside, I find myself in the family gathering area of the New York Governor's city residence. A row of flat panel TVs are installed side-by-side, suspended from the ceiling behind a wet bar. I sit on a couch and note a green twisty playground slide in the corner of the room, that acts as, *"a fast track to the basement."* A braided steel firehouse pole *(yellow with orange "bow shaped" steps)* threaded between the spiraling slides, serves as an alternative way for children to move between various levels of the home.]

. . .

[1141.2 / 3062] [**Fast images flash:** Chaotic news media. Incessant hand washing. The media roulette wheel stops on an interview of a grown man who reflects on his time in the Governor's residence as a child.]

[1141.3 / 3063] [I acknowledge a reporter for, *"remaining on the job while being in the throes of a viral infection."*]

[1141.4 / 3064] [A former Governor *(now out of body)* is held to account on things he said while in residence at the home.

"This is just one of many homes the family owns."

Hearing the dead man speak makes me, ***"more aware of all the money I've inherited from him."***]

[1141.5 / 3065] [A muscular man works out. I almost mistakenly consume his energy drink. The mother of the house comments in passing that she, *"has no idea what we're up to,"* as a couple of small dogs race through the property, off leash.]

[1141.6 / 3066] [I see people walking in and out of the house wearing drab tartan pattern jackets, and loose ill-fitting silk-paisley shirts with butterfly collars. Guys wear their hair longer than shoulder length. It appears that a *"mid-1970's trend may be primed for a reboot in the 2020's."* All I see is frizzy hair and thick dark rimmed glasses, which seem to turn people on.]

[1141.7 / 3067] [I get ready for a night out with my *"be-ins"*. I keep messing with my hair. I catch a glimpse of myself in a full-length mirror, noting my hair is styled in a tall off-center powder-blue beehive. Others wear their hair up similarly in different colors. We're planning on attending a party together later in midtown Manhattan.] //

⁂

MANHATTAN: #0024, #1214, #1251
BEEHIVE: #0089
1970's: #0006, #0175, #0365
BUTTERFLY: #0306, #1326
MIRROR: #1250, #1279

⁂

#1142 - April 7, 2020 @ 02:28 (San Francisco, California)

[1142.1 / 3068] [I'm on a ship at sea, chasing bb-like beings that roll across the floor, up walls and around the space. I corral them off in smaller groups in corners of the room. They're assumed to be, *"sort of dangerous,"* yet containable.]

. . .

[1142.2 / 3069] [I'm in a glass hotel. I can see a fire raging on the floor beneath a man who's sleeping in a chair. Purple and pink flames flash up through the floor. The carpet burns just under his feet. I bang on the thick glass walls in an attempt to rouse him. He awakens and smiles at me. He acts like he understands there's a fire below, but he doesn't grasp the severity of his circumstances. He's about to perish. I vacate the building unsure if he makes it out alive.]

[1142.3 / 3070] [THE CHILD and THE LITTLE PRINCE stand at the edge of a park during a rainstorm. THE CHILD gives THE LITTLE PRINCE a piggyback ride and contemplates jumping into a large puddle.

"Don't do it just yet...it's too deep!" I shout at her.

She decides to anyway. She rolls over and THE LITTLE PRINCE flips off her back, sending him skyward. THE CHILD rolls across the street. I catch THE LITTLE PRINCE and give him a quick glance up and down to make sure he doesn't have any cuts on his forehead. He's startled, but not injured. The three of us walk side-by-side holding hands.]

[1142.4 / 3071] [*I contemplate which friendships from high school could use a refresh after the current pandemic subsides.*] //

⁂

Maj. = ***3- THE CHILD: #1153, 12- THE LITTLE PRINCE: #1165***
PIGGYBACK: #0088
GLASS: #0007, #0015, #0021, #0032, #0043
REFRESH: #1202, #1300

⁂

#1143 - April 7, 2020 @ 03:43 (San Francisco, California)

[1143.1 / 3072] [I walk across the parking lot of a nightclub. I pay $10 to park. My car is the only one in the lot. I enter the club and descend to a basement level. Once in the center of the space, I look up to the doorway and see THE DEAR HEART *(consistent, supportive, and intuitive)* playing doorman and making out with a departing lover, after a romantic quarrel.

I hear a buzzing sound and, believe I feel a green hummingbird land on my right shoulder. I crane my neck and instead, see a giant crocheted fly with blue-green eyes. It's attracted to a similar sized object I've fastened to my opposite shoulder. I decide I want to sit in a eucalyptus steam room, shedding my clothes as I advance towards a dripping, opaque mint-white door.]

[1143.2 / 3073] [I'm in discussions with THE PRESS SECRETARY *(passionate, objective, and well read)* on how to best publish our forthcoming co-authored work.

"Seems the average turnaround time to acquire a proof is 18 days, based on the scope and requirements of our project."] //

⁂

HUMMINGBIRD: #0005

OPAQUE: #0081, #0125, #0250, #0394
PUBLISH: #0297
THE DEAR HEART: #1195

⁂

#1144 - April 7, 2020 @ 05:32 (San Francisco, California)

[1144.1 / 3074] [I drive a Go-Kart down a busy street to a valet in a restaurant parking lot. I'm early for a later reservation. The valet isn't yet open. I have to find my own parking and also pay the valet fee.]

[1144.2 / 3075] [I'm at a dinner party, challenged to decide between taking shots of vodka, eating breaded chicken sandwiches, or grabbing tennis balls with my mouth and placing them in a steel washing bin. Two tables of eight guests participate in the quirky, nonsensical game. We compete for a booby prize.]

[1144.3 / 3076] [I pick up a hitchhiking veteran. He doesn't know where he's going. His presence in my car creates confusion and challenges my driving ability. I wind up back in the restaurant parking lot where THE PILOT and I debate, *"what sized knife blade we'll need later."*

He's chosen a 4" switchblade. Once flashed, he holds it to his own neck, drawing a small amount of blood and a twinge of pain to *"keep himself awake."*]

[1144.4 / 3077] [A homeless man drives a rusty jalopy and picks me up while I'm hitchhiking. I ask him to take me home by way of *"Apple Blossom"* drive. He refuses. After making a loop, we wind up at the restaurant valet. On my way into the establishment, I grab a raspberry-sorbet-filled-chocolate cake donut. I believe the homeless man has a vendetta for me as I eat the donut. I ask for help from guests seated in the restaurant, but no one assists me.

"They all want me gone!"

The chase continues to a back patio. The homeless man takes a seat at a table in front of the evening's honoree, JOHN McCAIN.

"Senator McCain I'm so sorry for the disruption. I'm supposed to attend dinner with you later tonight." I say, noting the deceased Senator is startled by the homeless man's sudden presence at the table.

"Cindy, it's time for us to go," he says standing up and tossing a white cloth napkin on the table.]

[1144.5 / 3078] [I'm home in a dark bedroom. The homeless man has let himself into my apartment. My sister is asleep in a room downstairs. I feel a heavy presence behind me. While staring at a white wall that surrenders to shadow, I say,

"Don't you hurt her."

"I won't. She's fresh meat," he says as he slits my throat.

I feel the blade sever all the tissue between my windpipe to my spine. I can hear my last breaths gurgle and glug as I drift from consciousness and wake up.] //

⁂

Maj. = 6- THE PILOT: #1160
SHADOW: #0006, #0035, #0086, #0092, #0243, #0360
DONUT: #0148
THROAT: #0188, #0275
MEAT: #0033, #0088, #0187
KNIFE: #1236, #1319

⁂

#1145 - April 9, 2020 @ 06:56 (San Francisco, California)

[1145.1 / 3079] [I'm at THE EPICUREAN's home. It's vast and palatial with a magnificently manicured interior courtyard. Initially I think I'm a party guest, but am promptly made aware that I'm employed by an in-house caterer as a server. My team prepares a banquet hall for an evening gathering. THE NUN enters and takes a seat in a single chair positioned in the middle of the room. I kneel and hold her hand. I touch my cheek to the back of her hand and close my eyes. When I open them and look up THE NUN has vanished. I'm clasping a young woman's hand.]

[1145.2 / 3080] [A seven-piece rock band plays a concert supported by a large church choir. The venue occurs like an inverse impression of the Theatre of Ancient Greece. Steps lead up to the stage from where the music emanates. THE NUN and THE CHANNEL *(surrendered, awake, and devoted)* sing joyfully as members of the choir.]

[1145.3 / 3081] [Back in the mansion, the weather oscillates between misty and sunny. A group gathered is broken into smaller teams for a contest. My group is challenged to push a series of large oak bookcases in a serpentine pattern around the perimeter of the study, down a hallway, and into an otherwise vacant room. When we hit a kink in the route the entire house shakes. As we've moved the bookcases, we've also moved the foundation of the property.

An overzealous member of the team gives the cases a strong push in the opposite direction, shuttling them back through the path we've cut, and cascading entirely out the third-floor window of the mansion. They plummet like an overstretched accordion to the grass outside. She laughs at the impact of her brute display of force, though it's created a significant setback for us. We were within inches of completing the task. Action "fast forwards" and we seemingly cooperate to undo the misstep and win the contest, while setting a new *"house record."*]

[1145.4 / 3082] [Movie posters, props, and a variety of other antiques are on display at a silent auction in a salon.]

[1145.5 / 3083] [THE PIZZA DELIVERY BOY *(musical, opinionated, and judgmental)* talks about playing guitars and carries on about, *"hosting a party of his own."* He'll only invite people he knows because he's, *"paid for other people's beers too damn much and for too damn long."*]

. . .

[1145.6 / 3084] [I'm in a rustic kitchen in the servant's quarters. I stand over a deep fryer installed in the center island, making basketball-sized Poori. It's midmorning and the overhead lights are off. I've prepped matchbox-sized puzzle-piece-shaped pastries and a pumpkin filling with dark chocolate chips folded in, which will be combined later to create *"appetizer sandwich cookies."* The puzzle pieces have Van Gogh-ish swirls of blue and yellow frosting on the outside.

"They need to bake at 425 degrees for 8-10 minutes to 'fire and glaze' the frosting art to the cookies."]

[1145.7 / 3085] [I'm a teenager. I flirt with THE JAZZ TRUMPETER *(quiet, nerdy, and sweet)* while sitting on his bed. Some moments we're naked. Other's we're fully clothed.]

[1145.8 / 3086] [THE WEAVER debates whether or not people should move with their kids, *"out of their homes and into the streets."*]

[1145.9 / 3087] [I direct a movie. Aliens are the investors/producers. I disagree with their agenda. I abandon the project.]

[1145.10 / 3088] [A young woman is dropped off in front of a dusty saloon at 8:00am daily for breakfast, before reporting to prison. She's large framed. She has multiple tattoos of cartoon characters across her upper chest and neck. She has giant dinner-plate-sized spacers in her ears. Her attorney is a man. He wears a suit and chews on a piece of wheat as he waits patiently for her to eat.] //

⁂

Maj. = 0- THE WEAVER: #1146
Min. = ♥- THE EPICUREAN: #1161, ♦- THE NUN: #1216
RUSTIC: #0017, #0019, #0024, #0194
SEVEN: #0014, #0026, #0033, #0105
PUMPKIN: #0064, #0277
SANDWICH: #1277

⁂

#1146 - April 12, 2020 @ 03:09 (San Francisco, California)

[1146.1 / 3089] [I'm at an abandoned fast-food restaurant in London. An oxygen tank and a nitrous oxide tank have leaked fully into the kitchen. I stand at the perimeter knowing if I don't, I'll get high. When I look out a window, Scotland Yard has surrounded the building and intend to enter and apprehend me. THE ROBOT has been installed as a secret agent *"because of her precision and track record of successful execution."* Scotland Yard have accomplished more with her on staff for a single day, then they had in the prior month. She's acknowledged and loved by her team.]

. . .

[1146.2 / 3090] [I work on a movie set where the day quickly sails by. THE ROBOT is the lead producer who's stepped beyond her responsibility to the show to *"become the steward for all the garbage and trash accumulated during the shoot."* The show has vast waste management issues, and is presently poisoning the environment. She retrieves a key from a thief. A conversation ensues where the team debates the site's *"future dumpster needs."* The preferred dumpster dimensions are atypical and difficult to find for a movie set of our size. Finding the resolution consumes most of THE ROBOT's work day.]

[1146.3 / 3091] [People get haircuts and comment on how we, *"inspired them because we were the best-groomed bunch they'd ever worked with."*]

[1146.4 / 3092] [I soak off the day in a hot tub filled with foam, while talking with THE WEAVER on the phone.

"Did you have a good birthday, son?"

"Yes, for the first time in a while I prioritized rest and relaxation."

"That's good. That's what you did last year. It's working. Keep doing that."

I have a house key tied to a spring, wrapped around my mid-forearm. Two identical twin, muscular men enter the pool. I'm confused for a moment because I believe I've watched the same guy enter twice *(de ja vu)*. Another bright smiley guy who calls himself "SUPERMAN" cruises me for a moment, then encourages me to lower the key from my forearm to my wrist saying,

"It'll let the sunlight in to the spaces you tend to cover."] //

⁂

Maj. = 0- THE WEAVER: #1149
Min. = ♥- THE ROBOT: #1166
FAST FOOD: #0066, #0117, #0203, #0255
WRIST: #0086, #0293
KEY: #0324, #0386
BRIGHT: #1295, #1299

⁂

#1147 - April 13, 2020 @ 03:46 (San Francisco, California)

[1147.1 / 3093] [A giant house in San Francisco has been completely renovated.

"The original owners of the home were born in 1918."

It's my ideal home. The renovators occupy an office after we've taken ownership of the property. Small dogs run around unobstructed. A small patio through a pair of French doors can be found at the far end of the contractor's blue-walled office. A steep, slanted stairway connects each of the home's five floors. Each stairway is lined with plants. The landings between floors profile leafy plants from different continents. I share the house commonly with THE LAWYER and two other men. We each live on our own floor of the property, reserving one for group gatherings.]

. . .

[1147.2 / 3094] [I'm inducted into a secret society of percussionists and drummers in the basement level of a University library. I'm shown tips and tricks to make synthetic drums sound like a traditional kit.

"What's that ring-like trigger you use that sounds like a tabla?" I ask a dishwater blond haired man, who sits on his drum throne as members of a cycling team file through from an elevator to have their bikes serviced.]

[1147.3 / 3095] [I'm getting a team back together, and take suggestions for revisions to a shared statement of purpose. THE PEER *(bubbly, inventive, and demanding)* and I discuss everyone in our network we could tap for new roles at our firm. It'll be a few weeks until HR approves the 40+ roles we've requested to initiate our new global initiative, but we've gotten a head start.] //

⁂

Maj. = 5- THE LAWYER: #1150

PATIO: #0045, #0071, #0115, #0170

FIVE: #0182, #0188, #0193, #1098, #0365

ROLE #0007, #0077, #0106, #0156, #0206, #0251, #0324

⁂

#1148 - April 14, 2020 @ 03:35 (San Francisco, California)

[1148.1 / 3096] [I work at an office for the State of California, preparing a process to allow interstate travel, **post pandemic.** Travelers will be required to present a special lanyard to move freely across borders. The size of the print job, the age of the equipment, and the exceptionally short timeline has caused a perceived delay in the delivery of lanyards to those who have requested them.]

[1148.2 / 3097] [I perch on top of a shelf and watch a small grocery store's entire *"last day"* of business. The owners only announce the closure to their customers when they dim the lights and lock the door at the end of the day. The shopkeeper watches the last of his inventory leave in a brown bag. He places a small computer terminal where the register previously sat, *"for customers to place future online orders for home delivery."*

THE DANCER and others are sad the little shop has closed. It represented where they spent a lot of time hanging out when they lived in the city in their 20's.]

[1148.3 / 3098] [I'm at a school for gifted children. I walk upstairs, following THE TRANSLATOR and THE DEVOTEE. I enter a bathroom and go into a stall. I open a book and begin to read it. THE DEVOTEE comes in to check on me.

"What are you doing in there?"

"I just feel like singing," I croon through the door. We laugh.] //

⁂

Maj. = 2- THE DANCER: #1149, 19- THE TRANSLATOR: #1159

Min. = ♠- THE DEVOTEE: #1179

LANYARDS: #0139, #0248
LAUGH: #0072, #0183, #0189, #0204
SINGING: #1210, #1268, #1295
⁂

#1149 - April 15, 2020 @ 06:28 (San Francisco, California)

[1149.1 / 3099] [I have sex with a muscular guy in the back room of a house. Afterwards, I feel anxious. I remember that I haven't taken my Truvada. I look through a bunch of different pill bottles scattered around a movie theater floor. I find a variety of THE CARPENTER's prescriptions and grow startled when I discover his Viagra prescription and my Truvada prescription were errantly swapped by our pharmacist.]

[1149.2 / 3100] [I speak with an attractive man who claims, *"no one ever asks me out on dates."*

"Well why don't I take you out then?" I offer, but don't await his answer.

I get distracted, and follow a group of people who pass by, all wearing. We wait for another *"red shirt"* team member to arrive who appears to be running late. A young woman introduces the *"late runner"* to another friend of hers that I want to date.]

[1149.3 / 3101] [The family is together at a bar and orders cocktails. THE DANCER orders a drink that arrives served in a clear fish bowl, with orange sediment settled at the bottom. She looks disappointed.

THE WEAVER says, *"You have to stir it up. I've had that before. The vodka is just too much for me."*]

[1149.4 / 3102] [THE COUTURIER discloses she's been seeing a man who lives outside the city limits of Bucharest. He uses an obvious pseudonym. We recommend that she stop seeing him. From above, Bucharest looks like a flower, an atom...**a labyrinth.** All traffic flows in circles to the right. The only place one can make a left turn out of the city is at, *"the stem of the maze."*]

[1149.5 / 3103] [People set up tents from edge-to-edge of a giant campground. Signage is provided in English and *(depending on the day)* Spanish. A group of slightly confused guys on bikes gathers near a giant overhead banner that reads:

"PELOTON"

...then pedal through the site and disappear. THE LOGICIAN *(orderly, direct, and firm)* sets up her tent with her trainees. I introduce her to THE NURSE, who's forgotten that they spent a year in training together.] //

⁂

Maj. = 0- THE WEAVER: #1155, 1- THE CARPENTER: #1154,
2- THE DANCER: #1156, 13- THE NURSE: #1248

Min. = ♣- THE COUTURIER: #1240
LABYRINTH: #0024, #0027, #0053, #0065, #0376
ATOM: #0141, #1312
BUCHAREST: #0056
⁂

#1150 - April 15, 2020 @ 23:57 (San Francisco, California)

[1150.1 / 3104] [***NIGHTMARE! *** - I struggle to get out from under an invisible energy that wrestles from side-to-side in my bedroom. My body flips head-to-toe, toe-to-head, head-to-toe across my bed like a ragdoll. I constantly *"invite the light in"* to usher the unseen force away from me. I can't see what's holding me down.

I stand up and sprint around the house, noting the power is out. Post It notes have been left on all the light switches. I'm unable to read them in the dark. An odd amber-green dark light illuminates nefarious energies lurking the corners. I encounter THE LAWYER in the doorway of his bedroom. He stands lumbering over with each hand on opposite sides of the door frame, partially awake. He looks like an ogre in the odd amber-green light. He doesn't speak.

Before I run back to my room and shut the door, I turn on music and begin dancing. I put "We Found Love" by RHIANNA on repeat and dance myself *(and the house)* clean before falling back to sleep.

"As your shadow crosses mine...
What it takes to come alive...
We found love in a hopeless place...
We found love in a hopeless place..."] //

⁂
Maj. = 5- THE LAWYER: #1160
NIGHTMARE: #0035, #0172, #0352
INVISIBLE: #0299, #0310, #0339, #0380, #0397
LOVE: #1332
⁂

#1151 - April 17, 2020 @ 03:00 (San Francisco, California)

[1151.1 / 3105] [To escape the world I fill a bathtub, submerge myself to my eye line, then spend an entire evening shaving my stubbly legs underwater with a dull rusty razor.] //

⁂
ESCAPE: #1260, #1314, #1343
EYE: #1248, #1283, #1292
RAZOR: #128
⁂

#1152 - April 18, 2020 @ 01:40 (San Francisco, California)

[1152.1 / 3106] [*"Give it another month. Keep practicing."*]

. . .

[1152.2 / 3107] [I give a reading to a woman. My eyes are closed while I stand across from her. The flow of information is fast and intense. I speak quickly. A short-haired female teacher who wears glasses interrupts me and disrupts my flow.

"I've triggered the teacher."

I can see the karmic picture in her space that I've lit up via my channeling. I ask her to stop, apologize, and step away but she becomes defensive and combative. I complete the reading and walk through a steel exit door to a stairwell.

Once there, I see the teacher's belongings tossed at random across the stairs. It appears she's in the process of moving up one floor into a new apartment. I quickly *(and telekinetically)* gather her items into like groups so they're more easily transportable and simpler to find when she unpacks. When she turns the corner down the stairs to make another pass, she pauses for a moment, then appreciates what I've done to help her out.

We reconcile.

My clarity of vision and truth in speech overwhelm her. She remains unaware of my ability to see that in her.]

[1152.3 / 3108] [I'm an intern. I make repeated trips to the White House to work with The President. He's consistently drawn the ire of the people throughout his first term. After my third meeting with him, I understand he's misbehaving to please everyone who already hates him, to prove them right. I exit through one of three secret exits from the White House. Each is used for a different purpose. I leave through a side door, built for JFK to avoid the press during the Cuban Missile Crisis.]

[1152.4 / 3109] [I'm on Air Force One. I unbox a new device given to The President by DARPA. Three gyroscopic rings pop from the box, hover, integrate, and begin to spin.

"Perhaps it's a holographic camera?" I place a special hands-free headset in my right ear as the gyroscopic camera spins and whirs giving it the look of a carnival glass soap bubble. The device will allow me to safely address the public as a hologram, from-and-to anywhere on the planet.

"Maybe it's a cloaking device? I know I shouldn't have taken it from the package. He'll know that I know about the device."] //

⁂

DEVICE: #1216, #1319
RINGS: #1274, #1306, #1335
PURPOSE: #1274
GATHER: #1278, #1291, #1294

⁂

#1153 - April 19, 2020 @ 03:58 (San Francisco, California)

[1153.1 / 3110] [We prepare for THE CHILD's birthday party. She climbs up onto a set of bunk beds, slips between two twin mattresses, and disappears. I can hear her laugh as I reach my arm in to grab her leg and pull her out. When she *(and my arm)* emerge from the mattress, they're both covered in strawberry preserves. Curious what's in between the mattresses, I dive in. Once on the other side of the portal I'm in a "Winter Desert" in Siberia. I attempt to use Google to help me acquire directions home.]

[1153.2 / 3111] [I stand to the right of a cashier. I take two small clear cylinders filled with snack foods *(yellow puffs & chocolate squares)* from a point of purchase display. I stack a third on my arm, stabilizing it with my chin. I unintentionally leave without paying. People in the store don't notice that I take the items.]

[1153.3 / 3112] [I give a guy a blowjob. He's wearing a tuxedo. Mid-act he withdraws and zips up his pants saying, *"No I'm not supposed to do that."*

His small Asian father confronts him, then begins to beat his son *(and me)*, with a leather belt, culminating in him throwing us both out of the house.] //

⁂

Maj. = 3- THE CHILD: #1158

WINTER: #1220

POINT OF: #1221, #1228, #1249, #1313, #1335

⁂

#1154 - April 19, 2020 @ 05:17 (San Francisco, California)

[1154.1 / 3113] [I hear someone in the shower singing. I open the door thinking I'll find someone I know. I'm surprised to find a fully clothed man standing on a yellowish-gold-white grouted tile ledge.

"I made a mistake. I thought you were someone else," I say to the man as I back away and latch the door shut.]

[1154.2 / 3114] [I'm on a steam train that chugs along on a single, thick, rusted track. THE CARPENTER and I are passengers, and amazed by the strength of the engineer, who guides the train by rowing a giant iron oar].

[1154.3 / 3115] [Inside a house, a young girl cries. She wants to hang out with me. I hug her to console her.]

[1154.4 / 3116] [*"What are you doing?"* THE KIDDO (*methodical, curious, and comprehensive)* asks, as I take three folded Pendleton blankets from the back seat of my car. I intend to spread them out and lay on the wet rooftop of an urban apartment building.

"I may even have a foggy picnic."]

[1154.5 / 3117] [I walk through a house. A small Chinese boy stops to take a photo of me. I have no idea what he intends to do with it.]

. . .

[1154.6 / 3118] [I sit around a table with a group of women processing a phone conversation that's left me confused:

"THE ROMANTIC called me a week ago. He asked me to marry me. I said, 'Yes.' He quickly responded, 'Well then you'll have to take my last name.' I withdrew my acceptance and haven't communicated with him since. Why would I have done that? Why wouldn't I have chosen to change my name?" I ask the ladies.

The ladies don't speak. They continue to daintily nibble their triangular shaped crustless white bread sandwiches.] //

⁂

Maj. = 1-THE CARPENTER: #1155, 15- THE ROMANTIC: #1345
YES: #1207
SINGING: #1210, #1268, #1295
BLANKETS: #1220
THE KIDDO: #1243

⁂

#1155 - April 19, 2020 @ 03:58 (San Francisco, California)

[1155.1 / 3119] [I enter a sporting goods store attempting to buy soccer balls and foam rollers for party attendees. If I buy as many as I need, I won't be able to carry all of them. My bulk purchase will result in, *"a bounty of extra props."*]

[1155.2 / 3120] [I've been asked to lead a yoga class for a bachelorette party at THE EMT's *(direct, supportive, and motherly)* estate. THE COMPUTATIONAL LINGUIST *(inviting, optimistic, and artful)* will be among the 31 confirmed attendees. I've been provided with a thumbnail-sized image of each of the attendees, who appear *"generally well and healthy."* The majority of attendees are men. Apparently, this group ran a similar event as a fundraiser and raised an excess of $1MM. I dance around to some EDM before the event to psych myself up.

A young Asian man asks, *"What clubs do you go to?"*

"I don't. I have dance parties for one at home."]

[1155.3 / 3121] [*A summer camp scene:* Human adult camp counselors walk their campers around, pausing occasionally to have Pokémon battles. THE ORANGE PIG *(gregarious, romantic, and hyped up)* is among the adult camp counselors. The kids are asked to match their counselor to a Pokémon character with similar qualities.]

[1155.4 / 3122] [I'm tasked to find a list of sundry items at a local grocery store. A man named "Jeff," requests two rolls of specialty quilted patterned toilet paper with a thin white and grey vertical zigzag pattern.]

[1155.5 / 3123] [THE CARPENTER is extremely sick. He stays alone in a bedroom at GRANDMA's house to recover. He's feverish, and occasionally lets himself out to use the bathroom. THE WEAVER is concerned we won't be able to take our flight home from Iowa later that night.] //

⁂

Maj. = 0-THE WEAVER: #1156, 1-THE CARPENTER: #1157, 11-GRANDMA: # 1208
SPECIAL: #1218, #1302, #1322
PATTERN: #1211, #1222, #1251, #1286
THE EMT: #1330

⁂

#1156 - April 20, 2020 @ 00:36 (San Francisco, California)

[1156.1 / 3124] [I sit across from THE DANCER and THE ATHEIST who are seated on a couch by a kitchen. THE WEAVER is just out of earshot. They ask me if I'm, *"living up to my potential."* I don't know how to respond.]

[1156.2 / 3125] [An animal-like energy runs around behind me as I lay on the floor of my bedroom. It has small paws or hooves. It runs in a figure eight pattern overhead. I'm concerned it may trample me. I sit up quickly and look at my bedroom door, then wake up face down on the floor.]

*Note: *39 seconds of recording muffled. Whatever that galloping thing was didn't want to be remembered. **

⁂

Maj. = 0-THE WEAVER: #1158, 2-THE DANCER: #1157, 8-THE ATHEIST: # 1165
RESPOND: #1236, #1245, #1250, #1262, #1278
DOOR: #1279, #1284, #1291

⁂

#1157 - April 20, 2020 @ 04:16 (San Francisco, California)

[1157.1 / 3126] [THE CARPENTER and I stand on the driveway looking at the street when a blue hot rod speeds by and runs a stop sign. It squeals its tires, makes a U-turn, and doubles back across the intersection. We implore the driver to stop as he makes another high-speed U-turn, runs the stop sign, and then broadsides a neighboring car. The neighbor's car spins, then sputters to a stop as it crashes into the front door of a house. The blue car drives backwards into an open garage at the end of a cul de sac. The vehicle remains in full view as THE CARPENTER and I run towards it, demanding the driver, *"come out and take responsibility for what they've done."* The garage door begins to close. THE CARPENTER and I slide underneath it to pursue the driver as he ducks inside the house.]

[1157.2 / 3127] [Once inside the home, THE CARPENTER and I realize we've been trapped in a funhouse. As we attempt to find our way out, our various points of exit loop us back to the middle of the property. Walking through the funhouse, we open a door and realize we're moving quickly down the highway in a hollowed-out gasoline truck. On another pass, we hop a white picket fence as the lady of the house releases the hounds. Dogs jump the fence and chase us into the field. They attack me while I'm in THE CARPENTER's body.]

[1157.3 / 3128] [When we exit the house, the reckless driver and his entire family stand in the driveway and offer us a round of applause. A young miniature woman *(made of metal)* pirouettes like a dancer on top of her older brother's open upturned palm.]

[1157.4 / 3129] [I'm in Manhattan. I'm invited by ALANIS MORISETTE to attend a small club gig she's playing later in Washington Heights. I invite THE DANCER since it's close to her apartment, but she, *"has the baby and can't find a sitter on such short notice."*]

[1157.5 / 3130] [My female Asian friend prepares a tray of round yellow custards and pops them in the oven, intent on taking them to the show later in Washington Heights. She makes me review a catalog of photographs of every attendee from a party we previously attended. We cross reference the catalog with the guest list for the show so we'll recognize faces, and be primed for conversation.]

[1157.6 / 3131] [I'm with a group attending a tumbling class. The instructor teaches the group to do *"drop back"* backbends. She expects every student will be able to perform the skill immediately, though I know it's beyond the ability of most. We're encouraged to attempt the maneuver on a padded floor, lined up in an "L" shaped formation. Half the padded floor is flat, the other half is tilted at a 45-degree angle from the corner, composed of a trampoline that extends across the entire interior of a perimeter wall. Other people tumble nearby. I assume responsibility for teaching when safety becomes questionable.]

[1157.7 / 3132] [I'm lying on my back. A large toothy mouth in my belly repeats the phrase **"I'M DONE!"** over and over. I place my hands over it to muffle its volume. Over time it becomes smaller and smaller, silences, and eventually dissolves. When I remove my hands it's completely disappeared.] //

⁂

Maj. = 1-THE CARPENTER: #1171, 2- THE DANCER: #1158
ROUND: #1205, #1223, #1256, #1257
MOUTH: #1224, #1238, #1251
GUEST: #1202, #1302

⁂

#1158 - April 20, 2020 @ 05:56 (San Francisco, California)

[1158.1 / 3133] [THE DANCER stops by to give me an ice cream sandwich *(chocolate cookies with raspberry ice cream filling)*. She turns to walk up the street and says,
"I have to deliver this chocolate bunny to THE WEAVER."

THE CHILD exclaims an excitedly affirmative, *"YESSS!"* and pumps her arm as she and THE DANCER begin to cross the street.

"Come with me! Come with me!!!" THE CHILD beckons.

We walk to the end of the block and turn to the left. I look down and notice I'm holding an Easter Basket full of Marshmallow Peeps, Jelly Beans, Cadbury's Crème Eggs and other things I believe THE CHILD will like. As we approach the house THE WEAVER leans from a window and asks,

"Hey bud...have you grown a thick little pudge around your middle?"]

[1158.2 / 3134] [I'm in a gold walled room. I'm interrogated by the commanding officer of my naval ship for abandoning my post. I'm pushed to the ground. A group of men stand over me. My face is stepped on as I look to the side and see a wall of small succulent plants, immaculately manicured and placed on the interiors of small square black shelves arranged in an ornate *"geometric galaxy pattern."*]

[1158.3 / 3135] [I make eye contact with a "Cow-Eyed Brown-Eyed Baby" *(which turns out to be a miniature woman, who's mother to many children)* as THE DANCER pulls it back into the open cab of the car from behind the trunk.]

[1158. 4 / 3136] [I'm at work in a grocery store. I help people remove rotten pieces of fruit *(including a half-eaten orange)* from a display. THE CATHOLIC *(stubborn, devoted, and righteous)* has a social media identity that has multiple millions of followers. She's frustrated that people are interested in her struggles. I encounter THE CONNECTOR as we attempt to tape signs to a two-panel door that slides shut.

Horizontally placed slim rectangles of blue, white, brown and black denote different messages for customers to, *"group, gather, enter, and exit the building."*

We laugh in frustration because we're unable to keep the doors open long enough to affix the tape to the appropriate spot. An old man who stands on the back deck, gently guides us as we prepare the store for opening. ***"The overhead lights have still not been turned on."***] //

⁂

Maj. = 0- THE WEAVER: #1160, 2- THE DANCER: #1172,
3- THE CHILD: #1171, 4- THE CONNECTOR: #1166
Min. = ♣- THE CATHOLIC: #1249
FILLING: #1341
SHUT: #1229, #1314
FRUSTRATION: #1272, #1289, #1326

⁂

#1159 - April 22, 2020 @ 09:00 (San Francisco, California)

[1159.1 / 3137] [Two guys hooked up on a pool table in the basement of a coastal home and have angered the female homeowner. She's roped the doorway off to prevent other guests from descending a back staircase and seeing the mess they made on the green felt. One of the guys works for Facebook.]

. . .

[1159.2 / 3138] [THE TRANSLATOR offers me a job at a summer camp for gifted children. Inwardly I hear myself say ***"Yes"*** but my mouth says, ***"No."*** The job offer is rescinded.]

[1159.3 / 3139] [I walk through a busy grocery store, occasionally seeing familiar faces from my meditation school including THE CAROLER *(inquisitive, game, and transparent).* I stop at a freezer unit and look at spirals of, *"dynamically priced pork loin."* First listed at $100, the price changes in the moment to fit what the customer is able to pay. The meat is packed in injection molded plastic.] //

⁂

Maj. = 19- THE TRANSLATOR: #1178
POOL: #1271, #1277, #1299
BUSY: #1266, 1297, #1318
NO: #1319, #1322, #1340

⁂

#1160 - April 23, 2020 @ 06:06 (San Francisco, California)

[1160.1 / 3140] [THE PILOT and I sit in a tree.

He says, *"I'll be available later,"* as I climb across him from the branch where we sit to descend the tree trunk, nearly falling in the process. We're just high enough that were I to fall, I would break both my legs.

Together, we drive to a large house where we encounter THE KIND HEART who has grown a long black Mohawk fashioned into dreadlocks.

"Socially distant hugs!" I shout at them while gesturing from a couple body distances apart. I walk into a thicket and disappear.]

[1160.2 / 3141] [I sit in a grocery store waiting for my turn to shop. A sick family browses without wearing face masks. I admonish them.

THE LAWYER and his dad sit down next to me in a food court at the front of the store and say, *"There's slices of pizza on sale for a dollar. All you have to do is find a plate."*]

[1160.3 / 3142] [**Abstraction of masculine/feminine energies dancing and balancing. ** A woman shops. A man drives a car around a parking lot waiting to pick her up.]

[1160.4 / 3143] [I climb up a ladder to a treehouse in search of *"breakfast sandwich starters"* previously left in a vertical freezer. Muffin sized portions of Egg/Ham/Hash Browns are vacuum sealed in clear pouches. I look for bread and a microwave. The animal products have an odd, grey, gelatin-like quality.]

[1160.5 / 3144] [Woeful, pained, odd cries come from what sounds like a dying cat.]

. . .

[1160.6 / 3145] [I'm at home, upstairs with THE WEAVER. I go down a dark, unlit stairwell. When I get to the bottom all the lights on the main floor illuminate and reveal I'm completely surrounded by beings of all shapes, sizes, and varieties. They make cacophonous, startling noise as they press up against my skin.] //

⁂

Maj. = 0-THE WEAVER: #1161, 5-THE LAWYER: # 1168, 6-THE PILOT: #1199, 21- THE KIND HEART: #1199

ODD: #1241, #1302

SHOP: #1260, #1329

MAIN FLOOR: #1233

⁂

#1161 - April 25, 2020 @ 07:00 (San Francisco, California)

[1161.1 / 3146] [I'm with THE EPICUREAN and LADY GAGA in an office lined with file cabinets. She entrusts me with a movie poster she wants transported to her home. She doesn't want it to be folded, nor creased. She also has reservations when I suggest, ***"I'll roll it up and place it in a cardboard tube."***

"I'll make a special trip to Chicago and hand deliver it to your house," I say, intending to allay her fear.

The tone changes to friendly, creative talk when I ask her, ***"So with the Super Bowl...did you imagine the American Flag in drones behind you?"***

"No, that was a team effort. Many other people contributed. When you're the performer you simply sign up, show up, and do your thing. The rest of it seems to just 'happen' around you."

As I move closer to her and become desirous of a deeper friendship, I notice numerous others pull away. Most are women who say *(in one way or another)* that they're, *"fed up."*]

[1161.2 / 3147] [I urinate for what seems like a really long period. So long, I check my watch multiple times as I whistle.]

[1161.3 / 3148] [I drive a white car backwards into a gas station. When I exit the car to fill the tank, I notice I'm completely naked, but wearing shoes.]

[1161.4 / 3149] [THE WEAVER and LADY GAGA have been long time collaborators. They share a home at Lake Tahoe, where they've chosen to continue their work. THE WEAVER has recently agreed to take on some tasks as LADY GAGA's assistant, and the additional work has begun to take its toll on their creative friendship.]

[1161.5 / 3150] [I'm at a video store talking to a clerk about whether or not he can get me another copy of the poster I've been trusted to transport. It's not clear if I've done something to result in its damage/loss, or if I simply want one for myself.] //

⁂

Maj. = 0-THE WEAVER: #1162
Min. = ♥- THE EPICUREAN: #1246
LADY GAGA: #1180
CLERK: #1326
CREATIVE: #1239, #1240, #1253

⁂

#1162 - April 27, 2020 @ 07:22 (San Francisco, California)

[1162.1 / 3151] [THE WEAVER's exhausted and bedridden. I check on her by placing the back of my hand on her forehead. I kiss her, then turn out the light. The soft, pinkish-amber hue of a night light glows dimly in the corner.]

[1162.2 / 3152] [I leave a fully packed car idling outside a set of French doors on an otherwise completely dark street. When I open the doors, the lights are on, the bed has been made, and THE WEAVER is packed and ready to depart.] //

⁂

Maj. = 0-THE WEAVER: #1165
FRENCH DOORS: #1255
SOFT: #1235, #1279

⁂

#1163 - April 28, 2020 @ 06:16 (San Francisco, California)

[1163.1 / 3153] [I'm at a theme park with BOB DYLAN. I query him about his songwriting process.

He says, *"I just have a knack for getting people to tell me about their lives."*

BOB sits at an upright piano playing as I leave with a cohort. I run around a neighborhood and back into the theme park. While there, I keep searching for BOB because I want to get a selfie with him. Instead, I keep finding myself surrounded by a group of men who are trying to take showers. I stop to pee. I pee for a seemingly interminable period of time.

A proctor tells me, *"What you're doing won't make most people happy, but I'll let it slide."*]

[1163.2 / 3154] [An attorney has elected to represent two young boys, contrary to her typical clientele, as a way of favorably positioning herself for other prospective business.]

[1163.3 / 3155] [I walk around the park in search of "the correct location," but I keep moving to areas further removed from all exits. I've added significant travel time to my journey. I encounter a group of suit-wearing promoters who tout a new energy drink. They look like Mormon missionaries with their black ties, name tags, and *"high & tight"* haircuts. They've emptied the contents of a keg into a cube shaped vinyl bag. The liquid is purple/pink and may be carbonated.

"All these men are manically caffeinated."]

. . .

[1163.4 / 3156] [I pass by a display case filled with a variety of Lucite awards, illuminated from beneath with a bluish-white light. One award celebrates a banks' success for navigating a challenging interest rate environment during the "COVID Crisis." Some are shaped like curly Q's, loops, Chihuly-esque ornaments, which are intended to mimic the nonsensical and erratic fluctuations experienced in global markets disrupted by, *"the virus."*] //

⁂

PERIOD: #1304, #1343
NAME: #1220, #1235, #1236
DISPLAY: #1250, #1273, #1290

⁂

#1164 - April 28, 2020 @ 09:41 (San Francisco, California)

[1164.1 / 3157] [I'm in a shared house when I go to take a dump. I look back after attempting to shit for a while and see an earthworm writhing around in the bowl searching for dirt.]

[1164.2 / 3158] [I lay on my back, head downwards on a staircase. A man comes over to me who I initially perceive as familiar, but then isn't when he presses down on my hands, lays on me, and attempts to give me a massage. I struggle for a moment, then surrender. He has a Russian accent. When I come to, I realize he's a stranger, though I proceed with oddly familiar questions.

"How's the married life?"

"Grrreat!"

I'm startled when he identifies himself as "Pete" and introduces me to his wife. She has short blonde hair. They sit around a kitchen table.]

[1164.3 / 3159] [An airplane picks up speed. I watch the wings fold under the fuselage of the futuristic jet while the craft is pulled along a hilly, smooth, track like a thin-line rollercoaster from underneath by a ball and socket joint, fashioned from smooth white porcelain.] //

⁂

BOWL: #1204, #1249
FUTURISTIC: #1245, #1302, #1335
SPEED: #1251, #1267, #1275
ACCENT: #1288

⁂

#1165 - April 29, 2020 @ 07:09 (San Francisco, California)

[1165.1 / 3160] [I'm informed *"there's a dangerous entity in the corner of a room."* When my guide asks us to depart, it's time to go.]

. . .

[1165.2 / 3161] [I give myself a haircut. THE WEAVER seems disappointed with my decision.

"Why did you do that? Did you become impatient?" THE WEAVER asks.

"No, this was always the plan. I gave myself the idea that I was going to go 'all punk rock' and give myself a Mohawk. My hair was as long as yours!"

"No, it wasn't."

"Yes, it was, I just had an undercut."

She proves that her hair was longer by plucking a strand and comparing it side-by-side with one of mine. I assure her I made the correct decision. We walk through a woodland area. The greenish tone makes it feel as though we're in "The Matrix." We find ourselves on the only two-way street in a coastal town. A green sign indicates we're walking along "California" street.]

[1165.3 / 3162] [I have a breakup, or end a friendship. I write my farewell in purple ink while sitting across from the person. The letter is applicable to a number of, *"friends with either outdated or voided contracts."* At the conclusion of writing the letter, we decide where we want to go for dinner. He says he wants pizza.

"That's fine. Let me go collect the change I left in the vending machine so I can pay for it."

I walk to the machine, insert my arm into the snack slot, and as I sweep my lengthened arm from left-to-right, I find piles of stacked coins, wads of $20 bills bound together with paper clips, and multiple phones with cracked screens. The friend goes to grab the $20's.

I smack his hand and say, ***"Those are mine. You know that."***

Among the artifacts I pull from the vending machine are books that have warped pages, damaged by water. One of the covers has an image of ADOLF HITLER with his arms and legs cut off. His eyes are gouged out. Every hole/wound in his body has been packed full with sawdust and straw.]

[1165.4 / 3163] [THE LITTLE PRINCE cries until he's picked up and placed on THE ATHEIST's lap.] //

⁂

Maj. = 0-THE WEAVER: #1174, 8-THE ATHEIST: #1211, 12- THE LITTLE PRINCE: # 1166

PIZZA: #1329

CONCLUSION: #1319

⁂

#1166 - April 30, 2020 @ 06:54 (San Francisco, California)

[1166.1 / 3164] [THE DRUM MAJOR *(dedicated, methodical, and coy)* is getting married on the ground floor of a multi-level church. His entire family attends the ceremony. I take an escalator up to another level of the church. THE ROBOT and THE RAPTOR assign me to a special task for another wedding.

I'm to help them, *"facilitate the release of an Asian family from prison, so THE RAPTOR will receive his parade."*

I ascend to another level, and briefly encounter THE THINKER and THE FEELER. I meet a lesbian working the reservation desk named "Linda Evans" who is quick to point out she's, *"never been on TV and she is not to be confused with the actress of the same name."*]

[1166.2 / 3165] [I sit on a bed with THE CONNECTOR and another man debating *"the utility of video games."* I suggest they're not worthwhile. She's invited us over to watch TV with a group of friends. We're not aware we've been enrolled in a speed dating game. After a variety of interactions, I go to a hotel lobby where I'm accosted by a mobster who carries a large tray piled high with basketball-sized tomatoes. When the tops of the tomatoes are removed, they reveal the severed animatronic heads of people I've speed dated, resting inside, coated with seeds and red soupy residue. It's upsetting and bizarre.]

[1166.3 / 3166] [THE LITTLE PRINCE has been freshly bathed and lays naked on a countertop. He flips and falls towards the floor. I reach out and catch him on my forearm.] //

⁂

Maj.* = *4-THE CONNECTOR: #1168, 12-THE LITTLE PRINCE: # 1171
Min. = *♠-THE THINKER: #1215, ♥-THE ROBOT: # 1189,*
♦- THE RAPTOR: #1189, ♣-THE FEELER: # 1215
NAKED: #1280, #1299
CHURCH: #1226, #1264
HOTEL: #1203, #1222, #1229, #1255

⁂

#1167 - **May 1, 2020 @ 02:53 (San Francisco, California)**

[1167.1 / 3167] [I'm backstage at a concert, preparing to take the stage with a slew of costumed backup dancers. We're lined up in a single file serpentine pattern from one end of a long corridor to another. We give high fives and hugs as we advance towards the performance space. Once the house lights are up, a female pop star in a sparkling diamond dress sings in the center of a square shaped stage. I and other performers are positioned as nodes in a square grid around her. Some elements feel like we're tap dancing, or rapping canes, at an HBCU sorority step show.]

[1167.2 / 3168] [***"I'm 114 years old. Alcohol is the thing that killed those I love the fastest,"*** I declare while standing at a grocery check-out musing about how much everything will hurt, were I to actually live that long. I start thinking about how to protect my joints, bones, and muscles.]

[1167.3 / 3169] [A serial killer drives a car on a mountain highway. I sit behind him. I wave and yell at a woman on a bike who approaches from the opposite direction. She doesn't respond when I flail out the window. He parks the car. I watch him enter a restaurant and take a seat across from a prospective victim. Both men have wild black and grey hair. I blink once and observe the man crushing the dead body of the other man in an industrial trash compactor in an alley behind the restaurant. My surroundings suggest I'm near the Port Authority of New Jersey.] //

⁂

DIAMOND: #1248, #1293
WINDOW: #1205, #1208, #1209
GRID: #1284, #1295
HURT: #1334

⁂

#1168 - May 2, 2020 @ 00:47 (San Francisco, California)

[1168.1 / 3170] [I'm on the ground floor of a house. I ascend to the second level. The landlord lives above me. Her name is "Jennifer." THE LAWYER joins me as I take ownership of the property. I'm eager to show him a photograph that rests atop a TV on a mantle over a bar, as we ready the space for move in. THE CONNECTOR appears and informs me I've, *"finally arrived in San Francisco."*

I learn THE ACTOR used to inhabit the ground floor and vacated the property this morning, after living here for nearly a decade. I don't have the opportunity to say hello to him, or to wish him well on his next adventure. As we clean the space, the photograph disappears as I attempt to grab it. I reappear at a *(seemingly random)* new place in the house each time I attempt to grab the photo.

"Jennifer" comes inside my home. As I inquire as to the nature of her relationship with THE ACTOR, she's quick to express,

"Oh, I just love him! We were restaurant buddies for years. We would frequently go out on the town together. Perhaps we can strike up a similar situation."

"That'd be great. Honestly, I'm a bit confused because for a moment I thought that I dated him for a while when I lived on the other side of town. It's humorous that I lived above him all this time and never even knew it."

"You didn't. He just moved out an hour ago."

"Oh yeah, right. Derp."]

[1168.2 / 3171] [I stand out front of my new home on the small, manicured lawn. I observe a house across the street be built, lived in, and burned down many times in time-lapse-rapid succession. It's as though years pass in mere moments, just across the asphalt divide.

ANDREW W.K. is briefly a neighbor in one of the house's earlier life cycles. On the eighth round, the house is left to decay. The windows are smashed, then quickly boarded up with plywood, which becomes graffiti laden.

The dilapidated structure is doused with gasoline and set alight by a mysterious, bodiless hand that floats and pulses a few feet above the ground.

The mood is easy, playful and lighthearted.] //

⁂

Maj. = 4- THE CONNECTOR: #1191, 5- THE LAWYER: #1181, 10- THE ACTOR: #1206
ANDREW W.K.: #1248
HELLO: #1236, #1254, #1339
FLOATS: #1318, #1330

PLYWOOD: #1221, #1256

⁂

#1169 - May 2, 2020 @ 07:50 (San Francisco, California)

[1169.1 / 3172] [I'm on a gameshow where I'm tasked to crawl across a ceiling, while attached to a belay rope and harness on an overhead track. Tension from the rope allows me to stay tethered within inches of a blue lane, populated with different rows of oversized donuts hanging on strings. Sugar dusted, chocolate frosted, and other types whiz by as I collect and eat them, while advancing along the track. It becomes confusing and intense for a moment when competition breaks out between me and other members of my team, the host of the show, and, *"the person who took responsibility for setting up the course."*

The course warden sits on a couch behind me and kicks me hard once in the back.]

[1169.2 / 3173] [I've cleaned the house and unintentionally soiled the back of a white dress shirt with gloppy clumps of a fudgy brown sludge, sticky like molasses or tar. Rinsing with water doesn't release the stain. The only other white dress shirt I have has been similarly ruined by small patches and splotches of yellow paint.] //

⁂

WHIZ: #1258, #1275
ROPE: #1309, #1341
PAINT: #1241, #1276, #1311, #1327
STAIN: #1250

⁂

#1170 - May 3, 2020 @ 03:47 (San Francisco, California)

[1170.1 / 3174] [The scene is greyscale. I wander a residential neighborhood with a woman who resembles "FLEABAG." We leave the street whilst pushing a shopping cart. We enter a warehouse in search of a package that contains a book as we pass, *"questionable people doing questionable things."* Once we find the book, I immediately go home. While walking, I spot and wave to a male and female neighbor from afar. From outside they're grey, though I know he wears green, and she wears a warm shade of peach.

When I enter my home, the world ruptures and aches with vibrant color. I fall silent. I hand the book to an African American woman wearing a hijab. When she opens the book, it casts a brown light across her face, illuminating her in a rich shade of mocha. A father figure sits at an ovular dining table made of white marble, surrounded by hovering emerald encrusted ornaments. He works at a computer. I offer him a nod as I pass through the dining room without speaking.

I turn through the kitchen and hear a college aged man say, *"You're here! Go in there and make yourself comfy,"* as he guides me to a living room filled with Christmas decorations, a cheese tray, grapes, and gifts.

A miniature train on a track encircles the base of the tree.

My mouth waters. As I move towards the appetizer table to eat, a bell rings at the door. The young man welcomes the neighbors who say,

"We want to speak to your guest," they say entering the room and catching me with my mouth full.

"What have you been up to?" I'm asked.

I drop my arms to my side. The plate and napkin drop to the floor along with some cubes of white cheddar cheese as I break my silence and say,

"Throwing myself before the grace of God, and asking for the aligned guidance I need on the day, in the moment... And you can do it too! One day you may find yourself talking to Zeus. On another day, Juno. Other days, guidance may come from a 'pixie.' Maybe on occasion you'll encounter an angel from the highest choir? Just remember to ask. Ask every morning. Ask every moment. Ask and it's given."] //

⁂

AFRICAN AMERICAN: #1205, #1232, #1331, #1335
REMEMBER: #1220, #1228, #1277
ASK: #1284, #1295, #1297

⁂

#1171 - May 3, 2020 @ 05:49 (San Francisco, California)

[1171.1 / 3175] [I descend an elevator into a basement where I find THE CARPENTER, who learns how to use a peer-to-peer payment app. He's amazed when he instantly receives $500 as a test transaction, for a job he's scheduled to complete on a future date.]

[1171.2 / 3176] [I sit in front of a DOS computer screen attempting to access a game, played by other members of a team.]

[1171.3 / 3177] [Sacred items are tagged for sale at a grand cathedral. A table is listed for $10,370.

"LUCAS DVORAK?! I'll respect anyone who knows who he is!" A guy says as I look for artifacts to purchase.

"You mean, the master map maker? I've followed his work for years."

My response spurs the man to invite me into a secret chamber in the cathedral, where I'm permitted to experiment with a variety of heart-shaped whistles fashioned from precious metals. Some whistles are made of carnival glass and filled with glass beads that create fluttering staccato tones when breathed.

"P Drdrdrdr Dr Pl Bdpl Bdpl Bdp Lbdp Lbd!"

One of the bb's from a tiny whistle I audit, falls into my mouth. I spit it back into the instrument.

THE CHILD enters the chamber. We're excited to watch a parade.

"Respect please," she requests as we line up by a stained-glass window.

I'm excited. If I'm lucky, I'll be able to hold THE LITTLE PRINCE when the family arrives. I'm doubly excited by the prospect of introducing everyone to THE MAGICIAN after he concludes emceeing the parade. As we stand by the window watching the parade, my mind becomes fixated on taking home a heart shaped, *"ribbon whistle."*]

⁂

Maj. = 1-THE CARPENTER: #1184, 3- THE CHILD: #1172,
12- THE LITTLE PRINCE: #1201, 14-THE MAGICIAN: #1196
GLASS: #1223, #1235, #1240
EXPERIMENT: #1221, #1298
⁂

#1172 - May 3, 2020 @ 07:31 (San Francisco, California)

[1172.1 / 3178] [I'm on a cruise ship out at sea. I descend to a subdeck and watch MIKE PENCE give a demonstration on how to access a *"backup network"* without providing any visual aids that demonstrate the interface.

"It would be helpful if you would present what you're doing on a screen so others can watch...you stupid fuck (whispered)."

I proceed down a hallway, and turn right into a cabin where I see THE CHILD donning a party dress, and a manicure of gold sequins. ***"They're so glittery!"*** I exclaim as I usher her towards an elementary school event. She sits in front of a giant wooden table with a grid of hundreds of small hemisphere divots, which fill with small pastel bbs as children toss them by the handful. They fall and roll to the divots in unexpectedly beautiful and complex patterns. A glowing light passes beneath the table from left-to-right, creating *"the music of randomness."*

As the children play, a machine learning instructor informs THE DANCER:

"This lesson is cumulative. You have to fill everything out in advance before you can participate in this level. Be sure you place a cover over the icon of 'the Indian's' and one other avatar of your choosing at the base of the table. They're lit white for you to help assist with your selection. You must do this if you want the machine to function properly."]

[1172.2 / 3179] [I help a team of people complete an acting scene, with the support of a coach. The scene focuses on the adventures of a bellhop. The scene progresses through a desert and culminates with the lead actor navigating his way up a serpentine anthill-like passage composed of gritty sand. A time constraint, if unsatisfied, will result in the acting crew forfeiting $860MM in prize money. I'm hopeful they'll give me a kickback, because without my help the bellhop would not complete the task, and the crew would walk away with nothing.

"Maybe we'll set up an NGO or non-profit with the winnings?"

I think the key player is more interested in purchasing 26 private residences. I watch him scout property online, in various neighborhoods. His interests turn toward a huge white mansion on a corner lot with a gigantic dodecagonal bay window. A massive translucent chandelier mounted like a series of holographic razorblades suspended inches from the ceil-ing, hasbecome a conversation piece for the neighborhood. The home is world renowned for its architecture.] //

⁂
Maj. = 2-THE DANCER: #1183, 3-THE CHILD: #1178
NETWORK: #1318, #1323
MUSIC: #1284, #1293
PRIZE: #1237, #1303
⁂

#1173 - May 4, 2020 @ 05:46 (San Francisco, California)

[1173.1 / 3180] [I'm in a house where competitors are ranked from #1 to #30. They each design iron-on patches and contribute them to an oversized blue and white oxford shirt. Others look on as I continue to dutifully iron and seal patches to both sides of the shirt. Some people second guess where they've placed their patches and want to take them home after they've been adhered to the shirt.]

[1173.2 / 3181] [A young boy is intrigued by a math book. He reads problems he's previously solved, way into the wee hours of the night, with a flashlight. ***"Solutions and familiarity soothe him."***]

[1173.3 / 3182] [I quickly drive down an interstate with a group. One moment I'm on a city bus. The next I'm in a limousine. Someone famous may be at the back of the limo. We drive through a garage to avoid crowds of fans. We realize we've backtracked down a route we've previously traveled. ***"We'll likely be late to our intended destination."***]

[1173.4 / 3183] [Inside a house, a one-armed woman paints a wall and drips white satin liquid on the hardwood floor. A man who lives in the house *(and also shares an onsite workspace with his partner)* reveals he's been beaten repeatedly and severely. He hides the wounds on the left side of his face under layers of makeup.] //

⁂

MATH: #1301, #1331
LIMO: #1336
WOUNDS: #1220, #1271
FANS: 1272

⁂

#1174 - May 5, 2020 @ 05:02 (San Francisco, California)

[1174.1 / 3184] [I'm served a slice of "Red Mamba" cake as I stand in line with a group of similarly aged people. My trousers are inspected by a murder-of-floating-finger-pointing hands after I wet them.]

[1174.2 / 3185] [I'm at a house with THE WEAVER where we watch episodes of a TV show. We pick up the series in the fifth season, then decide to skip ahead to *"Season 20"*. The only notable change in the plot, tone, and characterization is the female lead has aged tremendously. The skin on her face proudly droops without makeup. We keep watching. After a few episodes, I exit the room in search of someplace to urinate. I peer inside a china cabinet that opens at waist level. I'm told it's a reasonable place to *"go"* since, *"there's only one set of china and an old picnic basket, within."* I soak the entire contents of the cabinet.] //

⁂

⁂

Maj. = 0-THE WEAVER: #1177
EXIT: #1205, #1217, #1228, #1234
SOAK: #1250, #1280
SEASON: #1256, #1299

⁂

#1175 - May 5, 2020 @ 09:07 (San Francisco, California)

[1175.1 / 3186] [I'm cleaning the house. While in the bedroom, I gather all the dust and fuzz balls from the carpets into a pile in the middle of the room. Upon inspection, I notice a variety of vitamins and pills scattered within the discarded pile. I become bored with cleaning and decide to masturbate. I've paid no attention to what I've chosen as lubricant. I look down and see my groin soiled with WD-40, which has dripped down my legs and formed dark oily pools on the white Berber carpet.

"I don't know how I'm going to clean up this new, larger mess."]

[1175.2 / 3187] [I walk down the back of an empty amphitheater, eager to register for a retreat. I've anticipated attending the retreat for months. I keep an eye out for my sponsor and group leader as I walk toward a table of people *(who from afar)* I see are busy assembling name tags and welcome packets for those enrolled. As I pass by a group of people seated in the back row of the amphitheater, I hear a breathy *"AHEM!"* from behind.

"Oh! You're wearing a disguise. I didn't recognize you," I say to my group leader as she shapeshifts back into a woman.

We both laugh at her prank.] //

⁂

OILY: #1231, #1295
CLEANING: #1228, #1259, #1300
DUST: #1343
EMPTY: #1208, #1251, #1258

⁂

#1176 - May 6, 2020 @ 03:44 (San Francisco, California)

[1176.1 / 3188] [I ride in a slow serpentine pattern in a boat around the interior of a house with low light *(akin to a "Tunnel of Love" ride)*. Plated food is reachable from the boat. It moves along a conveyor belt that flows in the opposite direction from the river. I grab a mug and wait to pass a coffee station. The regular coffee is empty. Decaffeinated brown water spurts into my cup as I slowly sail by.

"There is nothing to dress up the coffee with. No dairy. No sugar."]

[1176.2 / 3189] [I'm a restaurateur. I'm next to a group of people who've set up their food trucks uniformly in a row for a large public event, possibly a competition hosted by the public health department of our local municipality.

"We should wait to see who succeeds here and use their lessons learned to inform how to best jump start our reopening," I whisper to my business partner.]

[1176.3 / 3190] [I'm a contestant on a gameshow, which takes place in a mansion. One of the challenges is navigating a maze-like series of basement rooms. It seems haunted. I'm probably surrounded by ghosts, bu not frightened nor distracted by their presence. In one puzzle, I work with a partner to, *"inspire BRITNEY SPEARS to return to the stage to perform for sold out crowds."* We succeed. When we emerge together from the basement, I'm permitted to stay and offered an *"up level opportunity."*

Once on the main floor, the subsequent challenge involves having hot sauce squirted into my eyes. I'm paired up with a person from Berlin. Their gender is not specified. It's unclear which role I will embody. ***"Will I be the squirter? Will they?"*** A young man recently eliminated from the competition takes off his shirt and reveals he's wearing a heart rate monitor. As he jogs away, I grab him by the arm and say,

"You know I love you, right?"

"I know. I hear it. I just don't believe it yet..." his words trail off as he jogs out of the mansion, and down a cobblestone path towards the sunset.]

[1176.4 / 3191] [I may be in Colorado. I walk across the fences of backyards that segment different large parcels of land. The properties surrounded by the fences are upscale and luxurious. My entire family proceeds in a row, playfully balancing with our arms out as we walk along the fence tops. The mountains in the distance are breathtakingly beautiful. I jump off the fence when I see a laptop left on a glass table in a backyard, open to a login prompt. I reset my network password, which unlocks a secret pathway for us to advance along. We walk into the light and dissolve as I wake up.] //

⁂

BRITNEY SPEARS: #1249
SLOW: #1295, #1318
COBBLESTONE: #1246, #1274, #1278
EYES: #1280, #1281, #1284, #1301
MOUNTAIN: #1274, #1286, #1291, #1324

⁂

#1177 - May 7, 2020 @ 00:37 (San Francisco, California)

[1177.1 / 3192] [I'm at a library in the middle of a park. I walk through the property to an amphitheater where THE HILLBILLY and others are recognized for their service work during a recent large scale community crisis. A gift has been given; a stone cube with a hollowed-out space in its center, viewable from all angles.

"Is it a tesseract?"

A knot can be woven around the interior with a series of deconstructed cardboard boxes.

I'm surprised when I learn the mother of THE PERFORMANCE ARTIST *(inspired, fecund, and authentic)* wrote the poem recited to award recipients at the ceremony.

"My original intention was curiosity."

I observe the recitation of the poem and am moved to acknowledge the mother *(referred to as "Mary")*, as a group attempts to wind the cardboard-box-knot on the interior of the hypercube. They encounter problems completing the task. I intercede and weave the complex pattern in roughly a dozen steps, as the poem continues. A hush falls over the crowd. Many don't understand what they've just observed.

ping ping ping ping ping ping...DONE

I look up at the crowd of stunned faces and state, ***"I definitely practiced this before I got here. I just didn't know how to do it."*** The comment brings out some chuckles.

As the poem concludes, it brings me to tears. I charge forward, startling some with my unexpected presence.

"Mary,' I didn't know you were going to be here," I say to her as she sits next to a similarly ancient friend on a stone theater bench *(both wearing pastel dresses and Easter bonnets).*

"Baby, I always have and always will...be here for you," "Mary" promises.

I glance towards THE WEAVER and say, ***"I love you,"*** then look back at "Mary" saying, ***"...and Mama' I love you too."***

THE WEAVER understands the impact the old woman has made. As I hug "Mary," the sensation of divine love becomes so powerful that it wakes me up, with tear filled eyes.

THE LAST STANZA OF "MARY'S" poem:

"Baby, I know who you really are. I don't need to know your name."] //

⁂

Maj. 0-THE WEAVER: #1178
Min. = ♣- THE HILLBILLY: #1248
MARY: #1336
I LOVE: #1332
POEM: #1305
THE PERFORMANCE ARTIST: #1414

⁂

#1178 - May 7, 2020 @ 03:28 (San Francisco, California)

[1178.1 / 3193] [Groups of people play volleyball with balloons.]

[1178.2 / 3194] [I encounter THE TRANSLATOR. I give her a string of numbers I received during a recent transmission, including: *"ONE. POSITIVE THREE. ONE PERCENT TILT."*

In the midst of this she says, *"Remind me. Tell me '**dragon**,' later."*

I create a voice memo as I walk up a sidewalk towards a schoolhouse with yellow lit windows. THE NEUTRAL GUIDE sits quietly by the door in a rocking chair, reading a book.]

[1178.3 / 3195] [When I approach the window, the family stands around me. THE WEAVER says, *"Someone's here to see you!"* as she draws back a curtain, revealing THE CHILD on the opposite side of the window who yells, *"SURPRISE!"*

I feel sad because I'm not able to go outside and give her a hug.] //

⁂

Maj. = 0- THE WEAVER: #1183, 3- THE CHILD: #1201, 19- THE TRANSLATOR: #1388
Min. = ♥- THE NEUTRAL GUIDE: #1179
SURPRISE: #1284, #1343
TILT: #1307
BOOK: #1229, #1252

⁂

#1179 - May 7, 2020 @ 04:54 (San Francisco, California)

[1179.1 / 3196] [Five levels deep in dream, I record videos of THE DEVOTEE and THE NEUTRAL GUIDE at a retreat, though I don't physically attend, and I've never previously been to the venue. The timeline of the videos runs from the future, to past. I'm committed to record THE DEVOTEE from behind as I watch her bubble and space expand while she gives a public presentation on *"vibrational healing."* Children are present. It generally feels lighthearted. It may be a celebration of THE WORLDBRIDGER's lifetime of service to "the school." He may be contemplating departing the planet. He's dressed in olive-green-toned desert garb. His head is wrapped. He stands with a group of teachers having a meeting, one of whom is particularly excited by, *"the discovery of a central pattern."* The teacher now understands why he becomes triggered by sentences that start with decapitalized "t's."]

[1179.2 / 3197] [I walk towards a classroom and stand at the back with another small group of people. A woman dutifully gathers rolled up blueprints and places them under her arm in a honeycomb-like pattern. THE WORLDBRIDGER pops his head through the doorway and says, *"What's missing from this room?"*

Looking back over her shoulder, the woman pauses and mutters, *"The babies. That's right. I don't love my babies either."*

I'm taken aback by what sounds like an extreme comment. We drop the words through the grounding cord of the floor, invite healing energy to fill the space in the woman's bubble, and continue preparing for class. It feels like there are lurking things that want to be given a voice, but I'm not certain as to what they are.]

[1179.3 / 3198] [I record the prior two scenes, four times. My phone captures so much content it overloads the device, the images flicker, and I'm unsure if it has enough memory to capture it all. It doesn't. I wake up.] //

⁂

Maj. = 9- THE WORLDBRIDGER: #1187
Min. = ♠- THE DEVOTEE: #1289
PLANET: #1240, #1367
MEETING: #1243, #1291
BUBBLE: #1271

⁂

#1180 - May 7, 2020 @ 05:46 (San Francisco, California)

[1180.1 / 3199] [I stand across from LADY GAGA and ask her about her auditions for recording executives.

"You're talented, so you didn't have to fake it to make it like 'another' star. Would you mind commenting on the nature of that circumstance?"

"Look. Get ready for me to swear a lot. Let's walk."

She launches into a story about how one of her best male friends was denied a career because of the *"anonymous celebrity"* referenced. We walk down a staircase, and out a set of doors to the street before jumping into a pistachio-colored convertible.]

[1180.2 / 3200] [I find myself unwilling to date other people because ***"I'm comfortable with my circumstances."***

My assumption is, ***"anyone I would choose to date would likely be abusive or 'fucked up' in some sort of way."***] //

[1180.3 / 3201] [I stand next to the parked pistachio convertible. THE LOBBYIST wears a seersucker suit and leans against the vehicle while speaking to me:

*"Ooh, you're something. You can travel by either fancy car or... '**balon**.'"*

His absurd impression of a French accent causes me to buckle in half with laughter. I laugh so hard I wake up.] //

⁂

Maj. = 17- THE LOBBYIST: #1188

LADY GAGA: #1215

CONVERTIBLE: #1237, #1252, #1269

ABSURD: #1219

⁂

#1181 - May 8, 2020 @ 01:38 (San Francisco, California)

[1181.1 / 3202] [I'm in a funhouse game with THE LAWYER and a bunch of others. We compete to avoid being attacked by packs of wild animals *(Baboons, Tigers, and The Minotaur)*. All manner of creepy critters crawl around the interior walls of the house, floor, and ceiling. Giant screw-like cylindrical valves connect different areas of the property, threaded along the edges.

I teleport to different regions of the property. Some rooms are carpeted. Others have mosaic tiled floors. Some are dark. Some are light. Diamond shaped "accelerator pads" *(that look like giant floor jacks when viewed from above)* jettison players back through clear tubes to their point of origin at incredible speed, when touched.

I hold a magic wand. I can use it with moderate proficiency to keep the wild animals at bay. Thrash punk rock music serves as the soundtrack, while the game is active. I bound between different levels of the house with a single jump. The action starts fast and quickens. It's almost like I'm on a racetrack as I speed from point-to-point.

I realize at the conclusion of the game's first round, no one wants to continue. None of us want to *"get hurt."* We become aware that each of us have been selected to represent our **unique breed of monkey**.] //

⁂

Maj. = 5-THE LAWYER: #1193
INTERIOR: #1258, #1274, #1287, #1300
MOSAIC: #1337

⁂

#1182 - May 8, 2020 @ 06:19 (San Francisco, California)

[1182.1 / 3203] [I'm a teenage boy. I'm in the woods with others of the same age discussing different methods to trick our punk-rock-camp counselors. We hide fireworks in different sized boxes, which we later carry across the property on a 6' long plastic card table. One of the counselors is aware of what our crew is up to. Though one big "BOOM" and "BANG" from an explosion in a box on the table unexpectedly startles him.]

[1182.2 / 3204] [We're at an apartment. Various items on a shelf, including multiple video games and movies, contribute clues to a trivia game that ultimately determines the amount of explosive we can pack in our homemade fireworks.]

[1182.3 / 3205] [We're ushered to our box seats just before the curtain rises for an opera. Tonight's performance is Wagner. Our group is guided to watch from, *"a bed that seats three across."*] //

⁂

OPERA: #1213, #1242, #1248
PLASTIC: #1255, #1256, #1277
PUNK: #1336
CLUES: #1286, #1318

⁂

#1183 - May 10, 2020 @ 04:54 (San Francisco, California)

[1183.1 / 3206] [I'm at the rehearsal dinner the night before my wedding. We've gathered in a subway station. My husband-to-be is a cute young man. THE DANCER is my "Best Buddy."

"My Best Person."

She's concerned about something someone posted on my fiancé's social media account.

"I don't have it. I don't use it. I don't care what's on it. It's his business. He can tell me about it if he wants," I say to diffuse the tension.

My fiancé and I walk together down a staircase that splits in two halves down the middle. I choose the "Bad Boy" side and hop down from top-to-bottom on my left foot. He and I separate, and say good night. Soon after, I realize I don't have my glasses, and can't see. I've found a way to pay for the ceremony, the reception, and the rehearsal dinner but THE WEAVER objects.

"No, that's what your fiancé's family is supposed to do. Let them take care of it," she claims.

"I hadn't considered that possibility."

The next morning, I want support from THE DANCER, but she remains somewhat of a trickster.

"Can you please stop with the jokes? I just want to be with you today."

"Just ignore me!"

"I don't want to ignore you. I invited you here for a reason."]

[1183.2 / 3207] [I'm in London in a tube station. I meet up with some friends. I've brought along a series of colorful bath towels in paper shopping bags. My friends express a desire to take them home, but I intend to leave with all of them later. The subway system has a technology that scans the pressure of a passenger's eyes to confirm their identity and validate basic vital signs. Those with elevated temperatures are not permitted to ride. My friends are surprised when I offer to go to work with them, since I'm supposedly in London on vacation. The remainder of the ride is spent listening to recordings a popular band recently made in the subway tunnel.]

[1183.3 / 3208] [THE WEAVER is in the water. I'm on the shore. We see a wave in the distance and are worried for a moment that it will overtake us. THE WEAVER exits the water as the swell rolls in. We embrace, expecting to be swept apart and drowned. The wave crests and breaks. A small slosh of water hits our ankles.]

[1183.4 / 3209] [A guy purchases new hardware so he can hold video conference dates with his girlfriend.] //

⁂

Maj. = 0-THE WEAVER: #1186, 2-THE DANCER: # 1191
LONDON: #1220
ELEVATED: #1256, #1292
MIDDLE: #1330, #1331, #1336
WAVE: #1208, #1322, #1339

⁂

#1184 - May 11, 2020 @ 05:58 (San Francisco, California)

[1184.1 / 3210] [I'm sequestered in a hotel. I punch and crack a vertically-mounted wall-sized TV screen in a conference room. DONALD TRUMP stands nearby and seems offended.

"Go fuck yourself. I'll pay for it," I say as I walk away.

THE COWBOY *(rugged, handsome, and reborn)* runs hotel check out. He doesn't remember me, even though I can describe exactly what he looks like naked. My flirting has jeopardized my seat on a flight. I look for THE CARPENTER, then decide to walk to the airport by exiting the hotel, and trudging up a grassy hill in the direction of a bridge.]

. . .

[1184.2 / 3211] [I'm handed a box of my recent exam papers. I receive all D's. A couple of notes from the teacher in red ink read, *"See Me."* My work is incomplete. I've left the back-sides of some pages totally blank.]

[1184.3 / 3212] [Gang violence. I'm a woman. I'm shot in the mouth in slow motion. I can see the bullet race towards my face. It strikes and splits my teeth, scattering them like bowling pins. The roof of my mouth sears. I can taste burning blood on the back of my tongue. I'm worried I'm going to die as I feel pressure at the back of my skull increase.] //

⁂

Maj. = 1- THE CARPENTER: #1186
DONALD TRUMP #1382
GRASSY HILL: #1235
GANG: #1275, #1343
SLOW: #1237, #1249, #1295, #1318
SKULL: #1224, #1271, #1283, #1292

⁂

#1185 - May 12, 2020 @ 06:36 (San Francisco, California)

[1185.1 / 3213] [I have sex with THE PASSIONATE BRAZILIAN *(subtle, gentle, and open)* multiple times. He's in an open relationship. His husband is in the other room. It's playful and free. Most of the interaction takes place on a couch.]

[1185.2 / 3214] [I have a partner who's in a heterosexual marriage, intending to acquire a green card. He's concerned he's not going to be able to get a prescription filled. He requests, *"the special blue capsules that 'puff' when you place them in your palm."*]

[1185.3 / 3215] [I'm in a grove on a sunny wedding day, with a wedding party. I push GREAT GRANDMOTHER *(venerated, revered, and storied)* in her wheelchair under the shade of a palm tree for family photos. My expressions are awkward. My gaze in the images is downcast. I Photoshop a smile on my face, after the fact.]

[1185.4 / 3216] [THE SOUL SINGER *(vulnerable, feminine, and poetic)* resides in a doorless room at her residence. The space is softly lit. Visages of strong female beings are framed and proudly displayed on the walls. I'm captivated by an image of the Virgin Mary. THE REPATRIATES *(partnered, balanced, and grounded)* drift through a wall, surprised to see me. The reason for their visit is not clear, but I'm excited to see them.] //

⁂

GREAT GRANDMOTHER: #1255
WEDDING: #1241, #1280, #1320
BLUE: #1242, #1246, #1250, #1252
GAZE: #1256, #1282, #1318

VISIT: #1203, #1215, #1264

⁂

#1186 - May 13, 2020 @ 22:47 (San Francisco, California)

[1186.1 / 3217] [I ride in the backseat of a car at night. The air conditioning is supposedly on, but it feels so hot to me that my hands seem to be on fire. I repeatedly express my sensations of extreme heat to THE WEAVER and THE CARPENTER.

"It seems really hot in here. Can you do anything about it?" They don't understand.

When we arrive home, I promptly fall asleep on the floor, later waking up in a four-inch-deep layer of water that has flooded the entire area, and covers my hands well above the wrist as I press myself up. The water pours from a lit, modern master bathroom, through a hardwood floored master bedroom, and spills down a stairwell to the left like a dripping zig zagged waterfall to a floor below. As we mop up the liquid, my hands feel scorching hot while under the water, even though I'm assured by a guide that the water is cold.

The source of the leak is a loose shower fixture shaped like a "Y," a recent upgrade installed by THE ARCHITECT and THE DESIGNER. Water spurts from the top left arm of the "Y." I tighten the device to stop the leak, and point it towards a drain. Then, I search for a mop.]

[1186.2 / 3218] [A dad sells devices *(shower nozzles)* door-to-door. He's proud to tell his son he made his sales numbers for the month.]

[1186.3 / 3219] [I stand in the room of a child and extend my hands, offering healing while they sleep. Once complete, I join a group of friends to share our experiences. I'm afraid to express my knowing:

"The fire I experience flow through my hands is a healing tone of the divine."]

⁂

Maj. = 0- THE WEAVER: #1199, 1- THE CARPENTER: #1188

Min. = ♥-THE ARCHITECT: #1197, ♠-THE DESIGNER: # 1429

GUIDE: #1249, #1255, #1273

HOT: #1283, #1300

COLD: #1284, #1304

DIVINE: #1329

⁂

#1187 - May 14, 2020 @ 00:44 (San Francisco, California)

[1187.1 / 3220] [I attend a meditation class. I've checked in to a hotel with the intention of going to another "late night" class at a different location. I take a nap. I oversleep. People leave. I have challenges gathering my personal items, as I scramble to join them. My wallet is in the incorrect drawer. My credit cards are in the wrong holder. My shiny pink wallet is irrationally shaped. It closes flat. When opened, a tube to hold vertical stacks of quarters and toothpicks protrudes up from the fold.

I take an elevator to the ground floor. When I reach the bottom, I hear a woman working the night shift *(perhaps a being called "NAOMI?")* help clear rental car transactions on the hotel's register. I'm worried I'm going to miss a class led by THE WORLDBRIDGER, but I remember I don't have to physically be there, though the group has piled together *(in body)* in a 15-passenger van. I can still see where they are *(and what they're doing)* on my mental screen.]

[1187.2 / 3221] [Numerous sequences on a plane. I travel with a guy who always, *"gets the seat that he wants, when he wants it."* Some trips find him asking people in first class to relocate. On another, he gets an aisle seat upon first request. I go to the back corner of the plane. I take down the tray table and lay across it to catch a few winks. Each time I lay my head down, the plane nosedives into freefall.

"I'm in class! I've fallen asleep!"

I have nothing to worry about. Every time someone makes a comment about the beverage service, it causes the plane to rapidly lose altitude.]

[1187.3 / 3222] [I'm on a fast-moving train that collides with another slower train that runs in the same direction. Irrationally, after we crash our train casually rolls by the other train as though nothing happened. The other train slowed to accommodate a hobo wandering ahead of it on the tracks.]

[1187.4 / 3223] [I'm at a woodland retreat center. I've taken out my recorder because I believe I've said something *"intelligent"* or *"memorable"* to help a man and woman mend some core challenges in their relationship. I note that it's been recording for 993 minutes nonstop. I have no idea at what moment I said the thing I perceived to be, ***"smart."***] //

⁂

Maj. = 7- THE WORLDBRIDGER: #1200

15 PASSENGER VAN: #1343

FIRST: #1214, #1233

CENTER: #1241

⁂

#1188 - May 14, 2020 @ 06:05 (San Francisco, California)

[1188.1 / 3224] [It's the 1960's. I'm in a facility with painted brick walls decorated by previous visitors. I go with some friends through a "Congressional Security Entrance." A protest is underway inside the building. People angrily confront RICHARD NIXON. THE LOBBYIST has offered us access to the building. Flaky white paint between rows of bricks comes loose when I pick at it with my thumbnail, then peels away in long thick lengths as I pull on it. Messages are inscribed on the walls under the paint. Younger members of Congress *(early in their careers)* are protected by members of the secret service. The United States Men's Gymnastics team visited the facility a week ago. The carpet and the bathrooms were remodeled in celebration of their visit. I walk towards security and exit, dropping a chocolate baseball filled with candied orange wedges. I pick it up and eat the chocolate as I realize I may not be able to enter again. ***"I've crossed the threshold."***]

. . .

[1188.2 / 3225] [I search for different properties in California that are walkable to downtown. One's suburban, set on small tiers of wheat that ascend street-by-street to the edge of the housing development. One's in a country club. I wear a white T-Shirt and white shorts as I tour the properties. I don't seem to fit in the affluent neighborhood. Something about the properties feels fake and misleading.]

[1188.3 / 3226] [I'm with THE CARPENTER. We walk to the top of a staircase inside a house where he draws a shotgun and shoots at birds who have perched and nested on the semicircle window sills inside. We promptly depart the house by car. I drive. He attempts to distract me by offering a snack as I drive. A small refrigerator at his feet glows softly when he opens the door.]

[1188.4 / 3227] [A group of twelve young people have purchased a headboard made of flimsy particle board for $1000. They have the opportunity to transform the headboard into other products. One person suggests converting it into multiple sets of snow skis. The head entrepreneur, named "TARA" reminds the group that they, *"must hold on to the asset for an entire year before making any significant changes."* She discloses that her first love is bartending, and that she moonlights as an entrepreneur.] //

⁂

Maj. = 1- THE CARPENTER: #1190, 17- THE LOBBYIST: #1236
SEMI: #1235, #1278
CHOCOLATE: #1207, #1217, #1275
LOVE: #1332

⁂

#1189 - May 15, 2020 @ 04:50 (San Francisco, California)

[1189.1 / 3228] [THE VIOLINIST and THE BASS set up a tent at the mouth of a dirt road that exits a mountain highway. Every day, they walk from their trailer to the tent to perform for their patrons. When I walk towards the tent, I note THE RAPTOR and THE ROBOT have parked their semi-trailer in the neighboring lot. THE ROBOT lays face down in the dust. When I call her name, she stands and brushes herself off, then invites me to join her in the trailer. After a quick conversation, I'm made aware that she and THE RAPTOR are driving home for a couple of days, *"but will return to find their spot with the misfits later."*]

[1189.2 / 3229] [A guy plays the drums and throws one of his sticks into an empty city street surrounded by high rise buildings. He gets on a moped and speeds towards a large rope hundreds of feet long, which he grabs and uses to swing himself up a giant half pipe, and into the air overhead. He generates enough speed to keep the rope at tension. He stalls at the top and descends back down his path of ascent, perfectly meeting the edge of his tires to the lip of the half pipe on the return trip.]

. . .

[1189.3 / 3230] [Off to the side of the dirt road, I compose electronic music using a controller made of a series of tubes and pipes that run overhead and light up light a Tetris board when touched. The composition syncs with my laptop. The session is recorded.]

[1189.4 / 3231] [*"I HAVE ENOUGH."* I'm shown by a guide how to best prepare for a party. More fades that feels important, though I remember I'm taught something.] //

⁂

Min. = ♥- THE ROBOT: #1206, ♦- THE RAPTOR: #1206
TENSION: #1241, #1245, #1266
LAPTOP: #1310
DUST: #1343

⁂

#1190 - May 15, 2020 @ 07:48 (San Francisco, California)

[1190.1 / 3232] [I'm in a car with a husband and wife. The car pulls a trailer down a steep hill. We pick up speed. When the brakes are applied, the trailer flips. Its momentum whips the car around and sends the three of us tumbling around inside. I land on top of the wife. We're face to face. She's pregnant. The way we've landed *(surprisingly)* has protected the unborn child. We continue down the highway. ***"Appears we're on the way to Los Angeles."***]

[1190.2 / 3233] [In a hotel room. THE CARPENTER has purchased room service. THE AWAKENING *(fiery, masculine, and sought)* has taken residency in the room to the left. He's decided to delay his participation in a cycling event. A bald Navy Seal is holed up in another room with the blinds closed and the curtains drawn. The Navy Seal's done something he's not proud of, and debates surrender.] //

⁂

Maj. = 1- THE CARPENTER: #1191
STEEP: #1264, #1313
HUSBAND: #1224, #1246, #1295
WIFE: #1236, #1259, #1320
LOS ANGELES: #1248, #1259
THE AWAKENING: #1243

⁂

#1191 - May 16, 2020 @ 07:12 (San Francisco, California)

[1191.1 / 3234] [I take an exam proctored by a young man and an old woman. We're given the opportunity to review our notes just prior to the distribution of forms. The exam is one-page front and back, consisting of six specific questions on the content from a subchapter of a textbook. We must recreate the content verbatim. I don't know the answers.]

. . .

[1191.2 / 3235] [In an amusement park. All the rides in the park contain the word "DEMON" in their name *("DEMON DROP." "THE DEMON." "DEMON SPEED.")* We don't ride any of them. Overcast turns dark. THE CARPENTER, THE DANCER and I walk down a black asphalt path between two shallow grassy hills. The sprinkler system turns on and soaks us. We're happy and dance around.

We love that we, *"no longer have to stand in line for hours waiting for a water ride."*

I feel sad as I hold hands with THE DANCER. I realize I'm tugging her along, and have done so for most of my life. She takes the lead and guides me down a staircase.]

[1191.3 / 3236] [I'm in a canteen with THE CONNECTOR. We each order a glass of wine. THE CONNECTOR excuses herself to use the restroom. The server returns with three times the amount of wine we ordered. THE CONNECTOR returns as I goofily say,

"We've been overserved."

I have no idea how many ounces of wine I've consumed.] //

⁂

Maj. = 1- THE CARPENTER: #1195, 2- THE DANCER: #1208, 4- THE CONNECTOR: #1220

DEMON: #1208

SYSTEM: #1222, #1285

AMUSEMENT PARK: #1208, #1228, #1246, #1260, #1290

⁂

#1192 - May 17, 2020 @ 00:21 (San Francisco, California)

[1192.1 / 3237] [I sit at a computer while logging in and out of a variety of different online classes. I attend some for mere moments. Guidance suggests, *"It's ok to stay and receive just what you need. Every class. Every teaching is a healing."*

I have hundreds of sessions active when a pattern of octave tones emerges:

High...low, low, low.

Guidance proceeds, *"Every interaction contains an opportunity for the divine to mend itself. It's useful to not linger."*] //

⁂

HIGH: #1301, #1326, #1328, #1332

LOW: #1207, #1209, #1260, #1261

RECEIVE: #1206, #1245, #1248

⁂

#1193 - May 17, 2020 @ 01:33 (San Francisco, California)

[1193.1 / 3238] [I create an agreement to, *"hold my body at a specific frequency."* My bedroom is held at another. My home, yet another. As I sit and meditate, I acknowledge there are infinite agreements that occur at various levels of awareness. The atoms of the air constantly interact and renegotiate with the atoms in the field in an arrangement that eventually calls itself *"skin."* I revise my agreement to, *"hold a frequency that generates perpetual healing."* It produces tremendous heat. The body feels hot. I redirect the heat inward, sending swirls of gold, white, and diamond light throughout the agreement of my *"being."* The rest of the room *"beyond the agreement of the skin"* remains a cool, spacious, and neutral black. I realize I can shift specific agreements between atoms and molecules, which collaborate to create *"gut, heart and head consciousnesses."* The agreements can become infinitesimally small, or incomprehensibly large.

"I know for this period, it's best to keep things contained (wrapped with aligned intentions)."]

[1193.2 / 3239] [The body radiates intense heat. I have a strong desire to walk 20 miles before sunrise. I stay in bed repeating the phrase,

"I am always dreaming."]

[1193.3 / 3240] [Drinking water. Urinating. *"Drink more water."*]

[1193.4 / 3241] [I hover in front of THE LAWYER's door freely offering healing. He's struggling.]

[1193.5 / 3242] [I scroll through Instagram and see tremendous suffering. I offer prayers and healing to everyone through my thumb.]

[1193.6 / 3243] [I'm on a zoom call jamming with THE BEASTIE BOYS.]

[1193.7 / 3244] [I forgive incompetent leaders and thank them for showing me my own incompetence.

"I restart a practice of being loving, calm, and above all else, kind."]

[1193.8 / 3245] [I visit hundreds of exoplanets, though I'm taken with one that glows black and red. It has three suns that create different triangles in the sky. The form and direction of the "sun triangles" are used to derive a method of timekeeping on this bizarre foreign world.]
//

⁂

Maj. = 5- THE LAWYER: #1200
SMALL: #1204, #1206, #1210
LARGE: #1213, #1217
KIND: #1274

⁂

#1194 - May 17, 2020 @ 07:12 (San Francisco, California)

[1194.1 / 3246] [I've moved into a college dorm. The room hasn't been provided with a TV, which is the primary mode students use to connect to classroom lectures, complete assignments, and take exams. A course I'm enrolled in has an exam due later today, and I'm uncertain how I will submit my work. I share the suite with two other roommates. We're sober. We're playing a game where we have to discern the titles of popular songs and their *"feeling profile"* from pictographs. My clue is a stack of three, long, brown ovals containing gold symbols. The ovals are stacked vertically on a black background.

I have two cans of beer on my desk, which I turn on their side and cover with a stack of loose paper behind a book. Two cops enter the room, thumbs in their belt loops.

"Hey guys, is this where the case race is happening?"

"I don't know what you mean, officers."

"We got a tip that there was a party going on in here."

"We just moved in and there's no party happening."

The cops walk over to a desk and start thumbing through our personal property, even after we specifically do not express consent to search.

"You should respond to better information."

The cops become increasingly pushy. I'm neutral and cooperative. One of the officers decides to take our pizza.

"Well, that's upsetting. You're the kind of guy who'd steal pizza from a party."

They both make some nonsensical threats as they slide the cheese off the pie, leaving a swirled crust splattered with red sauce.

Unwavering, I tell them, ***"I'll take the classic style (threat) please."***]

[1194.2 / 3247] [Hockey players have been reshuffled into normal hourly wage jobs. *"The world's best goalie"* puts on a visor and ties an apron around his waist, while standing behind the counter of a mall food court restaurant. His manager is a teenager, who demonstrates how to properly use the register.] //

⁂

HOCKEY: #1313
OVAL: #1338
CONSENT: #1236, #1293
SYMBOLS: #1311

⁂

#1195 - May 18, 2020 @ 05:55 (San Francisco, California)

[1195.1 / 3248] [I'm with THE POSTMASTER and THE FARMHAND in a brick building. We take refuge during a large storm. We see four tornadoes touch down in the distance beyond a set of rolling hills. We go inside, managing to avoid being injured. When we emerge, the entire town surrounding our refuge has been leveled. THE FARMHAND seems a bit disoriented and doesn't want to be there, though she would've likely been killed had I not encouraged her to come inside to avoid the severe weather.]

[1195.2 / 3249] [I'm on an interplanetary mission stopping at all planets between Mercury and Neptune. I fly though the void of space alone without a spaceship.]

. . .

[1195.3 / 3250] [A fire in a saloon rages as THE CARPENTER and I sit and chat. We're across the street from the building, spared earlier by the tornados in **[1195.1 / 3248]**. I take a photo of the burned-out shell of the smoldering site when the damage from the fire is labeled a total loss. THE CARPENTER steps away. I encounter THE DEAR HEART who's sad after deciding to end a relationship with a boyfriend. He requests that we go grocery shopping together.

"Of course, we can do that," I offer and continue, ***"afterwards we can stop at my place and talk. I'll offer you as much healing as you need."***

"Do you still live at 'Such and so?'?"

"No, I've moved and at the moment I don't even know where to go."

"You don't know your own address?"

"It's so new, that you're right...I don't," I say with a playful laugh and shrug of the shoulders.] //

⁂

Maj. = 1- THE CARPENTER: #1199

Min. = ♥- THE FARMHAND: #1249, ♣- THE POSTMASTER: #1249

TORNADO: #1209, #1252

SHRUG: #1249, #1305

RELATIONSHIP: #1203, #1288, #1305, #1318

THE DEAR HEART: #1407

⁂

#1196 - May 18, 2020 @ 07:13 (San Francisco, California)

[1196.1 / 3251] [I'm in a house sharing casual conversation in a morning-lit kitchen with THE LALA and THE MAGICIAN. We talk about *"blind spots and opportunities for growth."*

"It's a year later and I'm still holding myself apart from 'that relationship,'" I say while spinning a pen on the table.

THE MAGICIAN offers, *"your geopolitical awareness toolkit could use a dusting off, and an upgrade."*

We rise from the table together and leave the kitchen, walking to a storage unit within the house, where I go through old personal effects and plastic crates of costumes. I find half a welding mask that holds a single solid lens within a thick silver frame. Contents have spilled from the back of one of my crates off a stainless-steel roller cart, and on to the floor.

I push the roller cart to an elevator and move between different levels *(some up, some down)*. I visit another locker where I retrieve a green duffle bag of other old costumes. I nostalgically rifle through the bag and try a couple on to reminisce. Some pairs of sunglasses have been smashed. Other items are falling apart. I place my items back in the crates on the cart, then depart.

I continue to the main level, where I encounter a group of people preparing for a wedding. Initially I wear a gold shirt and green corduroy pants. Others wear all white. I blink and discover we all now wear white angel robes with *"white -sparkly-puff-ball-halos."*

I'm offered the opportunity to switch, but it's quickly rescinded when the angel robe wearing friend says, *"You're basically already wearing the same thing."*

On the path between floors *(traveling up and down sets of stairs)* we pass a variety of familiar and friendly faces.

I'm left with a thought:

'Transformation comes at a cost of not less than everything."] //

⁂

Maj. = 14-THE MAGICIAN: # 1252
Min. = ♦- THE LALA: #1243
AWARENESS: #1278
ANGEL: #1214
COSTUME: #1239, #1278, #1304

⁂

#XXXX - May 19, 2020 (San Francisco, California)
****Two dreams, experienced as profound and hyperreal, requested to be forgotten**** //

⁂

TWO: #1304, #1306, #1311, #1312, #1317, #1318
PROFOUND: #1267
FORGOTTEN: #1248, #1278, #1309, #1326

⁂

#1197 - May 20, 2020 @ 06:19 (San Francisco, California)

[1197.1 / 3252] [A friend of mine is a scientist. His current work centers on a high-powered microwave device, which he demonstrates by taking aim at a watermelon, and destroying it. I go through my personal belongings on a picnic table behind a building and note the hour, realizing I have limited time to depart if I'm to honor an invitation I've received from THE ARCHITECT to substitute teach a yoga class at his gym. As I walk to the perimeter of the muddy property, two women nonsensically set up a makeshift slide in a deep rectangular hole, composed of two shovels that cross in an "X" at the center. I don't consider the slide to be a *"usable device."*

Downstairs at the gym I wait for guests to arrive. The time is five minutes past the planned start. I go upstairs to check with the reception desk and encounter a large group of people who have gathered for the class. My watch is set incorrectly, **it's twenty past the hour.** People are grouchy from the mistake, but I assure them I can ,***"teach them an effective class with the 40 remaining minutes (if they're game to take things at a faster clip)."***

We begin to move as a group. One student who typically teaches brings in a handheld speaker while talking into a head mounted microphone. His instructions drown out my cues. Each time I talk, he talks over me. The distraction is strong, and takes me out of presence from time-to-time. Another student wheels in a stack of chairs and sets them in rows. Class attendees choose to sit in the chairs. I pause and attempt to re-enroll students to the class, but they're content to sit staring at their phones. A couple stare directly through me like I don't exist.]

⁂

Min. = ♥- THE ARCHITECT: #1204
MICROPHONE: #1282, #1322
FAST: #1205, #1275, #1281, #1285, #1295
SLIDE: #1322

⁂

#1198 - May 21, 2020 @ 02:12 (San Francisco, California)

[1198.1 / 3253] [I'm at an amusement park. The scale of the rides and attractions is immense. I stand with THE SKEPTIC *(humored, playful and directive)* at the entrance to a "Dodge 'em" arena where we wander through an "antique bumper car" parlor. We ascend a pair of Penny Farthing bikes, welded parallel by frame, and pedal the unit around to a different ride that an Englishman suggested we take. The Englishman shares frustration with his inability to *"toss a basketball to himself"* while on what we discover is a, *"mammoth tower of a ride."*

I take on the *"basketball catching challenge"* and assume a seat in the center of a carriage that could sit four across. With a "whoosh" the carriage ascends a central tower more than 50 stories high, at such speed the basketball sticks to my lap and keeps me in place. Once at the top the carriage swings backwards, and I send the ball vertical. When I look back, I get scared at the prospect of falling and grip the upside-down carriage with white knuckled intensity. I request that we end the challenge and return to the ground.

When I arrive at the point origin, I disembark the ride and run to embrace my wife. She and I decide to run together hand-in-hand to the front of the park. As we approach the front gate, we watch a giant pendulum attraction with a C-Clamp-like carriage *(multiple stories tall and dynamically changing shape, like a robotic arm)* swing back and forth. Those on board the ride emit sensational screams and gasps. No restraints, nor supports are offered to riders, so those within, get battered around like bingo balls.

When my wife and I get closer, I see a series of long white brushes/bristles on the exterior of a C-Clamp carriage with small black-ball-cap-sized "bumpers" on them that sweep across the steel gangplank, which serves as the sole exit to the park. The brushes bring the ride to a complete stop.

I leave my wife, suggesting I investigate while she remains safe. When I successfully navigate between the flipping bristles as they sweep across the platform, I arrive at the ride operator's room. I encounter a tiny old toothless woman running the ride. She follows six simple instructions, each printed on its own white rectangular poster and mounted sequentially left-to-right, numbered from 1 through 6.

"Them's yers instructions to foller to help me stop this herre danggum ride," the woman tells me in a raspy hill-jack accent. She continues.

"You're 'gon hewp them yeeeout when it sleeers dern. Theeen yer 'gon hewp me git to that therrr uther ryde ta hewp me fiin mah huzbun."] //

⁂

SUPPORT: #1205, #1240, #1319
INSTRUCTIONS: #1208, #1268, #1289
ORIGIN: #1228, #1249, #1285
THE SKEPTIC: #1399

⁂

#1199 - May 21, 2020 @ 23:32 (San Francisco, California)

[1199.1 / 3254] [The homeless woman from my neighborhood strips naked on the street. She maniacally laughs when she discovers her period has started. Copious amount of blood runs down her leg as she leaps to a fire escape above me. When I look up, I see her atop a staircase surrounded on all sides by soil and leafy vegetation. Blood drips on my face in a rush, flooding my eyes and filling my mouth when I wince with disgust and yell. When I taste the blood, I sense Hepatitis C and at least three other pathogens on my tongue. Another woman attempts to grab my genitals through my pants.

I push her hand away and tell her, ***"No, don't. I haven't washed."***]

[1199.2 / 3255] [I sit on the covered red-tiled roof of a Mediterranean villa with THE WEAVER and THE CARPENTER. We peek through a series of Gothic style dormers, out on to a city built up into the walls of a mountain valley. The villa feels extremely old and positioned at the highest vista point in town. In a blink we find ourselves in a vacant cobblestone town square as the bell tower declares the time: **High Noon.** We walk through the closed town square noting the abandoned sports arena that's previously held events attended by upwards of 100,000 people. As we pass through the final gateway, I talk with THE PILOT and THE KIND HEART and describe the experience of the homeless woman bleeding on my face. THE PILOT is fascinated. THE KIND HEART is so disgusted by the anecdote he steps away to vomit.] //

⁂

Maj. = 0- THE WEAVER: #1204, 1- THE CARPENTER: #1204, 6- THE PILOT: #1222, 21- THE KIND HEART: #1235

PEEK: #1318, #1326

NOON: #1238, #1280

RED: #1214, #1215, #1222

⁂

#1200 - May 22, 2020 @ 02:51 (San Francisco, California)

**I dictate this twice before waking up and realizing I have to formally record it in 3D reality. **

[1200.1 / 3256] [My neighbors *(a father and his three kids)* stop by my front porch after they cross the street. The father tells me, *"The kids wanted to run experiments but I told them they needed at least four data sets, and right now, they don't even have one."*

They continue across the street in the direction of their home as the father shouts back toward me over his shoulder, *"The comp on the property your parents were interested in came in at $371,000."*]

[1200.2 / 3257] [I awaken with my head next to my door. The door is open, and closes on its own. I can hear THE LAWYER engaged in a heated conversation on the opposite side.]

[1200.3 / 3258] [I'm on a flight to Medford, Oregon with a female coworker. We fly over a cartoon landscape which we observe through the transparent floor of the airplane. Various land masses bear large embossed labels within their dash-and-dot borders. When we land, we share a car to a suburban home where we meet with THE WORLDBRIDGER, who immediately involves us in a variety of home improvement projects. He sits next to me at a dining room table walking through instructions for a task, then disappears. He reappears outside on the front lawn, viewable through the picture window. I open a sliding glass door and crawl up onto a 4" railing. As I crouch to stand, I see small well-placed stacks of square and rectangle trivet sized panes, on both the railing and a nearby workbench. ***"The interior of the house is ready for an update."***

When I go back inside, other students in attendance comment that they'll, *"take an encounter with THE WORLDBRIDGER anyway they can get one: In their sleep. While he sleeps. Face to face!"*

Conversations consistently center on, *"using sound as a method of staying connected to source energy."* As I look at a countertop of sundry items, THE WORLDBRIDGER appears at a coffee table next to me saying, *"Coconut milk isn't for you, but it reminds me of when I was a kid."*

His face distorts and inflates, then caves in on itself, leaving the impression of a skull in a small poof of a cloud. I start to cry uncontrollably. I'm not sure what needs to come out, but it feels like there's something lurking around my heart. I ask for healing and, receive it.] //

⁂

Maj. = 5- THE LAWYER: #1205, 7- THE WORLDBRIDGER: #1208
IMPROVEMENT: #1310
HEART: #1213
FACE: #1228, #1229, #1233
LAWN: #1273, #1305, #1307, #1314, #1343

⁂

#1201 - May 21, 2020 @ 05:29 (San Francisco, California)

[1201.1 / 3259] [I'm with the family at a house by a lake. THE CHILD bounces a basketball from the garage, up the driveway to the sidewalk, and back in a figure eight pattern. She's responsible for giving the property its name: **LAKE HOUSE**. THE LITTLE PRINCE bounds around nearby. THE LITTLE PRINCE is athletic, acrobatic, curious and remarkably dexterous...***for a baby.***

At five months old he can walk, talk, and gallop like a gorilla. He and I go on a series of adventures together, one of which includes scaling a large concrete wall to find a secret playground at the top, where we play. On our way down it becomes a bit precarious when we discover we might be climbing the large outward facing wall of a dam. I hold him under my left arm as I take small breaths *(and leaps of faith)* between gripping different hand holds of decreasing size on the wall. We ultimately descend to the bottom, where we lightly bounce off a series of five neon-green ratchet straps, pulled to tension at the base. We're able to step off gently, holding hands.

THE LITTLE PRINCE and I walk up a hill, stopping at a refreshment station for a Dixie cup of water. He drinks his quickly asserting, *"GRAPE!"* I realize I've made a mistake by giving an infant an energy supplement, and am further admonished by a TV that displays a warning in red capital letters on a white background:

ENERGY DRINKS POSE THE SAME RISKS AT ANY AGE.

I pour my portion in a steel wire wastebasket, crumple the cup, and drop it.]

[1201.2 / 3260] [I'm at a rally at a shopping mall where people hold up signs affixed to giant tongue depressors. When we leave, I take a bag of M&Ms and place them in a sack with other complimentary items. We've been divided into groups to complete a project.

I express to my group leader that, ***"it's the first time I've participated in something like this in the better part of a decade."***

He giggles and says, *"Same here."*

I briefly bump into THE GENIUS. I'm startled at first. I don't recognize him. His hair is short, wavy, and salt-and-pepper toned. He wears overalls. I tell him he looks cute. By the time I remember I have a gift in my bag for him, he's departed.] //

⁂

Maj. = 3-THE CHILD: #1220, 12- THE LITTLE PRINCE: #1216

RALLY: #1240, #1281, #1316

GENTLY: #1256

LEAPS: #1260, #1277, #1280, #1282

THE GENIUS: #1332

⁂

#1202 - May 23, 2020 @ 04:00 (San Francisco, California)

[1202.1 / 3261] [I make amends with THE GYMNAST *(forgiving, motherly, and neutral)*. I apologize for mean things I said back in high school.]

[1202.2 / 3262] [I'm backstage at a concert venue. The band wants a *"fisting demonstration"* during tonight's concert. People gather for a rehearsal of the spectacle.]

[1202.3 / 3263] [Concert attendees toss their phones across the venue to one another. They treat them like garbage.]

[1202.4 / 3264] [A young French woman stands behind the register at a refreshment stand. She becomes confused when a guest orders a *"fresh coconut."* She doesn't know what that means.

I tell her, ***"it's $6,"*** leave money on the counter top, and walk away.]

[1202.5 / 3265] [A young woman is about to be arrested for embezzling from the fashion label, where she's been hired for an internship. Similarly, a doctor is about to be sued and arrested for criminal malpractice. The doctor has administered multiple fatal treatments to patients who were otherwise well and healthy before their appointments.] //

⁂

TOSS: #1202, #1262, #1309, #1318

GARBAGE: #1320, #1343

CRIMINAL: #1223

APOLOGIZE: #1229, #1321

⁂

⁂

#1203 - May 24, 2020 @ 04:00 (San Francisco, California)

[1203.1 / 3266] [THE AESTHETE *(engaging, curious and artistic)* films a music video for an unreleased DAVID BOWIE song while showering. He's covered in *"black rainwater"* that slicks his skin like ink.]

[1203.2 / 3267] [I use a composting toilet at a hotel after walking through a fancy lobby during a formal event.]

[1203.3 / 3268] [An English mother offers to bake me a cake as I wrap up a visit with her son. I had a crush on him, but when his partner returned, I learned that the type of relationship I was intending for, simply wasn't possible. The departure is friendly and kind.] //

⁂

INK: #0202, #0260, #0374
BLACK: #0386, #0392
FORMAL: #0146, #0186
POSSIBLE: #0324, #0332, #0394
THE AESTHETE: #1228

⁂

#1204 - May 24, 2020 @ 07:45 (San Francisco, California)

[1204.1 / 3269] [I'm at a condo with THE ARCHITECT. He pulls a saran wrap covered bowl of chickpea salad from the fridge, which he terms, *"really old."* I believe it's my bowl, but he assures me that it belongs to, *"another woman."* When I pivot, I see THE WEAVER and THE CARPENTER seated at a table. Just beyond where they sit through a door, I see the neighbors; a Chinese couple with a small yapping dog. The dog isn't concerning, but the stench rolling from the neighbor's open door is. We don't know the origin of the odor, but we all seem to agree that it's probably a rotting human body.]

[1204.2 / 3270] [I take a walk in the dark down to the beach. When I get there, I realize I've left my shoes up at the house. I walk on the sand with socks. A group of guys playfully banter behind me, though I'm not able to hear what they're talking about.] //

⁂

Maj. = 0- THE WEAVER: #1208, 1- THE CARPENTER: #1208
Min. = ♥- THE ARCHITECT: #1429
CHINESE: #0094, #0173, #0254
GUY: #263, #0271, #0274
CONDO: #0036, #0063

⁂

⁂

#1205 - May 25, 2020 @ 01:40 (San Francisco, California)

[1205.1 / 3271] [THE VIKING ELF surprises me in the doorway of my home. He's recently had some rhinoplasty and wears a gauze bandage on his face. He hands delivers me a party invitation to his husband, THE TECHIE's birthday party.

"I sent you a text before I showed up."

"I must not have received it," I say checking my phone and scrolling through my messages, finding no indication of any mystery text.

The invitation is written twice in children's handwriting. Once in English, the other in Danish. THE VIKING ELF crosses the room and takes a seat on my bed as I briefly introduce him to THE LAWYER. After conversation naturally wanes, we depart and travel by car. THE VIKING ELF drives the vehicle from the back seat. Initially, the headlights are off as we zip down the road, which adds challenge to our travel. In some moments we swerve dangerously, which prompts me to grab behind me for the wheel *(a couple of times)* to keep the vehicle on course.

As we turn into a parking lot a group of people waves us to the shoulder, welcoming us to THE TECHIE's party. THE VIKING ELF nearly runs over the group as they flank the vehicle. Before we exit the car, we pause and I say,

"It's really good to reconnect with you. I'm glad we could go back to being friends again. I've missed you."

The suburban house is white smooth stone, has both round and kidney bean shaped windows, and is finished with a plum-colored roof. We enter the house, step around a banister and descend a couple steps before walking across a large central room, shaped like an octagon, as I'm introduced to *"the in-laws."* Once I've completed my run down the receiving line, I meet THE TECHIE who relaxes in a papasan chair. He's an older man with a pot belly and a beard; markedly different from how I'd pictured him in my mind's eye. I thank him for the invitation. He smiles and says,

"It's fine! I'm glad you're here. It's good for me to see who he used to like dating. It's funny, there's plenty of twenty-somethings and then a couple of older fuckers like us."

Next to THE TECHIE are stacks of "graph and puzzle books" that indicate someone in the family has been mapping out *"the gravitational pull of different sections of San Francisco."*

Someone suggests, *"gravity may influence real estate prices."*

"Really?"

"Well...we haven't been able to prove out a correlation but it's been a fun project and problem to attempt solving."

I'm invited to sit, and once my butt is in a chair the family's pet pig runs towards me then drops to its back, and lets me rub its belly. It athletically springs from its back to all fours with its ass pointed in my direction. I know it's about to shit, so I promptly rise from the chair and step aside. The family seems amused with my prognostication.

"You've spent time on farms!"

"Yep, that's true."

THE DULCE DE LECHE sits in another chair diagonally across from me to the right. As we talk through a variety of different subjects he considers to be *"the best,"* I determine he's excited for them because they're "novel" or "new" *(to him)*.

"You're seeking the answer to an unanswerable question. In business, you're constantly looking for updates to 'the model.' With space...how far out can you go? With a human body...how does it work?"

This goes on for some time.

"Did you know that a teaspoon of matter from a neutron star would weigh more than the Earth? We would never be able to hold it. Besides, its gravity would rip us apart before we could consider grabbing the spoon!"

It's unclear, though "the in-laws" may be embezzlers. At one point the mother "in-law" explains they own a building in the Tenderloin District of San Francisco.

"We're not slum lords, but we do charge our tenants proper rent."

I'm not convinced, as I look towards a series of shelves in a front room where coins and precious metals are loosely stacked. A projector set in the middle of the floor errantly casts an image at a blank wall, as an actor and actress enter and tour the property during the middle of the party. They evaluate the lot as a prospective site for filming a future scene in an as-yet-unfunded film.]

[1205.2 / 3272] [I've traveled with a large African American man, who I believe I've been mentoring. We're in an industrial warehouse on a property owned by a mob. A case containing a body is dropped from a car. Initially onlookers believe it's a movie. The young man says something and the action in the scene promptly stops.

The large African American man's awarded the, **"Keys to the Kingdom,"** the **"Keys to the Floor,"** the **"Keys to the Warehouse,"** all awards and prestige that typically take years of consistent participation to earn.

"He's taken a fast track."

I feel tremendous pride for his achievements. He's made a challenging decision, and I'm there to support his transition.

He walks alone between two rows of black trucks parked at 45-degree angles, all of which have the windows down and the stereo volume up, blaring hip hop. Another Black guy wearing a backwards ball cap leans out of the window of his truck as my mentee takes his *"ceremonial walk."*

"THAT MUTHAFUCKA!" Voices gasps in awe. Many expressions of seeming reverence. I hear others as I run towards him, the light, and the roaring sound. As I catch up to him, he drops to his knees, buckled over in disbelief. I grab him around the neck firmly, and hug him.

"You just sit here and savor this. Enjoy it."

I promptly run down a stairwell through a hallway, and wake up.] //

[1205.3 / 3273] [The process of traveling to the moon is told in Claymation and construction-paper-stop-motion-animation headlines:

"YOU SPEND THREE DAYS!
EXPOSED TO DAYLIGHT!
NINETY FIVE PERCENT OF THE TIME!
IT REQUIRES THREE PEOPLE TO ROTATE IN SHIFTS!"] //

⁂

Maj. = 5- THE LAWYER: #1207

Min. = ♦- THE VIKING ELF: #1271, ♣- THE DULCE DE LECHE: #1232

THREE: #0066, #0069, #0070, #0071, #0083

⁂

⁂

#1206 - May 25, 2020 @ 05:47 (San Francisco, California)

[1206.1 / 3274] [I'm in LA at a hotel. I skateboard through the property and encounter THE ACTOR, who's exercising on an elliptical machine. He's in town to play a role in a small theater production. Our interactions are friendly and familiar. Neither of us are in town for long. I invite him to a group hangout with THE RAPTOR and THE ROBOT later that day.

"Stop by if you have the chance."

Though unclear, it seems like we'll find each other on the beach under the sun later in the day.] //

⁂

Maj. = 10 -THE ACTOR: #1213

Min. = ♥- THE ROBOT: #1246, ♦- THE RAPTOR: #1337

⁂

#1207 - May 25, 2020 @ 06:44 (San Francisco, California)

[1207.1 / 3275] [THE LAWYER works on crafting a hollow egg formed, from white chocolate. It's finely decorated with royal icing, piped in delicate swooping patterns along the exterior. I help him complete a couple of heat seals to ensure it will hold together for the fancy dinner party planned for later tonight. The egg's a centerpiece for an old woman's table. He believes it'll take about two additional hours to complete the remaining detail. While with THE LAWYER, I field a courtesy call from a dental office in the Carolinas to confirm an upcoming appointment. I'm expected to remember a string of numbers to hold the appointment: 4 0 4 0 4 5 4 0 4 0 4 5 4.]

[1207.2 / 3276] [I'm on a reality TV show, where there's a financial incentive for being on camera the most. At the end of the series a count of scenes per character will be assessed. For each scene above the average number, a participant will receive an extra $200 *(regardless of duration).*]

[1207.3 / 3277] [Musical equipment is turned on, and set for play, in the middle of a public park. Techno plays at low volume. THE CAROLINA REAPER *(discerning, rugged, and distant)* approaches the equipment intending to power it down. When I ask him if it's bothering him, he huffily says, *"YES!"* and walks away.] //

⁂

Maj. = 5- THE LAWYER: #1235

SERIES: #0039, #0042, #0048

PUBLIC: #0009, #0394

HOLLOW: #0129

⁂

#1208 - May 25, 2020 @ 21:48 (San Francisco, California)

[1208.1 / 3278] [I'm at a roller coaster amusement park. I watch the family ride in the back seat of an otherwise empty train. They make multiple passes around the track, and eventually invite me to come along for a ride. I take a seat in front of them. The lap bar / chest restraint doesn't close to secure me in place at first, but I'm able to latch a buckle to provide myself some safety.]

[1208.2 / 3279] [THE CARPENTER returns from a trip ahead of schedule, wearing a gas mask. He disrupts THE EDITOR *(candid, erudite, and worldly)* and I as we make dinner plans. THE DANCER mentions she's been psychically tracking THE CARPENTER throughout his journey home, so she's not surprised by his arrival.]

[1208.3 / 3280] [We drive through a housing development, taking note of one structure set in the center of the plat that's a fraction of the width of other homes. It serves as a model and ad for a, *"new brand of energy efficient windows."* We park the car and enter the slim building. We hear THE DANCER talking to a young person about their, *"desire to race monster trucks."*

She reassures the young person, *"not to fear. The streets could be open again as soon as June."*]

[1208.4 / 3281] [THE CARPENTER sits next to GRANDMA and provides her with some instruction. She decides she's going to pass away. I blink, and when my eyes open, they're focused on a wedge of cake on a plate, on a gingham covered table. I glance up at THE WEAVER.

"GRANDMA's leaving," I share as we watch the bright color of the cake become dull. The color draining from the slice, indicates GRANDMA has left her body.]

[1208.5 / 3282] [THE WORLDBRIDGER describes a condition where emotionally reactive people have "Demon Danglers" latched on to their brains. The entities are able to control bodies and even speak through their hosts without them being aware of what's happening.

He says to, *"expect more of this as the current wave of collective suffering swells."*] //

⁂

Maj. = 0- THE WEAVER: #1214, 1- THE CARPENTER: #1215, 2- THE DANCER: #1213, 7- THE WORLDBRIDGER: #1216, 11- GRANDMA: #1225

DINNER: #0167, #0186, #0204

CAKE: #0022

⁂

#1209 - May 26, 2020 @ 02:34 (San Francisco, California)

[1209.1 / 3283] [I've been accepted as an MBA candidate at the Haas School of Business at UC Berkeley. I attend a *"new student info night"* in a large auditorium with large exterior facing floor-to-ceiling windows behind the lectern. I remove one shoe and sock. The odor from my foot permeates the room. A tornado strikes during a cocktail reception, and the ensuing pandemonium results in my phone being stepped on and smashed by another student. I get separated from my cohort, and in the process misplace my smashed phone. My personal items *(backpack, identification, etc.)* have all been lost. I want to find my phone, because it's the only possible way for me to contact my parents to let them know I'm safe. I have enough money to purchase a replacement, though I'm curious if they'll buy me a new one *(if I tell them a sad enough story).*

I enter a meeting space, and errantly find myself at an alumni event where I'm assimilated into a conga line between two much older men dressed in khaki pants and smoker's jackets. I become frustrated when someone hands me a "Class of XXXX" hoodie. I initially believe it's mine, but it's for another class.

I fly up and out of the building, then float above a parking lot in search of my items scattered by the tornado. I don't find them. I'm curious how I'm going to call home. I contemplate moving from San Francisco to Berkeley while I'm in school.

"It would make more sense financially and time-wise for me to relocate, if I'm certain I'll move forward with the program of study. I don't know if a daily hour commute each way on BART is worth it."

Seems expensive and low return. I have visions of myself bored with the lectures before they start, which makes me question if the program of study is a worthwhile investment.] //

⁂

STUDENT: #0033, #0390
EXTERIOR: #0396, #0016
INVESTMENT: #0141
ODOR: #0183

⁂

#1210 - May 26, 2020 @ 04:04 (San Francisco, California)

[1210. 1 / 3284] [I help attendees file orderly into an assembly hall. THE GOLDEN SHADOW and THE FLASH guide spectators as they enter. THE GOLDEN SHADOW requests I take position in the center of the floor. At the last moment she whistles at me and waves me towards a small stage at the back of the venue. An octagonal sound dampener surrounds our group, muffling the sounds of our music as the larger group continues to gather. A group of world leaders sings an off-key and dissonant rendition of a national anthem which is so out of tune, it's not recognizable. When the singing stops, the laughs of the larger group towards the leaders can be heard through the glass octagon, but are then quickly overwhelmed by applause. Unexpectedly, a young man stage dives into the crowd, carried around the floor, then back to the stage.] //

⁂

SINGING: #0235, #0375
OCTAGON: #0121, #0188
VENUE: #0229, #0298
CENTER: #0305, #0321

⁂

#1211 - May 26, 2020 @ 04:57 (San Francisco, California)

[1211. 1 / 3285] [I attend a concert wearing platform boots. I've seen the performer on previous occasions, and am excited to dance. The stage juts out into the crowd. As the curtain rises, the female performer walks across the front row of spectators and gives each a high five before ascending to her position for the show. It's impeccably timed and marked. The crowd goes wild.]

[1211.2 / 3286] [I rest as I write a screenplay. I watch a concert on television. THE ATHEIST grabs my feet and drags me along the floor in a figure eight. The pattern seems to cause ripples in space. Time dilates. Things slow to such a degree I consider myself catatonic, then fall asleep. When I come to, I use my forearms to pull myself up to a card table where I join a group of women, who take shots of Aquavit and Jägermeister between timed writing segments. They've already done two. I don't know if the third resting on the table top is for me.

THE RAJNEESH *(wise, elderly, and supportive)* sits at the far end of the table.] //

⁂

Maj. = 8- THE ATHEIST: #1216
CONCERT: #0327, #0336, #0340
RIPPLES: #0038
BOOTS: #0043

⁂

#1212 - May, 27, 2020 @ 05:05 (San Francisco, California)

[1212.1 / 3287] [I watch a family dispute unfold. It's challenging for a man's son to be questioned in a legal matter, when he's compelled to take the stand against his father and their family business. Depositions were previously held in a white corporate headquarters surrounded by a square perimeter, lined with trees.]

[1212.2 / 3288] [Parking a car at an angle up a hill.]

[1212.3 / 3289] [I tour a new office and am thoroughly impressed with the Chief Data Officer for a company that's produced an app that, *"links AI to various calendar services."*

"I want to work for her."

The team has some gaps in their knowledge, but each member holds a strong competency in a key industry. They don't know how to integrate information from financial services firms into their portfolio, and miss subtleties and regulatory nuance that degrade the success of their integration initiatives. They're working to shift their management team perspective.

Instead of considering recent failures catastrophic, they challenge each other to glean *"awesome learning opportunities"* and *"hidden wins"* for the betterment of future product releases.]

[1212.4 / 3290] [At the end of the day, a crew rolls by in a bus with the door open, all leisurely sprawled out within. It looks like they're styled and ready for a luxury blog photo shoot. They appear fashionable, and at the same time, totally exhausted.] //

⁂

DISPUTE: #0087
GAPS: #0027
AWESOME: #0009
TREES: #0032, #0036, #0048
⁂

#1213 - May 28, 2020 @ 06:48 (San Francisco, California)

[1213.1 / 3291] [I speak with BLUE IVY, who's about to go out on an errand with her dad. At the last moment she decides she'd rather stay home with mommy. Mommy says she can.

"What do you like to study?"]

[1213.2 / 3292] [I encounter OPRAH, who celebrates the completion of a giant pencil-looking structure erected by crane in Paris, France as an honoraria installation that *"champions education."* She pays the crane operator the standard union fee of $100.]

[1213.3 / 3293] [I walk through a promenade and see a projection crew/sound crew enter a venue to prepare for an evening event.]

[1213.4 / 3294] [I'm in a subway station where I encounter THE ACTOR. We decide to ride the "24 Line" together, abandoning prior plans to meet other friends. While on the subway we have a heart-to-heart.

"I have a niece now too."

"Cool. I have a nephew." I start to lose my space and go mushy in the mouth. As my voice changes while we're talking, I say,

"Do you hear that? I don't sound like myself right now. Before I lose my words: I never said 'Thank You' for modeling a graceful goodbye. I just wasn't. Thank you."

I offer a hug. Whatever was lurking in the space between us is purged. Once we separate, we rerun a familiar script:

"Didn't we have a good time?"

"Yes. We did. I appreciate you. I'm sorry I didn't just let go when it was over."]

[1213.5 / 3295] [A woman poses in public, showing off her exceptionally large, enhanced breasts *(and other cosmetically-altered body parts)*. They've been exaggerated to such an extent they almost look like an inflatable, puffy costume.]

[1213.6 / 3296] [A series of body builder men, dressed as centurions play out the same scene numerous times. They stab each other in the chest with a spade and lift the wounded skyward. They behead one another. Once bloodied, dismembered, and dead they reanimate and repeat. In one iteration they pause and say together,

"Why are we still doing this?"

They drop their weapons and shields, and chat casually as friends.]

. . .

[1213.7 / 3297] [THE DANCER passes me as I say, ***"Do you want to get some quality time together at the fair?"***

"Yes," she says and ducks into a small candle boutique to make a quick purchase before we continue together.] //

⁂

Maj. = 2- THE DANCER: #1216, 10- THE ACTOR: #1318
OPRAH: #1277
PUFFY: #0046
THANK YOU: #0059, #0063, #0125, #0390

⁂

#1214 - May 29, 2020 @ 06:18 (San Francisco, California)

[1214.1 / 3298] [I confront a group of people at a country-club clubhouse for blindly following an abusive evangelical pastor. They attempt to coerce me into joining their congregation. I ground and set my space, and hold it as the situation escalates. THE WEAVER goes missing. I'm concerned she's been kidnapped and brainwashed by the cult. As I look for her, the room miniaturizes. The people turn into rats.]

[1214.2 / 3299] [I watch MICHELLE OBAMA walk up a series of bleachers in an amphitheater with her wife. Their perfect spot for the upcoming event is behind me, and up two rows to the right.

"We've done it. We found the exact. Perfect. Spot," they say gleefully in unison.

I contemplate what it must be like to have every set of eyes in a room inspecting you, when you're doing something as simple as looking for a chair.]

[1214.3 / 3300] [A rat morphs back into the abusive evangelical leader in a room, where multiple young men inject themselves with steroids. I make eye contact with a security guard as I watch the leader duck into a conference room with an innocent young man. The security guard and I know the young man is about to be sexually assaulted.

"YOU KNOW WHAT'S GOING ON! YOU CAN SEE IT RIGHT THERE! YET YOU DO NOTHING???" I scream, while the security guard remains planted at his station.]

[1214.4 / 3301] [I follow a band of aging rock stars who are part of an *"evil-clown-heavy-metal act."* They've set up a series of farewell shows in Manhattan to conclude thirty years of playing together. They may call themselves "Demonic Sideshow." They drive around together in a VW Microbus with a red clown nose.]

[1214.5 / 3302] [A public health crisis has a solution funded by an angel donor. The project involves the creation and distribution of a completely white jigsaw puzzle. Upon the first die cut, the production team notices a variety of nonconforming pieces that nearly get packaged in with other outbound products. The printing error wasted the donor's money. A project team member speaks to the media about their plan to finish the work.] //

⁂

Maj. = 0- THE WEAVER: #1216
EYE CONTACT #0124, #0159, #0180, #0199
ANGEL: #0126, #0222
SIMPLE: #0047, #0060, #0066

⁂

#1215 - May 30, 2020 @ 01:09 (San Francisco, California)

[1215.1 / 3303] [I share company with THE THINKER and THE FEELER at their home. My vision becomes blurry as I take a seat next to THE FEELER. I stand and look for a restroom. I believe I have to go to another floor of the home, but they say,

"There's one right here next to the living room, silly."

It's been some time since I've been to their home. When I return, THE THINKER has changed clothes and now wears a red cardigan and looks like Mr. Rogers. He hugs me. **It seems out of character, but I like it.**

"I appreciate it, and it'll eventually overwhelm me because no one else has touched me in a really long time."]

[1215.2 / 3304] [Image of LADY GAGA skewered like a paper doll through the shoulders from left-to-right with a series of other brightly-lit, white mannequins. There's no blood. No grimace, nor pain. It seems expected and flawlessly executed as a PR stunt.]

[1215.3 / 3305] [I'm in a lecture hall *(in dire need of renovation)* where I tell THE CARPENTER, ***"This is where we invite public speakers like Nelson Mandela to give their remarks when they visit the bank."***

He and I stand on top of a giant grill cooktop. Ample quantities of charred matter crunches under our feet.] //

⁂

Maj. = 1- THE CARPENTER: #1216
Min. = ♠- THE THINKER: #1223
LADY GAGA: #1249
BANK: #0222, #0239, #0243
PAPER: #0250, #0260, #0261, #0266

⁂

#1216 - May 30, 2020 @ 04:17 (San Francisco, California)

[1216.1 / 3306] [THE DANCER has a stroke while spending the night at a friend's house. I hold THE LITTLE PRINCE while crying. THE LITTLE PRINCE doesn't understand what's going on, and cries in confusion. THE ATHEIST quietly stands nearby. THE WEAVER and THE CARPENTER enter the house to retrieve THE DANCER, who lays paralyzed on the floor, unable to speak.

Earlier, THE DANCER rented a *"body cage pneumatic device"* with her friend so they could get a *"trendy tattoo make-up treatment."* She had a seizure mid-session which became a stroke.]

. . .

[1216.2 / 3307] [The family stands in front of a giant floating cube with rows of human-sized faces. The object is a silvery grey. Each of the faces looks down at us as we silently present THE DANCER. The silence persists for a long time, until the cube of faces erupts in song and offers healing.]

[1216.3 / 3308] [THE WORLDBRIDGER spins around in his office chair to discover a pack of baby bears running up and down a series of neighboring roofs. The bears bound through a Technicolor portal to another dimension.]

[1216.4 / 3309] [I stand under a tree filled with bats. I pray as an invitation for them to migrate. THE NUN stands nearby supporting me.] //

⁂

Maj.** = **0- THE WEAVER: #1220, 1- THE CARPENTER: #1220, 2- THE DANCER: #1232, 7- THE WORLDBRIDGER: #1220, 8- THE ATHEIST: #1332, 12- THE LITTLE PRINCE: #1243

SILENCE: #0117, #0371

PARALYZED: #0376

⁂

#1217 - May 30, 2020 @ 07:44 (San Francisco, California)

[1217.1 / 3310] [A man and woman get off a bus. The man might be an abusive spouse. The frame and action are blurry and grainy.]

[1217.2 / 3311] [Quick scene in a casino-like space, where a man and woman rapidly open and shut waist-high cupboard doors. They remove gallon-sized tubs sealed with a layer of gold foil from a row of recessed circular holes cut into the particle board. They eagerly slice in through the foil tops and turn the tubs over in the center of the room. They create a large mound of gold foil wrapped chocolate coins. They split the mound into picnic baskets and attempt to exit the casino, with said baskets in hand. They're stopped by casino security. They've participated in a large scam. The money they used to play the cupboard game was funded from cash placed on a margin bet at a neighboring casino. The FBI records the actions of the suspects, their interaction with casino management, and local authorities.] //

⁂

BLURRY: #0015, #0061, #0132, #0140

CASINO: #0010, #0112, #0293, #0332

LOCAL: #0069, #0077, #0093, #0174

GOLD: #0009, #0017, #0022, #0024

⁂

⁂

#1218 - May 31, 2020 @ 07:05 (San Francisco, California)

[1218.1 / 3312] [I sneak around Russia with members of the US military. Large areas of the country are used as bomb test sites. Everyone is unemployed, though when I log on and inspect social media profiles of various people of interest, they appear to have seemingly "normal" and uneventful lives. I eat part of an unidentifiable roasted bird while sitting on the ground inside an aircraft hangar, in a playground four-square box with a friend.

"Properties are listed for sale, though no one can buy them because everyone is broke."

I tell my friend, ***"I've trained myself to go for weeks (and in some extreme circumstances months) without eating, which is useful. Those who eat on credit, wind up in extreme debt to the mob."***]

[1218.2 / 3313] [I'm the second-string stand in drummer for RAGE AGAINST THE MACHINE. I give cues to the stand-in drummer on stage from the side that result in him playing the incorrect beat for the song performed by the rest of the band. They completely pause and leave the stage. After a few moments, a cover band steps on stage and continues with the performance.]

[1218.3 / 3314] [A Special Forces group lands and executes a surprise attack on an unsuspecting group of enemy soldiers. The special ops group takes cues on where to travel next based on the most recent phone calls of those slaughtered.

Travel to, *"active connections where confused people on the other end of the line scream"* are prioritized.

The team travels without communication devices to eliminate the risk of being tracked by hostile governments.] //

⁂

TEST: #0008, #0025, #0049
STAGE: #0250, #0251, #0260
NORMAL: #0003, #0210
CREDIT: #0016, #0024, #0220

⁂

#1219 - June 1, 2020 @ 02:35 (San Francisco, California)

[1219.1 / 3315] [Climbing up footholds on the interior of Golden Gate Bridge. My counterpart who requested the trip decided not to join because he *"doesn't have the proper shoes."*

"You'll never do it. You'll never do it," I repeat as I climb up hand-over-hand.]

[1219.2 / 3316] [I attend a concert where most attendees have been dosed with LSD. The dosed revelers send videos to a friend, who was unable to join. A young woman wiggles her breasts playfully from side-to-side in front of a camera phone. She becomes loud, then challenges others to a *"push up contest"* to win *"more hits of acid."* I drop to the ground and crank out over a hundred repetitions. When I ask for my drugs, she walks away and gives them to other people, which leaves me a bit disappointed...***though unsurprised.***

Had I taken any acid, ***"I wonder how I would get home ,and what state of mind I would be in upon arrival."***

THE JESTER runs towards the backstage entrance of the concert venue. He performs a gyration where he rolls across a mattress and plops down on the floor next to me, doing his best impression of a scene from "THE RICKY GERVAIS SHOW," where a man rotates upsettingly while his legs dangle lifeless beneath the knee. The impression of an impression of a gross person attempts to be...***provocative.*** We laugh at the absurdity.

Others have gathered to celebrate "the doctor" though neither THE JESTER nor I know who "the doctor" is. He's known for creating popular memes and .gifs with the phrase "__________."] //

⁂

Min. = ♦- *THE JESTER: #1273*
ACID: #0053
CLIMBING: #0047, #0183, #0194
GROSS: #0045, #0250

⁂

#1220 - June 1, 2020 @ 06:23 (San Francisco, California)

[1220.1 / 3317] [Most of the scene takes place at a Winter Holiday Extravaganza, where I hold space with THE THERAPIST *(neutral, empathetic, and intuitive)* and a few other friendly students in attendance. In some moments we're down on our knees, prayerfully. With our hands extending up we meditate and "run energy" in public. THE WORLDBRIDGER suggests we take seats in chairs and,

"Do it like we normally do it."]

[1220.2 / 3318] [Scene where a classic car with a baby on the back-bench seat, drives through a room. A camera mounted on the ceiling of the car's interior gives an overhead view of the baby being blown by the wind. The baby suffers an *"initial wounding"* when the heel of one of its feet suffers a minor abrasion. The baby is an uncircumcised boy.

As the haunting image of the crying baby looms on screen, it's accompanied by a parable of how, *"life's smallest and seemingly inconsequential wounds tend to stay with a person the longest."*

A name scrolls beneath the image of the infant: **THE CARPENTER.**]

[1220.3 / 3319] [THE CHILD finds it funny to call THE WEAVER by the nickname "MAERS," which is also the name of a popular line of boutique hair care products. I feel sad because THE CHILD is quickly growing up.

"I'm afraid she's going to lose her willingness to be silly."

She'll be less likely to, *"walk or quack like a duck."* I decide to enjoy it while she still will.]

[1220.4 / 3320] [I take an international flight, and plan to travel with THE PORN KING'S MOTHER. THE CONNECTOR is present. She mentions, *"it's easier for certain types of people to travel internationally in pairs."*

"The only time some people get a proper night's sleep is on an international flight," THE CONNECTOR claims.

Cardboard boxes (4" wide, 3' long, 6" tall) are filled with RxBars, wrenches, vice grips and "thin & thick blankets" ready for travel. I'm supposed to deliver some of these packages to THE PORN KING's estate in London. The trip is short, which is to our benefit, *"because the packages decompose within 24 hours."* I tell THE PORN KING'S MOTHER,

"I've met your son twice, once at Burning Man, the other at his place of business. Though I know who he is, and I understand the circumstances that have contributed to his current reputation I don't believe he'll remember me."

I'm unsure how I'll pay for sundry expenses while in the UK. I only have US currency and no credit cards with which to transact, while abroad.] //

⁂

Maj. = 0- THE WEAVER: #1229, 1- THE CARPENTER: #1228, 3- THE CHILD: #1228, 4- THE CONNECTOR: #1226, 7- THE WORLDBRIDGER: #1253

BLANKETS: #0024, #0043

FUNNY: #0013, #0033, #018

INTERNATIONAL: #0050, #0224, #0332

⁂

#1221 - June 2, 2020 @ 00:30 (San Francisco, California)

[1221.1 / 3321] [The mood is generally dark and mysterious. I'm in the hallway of a sophisticated haunted house at night, surrounded by mental patients who scrape at their asylum cell doors. I descend under the floor and hold myself up, to crawl along a horizontal steel-rung ladder.

I feel little claws scratch at the left side of my back *(from the spine, outward)* along the ribs.

The experience corroborates some of the stories the patients told earlier in the evening about a, *"dark force moving between cell walls that creates psychic disruptions and interference while they sleep."*

I hear them make sounds of relief/validation as I pass beneath their cells and draw the dark force away. The patients are being used by an organization in a psychic experiment, though the intended outcomes aren't disclosed.

A large stone chalice seems to be a significant point of attraction for the:

"dark force."

One of the patients hides it, then initiates a countdown clock while assuring me and others that, *"the object safely rests with the proper person."* The patient then leaps from a catwalk with a cord wrapped around their neck in an attempt to hang themselves. The suicide attempt is not successful.

I scurry up the passageway I commonly take to access patients across various floors/dimensions/planes of existence, and am surprised to find it blocked off by a piece of plywood covered with large green vertical zigzag scribbles.]

[1221.2 / 3322] [I interact with KING KONG as he lurks over me from above. I hang from his chest by my knuckles, gripping the spaces between his abdominal muscles like cracks in a bouldering wall. I have to traverse his torso to advance to my goal:

The center of the building.] //

⁂

SOPHISTICATED: #0028, #0158, #0315
PATIENT: #0011, #0293
RELIEF: #0015, #0134, #0235

⁂

#1222 - June 2, 2020 @ 05:52 (San Francisco, California)

[1222.1 / 3323] [A MICHAEL JACKSON impersonator performs on a stage in a hotel ballroom in Indianapolis. Behind the performer, five large verticallyoriented rectangular mirrors are mounted at the front of the space where a wedding party is intended to sit for their reception. The space is dimly lit.

Most of the story follows me, following a couple who are suffering toxicity from contacting a bizarre red, gooey substance. I take a plastic liter bottle, place it under a hand pumped dispenser, and coat the bottom of the bottle with a swirly pattern of the mystery substance. I spin the bottle between my middle fingers *(holding it by the cap and bottom)*, and disperse the swirled goo up the side of the bottle in a near transparent layer. I fill the bottle with water, and take a drink without thinking. As I realize I've swallowed some of the toxic goo I overhear a suffering *(and now dying)* man say,

"When I tasted it, I tasted death. That's when I knew I wasn't going to be savable. My immune system was instantly destroyed."

The couple go on to describe the sensations they experience as the poison infiltrates the various systems of the body.

"It's a long, slow drag. The lethargy seems never ending, until the unexpected bursts of euphoria (which we've come to fear because the next slow segment doubles in length)," the woman laments.

THE PILOT sits quietly nearby. He says nothing, but I assume he's experiencing the same effects. I start accepting my fate.

"I don't have insurance, and I'm going to die young while breaking rocks in a quarry in Indiana. Indentured servitude appears to be the only partial antidote available to people like me."] //

⁂

Maj. = 6- THE PILOT: #1234
MICHAEL JACKSON: #1435
ANTIDOTE: #0014
FATE: #0050, #0199
BIZARRE: #0026, #0033, #0042

⁂

#1223 - June 2, 2020 @ 06:30 (San Francisco, California)

[1223.1 / 3324] [I'm on a football team with married couples. THE THINKER is on my team. I'm the team rookie. I run down the field and attempt to catch a pass intended for another receiver. The ball strikes the ground and splits into two oversized Cool Ranch Doritos. I catch the half that bounces toward me. The rest of the team sprints down the field, acknowledging me with hugs and high-fives in a big surge of sweat-laden musk.

"We may be playing as part of the conditions of our criminal sentence commutation."

Upon release, one of the wife's desires is to eat an entire, *"Choux Waterfall Tart."* She mostly anticipates its presentation on a round glass table top, where small divots at each 90-degree mark on the tart will slowly leak runny custard into small off-white rivulets, creating puddles on the glass. The couples flirt as the game clock winds down. It's unclear if I drop another pass the next time the *"chip ball"* is thrown in my direction.] //

⁂

Min. = ♠- THE THINKER: #1320
OVERSIZED: #0021, #0056, #0066, #0084, #0121
GAME: #0188, #0194, #0210, #0235
CONDITIONS: #0136

⁂

#1224 - June 3, 2020 @ 02:41 (San Francisco, California)

[1224.1 / 3325] [I'm on Montaña Larapata with THE KOAN *(strong, masculine, and productive)* and his wife. The retreat group is small. There's a sense the group must act covertly. Preparations are immediately taken to prepare for the evening ceremony. I'm not sure what my ceremonial intention will be.

Some people filter and cycle between two different cabins. THE SIREN *(songful, dutiful, and available)*, THE WARD OF GAIA and THE HEALER are aligned to co-facilitate. They commence their act of service by providing all participants with a lush green salad. Water outside the window sloshes like an ocean, where air would ordinarily be. I shake a jug full of tea bags on a thick white rope through the *"water window"* to create an infusion. Some excitement permeates the room, though my mood is subdued.

As we gather, the group is shown two different experiential paths to choose between:

1. ***The normal path.***
2. ***The fast path.***

I take the fast path. I befriend a playful husband and wife, who have created giant skull shaped helmets for them to wear during the ceremony.

THE SIREN expresses, *"three Scandinavian men plan on joining us whose dietary requirements include salted fish, dried nuts and alcohol."*

I revisit and shake the jug of tea bags in the *"water window."* I'm fascinated by the water-like quality of the air, which suspends small clouds of tea in *"poofs"* and *"dollops."*

I know I'm full of shit to clear, so I'm not certain as to what sensations may show up during the ceremony. I can taste the tar-like tang of ayahuasca at the back of my mouth and know,

"The night's work will be productive."] //

⁂

Maj. = 20- THE HEALER: #1345
Min. = ♦- THE WARD OF GAIA: #1412
RETREAT: #0181, #0189, #0193, #0309, #0337
CLOUDS: #0209, #0331, #0349, #0360
WORK: #0113, #0139, #0145

⁂

#1225 - June 5, 2020 @ 07:14 (San Francisco, California)

[1225.1 / 3326] [GRANDMA is cast in a new DEFTONES video.]
[1225.2 / 3327] [Women compete for attention on a reality show.]
[1225.3 / 3328] [Thick chunks of red meat are flipped on the grill.] //

⁂

Maj. = 11- GRANDMA: #1255
REALITY: #0013, #0015, #0019, #0023, #0024
MEAT: #0033, #0060, #0088

⁂

#1226 - June 6, 2020 @ 03:54 (San Francisco, California)

[1226.1 / 3329] [THE RODIN *(strong, flexible, and hands on)* and THE GOGO BOY *(distant, cerebral, and seeking)* talk about revisions and takedowns they've made in their social schedules since the start of the pandemic.

THE RODIN mentions he's, *"been staying near 'The Richmond' and working out at the gym near his office."*]

[1226.2 / 3330] [I eat soba noodles with THE CONNECTOR, THE BURLESQUE PERFORMER, and a tattooed man at a church. I've mistakenly eaten more than my portion. I drive to a grocery store intending to replace the overage I consumed.] //

⁂

Maj. = 4- THE CONNECTOR: #1240
NOODLES: #0327
SOCIAL: #0242, #0254, #0271, #0305
THE RODIN: #1288

⁂

#1227 - June 6, 2020 @ 06:54 (San Francisco, California)

[1227.1 / 3331] [**"HUMANS TRIUMPH OVER NATURE! ENSLAVED PLANTS! BILLIONS OF THEM!"**]

[1227.2 / 3332] [**Image of a map zooms out from a town, to swaths of land, a right angle in 3D, then infinite other irrational angle pivots. **]

[1227.3 / 3333] [I walk in front of a car driven by a lecturing ALAN WATTS. His words leave me weeping from their beauty. **He's my friend.**] //

. . .

[1227.4 / 3334] [I'm perched in a concrete tree. I watch a man without pants complete a run, wipe his brow with his jersey, then proceed inside his house. He exits moments later with two other men.]

[1227.5 / 3335] [I float horizontally face down above a drafting table where THE ARBORIST works.

I whisper, ***"I wanna suck your dick"*** in his ear that wears a carpenter's pencil.

We stand...*race down a hallway to a bathroom...disrobe*, and create the situation.] //

⁂

3D: #0024, #0116, #0225
FACE DOWN: #0035, #0153, #0301
CONCRETE: #0157, #0168, #0235

⁂

#1228 - June 7, 2020 @ 01:28 (San Francisco, California)

[1228.1 / 3336] [While on the set of a show, we work with a group of people where a young Black man is taught to hold his ground when he's attacked and bullied by others. One defensive tactic requires a razor blade.]

[1228.2 / 3337] [We pass by a stack of prop Rolex cases. Small Burberry lapel pins are attached to scarves presented in the cases. The tiny pins list for $480 per unit.]

[1228.3 / 3338] [I walk with THE CHILD around different areas of an amusement park *"so she can do her job."* She doesn't quite understand the value of informing people where she's going. She's supposed to help people on/off a ride. I give her some space to walk by her bosses and tell them where she's headed, yet she bypasses them and sprints down the path without saying anything. I grab her and we go back to our point of origin. The bosses have departed so I submit.

"Ok let's go do your job now."

We send text messages to those at our destination, informing them of our ETA. We find ourselves on a train platform where an arriving steam engine rolls to a stop. The doors open as we pass. THE FIDUCIARY exits the train car and begins to walk behind us. We stop and turn around to face each other, though it appears I'm a stranger to him.

"This is my friend!" I say, gripping THE CHILD's hand.

The introduction applies to *(and is intended for)* both THE CHILD and THE FIDUCIARY. THE FIDUCIARY travels with a short-curly brown-haired man. They comment, *"it's cute other kids are being taught to take on grown up tasks."* THE FIDUCIARY finally remembers my face after I say,

"I'm going to need your mailing address at some point."

His shorter counterpart answers, *"For sure. Look me up on Instagram. My feed is full of harps!"*

Is he an angel?

"No, but I make music like one," he informs me telepathically.

Another woman comes out to assist me in keeping THE CHILD on track. We're on our way to find THE CARPENTER, though the point of the journey is to, *"take it with THE CHILD and help her understand how to communicate."*

"PUT YOUR PHONE BACK IN YOUR POCKET SO YOU CAN GET TO WHERE YOU'RE GOING," we're firmly reminded by a bodiless voice.

THE CHILD is compensated $50 for her day's work.]

[1228.4 / 3339] [I enter a condo owned by THE AESTHETE *(styled, storied, and soused)* and THE FASHIONISTA *(creative, timely, and relevant)* while they're both out of town. I open a large safe recessed in the floor under a square of white carpet. I retrieve a guitar and cleaning supplies from the safe. Gravity pivots 90 degrees and I walk up a wall to exit the unit.] //

⁂

Maj. = 1- THE CARPENTER: #1233, 3- THE CHILD: #1235, 9- THE FIDUCIARY: #1407
GRAVITY: #0005, #0346
HARP: #0148
VALUE: #0046, #0160

⁂

#1229 - June 8, 2020 @ 06:09 (San Francisco, California)

[1229.1 / 3340] [THE WEAVER drives a Tesla at incredible speed. I ride in the back seat. Two 90 degree turns *(a quick left, then right)* have bales of hay stacked high on the outer curves. We approach them so quickly the car fishtails and we nearly crash. Once through the squiggle, we proceed down a dark highway. We eventually stop at an In 'n Out burger. A Black guy wearing a suit wants to show me the proper way to eat a "Double Double," but I'm in a bad mood and mutter,

"I can handle it."

My mood changes the tone of the room, and others perceive it to be a *"bad vibe."*]

[1229.2 / 3341] [While at a hotel on the Faroe Islands, I sneak around out of view of the staff. I walk through a large door that looks like a giant Hershey Bar and discover myself in the largest suite on the property. It's multiple floors tall with deep book shelves and a giant canopy bed on top of a cube-shaped platform at the center of the room. Beneath the bed is an entire other floor to explore, with parquet floors including "The master bathroom." The wood is dark blackish brown. The carvings in the shelving unit are intricate and delicate. When I leave the suite, I run face-to-face with the Black man from In 'n Out and apologize, but I ***drone on and it becomes weird.***

"It's probably better to stop while I'm ahead, so I'm going to just shut up now."

He offers me a big hug. He hands me my suit coat as I explain why I was upset.

"The two quick turns on the road scared me."] //

⁂

Maj. = 0- THE WEAVER: #1232
INTRICATE: #0014, #0015, #0080

⁂

#1230 - June 9, 2020 @ 05:24 (San Francisco, California)

[1230.1 / 3342] [I encounter CLAY AIKEN at a restaurant. He's with a couple of kids.
I tell him, ***"I'm looking forward to the next time you're on 'ELLEN.'"***
As he bounces a toddler on a hip, we discuss nonprofit strategy.] //

⁂
KIDS: #0093, #0129
RESTAURANT: #0171, #0229, #0256
STRATEGY: #0171
⁂

#1231 - June 10, 2020 @ 05:24 (San Francisco, California)

[1231.1 / 3343] [I swing on a red board suspended by two red ropes. A woman swings on a different board and ropes, on the same path of travel, in the opposite direction. She's at the bottom when I'm at the top. The scaffolding supporting the swing grows from a 10-foot structure to one that is hundreds of feet tall. The swinging goes higher, and eventually I've swung to vertical where I pause at length, dangle, and kick my legs quickly to prevent me from toppling to the other side *(where I would most certainly slam into the unsuspecting woman below)*. ***"She would not see me coming."*** I'm able to coax my body back to my hemisphere of the swing.]

[1231.2 / 3344] [A class of children practice their cartwheels. They're led by a teacher who seems bored and intermittently yawns. At left in the gymnasium, is a stack of dishes piled high in a sink under running water. When I take a seat to eat, I notice the food I've brought with me for lunch has spoiled. An avocado has a bubbly, effervescent quality. A cucumber that I halved lengthwise is spoiled and mushy on the inside. Both are gross and I eat neither. When I stop to talk to the female teacher, she comments on my shirt, which reads something to the effect of:

"I had my year of crazy. I had my year of party."

She says, *"I can barely do a day of party, I don't know how I would manage a year."*
We both look out the window and notice a large fire has consumed wooden art installations around the giant swing set in **[1231.1 / 3343]** . A wall of thick oily black smoke rolls in our direction. We're surrounded by a group of soot-covered people who emerge from the smoke and surround us, chaotically twirling and dancing.] //

⁂
SWING: #0141, #0145, #0310
CARTWHEEL: #0339
OPPOSITE: #0004, #0006
OILY: #0202
⁂

⁂

#1232 - June 11, 2020 @ 06:26 (San Francisco, California)

[1232.1 / 3345] [A family gathers in a new house for a weekend. THE DULCE DE LECHE *(conflicted, reactive, and upset)* doesn't stay and declares he, *"has to go back to work."*

THE DANCER has fashioned a spider web out of thick clear rubber in a doorway between THE DULCE DE LECHE and other areas of the home. THE WEAVER sits inside on a couch where she also regularly chooses to sleep. Guests are present. Two guys sleep in a room at the back of the house, next to a door to a large darkened auditorium.

I pass by them quietly so as to not disturb their sleep, pausing briefly to extend my hands over each of their bodies to offer them a,

"Prayer for peaceful rest and pleasant dreams."]

[1232.2 / 3346] [In a different house, a camera crew films a group of African American women who perform as backup dancers in a music video. They perform animated choreography on countertops with raw facial expressions and strong downward foot stomps that rumble the video.]

[1232.3 / 3347] [A man recently recorded a piece of electronic music. He plays the composition for me and, challenges me to identify what instrument he used to create it. I'm confused and unsure, though I manage to render a guess. He laughs at my incorrect attempt and from beneath the table on his lap, he places a tiny-contact-lens-sized drum on the table top that spans between us.

The drum oscillates from lens size, to an inch or two tall, releasing a sound similar to a timbale as its clear gel-like sides quiver when he strikes it.] //

⁂

Maj. = 0- THE WEAVER: #1233, 2- THE DANCER: #1233
Min. = ♣- THE DULCE DE LECHE: #1235
CAMERA CREW: #0060, #0131
CONTACT: #0023, #0045

⁂

#1233 - June 13, 2020 @ 07:27 (San Francisco, California)

[1233.1 / 3348] [Scene occurs on a college campus. I live on the main floor of a dormitory, but also have another unit in another building across campus *(and one floor below ground).*

I haven't met my roommate yet. He's left me a handwritten note on my bed along with a photograph so I'll know who he is when he later returns.

He's a marching band instructor.

Later we meet face-to-face and he tells me he'll, *"spend most of his time at the home of THE NINER'S FAN and THE POLISH PRINCE, who are no longer married."*

THE NINER'S FAN *(contrary, uplifting, and direct)* has remarried a much older man. I meet him for the first time as I pass them both walking on the street.]

. . .

[1233.2 / 3349] [THE WEAVER, THE CARPENTER and THE DANCER appear and then depart. I don't know where they're going.] //

⁂

Maj. = 0- THE WEAVER: #1241, 1- THE CARPENTER: #1249, 2- THE DANCER: #1235
ROOMMATE: #0015, #0133, #0194, #0395
PHOTOGRAPH: #0044, #0105, #0106, #0187
BELOW: #0390, #0392

⁂

#1234 - June 14, 2020 @ 04:15 (San Francisco, California)

[1234.1 / 3350] [I walk around the basement level of a large shopping mall. I bob and weave through a pinball machine-like arrangement of pop-up stands and kiosks where vendors of every variety attempt to peddle their products. I walk through without being baited by any of their offerings. I have a friend with me who repeatedly declares they are *"single."*

After we are together for some time underground, we pass under a corridor with a series of upside-down U-shaped lights that advance in rainbow shades from red through violet and pulse forward in sequence, suggesting a continued path of travel.

The friend says he'd *"rather go the other way,"* turns around, and disappears.]

[1234.2 / 3351] [I double back and pass through an exit door where I discover myself in a locker room as people change from exercise clothes into business attire. At the end of the locker room is a cubicle farm. People sit around idling, ready to accept new assignments. I walk through a well-lit space with an ascending white marble staircase, where a promotional banner denotes, *"a large liquidation sale is underway."*

I can see the ghostly whispers of people who had, *"both sold and purchased illusory products from a Ponzi scheme."*

The farce has left a stench of negative emotion in the room, which I occasionally react to when a waft hits my nose.]

[1234.3 / 3352] [I lay on my back on the floor next to THE PILOT, who holds a phone and shows me the constellation of my day's travel on a map.

"You have to make four jokes about the virus," he tells me, then promptly redirects his attention as a group of women gather around and start speaking down at us in Italian.] //

⁂

Maj. = 6- THE PILOT: #1235
CONSTELLATION: #0027, #0187
TRAVEL: #0204, #0224, #0242
DOUBLE BACK: #0025, #0236, #0323

⁂

⁂

#1235 - June 14, 2020 @ 06:44 (San Francisco, California)

[1235.1 / 3353] [It's snowing. I'm at a large CVS. I'm not wearing my glasses. I'm unable to see. A woman yells at me to get the attention of a person standing nearby. Seemingly the man's name is "Vince," and the woman has made several attempts to set him and I up on a date. I go outside, cross a street, and enter another store. I am still not able to see much. Everything is soft-edged and blurry.

"Being stood up on a date (or having an appointment broken via text message) should make the prospect of another meet up more desirable," I hear a chattering semi-persuasive voice say above my right ear.

I hear the comment as **bogus** and *"shoo"* the little confusion being off my shoulder as I wander blindly through the pharmacy.]

[1235.2 / 3354] [THE RECONCILIATOR holds up an abstract squiggle, framed under glass. With a smile she says, *"Hey look! It's a cat!"*

A single pencil line begins in the top left corner of the lithograph, and the squiggle progresses right, down, left, down and repeats. By the time the eye makes it to the bottom right corner of the print, what started as a graphite squiggle evolves into a continuous stop motion animation of a joyful, tumbling cat and the hijinks resulting from its choice making.]

[1235.3 / 3355] [I'm at a city park under a picnic shelter. THE DANCER arrives holding THE CHILD's hand. They sit at a table across from me. We discuss how THE CHILD is able to read proficiently, years beyond her societally defined grade level. I've purchased a collection of books as gifts for THE CHILD, which are easily viewable to her as they rest on the bench at my side in a clear plastic bag.

I distract her from seeing the books by standing up and inviting her and THE DANCER to an impromptu dance party.

THE PILOT and THE KIND HEART sit on a grassy hill a few meters away. We urge them to keep their distance if they decide to sit at a table. They lose interest in us, stand, and walk away into the surrounding brush.]

[1235.4 / 3356] [THE LAWYER departs on a bike ride after failing to coax THE DULCE DE LECHE *(sullen, doubtful, and tired)* to join him. THE DULCE DE LECHE sits in a desk chair behind me.

"I'm not allowed to participate in the Journey of Hope!" he says with a sob.

"What happened?"

"I'm not a member of the club, and I like to argue with members of the club."

"The way you put that; I wouldn't want you to be on the team either if I was responsible for building it."

He cries harder as THE LAWYER returns and parks his bike by the desk. He and I place a hand on each of THE DULCE DE LECHE's shoulders and comfort him by saying,

"It will be ok."]

. . .

[1235.5 / 3357] [I stand next to a canal. I walk towards a wire fence and clasp it as I peer through and observe two adult cranes that groom themselves just before they fall asleep. I decide to sit next to them and meditate for some time before walking back to the store.]

[1235.6 / 3358] [Scene in a modern mansion. I find rolled up cash scattered across a carpeted floor in a room with soft silver and grey light. I collect the cash, unroll it, and stack it. My vision is blurry but I'm able to differentiate between uncashed checks and ATM transaction receipts collated into the stack.

Once removed I fold the cash, then place it in my front right pants pocket.

Numerous meditation students converse nearby on charcoal toned chairs at opposite ends of a pale blue glass desk.] //

⁂

Maj.* = *2- THE DANCER: #1238, 3- THE CHILD: #1249,
5- THE LAWYER: #1238, 6- THE PILOT: #1310, 21- THE KIND HEART: #1310
Min. = ♦- *THE RECONCILIATOR: #1431,* ♣- *THE DULCE DE LECHE: #1341*
POCKET: #0044, #0069, #0100, #0102

⁂

#1236 - June 15, 2020 @ 02:23 (San Francisco, California)
**I believe I've recorded this encounter with exquisite detail until roughly halfway through the scene. I awaken and realize I have to start over. **

[1236.1 / 3359] [I encounter THE LOBBYIST, THE TEETOTALER *(sarcastic)*, THE AD EXECUTIVE *(observant)* and THE CHIEF OF STAFF *(peace keeping)* at a reunion event. THE TEETOTALER's quick to respond to a nickname she was given years back on an assignment:

AFRICA.

"Hey AFRICA!"

We wear military uniforms and discuss key moments from prior wars in which we've served. I scale an aluminum ladder after THE LOBBYIST begins to climb just ahead of me. The crowd gathered for the reunion pauses to acknowledge him for his devoted service and role in *"neutralizing The Chechnya Conflict."*

A series of buses arrives, each with a single destination for reunion attendees, who must get on the correct bus. **No transfers.**

THE HULA HOOPER *(contrary, intellectual, and self-humoring)* arrives with his wife. It's good to see them both, though I suffer an awkward moment when I greet her with an incorrect name. She believes I've said hello to someone standing behind her and briefly glances back over her left shoulder. I repeat her name correctly under my breath a few times to prime myself, likely appearing ridiculous and partially mad. Our interaction is brief.

"I have work to do with the kids, gotta hoop," he says as the pair each bring a steel ring to their hipline and hula out of sight.

The mood becomes suspicious and anxious. Someone's suggested multiple reunion attendees have been video recorded without their consent. I'm among the group who's allegedly been violated.

"Contents of the recordings should be considered culturally, socially, and professionally damning,"

reads an impromptu dossier distributed throughout the crowd.]

[1236.2 / 3360] [I watch a video of myself wandering the dunes of a blue-skied desert alone in 2005.]

[1236.3 / 3361] [When I conclude watching the video, I'm back at the reunion.

"I feel anger in my gut and it's the size of a quarter, but that quarter's as dense as a neutron star."

I become animated and enraged as I begin describing the methods by which I intend to torture the person who recorded me.

"I'll use a paring knife to skin their face! I'll extract their finger and toe nails with a pair of pliers, then plunge their bloody hand and foot stumps into a pile of salt."

The litany of potential techniques I espouse, cause those around me to feel increasingly gross and uncomfortable.] //

⁂

Maj. = 17- THE LOBBYIST: #1296
QUARTER: #0074, #0394
ANXIOUS: #0089
STAR: #0021, #0168, #0281, #0315
THE CHIEF OF STAFF: #1254
THE AD EXECUTIVE: #1335

⁂

#1237 - **June 15, 2020 @ 06:24 (San Francisco, California)**

[1237.1 / 3362] [I stand next to a car talking with THE VEGAN. As we chat, a green convertible with a tan rag top slowly backs into THE VEGAN and crushes her at the waistline between it and another vehicle. I bang on the roof, sides, and windows with open palms to get the attention of the driver. The driver side window retracts, revealing a small Asian man who gives me a smiling thumbs up.

"NO! You're backing over my friend!"

He doesn't seem to understand what's happened, nor my words, as he pulls forwards and closes the window with my right arm trapped at the shoulder joint. I'm able to jog with the slow-moving car as others rush in and flank the vehicle. The number of bodies surrounding the car is eventually enough to get the driver to stop. He retracts the rag top, releasing my arm.

As I make some circles to check my mobility, I reiterate to the driver that he nearly crushed my friend, and ran me over. The man grows deeply apologetic. With the car in park, he reaches in a cloth bag on the passenger side floor and pulls out a puffy vest that's a dull violet/drab blue color. He lifts it towards me and offers it as a gift. I hold it, but don't accept it as the man pulls out a similar colored piece of clothing and offers it to THE VEGAN saying,

"This is a wonderful workout shirt. $19.95 retail value."

She and I are both insulted he thinks this will resolve the encounter, though we understand it may be all he has to give.]

[1237.2 / 3363] [I play tennis with a White man who attempts to distract me by making disparaging remarks about KENDRICK LAMAR while on serve. I remind him that,
"KENDRICK's a Pulitzer Prize winner" as I hit kill shots back after every attempt.]

[1237.3 / 3364] [In a kitchen. Cooking for a group. Unclear.] //

⁂
FLANK: #0088, #0116
VIOLET: #0330
PUFFY: #0046
SHOULDER: #0056
⁂

#1238 - June 16, 2020 @ 05:11 (San Francisco, California)

[1238.1 / 3365] [THE DANCER shares a condo with THE LAWYER and I. I walk towards the front door intending to leave as it opens. THE AMBASSADOR *(engaging, light, and fun)* enters with excitement and expresses how happy she is to see me as she pulls a face covering down from her mouth and lets it hang from her neck. She runs towards me, arms extended, expecting to give me a hug. I back up quickly saying,
"No, no. Please stop."
THE AMBASSADOR is confused because she believes we'd made plans to hang out. As I walk around the unit in a circle I start yelling at THE DANCER.
"Why would you do this!!? I was getting ready to go and this has basically undermined everything I've tried to accomplish!"
When I approach THE DANCER, she slams a white door in my face, positioned directly next to the front door. I'm bewildered for a moment when she enters the condo via the front door. I walk towards her, and we pass through each other like clouds. She then makes a few dismissive comments, concluding with a reality check:
"It's not always about you. THE AMBASSADOR and I had made plans."
I make an additional veiled threat under my breath before noting THE AMBASSADOR's discomfort, whose sole intention for visiting was to have a fun afternoon and enjoy herself.] //

⁂
Maj. = 2- THE DANCER: #1243, 5- THE LAWYER: #1251
DISMISSIVE: #0012, #0397
HANG OUT: #0261, #0297, #0302, #0399
⁂

#1239 - June 17, 2020 @ 06:02 (San Francisco, California)

[1239.1 / 3366] [I've enrolled at a "Zen School." A variety of quick details sail by in a time lapse blur as I sit at a rectangular table in the back right hand corner of a room. A young woman is my instructor. She hands out a piece of paper with puzzles printed on both sides. I believe this is a homework assignment, but I'm surprised when she announces it's a pop quiz. I complete what I can, then turn it in to be graded. I take my seat and wait a few moments until my paper is returned without a score.

"There's no passing. No failing. You know how you felt when you interacted with the quiz. You assess yourself."

I do a spontaneous handstand on a desk, then disrupt a lecture by making screeches and Kung Fu kicks *(which seems a favorable move).*

"No grade?"

"When moved to back flip, just do," the teacher professes.]

[1239.2 / 3367] [Next, in a classroom, I'm tasked to construct a scale-model of a home that will fit on my desktop. I use handwoven cloth, wood, and other materials to construct my model during what seems to be a finite amount of time, though I'm informed by an out-of-body voice that, *"there's no such thing as time."*

Without the concept of time, the finished scale-model house instantly appears in front of me without any effort.]

[1239.3 / 3368] [I negotiate terms and conditions of a contract between two female musicians. They each had a list of prerequisites to be met, prior to performance which, were left unsatisfied at their last interaction, and thus *(...resulted in no concert).* They haven't spoken to one another in the years since.

I suggest they, ***"use their rift as creative fodder to mend fences."***

I pose a series of questions:

+ ***"What would happen if you planned to kick off your next tour in the Midwest, and one of you purposefully oversleeps on opening night?"***

+ ***"When the bus leaves for Florida the morning after, what would happen if it crashes and one of you dies?"***

The peculiar questioning continues until I wake up.] //

⁂

ZEN: #0391
PECULIAR: #0125, #0243
PUZZLE: #0065, #0187, #0243, #0273, #0359

⁂

⁂

PART 15 - FIAT LUX

#1240 - #1442

"You may say I'm a dreamer,
But I'm not the only one.
I hope some day you'll join us,
And the world will be as one."

-John Lennon

* * *

June 19, 2020 - October 18, 2020

⁂

⁂ 15.1 - RETREAT TO THE WOMB: 1240-1378 ⁂

#1240 - June 19, 2020 @ 01:23 (Louisville, Colorado)

[1240.1 / 3369] [I'm a virgin teenage boy. THE COUTURIER is a sexually active teenage girl. We sit together on her bed listening to music and talking. She invites me to my first sexual experience on the condition that I,

"Use it as a data point to later counsel straight men on how to be better lovers."]

[1240.2 / 3370] [I observe a public rally in support of an autocratic regime. A counterparty group of equal size surrounds and taunts those gathered to rally, until the regime devotees instantly disappear without a trace. A moment later, the counterparty group dissipates leaving me standing next to a shoddy, crudely constructed pulpit on the gravel shoulder of a rural county highway. I give the pulpit a swift kick and knock two small doors from its front, revealing a view of a cornfield. I stare at the corn waving in the wind for a moment until I'm startled both by the transition of day-to-dusk, and two men wearing camouflage trousers and hoodies who climb up a small hill behind the pulpit, drop their backpacks, and build a small camp for the night.

All sound stops. The stillness feels like the vacuum of space.

"Perhaps the atmosphere decided to end its contract with the planet and flew off to swaddle another heavenly body."]

[1240.3 / 3371] [I'm a shapeshifting spirit. Most recently I've taken up short term residence in THE EMPYREAN's *(skillful, clear, and collaborative)* house, and have pranked him by taking the form of his eight-year-old son in unexpected places in the home. If they're both in the kitchen and THE EMPYREAN steps away to use the bathroom, I manifest as his son washing my hands just before he walks in the door. If they're at the dinner table eating and he decides to grab a tool from the garage for a later project, I take a seat on the workbench and lightly bang my heels into the cabinet doors below, as though I've been waiting for him for lifetimes.

Each interaction is met with lightness and humor, and he's perpetually confused by his son's superpowers until I blow my own cover.

One evening while in my "son" costume I casually float in an orbit around the log-framed home, with large angular plate glass windows. I pass by the glass, where THE EMPYREAN and his son sit on a couch that faces out the windows as they talk. THE EMPYREAN does a double take, realizes I'm the impersonator, and invites me in with a smile. I pass through the window like vapor, then take a form twice as tall as my body.

"He's enlightened and awakened," THE EMPYREAN whispers to his son when asked who I am.

My eyes burst with tears and I cry as the acknowledgment hits me in the heart.

"I appreciate that's how you see me, but I can't accept the words because I don't believe them," I say drying my face as my lips quiver. I can barely utter the words.

THE CONNECTOR enters speaking at high volume, unaware of the holy moment, but ready to riff on projects and creative ideas.] //

⁂

Maj. = 4- THE CONNECTOR: #1242
Min. = ♣- THE COUTURIER: #1267
SPIRIT: #0018, #0610, #827, #1253
INTERACTION: #0059, #0628, #0850, #1217
THE EMPYREAN: #1289

⁂

#1241 - June 19, 2020 @ 06:11 (Louisville, Colorado)

[1241.1 / 3372] [Williams & Sonoma announces the opening of a new cafe concept in all their retail locations. Latvian Tea Cakes will be offered as the single specialty menu item. The cakes will be covered in Thai Iced Tea and served exclusively by Vietnamese associates.]

[1241.2 / 3373] [I'm in a basement where a single beam of outside light shines down from a window well, onto the carpeted floor. An odd tarantula *(its head atop the thorax, with legs extending from a common point beneath)*, scurries across the carpet. An odd cream colored "O" the size and thickness of a wedding ring highlights the center of its abdomen.

THE WEAVER and THE CHOCOHOLIC sit together at a card table talking. THE CHOCOHOLIC waves me over with a request to sign the back of a new debit card.

I look down and find a square of carpet sullied with refuse. I make it my priority to grab a piece of gold twine coated with a thin layer of dried gold paint, and yank it up an arm length at a time. I peel it up from the carpet leaving a shadowy series of squiggles and *"curly q's"* in the gold paint dried atop the carpet. When I give a final pull, the tension applied to the string dislodges a desiccated used condom *(coated with shit)* from the floor. It pops up and causes me to stumble backward a couple steps.

I crush the spider under foot as I walk to the table, grab the bank card, and dart up a flight of stairs. In transit, I bend the bank card horizontally in half. Once at the top of the stairs I hold the bent card between my index and middle fingers, and flick it on to a small white circular dish on a square table across the room, where a variety of other bank cards have come to rest in the shapes of "V's."] //

⁂

Maj. = 0- THE WEAVER: #1247
CREDIT: #0220, #0629, #0915, #1220
BEND: #0389, #0461, #0815, #1250
REQUEST: #0012, #0557, #0854, #1260
THE CHOCOHOLIC: #1404

⁂

#1242 - June 20, 2020 @ 6:42am (Omaha, Nebraska)

[1242.1 / 3374] [THE CONNECTOR and I share company around a wood burning stove in a cabin at night. We've decided to spend a long weekend together wherein we've *"prioritized rest, relaxation, and restorative activities."* We decide to add a few extra days to our planned sojourn. THE CONNECTOR places a call on an antique rotary phone, pausing to provide the operator with a code word necessary to lengthen our stay.

One morning we decide to take the car out for refueling, stopping at a 1930's era gas station for a fill up, while friends and family gather at the cabin. When we return, we discover a group of overall-wearing male friends collaborating on the construction of a wooden fence. They become overworked. As a group they collectively decide to pause.

Once paused, a faction decides to quit and walk off the jobsite. THE MANAGING DIRECTOR *(firm, unfettered, and precise)* and other friends from bygone eras may be overseeing the project from a hidden back room inside the cabin, though THE CONNECTOR and I don't check to confirm. After spending a few moments inside, an earthquake strikes, leaving the bracing that bolsters the house *(from beneath a ledge)* to become compromised and distressed. The steel ribs collapse into a pile of mangled metal noodles. The house on top topples shortly thereafter into a ravine. As we descend, all within share a fear that the roof will flatten us to corpsy pancakes once we strike the bottom.

I blink and find myself on the lip of the hill from where the structure once stood. A new retreat center is under construction. Backhoes till up the land. Gravel roads are freshly laid, and series of intricate steel I-beams *(all painted royal blue)* have been placed on what looks like a new group gathering space.

I blink again and find myself in a room with pine wood walls and floors. I can smell the fresh cuts of boards placed that day.] //

⁂

Maj. = 4- THE CONNECTOR: #1262
EARTHQUAKE: #0157, #0674, #0988
CABIN: #0309, #0427, #0826, #1307
WEEKEND: #0079, #0547, #0927, #1232
THE MANAGING DIRECTOR: #1412

⁂

#1243 - June 22, 2020 @ 06:57 (McCordsville, Indiana)

[1243.1 / 3375] [THE DANCER carries THE LITTLE PRINCE on her hip outside to play, inviting me to meet them later.]

[1243.2 / 3376] [Animated sequences for a forthcoming video game are developed by a popular Asian director. The anticipation surrounding the release of the game is palpable.]

[1243.3 / 3377] [I attempt to record something with my phone, but fail multiple times. I'm frustrated. Members of "TEAM NITRO" (THE IRONMAN, THE AWAKENING, THE KIDDO, THE CONJURER, and THE LALA) are present as I fail.]

[1243.4 / 3378] [I consider moving into a house when a PEE WEE HERMAN-looking real estate broker informs me that I'm,

"The next prospect on the list who the master tenant will meet." The meeting must happen imminently, per the broker, but I tell him to,

"Inform the master tenant that I'll make time to speak with him next week."] //

⁂

Maj. = 2- THE DANCER: #1249, 12- THE LITTLE PRINCE: #1273
Min. = ♦- THE LALA: #1285
THE CONJURER: #1281
THE IRONMAN: #1368
THE AWAKENING: #1368
THE KIDDO: #1368

⁂

#1244 - June 22, 2020 @ 09:08 (McCordsville, Indiana)

[1244.1 / 3379] [Car towed. Halloween Party. Intense, vivid, indecipherable action.] //

⁂
HALLOWEEN: #0017, #0761, #0902, #1304
⁂

#1245 - June 23, 2020 @ 03:04 (McCordsville, Indiana)

[1245.1 / 3380] [I fly along the highway at intense speed, quickly solving impromptu puzzles to receive a birth to a motocross race.
"I have to navigate a path from Idaho to Colorado to cast a ballot."]

[1245.2 / 3381] [A lie about being on a motocross team in order to acquire access to a garage space at a competitive track, where I can prepare for a prestigious upcoming race. I provide members of my management team with a manuscript printed on gold paper, along with my alternative identity and supporting credentials, which have been stolen from another qualifying participant. I hire dozens of engineers and crew to ready my vehicle for competition. A couple of crew members grow skeptical when we meet, expecting to see a different face associated with the name. I convince the curious to,
"Believe I am who I say I am."
Multiple people are escorted by legacy staff members who introduce me by my new alternative name. I almost correct the crew a few times, as I prime myself to respond to the new identity. I set to task, adjusting the tension to a series of six bands at the base of the stall where my bike is parked, causing the vehicle to rise up overhead. A media team becomes suspicious of my presence when my answers shouted across the garage in response to their questions, don't fit the personality of the racer. An extra layer of security prevents them from coming closer to me.]

[1245.3 / 3382] [The motocross bike has been enhanced with turbo boosters and a massive engine to aid my quest to cast a critical ballot in an election. A group of crew members upgrade a specific component related to the wheels. Another set of team members field test the electronic voting machine at the end of the track. The bike has a futuristic design made of sleek pipes with softly glowing components. As I take a final pass around the space before the race, I notice a copy of the distributed manuscript has been scattered along the exterior wall of the track.

As preparations complete, crew members peel off one at a time. I know that as I walk towards the bike *(now parked and idling at the start line)* I'll be the only one left when I mount it and prepare to ride.

"I don't have a team uniform, kit, nor fireproof suit."

I know I need one, but won't have one, which makes my participation hazardous and potentially lethal.]

[1245.4 / 3383] [The race concludes.

"I've won."

Though I've participated in a criminal manipulation with the identity theft, I'm given a pardon when others learn of how I've cast my vote.] //

⁂

LIE: #0012
VOTE: #0054, #0520, #0988
SLEEK: #0013, #0436, #0897
RACE: #0146, #0441, #0943, #1208

⁂

#1246 - June 23, 2020 @ 06:50 (McCordsville, Indiana)

[1246.1 / 3384] [I observe three men stand shoulder-to-shoulder on a small hill in a public green space. Time speeds up. The men remain stationary as a flurry of blurry activity erupts around them. Bursts of light leave layers of mulch, grass, and gravel in a disc-like form while the men stand in the center. A poured ring of concrete fills in around their bodies and eventually envelopes their heads. They're unbothered as the concrete cures and locks them in place. I find the circumstances humorous.]

[1246.2 / 3385] [I come to in the midst of a burst of activity, on a team at an in-house catering service, at a brick shaped mansion with a white painted exterior. THE ROBOT is present and shares affinity for another guy onsite who I'm not familiar with. I float backwards through walls to determine where I am. From outside the structure looking back, I learn I'm at THE EPICUREAN's estate. I observe activity within, without the visual obstruction of walls. I'm intrigued by the basement level which is currently under renovation, and later intended to be a customer service center for stakeholders of a highly sought hedge fund.

I fly inside and join THE ROBOT arm-in-arm. She and I walk the floor performing a four-eyed check of blue tape outlines that map out where desks and workspaces will later be installed. Once complete, I fly back outside and up about a hundred feet to determine my next task. I descend to ground level, and walk along a concrete sidewalk at the perimeter of the property until I discover a crack in the brick wall at exactly the height and width of my body *(when turned perpendicular to the wall)*. I close one eye to allow my vision to adjust to the dark and begin to shuffle with both arms outstretched like a T, sidestepping through layers of mortar, wood, and drywall until I reach the end of the tilted parallelogram-like corridor. When I reach the end of the corridor I know to turn right at the fork.]

. . .

[1246.3 / 3386] [Within the property, I find myself setting a table for 10 among a sea of others in a large banquet space. Mid-task I note the flatware used is oddly shaped at each place setting. Some forks have a tine or two bent 90 degrees from the root. Others have over bent necks. I'm most taken by ones that have unusually long, wide and flat handles with isosceles triangle cutouts, which remove most of the mass of the object and leave the tablecloth viewable beneath. When my attention shifts from the peculiar flatware, I'm asked by a man seated at the table to my right for a beer.

"Buddy, you're the third person I've asked. No one here seems to be paying me much attention."

I snap my fingers. A can of Fosters and a chilled glass appear on a silver platter on my outstretched palm. I serve the man the beer, and recognize him as THE ROBOT's husband, which I find upsetting.]

[1246.4 / 3387] [Another glance up from the table finds the banquet hall transformed into a stark black amusement park queue for a wild river rapid ride. The tables transform into bumper boat-like vessels surrounded by a thick ring of rebound-ready rubber. A lazy Susan at the middle of each vessel provides snacks as "rider-diners" rage down the winding river. I take command of a craft that jumps the bend, slides across a cobblestone path, and slowly slides to a stop after bouncing in to a retaining wall.] //

⁂

Min. = ♥- THE ROBOT: #1337, ♥-THE EPICUREAN: #1420
BEER: #0375, #0561, #0919, #1301
WILD: #0028, #0544, #0871, #1211
BLURRY: #0015, #0508, #0868, #1215

⁂

#1247 - June 24, 2020 @ 07:55 (Beavercreek, Ohio)
This sequence holds a tone of meditation, presence and healing throughout

[1247.1 / 3388] [I'm selected to assist a group of people run their energy in a large conference room. I lay out mats and coverings in advance of their arrival. Students are empowered to select what space in the room they wish to occupy. A group of six arrives, mostly women. I recognize one as THE PRAGMATIST *(psychic, transparent, and generous)*, and the rest as other *"fellow students of service."* They rearrange the mats into their own unique small clusters around the room.]

[1247.2 / 3389] [I'm a Trans Woman. I've befriended SAM NEILL and CATHERINE O'HARA who seem to be spouses and invite them into a five-way orgy with me and another couple. I grab SAM's hand and place it around my waist to flirt with him, but mid-seduction I find myself gassy, farting, and needing to take a shit. I excuse myself and enter a restroom, contemplating my desire to have a 1:1 interaction with SAM. As I sit to relieve myself, THE WEAVER startles me when she greets me on the commode immediately next to mine. She tells me *"she's done her homework by reading up on the stories of other Trans women and supports my transition."* There are no sidewalls, but a door can function as a privacy shield from a window to the street level. I'm not able to close the door. A group of women heading in to dinner can see everything.]

. . .

[1247.3 / 3390] [I'm a man. A male and female couple joins me in a taxi en route to a restaurant. We exit the car and walk through the front door, at which time the couple transforms in to a different pair of gay men. The three of us walk together through the restaurant, which turns into a den filled with beds. The beds are made up with different shades of red sheets. I see myself across the room as a Trans Woman having sex with SAM NEILL. SAM has a beautiful erection. I walk through the room arm-in-arm with the two men and wake up.] //

⁂

Maj. = 0- THE WEAVER: #1249
TRANS: #0176, #0452, #0976
RED: #0181, #0472, #0817, #1256
TAXI: #0003, #0512

⁂

#1248 - June 24, 2020 @ 09:38 (Beavercreek, Ohio)

[1248.1 / 3391] [Blueberries.]

[1248.2 / 3392] [At a concert. Behind a barrier. A man with a goatee debates moving from the back of the crowd towards the stage. It might be an ANDREW W.K. concert. I don't know the man, but I convince him to move ahead to a U-Shaped table, set center-stage at the front railing. He joins a familiar group of revelers who have just been delivered craft cocktails in highball glasses. A shadowy stranger delivers me an envelope with $150 in cash as *"payment for successfully influencing the goateed man."* At 2:58pm I receive an additional payment of $150 for *"arriving at the venue before 3:00pm."* I don't have a spending plan for the petty cash.]

[1248.3 / 3393] [I'm at a yoga studio with THE HILLBILLY. We discuss a new way of constructing public studio classes. A baby sits to my left heel who believes I'm its father. I repeatedly pick it up and set it down, making goofy sounds and faces, to the child's delight. THE NURSE pops her head through a doorway and attempts to offer an opinion. She becomes offended when we don't take her suggestion. She huffs and stomps away down a sisal-rug-lined glass hallway as THE HILLBILLY and I continue to brainstorm. The room fills with people, and the sound of live music booms from another room, so it's possible I've ***"bilocated and forgotten I've left a copy of myself at the concert venue next door."***]

[1248.4 / 3394] [THE GUITARIST and I walk towards a house. Air quality suggests we're in Los Angeles. Just before we arrive at the front door, we find a friend of ours *(a young Black man)* wearing a rust-colored leather jacket, lying face down and passed out in a pile of mulch. We roll him over and find he's vomited a massive amount of an odd, thick yellowish oatmeal-looking substance on the left interior panel of the jacket. Once we assure he's conscious, he asks us to leave him there. When we finally approach the white door with three small diamond windows, we find the doorknob covered in a similar puke-like residue. Another gunshot-like splatter of oatmeal puke viscously sticks at eye level. We enter the house and I awaken.] //

⁂

Maj. = 13- THE NURSE: #1319

ANDREW W.K.: #1350

DIAMOND: #0170, #0431, #0893, #1293

⁂

#1249 - June 25, 2020 @ 02:01 (Beavercreek, Ohio)

[1249.1 / 3395] [BRITNEY SPEARS lives on a dairy farm. She rehearses for the Superbowl halftime show on the back deck, in the center of a field, lined by a split-rail fence. A DJ stands in a booth nearby remixing LADY GAGA tracks with BRITNEY's catalogue. She practices in the rain to ensure she is, *"weather ready and won't slip if the elements are harsh,"* on the day of her performance.]

[1249.2 / 3396] [I sit at a picnic table. An obese woman wearing a mask hobbles towards me and takes a seat across the table next to THE CARPENTER. She wheezes and coughs as the two of them cynically chastise each other. I'm confused. I don't know why the woman is so angry. My guide informs me it's THE CATHOLIC. Her hair is long and thinning, and she's barely recognizable to me.

"I haven't seen you in 19 years," I say as I give her a hug and begin to cry.

She shrugs me off saying, *"DON'T do that. I can't help it. It's just how the energy is between us."*]

[1249.3 / 3397] [I walk through the door of an antique store in a small town in Arkansas. THE FARMHAND is the owner. She's 50% taller than the rest of us, and appears to be over 100 years old. Today's the final day the store will be open, after operating for more than four decades. She and THE POSTMASTER had run the business together until he passed away some number of years ago. The space is a simple open floor plan shaped like a long rectangle, with a series of square levels that each ascend a partial step as customers flow from the front to the back. THE WEAVER walks me by a wall of framed family photos on a sunlit side of the building, pausing nostalgically to share stories held still in the images. She introduces me to family members I've not previously met, most of whom are out of body, but talk with us from the photos.

A young man follows THE FARMHAND through her daily routine with a camera crew, documenting the origin story of the business for a movie they're creating. THE FARMHAND shares that she and THE POSTMASTER *"were on a leisurely weekend drive until she heard a guide tell them to stop and get out of the car. She knew to walk across a field and water a plant that had sprouted up from a block of concrete. She was moved by the plant's fortitude and took it as a cue to 'do the impossible' and open her own store."* As the interview progresses, THE FARMHAND removes her teeth and her cadence around the store slows. I tell her, ***"I want a hug."***]

. . .

[1249.4 / 3398] [THE FARMHAND leads a group of us on a walk to the site of another origin story. THE WEAVER, THE CARPENTER, THE DANCER and THE CHILD walk in order of descending height, down a concrete sidewalk that slowly rises and loops around, leaving a small teardrop-shaped patch of yellow grass at the center. THE FARMHAND expresses embarrassment when she admits she'd fallen in the teardrop shaped grass earlier in the day while she'd gone out for a walk after a large rain storm. The rain left the pavement slippery and she was unable to get up until, luckily, a member of the town's historical preservation society happened along the path and placed a call to local emergency services. The experience of helplessness was enough for THE FARMHAND to *"surrender the store and peacefully live out her embodied life."*

THE CHILD is a toddler and walks around the teardrop sidewalk multiple times. THE FARMHAND encourages THE DANCER to pull a waist high lever, resulting in the grassy center portion of the teardrop to slowly rise up 20 feet in the air, supported from beneath by a thin black metal pole that connects to the core of the earth *(expressed as a magnificent slow turning disco ball that sparkles when struck by sunlight)*. THE CHILD teeters close to the edge, when she sees the disco ball.

THE WEAVER calls out to THE DANCER, *"She's going to fall into the pit!"*

THE DANCER calmly walks towards THE CHILD, grabs her right ankle by the pants and threads it into a nylon loop, similar in teardrop shape, as THE CHILD topples in towards the glittery center of the earth. The grassy portion begins to retract to its point of origin. THE DANCER steadfastly clings to the loop which has snared THE CHILD's foot as the teardrop-shaped grass segment closes. THE DANCER's arm is likely crushed, though she's more concerned with whether or not THE CHILD has suffered injury. I cry. I don't know what to do.] //

⁂

Maj. = 0- THE WEAVER: #1255, 1- THE CARPENTER: #1256,
2- THE DANCER: #1251, 3- THE CHILD: #1255
Min. = ♣- THE POSTMASTER: #1257, ♣- THE CATHOLIC: #1252
LADY GAGA: #1282
BRITNEY SPEARS: #1283

⁂

#1250 - June 25, 2020 @ 06:21 (Beavercreek, Ohio)

[1250.1 / 3399] [I sit at a cafe table. I'm wearing a fitted sweater and a blue pork pie hat. GWYNETH PALTROW first takes a seat across from me, then stands and sits next to me on my side of the table. We have a conversation about possibly dating. She asks me if I can refer her to *"all-star web designers and coders."* I initially mishear her request and tell her,

"I don't have the correct skill set, but I can find someone who does."

I stand and walk to a half wall, pausing to bend over to lift a chair. Under one of the chair's slightly shorter legs is a stack of my business cards that act as a shim. The first card I grab is scuffed and has the impression of a square chair foot embossed in it. I walk back to the table which has transformed in to a coolly lit unisex washroom where GWYNETH rinses her hands in a sink. I stand behind her. My gob is full of mouthwash. I forget this as I respond to another of her questions, spitting fluid over her shoulder. The mirror turns into a cinderblock wall, against which the liquid ricochets, then lands on her cream cashmere camisole, leaving a neon blue splotchy archipelago near her right shoulder. I feel terrible for the mess I've made and reach towards the next sink to soak a wad of paper towels, which she'll hopefully use to blot the stain. She and I curtail our discussion and do not go on a date.]

[1250.2 / 3400] [I occupy a modern condo which has multiple black credenzas placed in a row against a wall-sized window.]

[1250.3 / 3401] [I'm in the starkly decorated ground floor bedroom of an average suburban home. I tidy the space by putting away the few Spartan items left on display as I anticipate the arrival of a royal guest.]

[1250.4 / 3402] [THERESA MAY has just been reelected Prime Minister of England in a surprise referendum.] //

⁂

BLUE: #0176, #0188, #0194
MODERN: #0404, #0429, #0437
PRIME: #0938, #1141

⁂

#1251 - June 25, 2020 @ 08:14 (Beavercreek, Ohio)

[1251.1 / 3403] [I teach a yoga class in Manhattan. I anticipate the arrival of THE SHARED HEART. My vision is blurry and I'm not able to discern who has filed into the practice space. I'm not able to find the sound system to set a musical mood in advance of class. A woman receives a private lesson in a corner of the room. We clap for her, before taking the elevator to a ground floor level to another practice room. The class commences and mid-session I completely forget the sequence I'm leading. Playfully, I begin asking the students,

"What do we do now?"
"MOVE!"
"What comes next?"
"BREATHE!"
"Third time's a charm?"
"SWEAT!"
"WHERE DO WE GO FROM HERE?"]

[1251.2 / 3404] [I watch a documentary that profiles fashion designer JUNYA WANTANABE. He's recreated a series of colorful thin-lined designer shirts that have become highly desired by young people. ***"They seem expensive for teenagers, but they're willing to pay a premium for the look."*** THE DANCER sits next to me watching and is eager to try sewing her own similar type of pattern from a bolt of colorful fabric she's previously not known what to do with. The documentary concludes with a single shot of the designer who looks towards the camera through a monocle placed in front of each eye. A larger magnifying glass is placed in front of his mouth just before he smiles as the film concludes.]

. . .

[1251.3 / 3405] [I've moved out of my apartment, leaving behind a small table and a single chair in an otherwise empty room.]

[1251.4 / 3406] [As I drive through a small town, I feel like the vehicle is moving well above the 25mph speed limit. There's no speedometer. I apply the break. Different people appear in the passenger seat: THE LAWYER, BUDDHA, ST. FRANCIS, ST. RAPHAEL, ST. MICHAEL, and CHRISTOPHER HITCHENS all stop through and chat.] //

⁂

Maj. = 2- THE DANCER: #1256, 5- THE LAWYER: #1256
ST. FRANCIS: #1442
MANHATTAN: #1043, #1141, #1157
SEQUENCE: #0035, #0047

⁂

#1252 - June 26, 2020 @ 07:37 (Beavercreek, Ohio)

[1252.1 / 3407] [I leave an office building and get in a car with THE CATHOLIC and THE MAGICIAN. We drive in the direction of a giant storm. As we barrel down the highway, THE MAGICIAN drops the rag top cover to the convertible. I look left and see a series of four tornados sweeping across a rolling hillside of farmed land. Rain strikes the left side of the windshield so strongly that it makes the glass look frosted and opaque. To the right the sky is blue and sunny.]

[1252.2 / 3408] [A friend hands me a book and suggests I read it. ***"I've read it before."***] //

⁂

Maj. = 14- THE MAGICIAN: #1359
Min. = ♣- THE CATHOLIC: #1295
CONVERTIBLE: #0159, #0610, #0698, #0726

⁂

#1253 - June 27, 2020 @ 08:19 (Beavercreek, Ohio)

[1253.1 / 3409] [I float as spirit with THE WORLDBRIDGER and THE PUBLIC MEDIUM. We observe a young boy and his mother painting a series of vertically mounted rectangular wooden panels with a series of horizontal rows containing Hebrew and Mandarin characters. I find their process beautiful and their creative connection soul stirring as I snap photographs of them playing and learning from one another.

"They're creating a translation tool."

We invite the mother and son to a game of freeze tag. Each time someone is tagged the pause is spent in prayer.

Just before unfreezing THE WORLDBRIDGER I tell him,

"Praying has served your body well. You look eternally youthful!"] //

⁂

⁂

Maj. = 7-THE WORLDBRIDGER: #1257, 18-THE PUBLIC MEDIUM: # 1407
HEBREW: #0618
PRAYER: #0139, #0309, #0742, #0818
FREEZE: #0402, #0496, #0520

⁂

#1254 - June 28, 2020 @ 05:47 (Beavercreek, Ohio)

[1254.1 / 3410] [I'm at a concert venue. I've been chosen to replace the bass player for the headliner. Their bandmate is recovering from hand surgery. I've been called away by another contract for a week's worth of performances. I inform the band that, ***"I'll need coverage for a couple of dates, but I'm locked in for the finale."*** The band members are two White men and a Black woman who has gorgeous braided dreadlocks. THE CHIEF OF STAFF *(good natured, loving, and supportive)* is among those nearby, sharing a conversation with a man in a suit. The three band members huddle together backstage as I prepare to depart. They shout at me to *"hurry back"* as I pause to say hello to THE CHIEF OF STAFF. I offer her and her friend tickets to the tour finale. Out on the parking lot I find a variety of Muppet-like puppets intentionally placed in front of inventory scanners in spots where I expect to see cars parked.] //

⁂

SURGERY: #0198, #0260
HUDDLE: #0688
HURRY: #0929

⁂

#1255 - June 29, 2020 @ 05:23 (Beavercreek, Ohio)

[1255.1 / 3411] [I'm in an old house with THE WEAVER, GRANDMA and another woman. We share space with another group of people gathered at the opposite end of the room. THE FAIRY GODMOTHER's mother has decided to retire for the night after she concludes her piano lesson. GREAT GRANDMOTHER, GRANDMA and two other women lay together in a bed behind the piano with the sheet pulled up to their noses.

THE WEAVER speaks at high volume, after I ask her repeatedly ***"to whisper in consideration of the ancestral women attempting to sleep."***

"Can't you whisper?"

"You've gotta get used to the noise."

Her response makes me mildly upset and we spend a few hours not speaking to one another. She's gotten her way, because my repeated use of the "F" word earlier was beginning to annoy her. While silent, I go to the back room and find THE CHILD asleep on a couch.

"We don't want to forget her," I tell THE WEAVER, breaking the silence.

"And the 'F' word...it's an amazing vehicle. When I was using it ad nauseum earlier it had no intention behind it. It was just a mouth sound."]

[1255.2 / 3412] [The small house opens into a large hotel lobby where hundreds of people have gathered for a concert. I pull a pair of French doors closed to guide concert goers in the proper direction. A few renegades break from convention, throw the doors open, and pass through in the *"undesired"* direction without purchasing tickets. There's no security enforced. No one seems concerned. Bodies congregated in a large ballroom overflow into an even bigger auditorium. I stand behind different groups of people who are queued behind rows of microwaves, which erupt piles of popcorn that dump into large black plastic tubs that can be, *"infinitely refilled by attendees so long as they remain inside the venue."*]

[1255.3 / 3413] [I rapidly descend a series of concrete hills on sleds, each time riding with a different partner. The sharp curves cause us to accelerate as we navigate each course to the bottom. I spend one descent high-fiving my partner behind me ***"acknowledging our proficiency."*** His legs are wrapped tightly around my waist, heels crossed, and placed in the space between my shin bones.] //

⁂

Maj. = 0- THE WEAVER: #1256, 3- THE CHILD: #1256, 11- GRANDMA: #1258
GREAT GRANDMOTHER: #1433
WHISPER: #0093, #0102, #0163, #0245
POPCORN: #0642, #0841
SHIN: #0874

⁂

#1256 - June 30, 2020 @ 05:57 (Beavercreek, Ohio)

[1256.1 / 3414] [I deliver supplies to a homeless family that lives on "Fairfield Road" on the former site of a garden center. They occupy the upper portion, of half of a simple wooden structure, among a series of three. The pairs of plywood cubes stacked atop each other look like three large dominos set upright in a tight row. The homes are held vacant specifically *"as shelters for transient immigrant single mothers."* My friends and I pass plastic bags of groceries up to a terrified and exhausted young woman. Once we've completed the task we proceed on to a previously scheduled dinner, where I'm supposed to have a role in an important business discussion.]

[1256.2 / 3415] [I attend THE CHILD's birthday party. THE WEAVER is there. The scene is rowdy and noisy. I'm taken in by chalk murals on a concrete wall. When I comment on the murals, another child's mother informs me, they were created by THE DANCER. When I ask THE DANCER about them, she tells me *"they were simple to create with a projector and a 'chalk by number' diagram that she first traced on the wall."* She directs my attention to slices of rainbow piñata cake with numerous deep shades of red and orange, plated and set on a round table with a red table cloth, which she believes is *"a greater achievement than the chalk murals."* When the time comes to open gifts, I realize I'm half an hour behind schedule to get to the dinner appointment. I have a quick exchange with THE CARPENTER, expressing that I want to make good on my commitments.

"There's no way I'll make it."

"You need to just go."]

. . .

[1256.3 / 3416] [I'm at THE BREAKS DJ's *(vivacious, talented, and pious)* new apartment, which she shows off to a small group of friends. The robust geometry of patterned squares and rectangles is set by tones of taupe, tan and white. Golden hour light floods in from a small rectangular window in the upper left corner of an undecorated, neutrally toned wall. The light condenses into a small rectangle that projects animated images on the headboard of her newly delivered bed, positioned in the center of the wall adjacent to the window. Light bends. THE BREAKS DJ believes the place is a substantial upgrade from where she just came from. *"I was in a basement for years!"*]

[1256.4 / 3417] [THE CHILD is extremely satisfied with her birthday party. She's overstimulated. I surrender and accept that it's the highest service to stay and take photographs of the piñata cake, which I then text to THE LAWYER. When I ask THE DANCER how long it took to complete the cake she dodges with a response, *"If I had to do it again, I could be finished in an hour."* THE CHILD is presented with a hallmark/prestigious gift, presented on an elevated table in front of all party attendees. She's distracted by a small rectangle of light projected on the wall on the opposite side of the room, until THE DANCER grabs her gently on both sides of the face from behind and directs her gaze back to the gift table.]

[1256. 5 / 3418] [The scene concludes with a percussion teacher *(a middle-aged Black woman)* seated behind a student at a drum kit, at the far end of the party venue. They practice paradiddles while tuning the drums and discussing their tonal qualities. As I approach the percussion teacher, she morphs into an older White woman with a large loose belly. She's certain the piccolo snare she's brought to the lesson is *"a half-step out of tune."* She knows different drums will be needed to match the key signature of a composition to be performed later in the season. I strike the piccolo snare as the woman gives the student feedback. I can tell she's annoyed, but I'm certain the drum is mine and that ***"I'm supposed to leave the party with it."***] //

⁂

Maj. = 0- THE WEAVER: #1257, 1- THE CARPENTER: #1259, 2- THE DANCER: #1257, 3- THE CHILD: #1258, 5- THE LAWYER: #1310

PROJECT: #0266, #0280

SNARE: #0463

SUBSTANTIAL: #0033, #0353

THE BREAKS DJ: #1344

⁂

#1257 - July 1, 2020 @ 05:14 (Beavercreek, Ohio)

[1257.1 / 3419] [I'm in Arkansas. I wake up from a nap on THE POSTMASTER's bed, located in a mattress showroom immediately adjacent to a Congressman's desk. The Congressman comes and goes, each time returning in a more negative mood. This becomes spookier over a number of days until one evening when he returns, he seems possessed by a demon. I call on THE WORLDBRIDGER for support, who helps me identify and isolate a *"diminutive energy"* that causes the Congressman to behave *"meanly."* THE WORLDBRIDGER softly pushes the entity out of the showroom. I see it outside the window as a small troublesome goblin, round in shape with tiny reed-like arms and legs, and a large gaping mouth which gnashes jaws lined with rows of jagged teeth. THE WEAVER enters to file a complaint with the Congressman's Chief of Staff. She's unaware of the disruptive goblin that's manipulated many of the man's recent actions.

The being and THE WORLDBRIDGER put me through my paces in a variety of *"spiritual training scenarios."*

One occurs in a parking lot where THE DANCER doesn't believe that *"people can be possessed"* and starts twirling goofily while making sounds at me. The entity matches posture behind her, overtakes her, and puppets her body around. I'm unable to call the goblin out. THE WORLDBRIDGER casts it from her with the raising of an eyebrow, as he meditates while holding a small bowl. I'm unable to see the energy but I know when it's in the scene.

In another, I flirt with a man. We disrobe and agree to have sex in a shower. The entity overtakes the man who slams the shower door in my face and laughs.

Yet another finds me negotiating the purchase of a car. The seller offers me a deal too good to refuse, which immediately indicates the entity has inhabited the man's body and is attempting to influence the transaction. I demand the entity, ***"Get out. Stop trying to scam me!"***

The last I recall finds me in a showroom. THE WORLDBRIDGER nods at me as he burns incense, affirming I've completed the day's exercises. I'm left feeling cautious. I'm not able to see the energy, but I'm aware of its tone and how to shift a space while it's present.] //

⁂

Maj. = 0- THE WEAVER: #1258, 2- THE DANCER: #1259, 7- THE WORLDBRIDGER: #1268

INCENSE: #0206

EXERCISE: #0295, #0489, #0538

SHOWROOM: #0502, #0796

⁂

#1258 - July 1, 2020 @ 06:22 (Beavercreek, Ohio)

[1258.1 / 3420] [THE CHILD rides a rollercoaster by herself while THE WEAVER and GRANDMA playfully observe from a public viewing deck.

"You can't get me!" THE CHILD shouts down with a giggle as the train crests the first hill and quickly descends at increasing speed. *"Wee! Woo hoo!"* she joyfully exclaims as the ride whizzes quickly through a series of corkscrews and helixes.]

[1258.2 / 3421] [I'm in the kitchen at a dinner party, with a group of five men. We're all leaning back around the interior "U" of a wraparound white granite countertop. I introduce myself to a guy with long curly red hair.

"My name's 'Chris.'"

"And 'Chris,' what do you do...for fun?"

He passes me a small red, repurposed greeting card on which he's scribbled *"ten tenets to unlock a happy life* "in a playful cartoonish script. All are obscured and fuzzy, save one which reads: *"First feel sad. Empty out. Feel every feeling. #KeyNumberThree."*] //

⁂

Maj. = 0- THE WEAVER: #1259, 3- THE CHILD: #1263, 11- GRANDMA: #1263

WHIZ: #0865, #0870, #0891

SCRIBBLE: #0323, #0337
GRANITE: #0770, #0919
⁂

#1259 - July 2, 2020 @ 04:22 (Beavercreek, Ohio)

[1259.1 / 3422] [A group of young men move ramp components from the basement of a home to the ground floor. They're intent on packing a car full for a college community service trip.]

[1259.2 / 3423] [Bridge construction. I exit a car and help a crew spread hot asphalt along its surface under a midday blazing sun. A portion of the bridge is enclosed. It's less stifling to be at work during those few brief shielded moments under the bridge.]

[1259.3 / 3424] [I'm driving with some friends. Initially the destination is undeclared, though after some discussion we select Los Angeles. A female companion's affirmation validates the route.]

[1259.4 / 3425] [I follow a musician who plays tracks by VANILLA FUDGE on a mobile Hammond organ that rolls around a parking lot on small wheels.]

[1259.5 / 3426] [THE WEAVER, THE CARPENTER, THE DANCER and I arrive home from a day trip. The kitchen is a mess. In the middle of cleaning it as a team, THE CARPENTER invites two scuzzy White men in for dinner after they knock on the door. Neither of them helps clean. THE CARPENTER suggests the two men join him in the basement to watch *"the new giant TV."* I'm perturbed because I'm tasked with finishing the cleaning and setting the table for dinner *(with places for our impromptu guests)*. I'm upset. I'm willing to be in service to our guests, but the way I was told has left me feeling marginalized. When the three of them ascend, ready to eat, I express my discontent.

"You didn't even ask us if we wanted to have dinner with those guys."

The guys disappear, then materialize on the other side of the kitchen, expectant of a home cooked meal from THE WEAVER, who's happy to feed them. This sets me off even more. I continue cleaning, crouching down and crawling into a giant Lazy Susan under the kitchen island to scrub out and clean up pickled foods remnants that have scattered and dried, stuck to the tray.]

[1259.6 / 3427] [I have a conversation with THE REINCARNATED *(fragile, gentle, and cerebral)* where she's attempting to determine which of her neighbors have survived a catastrophe. She's convinced THE CONSERVATIVE NEIGHBOR *(strong, forceful, and opinionated)* is dead, but I assure her that ***"he's very much alive."*** She replies, *"Well I hope his wife is still alive too."*] //

⁂

⁂

Maj. = 0- THE WEAVER: #1263, 1- THE CARPENTER: #1264, 2- THE DANCER: #1261
ORGAN: #0005
LOS ANGELES: #0699, #0700
WHEELS: #0801, #1197

⁂

#1260 - July 2, 2020 @ 06:07 (Beavercreek, Ohio)

[1260.1 / 3428] [It's the last day of summer. This is the final time I'll get to hang out with my friends until we all return home from college next year. Part of our hang out happens at an amusement park where we ride a bunch of rollercoasters. Mid-day to escape the heat, we enter a dark auditorium and watch the filming of a game show segment. When production concludes one of my buddies *(the one with the blue ball cap)* leaps onto another's shoulders. We proceed across a parking lot as a posse, while laughing and joking. I'm the only one with a driver's license. The guy in the ball cap falls backwards and cracks his head on the pavement. His head bleeds profusely. He nods in and out of consciousness as he asks me to, *"get the shop vac."*

It's critical that I contact park security as soon as possible to prevent my friend from dying. I use my phone to search for the internal emergency services number, but instead can only pull up a list of local non-park jurisdictions who aren't responsive when I call one after the next. I drop my phone and sprint across the parking lot, pausing to bang on a pair of closed sliding glass doors. They open slowly and I enter a customer service reception area. I run back and forth, weaving through the long steel piped rows, even though I'm the only person inside. I stand behind a white line as a single customer service representative works dutifully behind a desk. Cheesy elevator music plays at low volume in the otherwise silent room. The customer service rep calls me forward. As I get nearer, I can see he's an older White man with a bushy moustache who wears thick glasses. I submit a formal written request *(in triplicate)* for help.]

[1260.2 / 3429] [I'm behind the open hatch back of my car. I write on an oversized, white Post It note positioned in the trunk. I write everyone's name in the group with my arm extended from right to left, with the script upside down and backwards in all lower case with a thick blue, blueberry scented marker. As my hand feverishly prints, I realize I'm writing the content of a hold-harmless waiver that I believe will absolve me from responsibility, if my friend's injuries wind up being debilitating. It's intense and unresolved when I wake.]

⁂

SHOULDER: #0021, #0400
VOLUME: #0406, #0767
BLUEBERRY: #1248
LAUGHING: #1323

⁂

#1261 - July 3, 2020 @ 06:27 (Beavercreek, Ohio)

[1261.1 / 3430] [I'm at a coastal airport walking across a sunlit terminal to catch an international flight. I watch a married couple carry out *"person on the street"* interviews in different parts of a city, on different televisions, for a local morning show. The couple is incommunicado, which makes timing transitions between interviews challenging for the production team who's, *"on the hook to deliver a seamless episode in real time."* While walking, I pass by both the man and the woman as I advance towards my gate. Just before I board the plane the man and woman stand by the gate agent and introduce another young couple who've just gotten engaged.

The wind on the tarmac has dramatically picked up. I'm not sure where I'm heading, though it seems Bucharest is my likely destination. THE DANCER and I meet up in an overflow passenger staging area, but based on how vacant the airport is it's unlikely our flight is oversold. We carry spools of garden hose that we label *"firefighting equipment."* The hoses are connected to a water source and pressurized, which will make our transport of them onto the flight *"a messy proposition."*

"We didn't think this through."

An ENNIO MORRICONE soundtrack plays at low volume in the background. THE DANCER claims *"movies would be easier to follow without the music."* We look down together and see our hoses have transformed into antique fire extinguishers.]

⁂

Maj. = 2- THE DANCER: #1264
GATE: #0344, #0387
WATER: #0428, #0795
TERMINAL: #0878, #1148

⁂

#1262 - July 3, 2020 @ 07:38 (Beavercreek, Ohio)

[1262.1 / 3431] [Three Black men kneel together in a row on the pavement. They wear shorts. The two on the outside are dressed completely in black. The man in the middle is dressed from head-to-toe in white. They toss their pocket change on the ground in front of them. The guy in white says, *"Look at us! Two pennies and a nickel!"*]

[1262.2 / 3432] [Inside a local pub, people complain about the service. The owners have attempted to respond and resolve the issue by purchasing a single serving *"air fryer"* to make their signature chicken breast dish. A sign posted at the door reads: *"Our fryer is small. If you choose to dine here, please be prepared to wait for up to four hours for your meal."* I contemplate why they chose to purchase that model of equipment, when they have the means to buy and accommodate a massive fryer on premises.

"They won't be in business much longer."]

[1262.3 / 3433] [THE CONNECTOR is responsible for leading a group of people. She consistently disappears to make drug deals and returns at odd intermittent intervals. Each time she returns her skin is burned more. More of her hair is charred. On one return I find her next to a brick wall looking like a barbecued primordial dwarf. I curtly advise her to, ***"Start leading."***]

⁂

Maj. = 4- THE CONNECTOR: #1276
KNEEL: #0019, #0309
NICKEL: #0543, #0645, #0788
SKIN: #0844, #0874, #0876, #0891, #0900

⁂

#1263 - July 4, 2020 @ 03:46 (Beavercreek, Ohio)

[1263.1 / 3434] [I'm part of a prosecutorial team watching from across the gallery as the defense council readies their evidence. An arrested man is marched into the courtroom with a low ceiling as we bat various exhibits between our teams prior to the arrival of the judge. THE CHILD enters from the judge's chambers. She's ill. The courtroom fills with seltzer water as she points to areas of her body where she's broken out in hives. She points to the insides of her elbows, behind her knees, under her arms, and bottoms of her feet. The more attention she brings to them, the more they begin to swell and juicily erupt like pomegranate arils, leaving purplish red streaks all over her body. THE WEAVER and GRANDMA do their best to sooth THE CHILD by cradling her and rocking back and forth. I extend my hands towards her as an offering of healing, which *"encourages 'the virus' to move through THE CHILD's body as quickly and painlessly as possible."*]

⁂

Maj. = 0- THE WEAVER: #1264, 3- THE CHILD: #1266, 11-GRANDMA: #1295
VIRUS: #1122, #1163
ELBOW: #0618, #0628, #0745
JUDGE: #0017, #0034, #0050, #0265

⁂

#1264 - July 4, 2020 @ 04:41 (Beavercreek, Ohio)

[1264.1 / 3435] [I ride bikes with THE WEAVER, THE CARPENTER and THE DANCER across country. We're heading towards Arkansas as we pedal down a web of rural country roads. Two paths emerge when the dusty road is split by a grove of trees. We pause to decide which path we'll take. We encounter large bird-like beings of varying color. A red bird and purple bird occupy the path to the left. Rainbow turkeys of all other colors veer to the right. My bike is positioned to take the path at left. The red and purple birds conjoin in front of me into a single, larger pink-puce-fuchsia colored bird. It crosses the road, then veers off the path to the right.

We're not certain how much further we'll need to ride until we arrive at the airport. We stop in front of a large bronze church stationed to the right. Tarnished by the elements and "humming" with a greenish-blue tone, it looks like a hybrid of a pagoda and a ziggurat, with layers each slightly smaller than the next stacked up towards the sky, beyond the tree line. We're unable to count how many stories tall the tower rises. An alien script protrudes around the edges along each tier, pulsing and seeming to float a few inches away from the building like a hologram. The complex swooping script is colored gold as a striking offset to the rest of the structure.

The path to the left of the grove swiftly descends in a steep downhill. We're not clear on which path is correct for us. THE DANCER is convinced *"the high road is the quicker path to the airport."* I'm less certain and believe that ***"either path still will be roughly 85-100 miles from our destination."*** Neither option will be leisurely, if we're to make our flight later that day.

"The flight back to where we started, will come after our visit to the hospital, of course," we all communicate telepathically in unison.

The weather is mixed, patches of sunlight, some moments windy and rainy. From where we stand, we can see all the transitions, and our destination way off in the distance. As we pedal away, I look over my shoulder at the church, which from a distance looks like an antique ceramic Christmas tree. The script on the exterior seems to creep along and scroll vertically. None of us are able to decipher any of the messages it communicates.] //

⁂

Maj. = 0- THE WEAVER: #1266, 1- THE CARPENTER: #1266, 2- THE DANCER: #1266
ARKANSAS: #1249, #1257
CROSS: #0820, #0872, #0874, #0887
HOLOGRAM: #0452, #0511, #0518, #0559

⁂

#1265 - July 4, 2020 @ 08:00 (Beavercreek, Ohio)

[1265.1 / 3436] [Unclear scene in a house.]
[1265.2 / 3437] [On a road trip.]
[1265.3 / 3438] [People gather on a driveway and leave their equipment for a yoga class that I've agreed ***"to teach tomorrow at 10:00am."*** One woman brings a rolled up, damp, and moldy carpet runner to use as her mat. When she drops it, it soggily splatters dinge on other personal items left by others. She doesn't feel the need to clean any of it up.] //

⁂

HOUSE: #0278, #0282, #0288
YOGA: #0529, #0532, #0551
TOMORROW: #0867, #1053, #1084

⁂

#1266 - July 5, 2020 @ 03:28 (Beavercreek, Ohio)

[1266.1 / 3439] [We're contained to our own space in the dark, in the middle of a noisy, busy group of people. The family sets up an *"autonomous zone"* in a small hexagonal/octagonal space by marking edge points with rebar and running yellow and orange ratchet straps around the perimeter. The sides of both shapes expand and contract. Lengths of braided human hair *(multiple shades)* extend to opposite corners of each shape. Initially, the perimeter is set at ankle height, intending to serve as a tripwire for intruders. We work as a group to adjust the rebar to waist and neck height. THE CHILD becomes upset when a momentary loss of tension in the ratchet straps causes the perimeter to droop. It sags limply for mere moments. THE DANCER consoles THE CHILD as I work with THE WEAVER and THE CARPENTER to quickly restore tension to the shapes.] //

⁂

Maj. = 0- THE WEAVER: #1267, 1- THE CARPENTER: #1269,
2- THE DANCER: #1271, 3- THE CHILD: #1267

ZONE: #0168
TENSION: #0405, #0466, #0682, #0725
HEXAGONAL: #0895
OCTAGONAL: #1210
⁂

#1267 - July 5, 2020 @ 04:21 (Beavercreek, Ohio)

[1267.1 / 3440] [Borrowing money from THE COUTURIER.]

[1267.2 / 3441] [I'm in a cubicle with a group of recent college graduates, one of whom is convinced a piece of new software is poised to revolutionize the world of financial accounting. I tell them,

"The vision is profound, but you'll find your promise will cave when you discover:
1) Your process and product are incomplete and
2) Your inputs may be incorrect...maybe both."

Stunned by my lack of enthusiasm, the young professional asserts, *"That's just not the case. We're prepared for all scenarios."*]

**I AWAKEN from this next segment three times, dream within a dream within a dream, believing I've recorded it before I awaken and dictate my remembrance. **

[1267.3 / 3442] [I walk through a series of hallways that looks eerily similar to a building where I've previously lived, with a small kiosk and attendant placed in front of every open door. At the kiosk table are hand painted miniature figurines. Their detailing is exquisite. For some reason I'm concerned whether or not the artisans have sufficient inventory on hand to sell. I'm also convinced the high demand for the objects will result in theft. I enter a bathroom, interacting with a vending machine at chest level as I pee into a urinal. I roll coins through a slot, they pivot and speed down a series of small Donkey Kong-like ramps in front of me, shielded by glass. Some of the coins have holes at their center, which give them a lighter hand feel as they're deposited into the machine. THE WEAVER calls out to me from behind and informs me THE CHILD has been awarded, *"Student of the Year, Across All Grades!"* The excitement in her voice is palpable. My attention remains on depositing coins as I continue urinating.] //

⁂
Maj.* = *0- THE WEAVER: #1272, 3- THE CHILD: #1269
Min. = *♣-THE COUTURIER: #1322*
DONKEY KONG: #0034
CUBICLE: #0063
⁂

#1268 - July 5, 2020 @ 06:11 (Beavercreek, Ohio)

[1268.1 / 3443] [I stand in line to retrieve a tray in a small buffet line. When I get to the front, I see PAUL MCCARTNEY standing by a Hobart industrial dishwasher, singing to a woman who stands by a cashier across the room.

"That's the best dish dog job ever!"

I buy my food and take a seat at a nearby table, pausing to note the tremble in my hands indicates I'm over caffeinated. ***"I don't need any more."***

"If I keep doing things the way I'm doing them, my mood will quickly erode," I think to myself.

Nearby, THE WORLDBRIDGER distributes a document for students to fill out. He takes a brief call just after he provides instructions for a tool to practice, for those present. My copy is different from the others. It has red page numbers in the top right corner. The numeric series *"5-9-1-2"* is repeated on every page.] //

⁂

Maj.** = 7- **THE WORLDBRIDGER: #1295

FIVE: #0073, #0126

NINE: #0568, #0621, #0755

ONE: #0897, #0899

TWO: #0901

⁂

#1269 - July 5, 2020 @ 08:14 (Beavercreek, Ohio)

[1269.1 / 3444] [THE CARPENTER and THE CHILD stand in silhouette by the driver's side door of a red and white two-tone classic convertible, facing out a garage looking on a vast rolling blue skied prairie. The convertible top is down. The passenger side of the car is parked inches away from an incredibly tall concrete wall.]

[1269.2 / 3445] [I'm in a dormitory with a set of roommates. One departs on a date as I leave to study. When I return, the other roommates have packed up and left. The space is now ***"my room."*** The rectangular window in the door has been shattered by a gunshot, its fragments held in place by a mesh of wire.] //

⁂

Maj.** = 1- **THE CARPENTER: #1271**, 3- **THE CHILD: #1271

PRAIRIE: #0945, #1097

MESH: #0637

CONCRETE: #0157, #0168, #0235

⁂

#1270 - July 6, 2020 @ 02:06 (Beavercreek, Ohio)

[1270.1 / 3446] [A movie scene is filmed in a swimming pool at night. One of the poolside attendants has a disfigured left foot. Between takes an inconsistency in the protagonist's lines is pointed out to the director by the screenwriter. The protagonist is a womanizer and surrounded by females.

"ACTION!" the director calls to begin filming a climactic scene. We begin splashing in the water and running lines.

The protagonist goes off script and shouts with a laugh, *"I'm an expert in art!"*

A "gotcha" moment instantly unfolds and everything on set goes dark. Someone calls out the protagonist's incompetence and habitual lying. I add in a dangling line of dialog,

"The real question is: why is someone like you in the part of the pool reserved for players familiar with at least 15% of a declared topic? You missed the one question to which you're supposed to know the answer."

"Because in this context, revealing incompetence is part of the 'art,'...duh." riffs the protagonist.

"CUT!" Action wraps. No further filming takes place. Cast and crew exit. Production on the movie abruptly concludes.] //

⁂

SWIMMING: #0302, #0323
PRODUCTION: #0645, #0745, #0793
CONTEXT: #0998

⁂

#1271 - July 6, 2020 @ 05:46 (Beavercreek, Ohio)

[1271.1 / 3447] [I'm at a theme park in a restroom. I encounter THE VIKING ELF. He and I have sex there *(which we've done many times prior to this encounter)*.]

[1271.2 / 3448] [I blink and find myself banking hard to the left on a wooden roller coaster that roars twice through a stainless-steel tunnel. Both layers are stacked atop each other and are shaped like a series of silver frames that jut out as the train passes across a rickety track beneath. The wind rushes and the frame freezes mid-action.]

[1271.3 / 3449] [I'm with THE CHILD in a public pool taking a synchronized swimming lesson. She swims to the center of the pool and meets a grey-haired man. I believe he's part of the class and we're switching partners for an exercise, but he abducts her from the pool and disappears. I'm shown a vision of a fryer basket with small breaded meatballs pulled from a vat of hot oil. The fryer basket becomes a stainless-steel transport box that the man places in a storage compartment of a scooter, which he rides to a large mansion with ivory columns. I follow him and watch him take the box inside the house. I bang on the door repeatedly until it opens on its own, revealing a pornography production site within. The mansion is located on the rear side of a popular restaurant. Guests in the dining room are unaware of the crimes involving children perpetrated in the basement. I glance down a stairwell to a dimly lit bottom floor where some sinewy and sinister looking people *(most of them nude, dirty, and bearing wounds and sores)* skitter into the darkness. Without any rush, I walk to the bottom and grab a woman by the hair and throw her to the floor. A group of other abusive women sit with backs against a wall. They watch me place my knee on the back of her head and begin slowly grinding it back and forth on the carpet.

THE CARPENTER enters dressed in combat fatigues, followed by THE DANCER who admonishes me saying, *"Never let anyone else take your children anywhere."*

She grabs THE CHILD by the hand and walks her out into the light. I feel terrible and embarrassed, but relieved she's ok. I explain to THE CARPENTER that I've discovered a ring of child pornographers and these women are responsible for raping hundreds of children. The women snicker and laugh when I call out their crimes.

"Bitch, he's military...he'll snuff you out fast," I say with a snap of my fingers.

The demeanor of the woman under my knee shifts from mania to fear while the other two by wall continue to laugh.

"You might think this is a joke, but this is what you get for banging children," I say, continuing to grind the woman's face under my knee through the hunter green carpet, the wood, and into a concrete floor which shreds the skin from her face. Blood spills forth as I feel the front of her skull chip away. She gurgles and gasps through bloody bubbles as the life-force drains from her body. With a smile I say to the other two women, ***"neither of you are leaving without first drowning in your own blood."***

Books topple from a high shelf and strike the doomed women as the one trapped under my knee goes limp and dies.] //

⁂

Maj. = 0- THE CARPENTER: #1272, 2- THE DANCER: #1275, 3- THE CHILD: #1273
GRIND: #0088
LIGHT: #0797
TRAPPED: #0871, #0943, #1089

⁂

#1272 - July 7, 2020 @ 03:03am (Beavercreek, Ohio)

[1272.1 / 3450] [I hitch a small trailer to another larger trailer, hitched to the back of THE CAMERAMAN's truck. He drives off with it. Once out of sight I meet THE WEAVER and THE CARPENTER at a hotel. THE CARPENTER expresses frustration because the type of reservation has a specific, immovable check-in time and my name is on the reservation. A small English-speaking rat is a member of the family who's joined us at the hotel. He jumps precariously between different areas of a wooden staircase that doesn't have railings. I'm worried he'll fall.]

[1272.2 / 3451] [I interview JOHN LENNON where he describes his favorite experiences with THE BEATLES in the recording studio, and the *"techniques employed to achieve particular sounds and unique tonal qualities based on the tool available."* Our interview is cut short when he's chased into a phone booth by a mob of ravenous female fans who try to break through the glass doors and tear his clothing and spectacles from his face. Once bare skinned, he's licked and poked repeatedly. He and I connect psychically. I hear him surrender and accept the circumstances.

"Mate, this is just what happens when you become too famous. To an outside observer your life seems full of appreciation and gross adulation, but it's actually the hallmark of isolation and chaos."] //

⁂

Maj. = 0- THE WEAVER: #1275, 1- THE CARPENTER: #1280
TRAILER: #0043
FAVORITE: #0541, #0648, #0754
STUDIO: #1077, #1096

CHAOS: #1282

⁂

#1273 - July 7, 2020 @ 05:14 (Beavercreek, Ohio)

[1273.1 / 3452] [THE JESTER has completed a full renovation of a home in Colorado. I'm relocating from California to Colorado with THE CHILD and THE LITTLE PRINCE. We leave a hotel together, which transforms into the house across the street from the renovated property. A large sprinkler waters a straw covered patch of seeded land on the front lawn at night, where a few children of our future neighbors play. I proceed with THE JESTER on a tour of the property. Everything is black and still. No lights are on, though we're able to see everything clearly. An attic has been removed to create a vaulted/cathedral ceiling which renders the previously congested living room vast and spacious. He points to a lofted bedroom and bathroom, newly installed at the back of the property.

"The renovation is permanent. Setting it back to what it was, is a full demolition job," he says as he shows me to my new room through the kitchen on the ground floor at the rear of the property. I'm mostly delighted to finally have my own bathroom.

I brush my teeth, and part way through I realize I'm not wearing my glasses. My vision goes fuzzy as I stumble around furniture placed between my bedroom and the front door. As I become woozy and off balance, I look at my left hand which clasps a tube of commercial sealant, which I've used to brush my teeth. It's toxic and has absorbed into my bloodstream.]

[1273.2 / 3453] [I'm shown by a guide that I'm supposed to ask THE SEASON *(connected, surrendered, and comedic)* for her comments on cassette tape for inclusion in an art installation for *"the school,"* which will be on display at the hotel beginning next week.] //

⁂

Maj. = 3- THE CHILD: #1275, 12- THE LITTLE PRINCE: #1298

Min. = ♦- THE JESTER: #1308

HOTEL: #0007, #0009, #0115, #0170, #0301

PERMANENT: #0545

⁂

#1274 - July 8, 2020 @ 01:43 (Beavercreek, Ohio)

[1274.1 / 3454] [I'm simultaneously **"the father and the son"** who encounter a humanoid extraterrestrial, roughly 5'5" tall with a flat, enlarged head and large binocular circles for eyes. It's tan colored. Its skin looks wet, but it's sheer, rubbery to the touch, and reflective. It has an exquisitely muscular back, though its spine, scapula and hips make impressions through the skin. It's a kind and playful being, with us until we begin to scramble together up a square interior perimeter staircase for five floors *(starting from a small cobblestone courtyard surrounded with wrought iron gates)*. I lead as the father, the being in between, and me as a teenage son at rear. The being is excited to get to the top of the building.

As the teenage son, I notice a shortcut where if we pass in front of a series of iron maiden-looking spikes at one corner of the stairwell, we can advance up a level effortlessly. I'm successful as the teenager, but suggest the alien, me as dad, and neighbors who have joined in the ascent, continue with the straightforward and less risky option up the stairs. I land at the top of the large urban apartment building and look up to see a large circular mothership that has a series of blue and white dots on the bottom, that join to create larger dots, until a few remain and begin spinning like the dial on a rotary phone. We believe we're going to be taken up with the alien. Instead, the remaining dots focus to a single large prismatic dot in the center of the craft that instantly zaps the tan being up. Massive amounts of firework shells detonate around the craft, startling the crew inside. The craft instantly disappears.

I, along with the remaining humans, walk back down to the cobblestone courtyard. We play a game together on a small square grassy patch at its center. I tell myself *(as the father)*, ***"I'm really happy I had that experience with you. If you ever need to be reminded that it happened you let me know."***]

[1274.2 / 3455] [I ski downhill quickly in a glossy video game-like environment of blue and white icy crags. A Technicolor twilight sky raptured by aurora borealis lights the path. I pause midway down the mountain to collect shiny black rings from beneath a vending machine. I drop to my belly and sweep my right arm as far as I can from front to back, right and left, drawing forth a variety of objects including some discarded cardboard, and fountain pens. A fellow skier asks for a pen, and a small interior square of cardboard from a Cabbage Patch Kids doll on which to write a note, but I tell him, ***"I already intend to use the cardboard for a similar purpose."***] //

⁂

FATHER: #0333, #0337
SON: #0678, #0748, #0768
ALIEN: #0831, #0847, #0893, #0914
RINGS: #1306, #1335

⁂

#1275 - July 8, 2020 @ 04:30 (Beavercreek, Ohio)

[1275.1 / 3456] [I want to order a ring with a dark blue gemstone set on a black band. THE DANCER is on the phone with a group of artisans who live in a far wing of the house. *"They're output is inconsistent. You'll want to consider buying your ring from someone else,"* she suggests while placing a hand over the phone receiver mid-conversation. I could simply walk to the other end of the property to discuss the transaction face-to-face, but that would be considered a ***"fatal breach of business protocol."*** I decide to go anyway, and encounter the artisans sitting and eating together at a common table. No one says a word, but it's clear they want me to leave.]

[1275.2 / 3457] [THE CHILD is a mermaid lounging in a carpeted room, facing a corner. Both hands are placed under her chin as she observes some microscopically small activity I can't see.

"I wanna know what's going on with the tiny machines!" she exclaims as her little tail flops back and forth on the royal blue carpet. Her hair is long and braided, with each strand a unique shade of seafoam green, purple, and yellow. She doesn't want to go to bed, and is up **way past her bedtime**.]

. . .

[1275.3 / 3458] [I arrive in the desert at night with THE WEAVER and THE SOUL SISTER *(affirming, loving, and candid)*. The desert is populated with different camps/tribes who've established dazzlingly lit frontages with multiple fire barrels burning along what I perceive are the borders for each group. THE WEAVER points at a small seemingly unclaimed patch between two large groups and suggests we set up camp there. We're unaware that the area is a "no-man's land" between two rival gangs.

"It's best if you're able to sleep with a lot of ambient noise," I suggest though neither of them understands how loud things here will eventually become, as others arrive.

None of the faces in the surrounding camps are familiar to me. I enter a well-lit camp to meet new friends. I sit down at a full common table where no one *(save me)* wears a face covering. ***"It's been multiple years since I've been in a similar situation, and that was before the virus came and killed off a bunch of unsuspecting people."***]

[1275.4 / 3459] [55mph speed limit signs are posted every 50 feet along the streets of a suburban housing development. Cars whiz by at incredible speeds as I walk along a sidewalk.]

[1275.5 / 3460] [THE DANCER appears and says, *"I need to go home."*]

[1275.6 / 3461] [TOM MORELLO teaches a master class in cooking breakfast food. Today's construction is a waffle-like item produced on a large rectangular iron the dimensions of a theater sized television. Once the batter has formed, the iron infuses the mold with a combination of chocolate and caramel, and coats the outside of the *"little squares"* on the waffle. Each square has a small hole punched in the center. From a distance the giant waffle appears to be perforated. The episode is from a forthcoming online series where *"rock stars cook their favorite foods for their fans."*] //

⁂

Maj. = 0- THE WEAVER: #1277, 2- THE DANCER: #1278, 3- THE CHILD: #1281

MERMAID: #1334

ROYAL BLUE: #0112

CARAMEL: #0606

AMBIENT: #0819, #0966

⁂

#1276 - July 8, 2020 @ 05:30 (Beavercreek, Ohio)

[1276.1 / 3462] [I observe myself riding in the backseat of a car with THE CONNECTOR, who watches me wake up and dictate the same dream into my phone multiple times:

"Contestants prepare their projects for evaluation. The contestants are sick. Each is allocated a key on an oversized piano (six inches wide and three feet long) to install their work. Once complete, I'm given the go ahead to fly overhead and "dress" their presentations with small dollops of gold paint and glitter. One piece is placed beyond the one-octave keyboard on its own unique red key (a literal "high

note"). The work belongs to THE MIDWIFE (mysterious, gracious, and curious) and is most easily described as a 'mandala composed of fruit.' I believe the work will spoil, though her intent is to eat it once it's been installed."

As I BEGIN AGAIN, THE CONNECTOR touches my arms and says, *"You've said the same thing multiple times. Wake up."*] //

⁂

Maj. = 4- THE CONNECTOR: #1289
FRUIT: #0024, #0516
GLITTER: #0768, #0755
KEYBOARD: #0825, #0853

⁂

#1277 - **July 9, 2020 @ 01:07 (Beavercreek, Ohio)**

[1277.1 / 3463] [OPRAH owns the New York Yankees and stars in all the advertisements shown in the stadium before each game. Her smiling, animated image is everywhere. She also provides game commentary through stadium speakers in a calm and soothing tone, once competition is underway. A gorgeous golf course contained within the stadium compound can be accessed as an additional form of amusement.

I'm seated in the upper deck with my feet on top of the next lower row of blue injection molded plastic seats. A young Black woman sits down next to me wearing rust colored boot cut trousers and a slim, black-and-white striped top. A cordovan handbag dangles from her left forearm. She laughs while eating her popcorn when I incredulously state, ***"I wasn't aware that OPRAH had purchased the franchise."***

"I thought she'd inked a global licensing deal to exclusively provide all the commentary for the next thirty years,"

"Well, that's mom. She's always got a trick up her sleeve," the woman replies. Without her needing to confirm, I realize I'm speaking with OPRAH's adult daughter. The stadium is empty, except for us. The team hasn't yet taken the field. Multiple players have fallen ill.]

[1277.2 / 3464] [A young female artist presents an abstract to a funding committee. She wants to produce a series of photographs of *"nude waistlines of men who have tiny painted penises and average sized scrotums."* I'm the treasurer of the committee. Other committee members are seated on either side *(two to my right, one to my left)*, behind two 6-foot rectangular tables. As the artist clicks through a presentation projected onto a white wall, she requests $2300 to bring her vision to fruition. The check is placed in front of me and requires my signature. Two other committee members have already signed it. The artist grew up in a household where secondary sex characteristics were not sexualized, so she's surprised when the committee probes her underlying intention for producing the series of images.]

[1277.3 / 3465] [On the golf course within the Yankee Stadium compound, a group of men lock arms along the top ridge of a sand trap where a golfer attempts to chip out. THE WEAVER and I look on from a distance as she questions, *"I don't remember that being allowed?"*

THE WEAVER then begins to reminisce on how she used to pool her money with other kids when she was in grade school to buy sandwiches in the lunchroom. She shows me an image of her and the other kids laying on a long dining room table comparing the lengths of their legs.]

[1277.4 / 3466] [A baby, not yet able to speak, likes to choose what it eats for lunch. If dissatisfied or unheard it leaps from the highchair to the floor and cries. As THE WEAVER and I watch this she tells me, *"I was letting you choose flavors of things before you were even a year in that body."* The baby slides down the wall, plops on the floor, and crawls over to me and looks up just before I wake.] //

⁂

Maj. = 0- THE WEAVER: #1281
OPRAH: #1388
GOLF: #0160, #0236, #0265
NUDE: #0450, #0597
PLASTIC: #0862

⁂

#1278 - July 9, 2020 @ 04:33 (Beavercreek, Ohio)

[1278.1 / 3467] [I drop my olive-green cloth backpack in a storage room with a bunch of other student belongings. We leave together for an assembly. I realize I'm 18 years old and soon to be 19 and don't recall why I'm still in high school. There's some confusion about what remaining coursework I've yet to complete. ***"I know I've already graduated once before in 1997, so is there a reason I'm supposed to be here which I've forgotten?"*** After the assembly I'm not able to find my backpack. All personal articles were removed from the storage closet and moved to a ballroom, where items are separated and stacked, though I'm not sure of the sorting criteria. Color? Size? First letter of last name? No one seems to know and isn't able to help me as I look at different shelves of bags in the richly colored room. A cocktail hour is underway in the retrieval room. I bump into THE DANCER and say, ***"My keys, ID, wallet...everything is in that bag. I don't know how I'm going to find it. I'm never going to get out of here."***]

[1278.2 / 3468] [A father and young child swim together in a brown water pond in the dark. I walk around the perimeter towards a small, white, glowing square nestled in among the cattails. I cut across the pond and walk through the water, not on the surface, but a few inches beneath, until I reach the small light. I discover a small 4" square, black-and-white television playing old cartoons featuring cats and mice dancing. The TV is inside a clear plastic backpack. I retrieve the bag and walk back towards the hotel. THE DANCER touches my right arm saying, *"You dug that out? It's been there forever."*]

[1278.3 / 3469] [I'm at a resort, where the energy is rising. People are partying. Most attention is focused on becoming contestants on a reality show. Prospects *(wearing swimsuits)* advance up along a winding cobblestone path, passing various gateways and challenges in an attempt to get access to a VIP event at the top. I've made it to the "costume level" where a subset of players gathers under a large gazebo, in a serpentine queue. They pump up, cajole, and challenge each other before advancing to the next level of the competition.

A few guys have costumes similar to mine. I'm painted in gold from head to toe. I'm also wearing a red Hawaiian shirt with large white flowers. Other guys do their impression of being "Oscars." My body stays on the ground. My spirit flies upward to get a macro view of the pending challenge, which seems to involve navigating through a human barricade made of large muscular Caucasian men. As I advance up the cobblestone path with the group of prospects, someone behind me hits a small ball *(racquetball? Squash ball?)* up in the air. Another yells, *"LOOK OUT!"* and those around me crouch and wince as it strikes the top of my head and bounces upward. The strike doesn't bother me and I continue to walk up past a large muscular man to my left. The ball bounces off my head a second time, causing me to glance skyward while I continue to walk. I spot the ball and wait for it to drop, performing a bicycle kick and launching it with my foot towards a set of large iron gates. The maneuver impresses the *"human wall"* and other contestants so much they give me an instant pass to: *"GET UP THERE!"*

I pass through the gates and enter the party, where I greet people who climb various trees and ladders to access gathering rooms of different sizes; some for one-on-one conversation, others meant for large groups. Some of the men treat the ladders like obstacles, pausing to perform pull ups and other strength training exercises. Some players take pauses to speak intimately. Everyone's clothed. The interactions are playful and "G" rated.

I discover myself in an auditorium with walls composed of large screens. The walls are illuminated with colorful, repeated 1000pt font phrases presented in cursive. **"The ONLY time is PASTRY time!"** and other quirky semi-nonsensical phrases flash on the screen in yellow, magenta, and cyan as the background color toggles between black and white. I feel like I'm going to meet a long-term partner here as I interact with a variety of faces and personalities, but I don't.]

[1278.4 / 3470] [I've taken a new job in an office. People at the firm only communicate through video texts. Every word is recorded. I find the delay bothersome. ***"I prefer face to face conversations. I prefer immediacy."*** I have more than a dozen videos to watch and respond to. ***"Bleck."***] //

⁂

Maj. = 2- THE DANCER: #1279
CARTOON: #0277, #0393
COBBLESTONE: #0494, #0527, #0548, #0561
TREES: #0924, #0939, #0963, #0970, #1011
BACKPACK: #1304

⁂

#1279 - July 9, 2020 @ 05:54 (Beavercreek, Ohio)

[1279.1 / 3471] [I'm in the basement level bathroom of a dormitory. The overhead lights are off, but soft morning light pours in from windows along the tops of the walls. Large shower-cap-looking objects hang from the ceiling in front of stalls and urinals, meant to be facial and corporeal shields from airborne contaminants. A group of guys stand in front of the stall I want to use to take a shit. I turn around and close the door as one pops his head over the top and asks me if I want to hook up. **...THE SCENE SPEEDS UP AND GOES BLURRY...** I find myself in the top bunk of a bedroom making out with a blond-haired smooth-skinned guy.

"What are you into?"

He blurts, *"Coke,"* while biting my upper lip and exhaling into my mouth.

"I'm not, and I don't have any," I say as I look up and to the right towards his closet.

The spirit of THE DANCER appears to my right and says, *"What you want is up there on the top shelf."*

I woozily stumble out of the room, and down a hallway into the bathroom where the blonde guy and I met. I brush my teeth, shave, and wash my face only looking up after I've completed my grooming. I'm startled when I see my body in the mirror without a head. I walk to the left, pausing to note that in each mirror, my head is still gone. I become perplexed and unsettled. A woman with dark shoulder length hair enters and stands to my right, primping and painting her lips.

"Can you see my head?" I ask.

With a laugh under breath she says, *"Yeah, don't worry it's still there,"* and then dabs her lips on a piece of tissue.

The blonde man and his roommate enter the bathroom and stand behind me to the left. My head reappears. I notice my appearance can shift, by simply saying what I want to see.

"Long hair." My hair grows to waist length.

"Bald." My hair instantly vanishes.

"Tall and lean." Bloop.

"Short and pudgy."

The awareness is new to me, but seems to be familiar to the guys who are humored by how astonished I am by the instantaneous changes. A dozen or so people sit on the tile floor to the left, looking towards the wall of sinks and mirrors. The ethnicity of the group shifts, then becomes a large Hispanic family. A daughter stands up and says, *"Daddy can I show him?"* After a nod from her father, the girl jumps, landing with her legs wide and arms out. Her body is shaped like a star as she confidently declares, **"LAKE TITICACA!"** The group laughs and claps, and wakes me up.] //

⁂

Maj. = 2- THE DANCER: #1283
MIRRORS: #0056, #0189
LEAN: #0622, #0726, #0732, #0748
BALD: #1082, #1126, #1190
TOP SHELF: #0444

⁂

#1280 - July 10, 2020 @ 05:54 (Beavercreek, Ohio)

[1280.1 / 3472] [I lounge on a white leather couch in the living room of a compound with THE KANGAROO. He wears a cowboy hat, nothing else. He leans in to kiss me, pausing to tell me that *"the value of the property has risen $208,000 overnight."* He's one of eleven members of a consortium that each have an equal ownership stake in the residence.

"How much did those pocket doors cost THE CARPENTER to install? The white ones at the far end of the main level off from the kitchen."

"I'm pretty sure they were there when they moved in 25 years ago, but I'm certain he could give you a contractor's estimate. He'll probably hook you up for the cost of materials, if you want him to take the job."

We spend the rest of our interaction in the compound playing naked hide-and-seek with one another. We pause in different rooms and engage in different sexual acts when one of us finds the other. In the last rendezvous, he disappears down a hovering staircase towards a basement, and leaps into an unmade bed. A couple nearby inspect each other's formal wear just before heading out for an afternoon wedding. As they exit the building, a whoosh of arctic air rushes in and up the corridor, causing my naked body to tense up with gooseflesh.]

[1280.2 / 3473] [I'm at a revival with THE CARPENTER. We give each other some final words of encouragement before we head out to a congregation and lay our hands on people, desirous of healing. We work in opposite directions, eventually crossing paths at the far end of the venue. We both place our hands on a teenage boy with Down Syndrome and close our eyes, while the young man laughs and soaks in energetic prayer.]

[1280.3 / 3474] [A low, steady voice repeats, *"Step. Step. Half Step. Step. Step. Step. Half Step. '**Major.**'"*] //

⁂

Maj. = 1- THE CARPENTER: #1284
Min. = ♠- THE KANGAROO: #1425
HIDE: #0006, #0036, #0051, #0115
SEEK: #0437
STEP: #0815, #0819
DOWN SYNDROME: #0405, #0834, #1014

⁂

#1281 - July 11, 2020 @ 01:30 (Beavercreek, Ohio)

[1281.1 / 3475] [I'm at a rally at a large indoor arena. The environment is active and supportive. I'm on a catwalk above a crowd with another man. He and I are stuntmen. He and I hang from a girder by our fingertips. He intends to drop through numerous layers of sheetrock and metal, clearing a path for me to fast-follow. Instead, we decide at the last minute on an alternate route that will bring us to the ground together. We select a different drop position. The person attempting the stunt immediately before us mirros their approach on a still image they'd found on the internet. At the bottom, they land perfectly balanced on both feet, on the shoulders of a person standing beneath them. The person beneath explodes. We release and freefall, our feet punching through dozens of layers of colorful tissue paper as we descend to the concrete below.

"Did I hit my head?" I'm disoriented.

"Was I supposed to let go three seconds after he did?" My eyes are closed.

Once safely at the bottom, THE CONJURER *(practiced, dedicated, and quiet)* presents me with a T-shirt to acknowledge my bravery. I proceed up a ramp and turn to the right to meet up with other successful members of my team. THE WEAVER doesn't want THE CHILD to sit anywhere near the drop zone for the stunt, and repeats herself until I speak her comment back to her: ***"I'll contact the airline to make sure I reserve a seat that's far enough away from that place."***]

⁂

Maj. = 0- THE WEAVER: #1282, 3- THE CHILD: #1284
DROP: #0154, #0257, #0306
CATWALK: #0404, #0620, #0757, #0765, #0773
SHOULDERS: #0857, #0867, #0887
EXPLODE: #1366
THE CONJURER: #1368

⁂

#1282 - July 11, 2020 @ 03:04 (Beavercreek, Ohio)

[1282.1 / 3476] [I step up onto a bus. The bus driver hears a MADONNA song come on the radio and decides to turn it up and sing at full volume. The recording quality is muffled and degraded because of her choice of microphone usedin the studio. ***"That's the reason I like LADY GAGA better,"*** I say while taking a seat, pausing to notice LADY GAGA is seated next to me with a cherub faced man with curly blonde hair who wears a navy-blue three-piece suit with a near invisible white pinstripe. I see a small gold pocket watch chain drop from his vest like a small upturned mouth that seems to talk as he moves. At the next stop they exit the bus and declare they're *"going shopping."*

The bus turns down an alley with a road slanted at 45 degrees to the left. The day turns to night as the bus pivots to the right on to an even narrower road with a steeper pitch. Large visible signage on both streets prohibit the passage of buses. THE WEAVER leaps up and runs behind the driver excitedly saying, *"You know you can't go down this way!"* The bus driver doesn't speak English and doesn't understand that the bus is about to topple over. The bus falls to the right, and grinds to a sparky stop.]

[1282.2 / 3477] [In a blink, I'm on a sidewalk across the street from the crashed bus observing people collecting their things.

"I could drive the bus. She's obviously fired...right?" I say to an old man who's collected his personal items from the wreckage in a small cardboard box.

He nods and says, *"I could drive too."*

LADY GAGA and the blonde suit-wearing man pass by me with shopping bags, surprised to see the bus has crashed. My gaze is slightly up cast as I look past the chaos a few feet away. The suit wearing man tugs on my right pant leg saying, ***"Bring it down to this level."*** We laugh.

"We're the same shady bitches we've always been," we say in unison as we giggle and hug one another.] //

⁂

Maj. = 0- THE WEAVER: #1283
LADY GAGA: #1344
SIDEWALK: #0384, #0390
DEGREES: #0905, #1085, #1145

⁂

#1283 - July 12, 2020 @ 02:14 (Beavercreek, Ohio)

[1283.1 / 3478] [THE DANCER and I sit together in a hot tub discussing her recent choreography session with BRITNEY SPEARS. THE DANCER is pregnant, yet able to move with the same degree of fluidity in her demonstrations without carrying a child.]

[1283.2 / 3479] [THE WEAVER points at a small desk chair hidden behind a stack of items at an estate sale. I think it's a piece of junk, but THE WEAVER's taken by it. A small diving board-looking plank is affixed to the seat of the chair. We contemplate its addition. THE WEAVER and I are invited to view an alternate reality *"held by the chair, wherein as people sit in it, they instantly disappear or turn to stone."* After I watch a few people disappear, I nonchalantly walk to a large plate glass window and look down on a red rock canyon. While gazing at the rust-colored lines with soft eyes, oversized impressions of faces *(those who've disappeared)* stretch forth from the rock wall, wincing and grimacing before they freeze. Those who turn to stone in the seat levitate across the room and come to rest on circular podiums, *"prominently displayed for eternity."* I copy and paste a text to as many people as I can, ***"BizR. U gotta chk this out. Utterly ridiculous."***]

[1283.3 / 3480] [I walk to the desk chair with a group of friends. A small cardboard box on top opens, lit under a dusty column of gold light. We peer in and see a single red rose growing up through the eye socket of a stone skull.] //

⁂

Maj. = 0- THE WEAVER: #1284, 2- THE DANCER: #1284

RUST: #0043, #0202, #0339

PEER: #0567, #0748

ROSE: #1074

⁂

#1284 - July 12, 2020 @ 03:53 (Beavercreek, Ohio)

[1284.1 / 3481] [THE WEAVER packs up THE CHILD's old toys, to help THE DANCER prepare for a trip. Particular attention is paid to a Styrofoam box, in which dozens of small batteries are vertically placed in small holes in a grid. A top piece of equivalent shape and size will keep the batteries in place during transport, though there's a bit of a struggle to get it to fit.]

[1284.2 / 3482] [THE CARPENTER drives an SUV *(with the family inside)* through a square concrete tunnel that banks hard to the right. We nearly crash into the side wall near the end of the tunnel, but narrowly avoid catastrophe and continue on to dinner. He suggests that we stop to meet a friend of a friend who's eager to show us in and involve us in a board game testing party, attended by his neighbors and their children. The home is a long rectangular room, naturally lit, with small square tables *(four chairs filled around each)*. Each table has a different game. We're invited to try them all. I find THE CARPENTER's friend to be delightfully cerebral and geeky. I think he's cool and I want to hang out with him more.]

. . .

[1284.3 / 3483] [The family walks shoulder-to-shoulder through an open-air mall with red brick streets. The light suggests it's golden hour. THE WEAVER and THE CARPENTER hold hands as she says,

"Check it out. They've installed so many more security cameras since we were last here."

I count between 30 and 40 before I lose interest. We're supposed to stop at a bakery to pick up a specialty order of cookies for THE CARPENTER's birthday. He makes a sarcastic comment to THE WEAVER, as he holds the door to the bakery. She rolls her eyes and he looks at me, smiling with a wink. THE WEAVER asks a service rep to check the back for a particular type of chocolate chip, as she surveys a cold case filled with cured meats that THE CARPENTER would most enjoy. She selects two landjaeger and motions for me to retrieve a box from a counter at the back of the store. I open the box and see "Open Face Homemade Oreos," which initially confuse me. The cookies are 2" x 2" square, with a layer of white frosting atop a black cake base. I tell THE WEAVER,

"We would've been better suited to come here first thing if you really wanted those chocolate chips."

"Not true. They start to pull their inventory off the shelves at 4pm. You just need to ask them to get what you want."]

[1284.4 / 3484] [I'm 6 or 7 years old. I'm at a music store, standing on a stool flipping through stacks of records with THE CARPENTER. We listen to classic rock through different sets of headphones.]

[1284.5 / 3485] [A group of young women plan a surprise 21st birthday party for one of their friends in Las Vegas, Nevada.] //

⁂

Maj. = 0- THE WEAVER: #1289, 1- THE CARPENTER: #1292,
2- THE DANCER: #1289, 3- THE CHILD: #1303
CHOCOLATE CHIP: #0014, #0043
BAKERY: #1016
STOOL: #0561

⁂

#1285 - July 13, 2020 @ 04:31 (Beavercreek, Ohio)

[1285.1 / 3486] [I'm on a college campus in central Missouri in the 1990's *(based on pop culture references and political propaganda).* I witness a group of five students seated around a conference table in a student union complete a revision to a code base and run a compiling program, intent on running some tests once it completes. I don't know what the purpose of the code is, but I'm intrigued as I watch the system reboot and come back online. A postage-stamp-sized-purple-microchip icon with a smiley face in the middle winks at the students who clap, cheer, and whistle at the arrival of "The Origin." Each student uploads an additional plugin that creates another equally sized icon of other colors, which begin to move around the screen and interact with "The Origin."

Satisfied with their output, the students decide to rent a car and leave campus for the weekend. I'm invited, but I have other commitments to fulfill on campus. They drive away as I'm left pondering where I've parked my car. I'm a new student. It's my first day onsite, and I'm not familiar with the campus layout. I walk to a convenience store *(at a gas station in a mall),* walk to a basement and turn left. I take a seat on an inflatable mattress and watch a small TV mounted in the top corner of a wall until a janitor asks me to leave so he can mop the floor. I tell him I'm on my way back to campus. I'm wearing a red cardigan with the letters CMS embroidered in black, in the front center of my chest. Each letter is outlined with white and red.

I encounter THE LALA as I walk through a well-lit underground tunnel on my way back to campus. She's a student and offers to help me find my way. Fast moving men wearing suits rush through the space like grey streaks of light, and bounce off THE LALA who is unaffected by the collisions. She doesn't' seem to notice the bumper car-like interactions as we walk and talk.

"Will you give me a ride back to campus?"

"Yes."] //

⁂

Min. = ◆-THE LALA: #1368

ORIGIN: #0358, #0397

CODE: #0484, #0518, #0606

UNDERGROUND: #0880, #1130

⁂

#1286 - July 13, 2020 @ 06:40 (Beavercreek, Ohio)

[1286.1 / 3487] [**Dream runs entirely in reverse** - I'm at a party with ERYKAH BADU, I walk backwards away from the party and eventually find myself at a car rental desk. A Black man with hip-length dreadlocks named "ECNIV" (Vince) stands next to me at the counter. He and I walk backwards together down an orange, tan and white colored corridor and are joined by two others, an average white woman and man *(both in their 20's).* We continue walking backwards and it's clear the four of us are friends. We're moving in reverse towards another rental car counter after moving through a series of buildings, up and down stairwells. I'm afraid I'm going to trip even though I know I've already taken every backtracked step. "ECNIV" peels away from the group and I find myself standing next to the average White man at a bus depot, staring at a lone pink mountain peak in the middle of a white powder covered range. A series of riddles and puzzles run in reverse, offering clues as to where our rental cars have been parked:

- A group of men stand in front of us in a pattern on the floor, to unlock access to the rental car desk.
- A red leather-bound book hovers in front of my face with the answer to a riddle, and systematically rewinds through the seven clues that lead to the answer.
- A puzzle is solved under a staircase. Balls of white light point in the direction of the red leather-bound book.
- A solo sexual encounter where I use my forearms to push away other parties that want to involve themselves.
- *.... many other scenes unwind and reveal clues until...*

The young White man and I debate whether or not we're at the correct bus station, and move backwards on to a city bus. As the bus drives backwards, I'm certain I've left my rental car in a neighborhood two stops back. Once there, I believe I'll be able to retrieve the car and advance forward to return it on time.] //

⁂

ERYKAH BADU: #1387
RIDDLE: #1295
PINK: #0816, #0820
LEATHER: #0549, #0557, #0726
RETURN: #0016, #0022, #0034, #0045, #0048, #0060

⁂

#1287 - July 14, 2020 @ 05:05 (Beavercreek, Ohio)

[1287.1 / 3488] [I'm a young boy, freely passing between the "male" and "female" sides of a prison. I wear my favorite pair of gold boots to cheer up my female friend, who asks me to call her "mom." A prison lock down is followed by a cell inspection, which causes me to remove the boots and leave them in her cell. Her cell is decorated like a small country cottage. I leave her, exit the building, and walk along the interior of a perimeter fence to return to my assigned side of the prison. Far more stringent controls are put in place to monitor guests and future visitation.]

[1287.2 / 3489] [I hastily move out of an apartment and into another one across the hall. I hang a cork board next to an abnormally deep window box at right. I hang a second smaller black frame filled with woven black and silver ribbon. I press a few colored push pins into the smaller frame, while I decide which boxes to unpack. A medium sized box in the window rests heated by the late morning sun. I look inside and find a dozen lemons and a similar count of large eggs, four of which have hatched. Three baby swans have died in their shells. A fourth clings to life as I scramble to get it some water. It dies just as I return.]

[1287.3 / 3490] [I'm on a boat docked in a marina. Servers set dinner plates in front of me and three other friends. A news alert on a table top television notifies us *"the marina has been closed indefinitely,"* and we *"must leave immediately."*]

[1287.4 / 3491] ["THE PRESIDENT" is interviewed in a conference room by a member of the media. During the conversation I walk in and place a black, seven-foot-tall accordion room divider between them.] //

⁂

LEMON: #0407
SWAN: #0043, #0285
DIVIDER: #0083
ACCORDION: #0125, #0160

⁂

#1288 - July 15, 2020 @ 05:56 (Beavercreek, Ohio)

[1288.1 / 3492] [I take a palm full of vitamins then salute judges to commence my pass at a world championship tumbling competition. I'm in a relationship with THE RODIN *(fit, attractive, and active)*, who manifests as a muscular wrestler that performs a floor routine at the same time I tumble. He pauses between passes to pose for photos in front of the large audience that's assembled. The camera flashes distract him and catapult him back in time to a childhood memory:

~he holds a spool of yellow raffle tickets on his left wrist as he feverishly scribbles with a pen on paper with his right hand. ***The more he scribbles, the younger he becomes.*** *The note is intended to remind him that his sister recently gave birth. The more he scribbles, the more childlike and incoherent the words on the page become. He's confident he'll "remember the most important details when questioned later." He believes he's regressed to age six when the writing concludes. ~*

When THE RODIN returns to the present, he's completed his routine and swallows a mitt full of supplements, taking note that people in the crowd speak with a British accent as he draws large gulps of liquid from a water bottle.]

[1288.2 / 3493] [THE CONFIDANT becomes increasingly angry with me. He slams a piece of blank white paper on the desk behind me. I turn around and write down an example of a ***"made up problem,"*** which further agitates him and causes him to fume with rage. I write the word ***"incommunicado"*** at the bottom of the page, and he storms out of the room.] //

⁂

Maj. = 16- THE CONFIDANT: #1372
TICKETS: #1254, #1255
FUME: #0502, #0596
BIRTH: #0007

⁂

#1289 - July 15, 2020 @ 08:01 (Beavercreek, Ohio)

[1289.1 / 3494] [THE DEVOTEE leads a class where attendees learn how to throw a proper dinner party. Eight students have gathered around a table. THE DEVOTEE provides instruction from the side of the room. Two placemats are brown. The other six are white. The initial group task is to determine where each is best placed. A photo booth machine allows us to zoom in to a microscopic level where we can alter environmental details *(adding space, changing color, etc.)*. Class is scheduled to conclude at 11:00pm, though a glance at my wrist suggests it's already 11:26pm. I select the option to print my altered photograph, but I'm interrupted by a prompt for payment: **"Any unpurchased amendments will be discarded."**

THE EMPYREAN *(masculine, engaging, and productive)*, THE CONNECTOR and THE INTELLIGENCE OFFICER *(contrary, smart, and short tempered)* join me in the photo booth. THE INTELLIGENCE OFFICER annoyed with the machine's interface says, *"I have to point a gun at people all day long. It's annoying to have to point my finger at this machine so it'll print."*

THE DEVOTEE pops her head through the machine's screen and informs our group that it's time to wrap up. She concludes class with a vulnerable share about her biggest current challenges with interpersonal communication.]

. . .

[1289.2 / 3495] [I show THE WEAVER a photo of a blue rooftop tennis court that a former lover's installed on top of his condo building. The photo receives a variety of positive comments online. She looks at me as she says, *"It's good to see what the grandbabies are up to."*]

[1289.3 / 3496] [THE DANCER expresses frustration at how I've chosen to write this book. She points to my most recent draft saying,

"You didn't give sufficient detail. Read the passage again."

"That's not the point. I can't write out every bit of detail and dialog. It would be arcane"] //

⁂

Maj. = 0- THE WEAVER: #1301, 2- THE DANCER: #1293, 4-THE CONNECTOR: #1304

Min. = ♠-THE DEVOTEE: #1306

SUFFICIENT: #0182

MICROSCOPIC: #0430, #0552

GUN: #0829, #0832, #0843, #1050, #1086

⁂

#1290 - July 15, 2020 @ 09:43 (Beavercreek, Ohio)

[1290.1 / 3497] [I'm shown a map of a human mouth while attending a lecture on *"how to exploit a person's taste buds."* According to the teacher, *"Sweet always cancels out bitter."*]

[1290.2 / 3498] [People queue in front of a store built into the trunk of a giant paper tree, to buy a new book, copies of which are printed on demand by way of a large cartoon-like Rube Goldberg machine that begins in the tree branches and meanders to ground level. I've run a print job for 100 copies of a highly desired text, which I quickly learn is peppered with errata. The errors have been purposely left uncorrected. The cover of the book errantly has the word **"doctor"** printed across itmultiple times, as well as on the binding. On an inside display shelf rests two previously unreleased "Dr. Seuss" books. I pick up a copy of one titled "THREE FOUR TWO!" presented with a soft blue cover, and an impression of a dove consuming the top right quartile. I place the book under my sweater and walk out of the store into an amusement park.]

[1290.3 / 3499] [A teenage mother has sex with her new boyfriend in her parent's bed. The parents are fine with it because they *"know where she is."*] //

⁂

TASTE: #0033, #0039, #0090

SWEET: #0566, #0614, #0634

BITTER: #0088, #0401, #0929

⁂

#1291 - July 16, 2020 @ 07:25 (Beavercreek, Ohio)

[1291.1 / 3500] [Band practice in the basement. A bunch of us have gathered. All of us can play a variety of instruments and can change roles within the band, on demand. I'm intrigued by a new synthesizer rig someone's brought to the space, which appears to be controlled by three smartphones, plugged in to side-by-side recessed ports just above the keyboard. The rectangular ports are outlined with a soft thin line of green-white light. A subset of musicians gathers and leave, intent on meeting with a manager whose office is just beyond a tall black accordion room divider. The office manager is a man with a beard who wears a short red dress.]

[1291.2 / 3501] [I walk towards a house in the middle of the night. The property is under construction. A mountain lion walks out a back door and towards me.]

[1291.3 / 3502] [I prepare for my first morning at a new job. I'm a nurse. Once on site I'm instructed to set up a reception area for overflow patients. Some may need to receive care in areas that ordinarily serve as offices. We don't have any plastic gowns to wear over our scrubs. I'm a bit disappointed that I'm going to get my sweatshirt dirty. It must be burned at the end of my shift.] //

⁂

MIDDLE: #0094, #0141, #0150
OVERFLOW: #0586, #0646
CONSTRUCTION: #0805, #1089
SHIFT: #0219, #0251

⁂

#1292 - July 17, 2020 @ 06:08 (Beavercreek, Ohio)

[1292.1 / 3503] [I'm in a car, crossing a long straight bridge over an ocean at right. THE CARPENTER nearly drives off into the sea when his attention is taken by the majesty of the water.]

[1292.2 / 3504] [Curiously, I take a straight pin from a cushion and plunge it a couple of inches deep into the *"white to the right of the iris of my left eye."* I understand I didn't need to do it, but I was drawn to the novelty. I remove the pin, which brings audible gasps and concerns from others gathered in the study. Many express worry my left eye will deflate and fall out of my skull. I squint to prevent that from happening, though I don't feel any change in the pressure of my eye.]

[1292.3 / 3505] [I'm in a department store observing a fire sale on *"Russian produced goods."* I can buy a yoga mat for $6, and a variety of other props for pennies on the dollar.]

[1292.4 / 3506] [I'm a woman. I kill another woman and leave her corpse on an elevated bed, dressed with white lace sheets. A neighbor discovers the body and calls the police. I attempt to flee the scene when a director calls, *"CUT!"* The frame pulls back to reveal I'm on the set of a soap opera.] //

⁂

Maj. = 1- THE CARPENTER: #1295
SKULL: #0957, #0987, #1184, #1200
PRESSURE: #0527, #0540, #0607
POLICE: #0145, #0161, #0278, #0397

⁂

#1293 - July 19, 2020 @ 08:02 (Beavercreek, Ohio)

[1293.1 / 3507] [I'm with THE DANCER in a large rehearsal space. We prepare for a public performance. I dance and leap, accompanied by loud orchestral music.]

[1293.2 / 3508] [A man is promoted to a CEO role at a small community bank. He's congratulated by the entire staff and walks the floor for individual acknowledgements. When he arrives at my desk we embrace, then hold one another at the forearms for a few moments. In unison we say, ***"I consent,"*** before grabbing each other's butts at the same time.]

[1293.3 / 3509] [***"I'm concerned I don't know the choreography, nor lyrics. I don't have tools to help me, but I'm confident I can put on a good show."*** I walk through different rooms in a public venue, pausing as I get a glimpse of a long performance hall just before its glimmering diamond doors close. I want to go in.] //

⁂

Maj. = 2- THE DANCER: #1294
CEO: #0113, #0193, #0281, #0306
CONSENT: #0747
DOORS: #0820

⁂

#1294 - July 20, 2020 @ 07:24 (Beavercreek, Ohio)

[1294.1 / 3510] [THE DANCER and I convene at a large ranch home in Montana. Our planned excursion to a theme park is delayed when our hosts suggest we look through various knick knacks and family items they're looking to sell on premises. The elderly female owner of the ranch complains that we *"aren't following appropriate public health protocols,"* though their home is unkempt and filthy. We walk through a series of accessible ramps, passing by large rooms with portals to different realities *(a shopping mall, a park, a hotel, restaurants, and so on)*. While passing by the theater I see a porn star.

"You're attractive!"

"I'm so much more than that," he replies with a yawn.]

. . .

[1294.2 / 3511] [I ride a carousel horse that leaps from its hinges and gallops down from the sky towards the Napali Coast. The horse penetrates the mountain, stopping at hidden municipal subway stops within. I ride the horse one stop beyond my intended destination. I dismount and walk down two different wide staircases carpeted with red velvet. I pass through a pair of gold doors to get entry to the subway, knowing I have to ***"backtrack to reconnect with the family."*** As I ride the subway, other members of the family gather at each stop. People introduce themselves to me as family, though I don't recognize them. The interactions are curious, friendly, and engaging. The family expands.] //

⁂

Maj. = 2- THE DANCER: #1300
GALLOP: #0683
HEALTH: #0845
FAMILY: #0006

⁂

#1295 - July 21, 2020 @ 08:00 (Beavercreek, Ohio)

[1295.1 / 3512] [THE CARPENTER drives a truck. The wheel is on the right ride of the vehicle. I'm the passenger, riding to his left. The day is bright and sunny. We're driving on a country highway that's recently been repaved. The road is oily and black. I ask THE CARPENTER to stop texting while driving and place his attention back on the road.]

[1295.2 / 3513] [I walk into a restaurant and down a stairwell to a community table where generations of family members are seated. THE CATHOLIC *(devoted, cynical, and upset)* stands and attempts to sneak away from the dinner without being noticed. She's very old, and frail. Her head's wrapped in a red scarf. Just before she exits well all yell, ***"HAPPY BIRTHDAY!"*** in unison, which is enough to get her to pause, turn around, and crack a small smile. GRANDMA sits at the head of the table.]

[1295.3 / 3514] [I walk up a stairwell in a modern home. I'm greeted at the top by a husband and wife who point towards the corner of a large family room with dark hardwood floors. I walk to the corner, and discover a curved tabletop length of glass resting upturned on its side like a ribbon. The floor where it rests has a liquid quality as I cross it. I lift the glass ribbon and see etching in a language I don't recognize. When I place it carefully back on the floor it warps and bends. ***"The glass may be cooling off too quickly."*** The husband and wife are not concerned with the shift in shape.]

[1295.4 / 3515] [I'm in a cinder block walled room that's been painted a mint green tone. A simple roller cart near the wall holds an old television and a VHS player. I press the "fast forward" button to wind the tape within, all the way to the right side of the cassette. When ejected, the spool creates a bulge on the right half of the cartridge that must be evened out by placing the object within a white plastic mesh of equivalent size that fits the exterior of the object much like a taco shell.]

. . .

[1295.5 / 3516] [I'm enrolled in a sophisticated game in a large house, spread across its innumerable floors. At the start, I stand in front of a wall sized contract headed with the boilerplate phrase: "**THE WORLDBRIDGER'S SMORGASBORD**" replete with a highly detailed list of rules and considerations printed in a font so small it's unintelligible. As teams break out and begin play, familiar voices can be heard within the property.

THE HANDYMAN leads a group through an exercise on an upper floor. Initially, THE CARPENTER and I attempt to solve a musical riddle by singing in harmony, but when we're unsuccessful we're instead given a lesson by a stern female teacher. I observe dozens of groups engaged in different tasks that challenge their collective skill sets, often using diagonal passageways and elevators to move between areas of the house. At the bottom of one such passage, I discover a series of three, palm-sized statues of blue kittens positioned in a small equilateral triangle in the corner of a room. The kittens are faced away from each other. Small blue lasers create a security grid across the room, which I break as I step through. A secret door opens in the wall to my left.]

[1295.6 / 3517] [I'm handed an exam paper covered with red ink. Answers to the exam increase in difficulty and sophistication as I read the document. A note at the top informs me that I'm days ahead of the class, and requests I, *"slow down to allow others a chance to synthesize information."*] //

⁂

Maj.* = *1- THE CARPENTER: #1299, 7-THE WORLDBRIDGER: #1335, 11-GRANDMA: #1305

Min. = *♣-THE CATHOLIC: #1356*

MINT: #0053, #0055, #0309

VHS: #1302

⁂

#1296 - July 22, 2020 @ 08:00 (Beavercreek, Ohio)

[1296.1 / 3518] [A skinny White man with arm sleeve tattoos directs a group of people up to the second-floor gallery in a co-ed fraternity house for an initiation ritual. THE LOBBYIST is among those present in the line of neophytes. He holds a photo album full of Polaroids at his chest.]

[1296.2 / 3519] [I take planes of decreasing size as I puddle-jump between islands *(as the islands themselves decrease in size)*. The count of passengers on the flights decreases until I'm left alone and piloting a small glider. I land on an island that's been built up with resorts and tourism infrastructure, but I'm the only person there.]

[1296.3 / 3520] [Inside a hotel lobby, I look at an octagonal diagram on a screen that pulses and undulates, drawing my attention to my seat assignment at *"position 57,"* which is irrationally set next to *"position 1."* I shake my head in confusion and walk down a grey hallway in search of peanut butter cookies, stopping to rifle through cupboards and cabinets to no avail. I remain the one person onsite. My surroundings are immaculately clean and sterile.] //

⁂

STERILE: #0125
TATTOOS: #0455, #0597, #0644
PEANUT: #0845

⁂

#1297 - July 23, 2020 @ 06:51 (Beavercreek, Ohio)

[1297.1 / 3521] [In "The Highlands" I stand in line at a mall kiosk waiting to print documents. A group of people in front of me huddles around a computer terminal debating which pieces of propaganda need to be reprinted in triplicate that will later be posted in "The Midlands." A small bald man frantically enters from a door behind me, after sustaining a blow to the right eye with a baseball bat. The white of his right eye has turned black. When I ask him if he needs help, he refuses and assures me he can do his own research on, *"how to cope with a detached retina."*]

[1297.2 / 3522] [I contemplate ways of traversing a busy one-way bridge in the opposite direction to get home. Cars zip by and honk as the sun sets.]

[1297.3 / 3523] [I ATTEND A "COMPETITIVE FUNERAL," where participants are invited to leap into an Olympic size lap pool. I place a stack of books on an end table, and walk by a group of mourners who hesitate leaping into the pool. They're concerned they'll ruin their clothes. I pass by an elderly family member, perhaps the widowed patriarch, who sits quietly in a wheelchair roughly 20 feet from the edge of the pool. He's eager to watch "the race," giving me some reassurance that, ***"our group has appropriately decided to honor the dead by swimming"***] //

⁂

TRIPLICATE: #1260
FUNERAL: #0124
PROPAGANDA: #0806, #0944
OLYMPIC: #0036, #0069, #0071, #0076

⁂

#1298 - July 23, 2020 @ 09:01 (Beavercreek, Ohio)

[1298.1 / 3524] [I experience different bodily appendages as detachable. My fingers pull apart from my body and click back into their joints when they become purple and discolored. I run similar experiments with my toes, ankles, wrists, and penis. I take photographs, which in this reality amounts to the same behavior as masturbation. Each body part straightens and snaps like a *"slap bracelet."* I marvel at the novelty.

I stand up and look around, taking note the layout of the upper level of the house has completely changed. The now open floor plan has a nursery to the right, where a crib holds a cooing and babbling version of THE LITTLE PRINCE. He may be asleep. I don't go over to look at him because I may rouse him unnecessarily. To the left are a variety of toys that children have left scattered around on the floor after a morning play session.

I take a seat at a table and remove numerous pieces of broken technology from my pockets. I place my phone on the table *(and a cracked glass ring atop the phone)* before I decide to go for a swim.] //

⁂

Maj. = 12- THE LITTLE PRINCE: #1332
PURPLE: #0088, #0125, #0168, #0177
SWIM: #0773
CRIB: #0019

⁂

#1299 - July 23, 2020 @ 09:56 (Beavercreek, Ohio)

[1299.1 / 3525] [I get on a bus at night with THE CARPENTER. I'm unable to find my face covering, so I place my nose in the crease of my left elbow. As I take a seat, I note multiple single use medical masks discarded on the floor of the vehicle. As we sit facing out the window, we pass by a different rock band performing at each stop. One band has three members dressed in all black, standing with their instruments on black road, in front of a black wall, lit by two large white spotlights angled perpendicular to the wall.]

[1299.2 / 3526] [I pass through a locker room en route to a public pool when I hear a small child crying. I grab a small peppermint patty wrapped in bright pink foil, noting a small microchip in the wrapper crease as I tear into it. The small candy within is a circle with a cartoon-like bite mark taken from its lower right quadrant. I pop the chocolate in my mouth and approach the crying child, who's naked and facing the corner nearest the exit door. The child has long blond hair, and I initially believe it to be a girl, perhaps 6 years old. When I ask where its parents are, the child reveals itself as a boy named "David." I wrap him in a fluffy white towel. His tears cease. While wearing the towel, he turns into a small white rabbit and hops towards a large sunny window by a different door. A group of woodland creatures congregate in front of the window and begin to excitedly jump up and down, happy to be reunited with their long-lost friend. I open the door. The rabbit hops out. The pack of animals disappears into the lush green jungle-scape, bathed in soft yellow-gold sunlight.]

[1299.3 / 3527] [I turn towards a wall and see a variety of images projected within a clear plate glass window. One of the six screen tiles shows the progression of a musician from young pianist, to lead vocalist in a rock band, to a mature solo artist. Another of the six, I touch. It pulls me through to a large club house with a glass wall at its far end. An oversized couch filled with 30 teenagers sits in front of a young rock band that rehearses. Between songs the guitarist shows me his rig, then invites me to check out his secret amplifiers that are set up behind a set of gym risers nearer to the back window.]

[1299.4 / 3528] [I stand in front of a bakery display case and watch a woman place orange and black frosted cupcakes out for sale. She expects them to sell well during the fall season. She organizes another tray of large book-sized graham cracker treats *(filled with black-and-white checkerboard marshmallows)* taking a pause to scoop two wilting ones from yesterday's lot from a bottom shelf, hiding them behind today's presentation.] //

⁂

Maj. = 1- THE CARPENTER: #1303
QUADRANT: #0887, #1082
FLUFFY: #0066, #0350
LOCKER: #0021

⁂

#1300 - July 24, 2020 @ 01:39 (Beavercreek, Ohio)

[1300.1 / 3529] [THE DANCER and I wake up together on the floor of a neuroscientist's compound. The room is familiar to both of us. I explore the property alone. I arrive in an atrium in the center of the building, and am guided to cross a carpeted interior courtyard, intent on ascending a staircase at the far end that zigzags up and to the left. I stop at a mezzanine to use a glass-doored bathroom marked "private." The floor's wet. Someone's recently taken a shower. A tile and glass staircase leads to another steam covered glass door. I errantly rub my hand on the door to wipe away steam, which doesn't have the intended effect. Confusingly, steam only covers the opposite side of the door, though where I stand is hot and humid. The shower is beautifully appointed. An entire interior layer constructed from clear-glass square-tiles, *(which hover a foot away from an outer layer of royal blue tiles on all sides)*, have finely etched images which alternate between botany catalog images of flowers and complex multi-dimensional shapes. After seeming eons of appreciative inspection, I turn and leave the "private" bathroom and resume exploring.

If I continue upward and to the left, I'll eventually arrive at *"the scientist's master suite."* A map of the property shines in gold in the center of my head as a reminder that I've been here many times before. I continue down a hallway, which opens up to a massive aircraft hangar. My path converges with the neuroscientist and others who take a walking tour while loading roller carts full of household cleaning supplies *(rubber gloves, garbage bags, paper towels)*. The neuroscientist suggests we pause at a canteen for refreshment, then commences a lecture on ***"the science of sleep"*** as we replenish our water bottles. I infer there are areas in the home that are truly off limits, but receive no feedback from the neuroscientist as I open different doors at my discretion. He seems creepy. I question his intent. I press the steel bar on an exit door and leave through a back alley.] //

⁂

Maj. = 2- THE DANCER: #1301
ATRIUM: #0033, #0128, #0188
FLOWERS: #0710, #0735
PRIVATE: #0905, #0926
CANTEEN: #0080

⁂

#1301 - July 26, 2020 @ 02:55 (Beavercreek, Ohio)

[1301.1 / 3530] [THE WEAVER enrolls me as a part time employee, to assist with the deep cleaning of a neighbor's large mansion across the street. We enter through the garage, passing by a large clear vessel containing hundreds of thin, colorful layers of sand. Guests can take a scoop and pour it in a small jar of their own when they depart as a reminder of their visit. Once inside, we begin cleaning the dirty aftermath of unpleasant guests, who we quickly learn are an older brother and sister of the neighbor. THE WEAVER finds a dirty diaper in a corner of a bedroom, while we clean other rooms in the house. I'm mildly grossed out. THE WEAVER laughs, *"Let me show you something that really stinks."* Waving at us with her index finger, we follow her up a white marble spiral staircase and walk towards a *"bolted on"* addition at the back of the house. Three large rooms have been left in disrepair by the neighbor's older siblings and children. One of the children has taken residence in a long open hallway with vaulted ceilings, with a single small blob of a skylight in the far upper right corner of the space. Light shines down on the non-binary teen, who practices songs with their, *"revolutionary rock band."*

THE WEAVER asks me pointedly to, *"Do the yard."* I acquiesce. Once complete, we rendezvous with the neighbor, who discusses the declining health of her aging siblings and the impact it's had on her ability to keep the house clean. We walk together up a back staircase. The mansion continues to grow in scale, the higher we climb. We pause and stand by a railing on the second floor on a multi-level vista point. I peer over the railing and see a dark hardwood beer garden that fills with people who pile in from numerous hallways below. The bar is composed of cherry wood and sports intricate scalloped carvings. THE DANCER and I agree that she and I have both worked at the venue previously and have, *"used its prestige to close numerous high-profile deals."* We stand there interminably watching people advance through the grand atrium of the mansion in time lapse. THE WEAVER breaks our hypnotic observation saying,

"You'll want to note whether or not the space can hold its own with these forces. At what point does it become unlivable as a home?"

We're reminded of our exciting experiences, and nearly blurt out a premature affirmation. The atrium grows increasingly spacious, elegant, modern, and rich in feeling. As I look down, I see levels of the mansion spiral deeper into the ground, beyond what my eyes can bring to focus.] //

⁂

Maj. = 0- THE WEAVER: #1305, 2- THE DANCER: #1320

DIAPER: #0728

SPIRAL: #0024

SIBLING: #0895, #0947

⁂

#1302 - July 26, 2020 @ 04:53 (Beavercreek, Ohio)

[1302.1 / 3531] [I've taken up short term residence in a guest house, which I share with a rich teenage boy, who inhabits a recessed loft that runs the length of the right-hand wall. From my desk it looks like a tunnel in an oversized ant farm. After returning from my daily errands, I drop my bag on my desk and discover a small green diary he's left as a gift *"for special notes and stories."* It changes size as I flip through it. Some moments it appears it can hold LPs, in others VHS cassettes, and compact discs in others. With each flip, different milk crates filled with the appropriate technology line the far wall of my room, then immediately change to what corresponds to the slots in the book.

The rich teen doesn't get along with his father, and may be at risk of getting thrown out of the house. He consistently hosts parties. He might have a drug addiction. After a particularly rowdy party he has sex with a muscular older man. I'm assigned a page, who informs me the young man is, *"trying to offload all his old technology on you, sir."*

Later at dinner, I interact from a distance with other members of the family. I'm in quarantine with the son in our own wing of the house. Something strikes me as odd and futuristic, mere moments before I awaken.] //

⁂
ANT FARM: #1100
MILK: #0790
DISTANCE #0214
ODD: #0191
⁂

#1303 - July 26, 2020 @ 08:08 (Beavercreek, Ohio)

[1303.1 / 3532] [THE CHILD rides a bike and crashes it into a workbench. She doesn't know how to use the breaks. She rides away, pausing to ditch the bike after making friends with a man who has robotic legs.]

[1303.2 / 3533] [THE CARPENTER and I print out volumes of documents at a table in a diner as the owners finalize today's menu, which they scribble in black ball point pen on a large piece of butcher paper. Once complete they post the butcher block scroll on the wall. The descriptions for today's specials make my mouth water.

I blink and the scene restarts. THE CARPENTER disappears and is replaced by two similar aged men. The three of us seem to be stuck in an infinite loop. A small square monitor is mounted up and to the right of the kitchen service window. ***"If we snap a photo of a hologram on screen at a precise moment, we'll receive a prize."*** The repeated experience becomes increasingly frustrating, as the guy who appears to win is not awarded his prize because the caption and hashtag attached to his image, *"was submitted in English on an out-of-date tablet."* In this reality, English responses are only valid for 30 seconds before they erase themselves.] //

⁂
Maj. = 1- THE CARPENTER: #1309, 3- THE CHILD: #1309
ERASE: #0323
INFINITE: #0747
MENU: #1241
⁂

#1304 - July 27, 2020 @ 01:49 (Beavercreek, Ohio)

[1304.1 / 3534] [I'm on a party cruise with THE CONNECTOR and others. We watch a concert video as the boat pushes back. The video features a Halloween DJ set, where the performer wears a hybrid *"wolfman-Dracula"* costume while performing in front of a massive indoor arena crowd. I fall off the side of the vessel and plunge into the cold dark water below. Though I'm more likely to drown, my concern remains on the backpack I left aboard, which has my necessary prescriptions.]

. . .

[1304.2 / 3535] [I befriend a young Asian girl, within what I believe to be a submarine. We walk from end-to-end solving puzzles by pulling different series of levers from their upright positions in the walls. She asks for my help in pulling two pressurized valves on the far end, resulting in the opening of a small door. We walk through the bright white doorway and find ourselves at an open-air market in an Asian speaking country. The lack of signage impedes my ability to know where we are, with certainty. Some people realize we don't have passports nor customs forms, but offer us assistance because they, *"know it will be challenging for us to get home."* Some steal items from the market as they help us.]

[1304.3 / 3536] [A girl's father walks up behind us and takes a seat, as I help her memorize the periodic table of elements using flashcards. She climbs up onto his lap and continues to practice. The father does not recognize the girl as his child. I hold up a card with three small dots obscuring the syllables of the answer. *"HE-MUH-TITE,"* she says, pointing at each dot. Though she's confident, her answer is incorrect.]

⁂

Maj. = 4- THE CONNECTOR: #1320
INDOOR: #0137, #0233, #0275
SYLLABLES: #0933
MEMORIZE: #0014
LEVERS: #1304

⁂

#1305 - July 28, 2020 @ 08:05 (Beavercreek, Ohio)

[1305.1 / 3537] [THE WEAVER points to where the back lawn is overgrown, as a result of *"too much sauna-ing in the backyard."* The grass is tall and will be difficult to mow. *"GRANDMA and GRANDPA never had a similar problem,"* she says with a shrug.]

[1305.2 / 3538] [People author lists to outline their *"ideal lives,"* then build scale model dollhouses as physical reflections. The exterior of the houses will be evaluated by a panel of judges who will inspect and manipulate them. As the judges move between podiums, they note the insides of every model are filled with "so much weighty matter" *(objects, emotions, desires, and memories)* that they sag and bow when pulled from their presentation stands.]

[1305.3 / 3539] [A man sits by a pool in a bathrobe and recites a poem, lamenting what it's like to be, *"too beautiful."* His heir of elitism is not attractive. His lyrical references about how, *"real estate prices in East Hampton are on the rise,"* seem awkward and tone-deaf.

"They've always been high."]

[1305.4 / 3540] [People start a new relationship, then retire to a bedroom to make love. I stay in another room and crawl behind the headboard of my bed on my elbows and find a pad of paper where I confirm a list of desires I've authored in a secret code. I utter a few pleasure-laden groans while reading from the list, before standing and walking out of the bedroom.] //

⁂

Maj. = 0- THE WEAVER: #1309, 11-GRANDMA: #1333

Min. = ♥- GRANDPA: #1356

IDEAL: #0887, #0948, #0962

HEADBOARD: #0035, #0168

SAUNA: #0232, #0314, #0820

SECRET CODE: #1001

⁂

#1306 - July 29, 2020 @ 08:58 (Beavercreek, Ohio)

[1306.1 / 3541] [THE DEVOTEE meets with me in a white-walled basement after concluding a lecture. I ask her for her future availability to schedule a consultation. She walks me to a computer and uses a mouse to highlight an icon of a small woodland cottage. She wants to enroll me in a retreat she's leading in the spring. The cottage is available to rent.]

[1306.2 / 3542] [I walk into a tiny boutique where a polished, expressive man hangs clothes on racks. He offers me a job. I ask him how many different SKUs he holds in inventory. *"Fifty,"* he says while sweetly placing a kiss on my nose.]

[1306.3 / 3543] [I look in a mirror and see two small rings on the surface of my skin, one on each cheek directly to each side of my nose, the size of a halved green olive. The skin appears irritated and about to rupture.

"I've contracted an incurable disease that will eventually eat the skin off my body."] //

⁂

Min. = ♠- THE DEVOTEE: #1378

COTTAGE: #0028, #0040, #0222, #0282, #0284

FIFTY: #0710

CHEEK: #0001

LECTURE: #0025

⁂

#1307 - July 30, 2020 @ 07:30 (Beavercreek, Ohio)

[1307.1 / 3544] [A large confederate flag on a pole behind "Dwight's" desk hides a red, white and blue swastika on the reverse. The flag's taken down as the team prepares for a party. One guy fills bowls with M&Ms. The group gathered grows annoyed with the distorted flag. "M&M man" grabs the crudely folded fabric and tosses it out on the lawn, inviting unwanted guests to make a tent.]

[1307.2 / 3545] [I awaken in a group discussion about how people with Master's degrees make six figure salaries upon enlisting in the military. Some cadets discuss where they would take vacation.]

. . .

[1307.3 / 3546] [Image of an overloaded dump truck. The cabin tilts up. The front wheel drive axle spins, but the vehicle won't move.]

[1307.4 / 3547] [I debate titles for my long form podcast.] //

⁂

FLAG: #0131, #0309, #0334
M&M: #1201
VACATION: #0622, #0682
MILITARY: #0013

⁂

#1308 - July 31, 2020 @ 08:11 (Beavercreek, Ohio)

[1308.1 / 3548] [YOKO ONO creates art out of discarded food at her urban flat. The sculpture is numerous stories tall.]

[1308.2 / 3549] [I walk behind myself, climbing up a flight of stairs. My hair is long, one portion at the center falls to my waist, the rest at my mid-back.]

[1308.3 / 3550] [THE JESTER appears, then quickly dissolves.] //

⁂

FLAT: #0002, #0006, #0009
LONG: #0694, #0695, #0725, #0733, #0750, #0764
QUICKLY: #0814, #0815, #0817

⁂

#1309 - August 1, 2020 @ 10:00 (Beavercreek, Ohio)

[1309.1 / 3551] [I tie the end of a rope in a knot around a transistor radio. I turn the radio on and tune it to 103.7FM. After spinning the rope overhead like a lasso, I toss it into a swimming pool. THE CHILD catches it like a football just before breaching the surface of the water. The rope splashes, sinks, then swings like a pendulum from deep end, to the shallow. THE CHILD walks out of the water holding the radio and rope at tension.]

[1309.2 / 3552] [I work with the family to reorganize and redecorate one half of a duplex. We've resided there for years, but the time has come to move. As we configure kitchen appliances, I've forgotten that I'd been cooking a savory cheese galette in the microwave. After the appliances have all been set in their new position on the opposite wall, I remove the tart and discover the cheese is not melted, and the pastry is underdone. We eat it anyway. THE CARPENTER requests I join him in the back yard to hoist picnic tables, and large corner reinforced steel "L's," on to storage racks that tuck away neatly into the fence. The occupant of the other half of the duplex is miffed to learn THE WEAVER took a roller cart for the morning to assist with the move *(even though the task was completed and the cart had already been returned)*. We reposition a guest room toilet in a previously unused area of a walk-in closet. Once complete with our projects, we're amazed by how spacious the property now seems. The neighbor down the street who's taking occupancy tomorrow will be able to make a swift adjustment to *(what will be for them)* a downsized living space.] //

⁂

Maj. = 0- THE WEAVER: #1310, 1- THE CARPENTER: #1310, 3- THE CHILD: #1318
RADIO: #0897, #1072
CHEESE: #0547, #0787, #0793
SPACIOUS: #0019, #0033, #0059, #0113
HOIST: #0402, #0760

⁂

#1310 - August 2, 2020 @ 03:27 (Beavercreek, Ohio)

[1310.1 / 3553] [Candidates vie for elected positions in different west coast cities. A delicate civil balance hangs on the funding and completion of key infrastructure improvements *(bridges and tunnels linking various municipalities)*. I'm accountable for the on time, on budget delivery of a new bridge. A scandal disrupts incumbent leadership, forthcoming elections, and tosses the portfolio of projects into disarray. A mass exodus of urban dwellers to smaller coastal towns, swiftly impacts prospective funding pools for out-year investment and recurring maintenance. The political balance collapses and everything spontaneously combusts into white hot flame.]

[1310.2 / 3554] [I live in a three-story building. THE PILOT and THE KIND HEART live above. THE LAWYER lives below. A huge fire rages on the third level, so hot it warps space-time. I call 911 and work to hurry everyone I see, out of the building. I recently purchased a gold square laptop, and a flat's worth of new furnishings. I retreat to the street and see the fire raging, deeply saddened that everything within will be considered a total loss. I'm most upset about the upstairs set, because everything they own has been reduced to char.

Eight fire trucks arrive and squelch the inferno from all angles. When I'm allowed to enter the building, I note my unit has mostly suffered water damage. The coal black ceiling gives hints as to what may have happened if the fire was left to its devices for a few more moments. I'm surprised to find the gold laptop and other electronics untouched by the fire and water.

I've left the door open. A young man who dates another neighbor down the hall, looks in and removes a framed piece of illuminated medieval calligraphy from the wall.

"Yo. Yo. That's mine. DUDE!" I yell to the brief bewilderment of the young man who's certain he's in his own apartment.

I kindly inform him that he's not at home. He drops the frame and runs away. I push the walls of my condo out in every direction to make space for piles of burned trash left in other areas of the building, which people rummage through to find relics from their pre-firestorm lives. I stack a series of street signs next to an upright piano as an older man and woman enter to collect some of their partially salvaged property.

THE WEAVER and THE CARPENTER offer THE PILOT and THE KIND HEART a place to live while they determine their next steps, though they politely decline the interim home.

The respite home's an hour away from where THE PILOT and THE KIND HEART work, and neither are willing to make that long of a daily commute.] //

⁂

Maj. = 0- THE WEAVER: #1320, 1- THE CARPENTER: #1311, 5- THE LAWYER: #1335, 6- THE PILOT: #1404, 21- THE KIND HEART: #1404
FLAME: #0012, #0035, #0065, #0189
GOLD: #0540, #0545, #0547, #0550, #0572
PIANO: #0908, #0919, #1134, 1163

⁂

#1311 - August 4, 2020 @ 06:49 (Beavercreek, Ohio)

[1311.1 / 3555] [A bass player for a rock band shows up late for a gig. Contract negotiations for a forthcoming album took place with each band member individually offsite, earlier in the day. THE CARPENTER insists, *"it'll save a lot of future back-and-forth when the group returns to the studio to track new material."* The bass player walks up a concrete driveway divided into incongruent segments by a two-inch band of shiny gold tape. The X at the end of the tape denotes where the bassist will stand to perform. Known for his short temper and throwing hissy fits, the bass player seems to hold an unfair degree of control over the group. If the show doesn't go the way he wants, he'll pull a handle on a cord suspended just above his head and bring the music, the venue, and the entire action of the scene to a grinding halt.]

[1311.2 / 3556] [Two people practice writing *"the script of the spirit"* with paint brushes dipped in ink. Later they'll offer a prayer to ask the "god of rain" to relent. Both people produce what they believe are the same, appropriate magick symbols, though their output appears vastly different when I'm asked to review their creations.] //

⁂

Maj. = 1- THE CARPENTER: #1320
SCRIPT#426, #0556, #1101
BASS: #0554, #0580. #618, #0666
NEGOTIATIONS: #0097, #0500

⁂

#1312 - August 4, 2020 @ 08:14 (Beavercreek, Ohio)

[1312.1 / 3557] [An orb of silver light asks me to telepathically interview two ants from a colony outside a house, who've been instructed to journey inside to retrieve water from a freshly cleaned toilet bowl. The male ant has a robust multi-point checklist and complains, while the female ant simply does her job masterfully and without any need for extra assistance. She carries a low volume murmur of irritation towards her cohort.]

[1312.2 / 3558] [The moon captures me in a tractor beam of white-gold-light and infuses my aura with a transmission from an ancestral language. I feel communication barriers between the atoms of my body recede. I feel nourished, energized and healed.] //

⁂

ORB: #0086, #0146, #865
JOURNEY: #0011, #0047, #0053, #0076
HEALED: #0098, #0384, #0896
TOILET: #0488, #0538, #0586, #0613

⁂

#1313 - August 6, 2020 @ 05:02 (Beavercreek, Ohio)

[1313.1 / 3559] [I'm at a postal distribution hub where I observe mass volumes of variable sized packages shuttle across a complex network of conveyor belts. Packages are initially wrapped in purple vinyl, then subsequently sealed in clear plastic cling. Three large cylinders are loaded onto the conveyors, and quickly routed up a steep incline. They spin slowly in a counterclockwise direction as they're wrapped up. Shorter women are tasked with removing air hockey tables from a box truck. They're told to report the size and weight to onsite management so they'll be properly inventoried. The women are concerned the tables are too heavy for them to lift.]

[1313.2 / 3560] [I'm in a shopping mall. People gather by a point of sale, when they've been instructed to take their break. I walk down an aisle and feel alone. I pick up a fur lined charcoal fedora *(microscopic black and white checkerboard print)*, with a single red feather sticking from the band. The hat has no price. ***"Is it Gucci?"*** I try it on in front of a mirror that reflects a wall of single socks behind me for sale, a la carte.] //

⁂

FEDORA: #0277, #0450, #0579, #0790, #0876
CONVEYOR: #0007, #0014, #0322, #0534, #0621
HOCKEY: #0452, #0535, #0886, #0990
PURPLE: #0498, #0595, #0613

⁂

#1314 - August 7, 2020 @ 02:48 (Beavercreek, Ohio)

[1314.1 / 3561] [I'm in a house with a group of people who lock up and shut off lights, just before heading to bed. We realize one of the exterior doors has been open for hours. Someone recalls letting another person they didn't know enter the home before sundown. The stress of, *"not locking someone out who should be allowed,"* is greater than leaving the home unlocked and vulnerable to strangers. I leave my body and observe the scene in third person, floating to the garage and witnessing a person in front of a truck who's encouraged by another to, *"take off and get going."*]

[1314.2 / 3562] [I run for political office. The stress is so acute that the only way I can cope is to grind my teeth. I grind my teeth so hard while looking at myself in the mirror that I break both the top and bottom rows.]

. . .

[1314.3 / 3563] [I sit in a car at night. Someone else drives the car off the road, up a hill, and on to a lawn. Someone captivated by *(and filming)* a flying squirrel unintentionally captures the car in flight, crossing the lawn, and then plunging down another hill. We attempt to escape our pursuers, knowing we've just committed vandalism. We stop the car at the bottom of the hill, exit, and run, knowing our pursuers can track our location through our phones.

"You cannot get away. We always know where you are."] //

⁂

GRIND: #0772
FLYING: #0500, #0561, #0655, #0725
TAKE OFF: #0071. #0494, #0540, #0601, #0762, #08023

⁂

#1315 - August 7, 2020 @ 04:10 (Beavercreek, Ohio)

[1315.1 / 3564] [I walk through a small English boutique and compliment a woman on her choice of bra. An older gentleman who looks like BILL MURRAY invites me to dinner. I may be a woman. BILL and I sit down for dinner on the same side of the table. After eating, I decide that I want to pay and leave. BILL gets the check from our server, then stands and leaves the table to speak with a business associate. I glance across the table, reaching past chunks of half chewed sausage scattered across it, and grab the folio. I open it and take a glance, learning our total is $230. I close the folio and place it on top of a file folder I've dropped on the table top. I'm unnerved. My teeth are loose. BILL returns to the table and takes a seat across from me with a different acquaintance. He introduces the unnamed man to me as his "mentee." BILL remains unaware that I want to pay. We're still seated at the table and talking when I wake up.] //

⁂

TEETH: #0500, #060, #0897, #0973, #1044
ENGLISH: #0578, #0831, #0851, #0933
CHEWED: #0151

⁂

#1316 - August 7, 2020 @ 05:31 (Beavercreek, Ohio)

[1316.1 / 3565] [We rent a second story cabin at a public pool. Tiny rooftop cabins can be rented for a smaller fee. It's free to stay in the cabins at pool level, but you have to pay to use the pool. Neighbors make bets with each other to leap from their balconies to the water. They encourage each other to take increasingly larger risks. The splashes create abnormally large waves. The level of fun increases. Some old women in the pool are concerned, *"the splashing will ruin their perms."* They prefer the water to be flat, splash-less and serene.]

[1316.2 / 3566] [I'm in a factory showroom with THE ALIEN NATUROPATH *(intuitive, quick, and intellectual)* and members from his professional association for a portfolio review. Their cash cow company produces specialty potato chips and has produced consistent returns for decades. They've gathered today with leaders from an incubator, who demonstrate a technology that will restore a blind person's eyesight, through a breakthrough process termed, **ROCD,** *"reversal of cell death."* A single drop of a new therapeutic costs $400, which can be injected directly into a patient's eye. Sight restoration in clinical trials usually occurs before the patient leaves the office. Government programs refuse to subsidize the procedure. People rally on behalf of the blind at City Hall so everyone can see, *"eye to eye."* When I ask THE ALIEN NATUROPATH for his impressions on the new vision restoration therapy, he politely refuses and suggests we collaborate on updating his financial management model.] //

⁂

CASH: #0683, #0801, #0805
POOL: #0538, #0561. #06022
SHOWROOM: #0502, #0796
DEATH: #0496, #0519, #0682

⁂

#1317 - August 7, 2020 @ 06:03 (Beavercreek, Ohio)

[1317.1 / 3567] [I join a coed cross-generational cycling team. On the day of our first ride, I immediately get a flat tire. I abandon my bike and begin jogging on the shoulder of the road. A woman behind me picks up my bike and wheels it along as she rides, shouting to me that my rear brakes don't work. I run down a highway. Some other team members speed by me on a downhill. I catch them as I jog up the next hill. We crest the summit together and once at the top, marvel at a large capitol building a few miles up the road. It's further away than we think. The group arrives at a familiar hotel. I'm handed my bike and carry it down multiple flights of steps. I pass a sign near the concierge that reads: **"OHIO. LOST PHONE."** I arrive at the front door after crossing a parquet checkerboard floor. I'm greeted by two female members of my team, one of whom rolled my bike along as I ran.

"How'd your day one go?"

I wake up before I receive an answer from either of them.] //

⁂

HIGHWAY: #0720, #0815, #0887, #0974
CAPITOL: #0341, #0395
FEMALE: #0496, #0544, #0550, #0561
FLAT: #0557, #0560, #0610

⁂

#1318 - August 7, 2020 @ 07:09 (Beavercreek, Ohio)

[1318.1 / 3568] [A sophisticated network of zip lines allow city dwellers to quickly and athletically traverse neighborhoods. At busy intersections, riders must use their judgement to determine when they leap and zoom, else accept the risk of being broadsided by municipal buses. Residents segment themselves into two factions. Those who don't use the zip lines chastise residents who do, accusing them of unfairly driving up local taxes, necessary for maintaining the network. I take a swing, and narrowly avoid being struck by a fast-moving bus from my right. I slow to a stop at a platform and walk down a ramp. The cool overcast day leaves the buildings a muted bluish-green tone. I pass by an elementary school, then a power plant, then another building I don't easily recognize. All buildings in town have a small bronze plaque with the current name for the structure, along with a historical listing of all other parcel uses.]

[1318.2 / 3569] [I peek in on THE ACTOR and his partner in their "C" shaped condo with salmon toned walls. The carpet is unfinished and extends up the walls. A small living room just in from the front door, spills into a narrow hallway to the left. A small bathroom and kitchen off to the right fill the space otherwise occupied by their "L" shaped boudoir. They rest on a futon *(which transforms nightly into their bed)* at the back of the unit. I sit on the couch. They wake up and begin communicating to each other exclusively through crossword puzzle clues. Today is their third anniversary. The partner puts three puzzles on the table in a row, with the clue, "**Mistake! Mistake! Mistake!**" written underneath each. Their attention moves to one another. They become amorous. I stand and walk out, pausing to turn, and toss them a small bottle of lube as I pass through the doorway.

"Children's soap?" they say quizzically when they inspect the bottle.]

[1318.3 / 3570] [THE CHILD gazes at a six-inch cube of glowing glass with a beach scene etched at its center. The cube floats at sternum level about a foot from her body in a mint white orb of light.

"Look! It's my self-portrait!" she says with a joyful toothy smile.]

[1318.4 / 3571] [Sitting at a cafe table, THE ACTOR tells me he's dated a dancer for a number of years. I tell him my most recent long-term partner was a dancer as well, though I express I've been single for the last five years. *"Lovingly dancing with those who dance,"* is where he and I find common ground in our adult relationships.] //

⁂

Maj. = 3- THE CHILD: #1326, 10- THE ACTOR: #1339

ATTENTION: #0498, #0506, #0521, #0524

CUBE: #0597, #0615, #0640, #0647

ADULT: #0541, #0575, #0813

⁂

#1319 - August 8, 2020 @ 03:52 (Beavercreek, Ohio)

[1319.1 / 3572] [Two marketing teams compete with each other on a campaign. Oddly, they train for a rowing competition on land. All wear hypoxia masks to increase their lung capacity. THE NURSE is part of a team I support as an alternate. I take position behind a young man and assist him with an exercise by pressing my shins into his back and lifting his arms above his head. Our "on land" training device begins to quickly crabwalk along the ground. When we complete an exercise, I look down and see the young man's feet are encased in purple wax up to the ankles. I take an exacto knife from my pocket and cut circles around his feet so he'll be able to extract his body from the training device at the conclusion of practice.]

. . .

[1319.2 / 3573] [I walk into a small galley kitchen. I pause to fist bump THE NURSE before hopping up on to a countertop, taking a seat, and chatting with other team members. Mid-conversation we realize we're no longer wearing our face coverings. A coach calls us out for egregious non-compliance. THE REANIMATOR *(artistic, musical, and flattering)* enters with his older brother and gives me a quick hug.

None of us wear our masks.

I'm interested in where he purchased his designer knit sweater, which boasts a complex black, blue, and green geometric pattern. A small tan haute couture label on the neck of the piece below his left ear is too small for me to read.] //

⁂

COMPETITION: #0001, #0034, #0376, #0725
KITCHEN: #0487, #0498, #0541, #0550
LUNG: #0613, #0671, #0698

⁂

#1320 - August 8, 2020 @ 05:47 (Beavercreek, Ohio)

[1320.1 / 3574] [I stare at a neighboring mansion from a moonlit window.]

[1320.2 / 3575] [I attend a wedding where THE CONNECTOR gets married to THE INTROVERT. The wedding party hides in a closet before the processional.

A theatrical production precedes the ceremony, that overly taxes the venue's electrical circuitry and trips a series of breakers, leaving attendees in the dark.

The wedding party moves into position on a series of band risers. One bridesmaid on the lowest step leans back too far and causes a domino effect, knocking everyone down. The members on the top bleacher fall off the back, and topple over a painted canvas backdrop of a cathedral and altar.

THE CONNECTOR uses a golf-putter-like cane as she walks down the aisle, which THE INTROVERT gave her on their first date. Once the lights are restored and the wedding party is in place, the ceremony proceeds rapidly.

At the reception, THE EXTROVERT stops by my table to chat. He's retrieved six cupcakes from a garbage can that he'd seen me contemplate eating earlier, and boxed them up for me as a gag gift. He falls backwards when he trips over a banquet chair. His wife and adolescent daughter swoop in and help him up.

Later, we gather in a kitchen with THE WEAVER and THE CARPENTER to help THE DANCER with final preparations for her wedding.

"Oh, this should be the easy one," THE WEAVER claims.

We head back to the wedding venue. THE THINKER pulls the discarded processional golf club from the garbage and hands it to me. I pass it back to THE CONNECTOR.

I'm shhh'd multiple times by another wedding party that hides out in the closet.

I encourage them to come out, but they're looking forward to being sprung as a group when the ceremony begins.] //

⁂

Maj. = 0- THE WEAVER: #1329, 1- THE CARPENTER: #1326,
2- THE DANCER: #1326, 4- THE CONNECTOR: #1328

ALTAR: #0217, #0251, #0396, #0887

⁂

#1321 - August 8, 2020 @ 06:29 (Beavercreek, Ohio)

[1321.1 / 3576] [I meet the owners of a pub at a party. They invite me to leave the party and join them at their place of business. I enter behind them and take a seat at a low, stainless-steel counter near the register, as they proceed to the service side of the bar. When they turn around, neither of them claims to know me. They apologize for the misunderstanding and serve me their signature cocktail, the "Whiskey Dick," a brown liquor base, pickle juice, garnished and cooled by a frozen "fingerling" gherkin. I'm presented with a complementary main of braised pork shoulder *(their house specialty)*. I become quite tipsy as I devour the meal.

I move my chair to an alley, and take a seat by an empty bike ramp noted as, "Team Parking." THE HOPE *(youthful, curious, and energetic)* is part of their "street team" and currently out on a delivery.

When asked if I'd be willing to meet THE HOPE halfway with an incremental addition to an existing order, I'm quick to acquiesce.

"Sure! It's not that far. Just like...four or five blocks from where I live. *hiccup*"

As I reference the proximity of my dwelling to the end point of the errand, the owner chuckles, which helps me infer I'm actually much farther away from home than I understood. I contemplate a rendezvous point and send THE HOPE a text. ***"Do I order a car? Do I rent a scooter?"*** I opt against the scooter. I'm coherent enough to know I'll fall over and crash.

The owner hands me a stack of 20 round yellow decals to place on people's cars, and a stack of equivalent size for THE HOPE, casually inquiring as to whether I'm still willing to travel across town to meet him.

I've been staring at a brick wall for an unknown amount of time. When I refocus, I ask the owner if he wants to expand his street team. He replies with a *"Sure!"* and hands me another stack of blue square stickers.

"We'll take customers any way we can get them. Please just go."] //

⁂

PARTY: #0724, #0755, #0767, #0773
RENDEZVOUS: #0043, #0158, #0186, #0917, #0976
YELLOW: #0725, #0764, #0770, #0850
EQUIVALENT: #0100, #0397, #0409, #0668, #0807, #0955

⁂

#1322 - August 8, 2020 @ 07:40 (Beavercreek, Ohio)

[1322.1 / 3577] [I attend a party at ALEX GREY's urban estate. Today is his wife's birthday. I enter a ballroom with an end stage set, where a DJ performs as the artist's wife stands and receives gifts of karaoke from adoring guests. I'm handed a microphone and sing her a song. When I complete the song, she, the DJ, and I are only three people in the room. Other rooms are sparsely populated. I wave to THE COUTURIER in one. I wink at THE FAITHFUL ONE *(sweet, devout, and open)* in another as he talks with a small group of men. Most of the estate furniture has been removed in anticipation of an onslaught of visitors. THE OLD SOUL *(direct, skillful, and understanding)* takes to the turntables, instantly attracting a larger, swooning crowd that croons in unison to the birthday honoree. Scavenger hunt games are facilitated in another wing of the building. One involves reading clues on scraps of paper *(with phone numbers to call scribbled across them)* to complete a riddle *(though I'm not certain of what to do with any of them).*

ALEX GREY has short hair and wears khaki trousers *(both of which seem out of character).* I tell him I appreciate what he's created, and that his home is, ***"very very quite large."***

"It's truly spectacular what you're doing here. It's amazing! Please keep doing it." I fawn.

"To be what's spoken through you, is why we do what we do."

I walk to a pair of steel doors, each with a slim, red, eye-level slit at the center. I take a moment to glance through each, and discover he's placed a photograph slide across both that gives a different impression of an equally expansive *"back yard."* I believe they're holograms, or an artist's perspective trick, because I understand the house is surrounded on all sides by other property. I become skeptical after extensively touring the inside of the house. I fly out a window and around the perimeter of the property, confirming it's *"the biggest private landlocked parcel in the city."* No other property within the city limits will ever have a larger footprint. **Only vertical additions can be made**. No other land annexations are possible on the peninsula. The owners are unsure of the appraised value of the estate, though it's rumored to be worth tens of millions of dollars. **It's huge.**

"That's a great trick!" I say to ALEX GREY with a gentle laugh, but he doesn't understand what I believe to be funny. He waves at me to follow him, then stacks two banquet chairs and carries them to an empty garage, softly lit by a dusty gold stream of light. As I look left, I see a giant bunny rabbit wearing stylish white boots. I stare at it, as it slowly chews a length of brown grass, and infer it'd rather not be bothered. I walk out a door and up a concrete stairwell to the left that spills out onto a large, bustling, waterfront resort promenade. The size of the pool and the volume of people catches me off guard, as the reality from the back door differs from my understanding of how the property is laid out. A young boy with special needs is crouched down under a concrete archway at the bottom of a different stairwell. I approach him and see his body covered head-to-toe with acne. He's unable to speak, but I share conversation with him.

"Is your father ALEX?"

"Hey don't bother him. He's my son!" an aggressive woman shouts at me.

"I'm sorry, was I bothering you?"

The son offers a smile as a response.

I look to the right, and see a wall of ten-foot square-wood panels, painted with political propaganda. The further away they are, the more decayed and rotten the panels become.] //

⁂

GARAGE: #0023, #0025, #0039

FOOTPRINT: #0157, #0842, #0917

TRICK: #0250, #0887

⁂

#1323 - August 9, 2020 @ 01:35 (Beavercreek, Ohio)

[1323.1 / 3578] ["Katie" is a pundit on a conservative news outlet, who's consistently made a laughing stock and parodied by her contemporaries on other networks. After numerous spoofs, an actor who portrays "Katie" feels lost in the character and claims she's, *"out of integrity with her personal values."*] //

⁂

CONSERVATIVE: #0154, #0633, #0744
INTEGRITY: #0540, #0628, #0768, #0927
LAUGHING: #0699, #0773, #0808, #0937

⁂

#1324 - August 9, 2020 @ 03:23 (Beavercreek, Ohio)

[1324.1 / 3579] [I attend a webinar on effective workplace applications of machine learning *(cross training employees, and conflict resolution).* The facilitator and an executive field questions from the group. I type a question into a chat window and realize I'm the only person attending remotely. I'm curious about the current precision of AI responses. The executive uses a term I haven't heard before, and I ask him to repeat and define it. They're more interested in answering questions submitted by those physically onsite.]

[1324.2 / 3580] [I ride dirt bikes up a hill, through a woodland area, with friends. We crest a hill and turn left on to an empty mountain highway.] //

⁂

DIRT: #0193, #0445, #0481, #0571, #0696, #0979
MACHINE: #0774, #0819, #0829, #0842
CURIOUS: #0715, #0783, #0790, #0828, #0871

⁂

#1325 - August 9, 2020 @ 04:47 (Beavercreek, Ohio)

[1325.1 / 3581] [A coworker drops me off at the hospital.
"It's probably the last time I'll see you for a while," she says whilst giving me an embrace.
She has cancer and proceeds to another hospital to receive treatment.
I sign in at the registration desk, then proceed downstairs to the basement where I encounter a red headed man and woman arguing about the best way to lead a group. The woman doubts herself, but the man assures her she, *"has the skills to do a world class job."*] //

⁂

HOSPITAL: #0321, #0466, #0469, #0476, #0534
CANCER: #0476, #0740, #0824
WORLD: #0786, #0795, #0803, #0927, #1087

⁂

#1326 - August 9, 2020 @ 06:01 (Beavercreek, Ohio)

[1326.1 / 3582] [I wait for my name to be called to confirm a standby seat on a flight to Miami, Florida. I sit at the end of a row of chairs, my vision obscured by a horizontal stainless-steel tube.]

. . .

[1326.2 / 3583] [THE CARPENTER, THE DANCER and THE CHILD set up a toy race car track perpendicular to a large plate glass window segment of a public mall, in order to prevent cars from getting lost in the sea of two directional foot traffic. THE DANCER expresses some frustration because, *"she knows how to do it best."*]

[1326.3 / 3584] [I walk through a series of corridors backstage at an arena while a concert takes place. I stock the shelves of a concessions kiosk with books. I test my Lucite Rube Goldberg machine positioned along the entire back wall, to confirm it functions properly before customers interact with it. I drop a red rubber ball through a slot at top right and watch it bounce and zigzag through a variety of spiral chutes and ladders. When it arrives at the bottom, a Lucite toothed conveyor belt stops, and the ball bounces until it becomes still, a few feet from the bottom receptacle. I stick my arm through a waist high slit and grab the ball to remove it from the machine.

I peek around a corner, finding a man taking a nap seated upright. I tap his shoulder to wake him up. He's startled for a moment, then playfully proceeds on his path. I continue stocking my shelves to prepare for the eventual flood of customers once the concert finishes. GOVERNOR MIKE DEWINE passes through with his chief of staff. They pause to look at a few books, neither wearing face coverings. I've forgotten to wear a face covering too. The absence of the mask makes me think, ***"they've given me COVID19."***]

[1326.4 / 3585] [I'm in a press room at a concert venue. An androgynous being dressed in black crawls towards me on hands and knees. It stands in front of me, looming taller than expected on platform boots, and begins to dance. I'm seduced by its movements, and surprised when it lunges at me. It bites around my front left sternocleidomastoid through to my carotid artery *(its chin nestled on my Adam's apple)*. After latching on for a few seconds I realize what is happening. I get embarrassed at the thought of getting a hickey. The jaws release and the being yells, *"ONE!"* waving to a woman who hands me a fundraiser pledge form. The vampire plants a purple stamp of a butterfly on top of my left hand, then places the inked block in my palm and wraps my fingers around it.

I walk to a register, present my form, the block, along with a donation of $10 to a clerk and turn to exit.

"No! The block is for you," she calls to me as I walk away.

I see a guy sitting on a couch, but I'm unable to make out his face. It's all blurry.

"Hey! Dude! It's 'Eric!' From another lifetime!" he says. I stare at him for a few moments and the blurry face becomes pixelated, then comes into focus. When I ask blurry faced "Eric" where he lives now, he mutters, *"You know I can't tell you that."*] //

⁂

Maj. = 1- THE CARPENTER: #1329, 2- THE DANCER: #1327, 3- THE CHILD: #1334
ZIGZAG: #0017, #0972, #0987, #1058, #1094, #1155, #1121
CLERK: #0033, #0050, #0064, #0575, #1110, #1161
BLURRY: #0569, #0925, #1215, #1217, #1235

⁂

⁂

#1327 - August 9, 2020 @ 07:45 (Beavercreek, Ohio)

[1327.1 / 3586] [I'm on a rooftop speaking with my neighbor through a glass partition. I'm unable to hear him. I walk closer to the window and pull a sliding glass door open. THE GYM TWINK *(fit, flirtatious, and doting)* is by the neighbor's door. At a glance it appears he's missing both legs below the knee, though when I take two steps to the left, I see he's sitting on his heels. I pop my head around the glass and offer a ***"Good morning!"***

When I inquire about the young girl running about, the neighbor is quick to say he's *"not the parent, but solely her daytime caregiver."* The young girl wears a dress with blue and yellow squares that matches the paint job on his fence. In some moments she blends in and fades away as she walks around.]

[1327.2 / 3587] [I practice a parallel bars routine in a gymnasium. I'm eager to learn a new front flipping dismount. I'm 10-12 years old.]

[1327.3 / 3588] [I sit at a silver drafting table with THE DANCER. She and I thumb through a table-sized book with thin platinum pages. Detailed information on any topic, beautifully scripted, and accompanied by illustrations generates on demand, once a reader's request for information is spoken. I compare the book to a similar sized silver tablet computer, set in a silver frame. Though the tablet is brand new, the frame has started to split at the diagonal corner seams. I consider the tablet, ***"cheap."***] //

⁂

Maj. = 2- THE DANCER: #1333

GLASS: #0701, #0732, #0746, #0748

SILVER: #0755, #0788, #0811, #0820, #0848, #0929

DIAGONAL: #0383

⁂

#1328 - August 10, 2020 @ 06:59 (Beavercreek, Ohio)

[1328.1 / 3589] [THE CONNECTOR drives an RV and parks in front of a warehouse. I'm her passenger. She lets me out and I walk inside. Upon entering the warehouse, I find members of a rock band lounging around on oversized red couches. I walk to a blackboard and write the word "**GOJI-**" in red chalk. They clap and yell, "**RA!**" as I place the chalk down. I've been hired to replace the outgoing bassist, who finishes laying down a track for a song called, *"Remembrance."* He powers down the amplifiers, hangs his instrument around my neck, and gives me a high five.] //

⁂

Maj. = 4- THE CONNECTOR: #1344

WAREHOUSE: #0830, #0918, #0950, #1138, #1170, #1205

RED: #0699, #0706, #0720, #0725, #0762

INSTRUMENT: #0747, #0757, #0787

⁂

#1329 - August 11, 2020 @ 04:30 (Beavercreek, Ohio)

[1329.1 / 3590] [I sit with the family at a long dimly-lit dinner table. We eat pizza. When we finish, I state that ***"I feel ill and this is the last time I'll eat it."*** THE CARPENTER and THE WEAVER stand and leave the table, intent on shopping for new outdoor furniture. I'm concerned for THE CARPENTER's health. He seems sickly.]

[1329.2 / 3591] [Fatwas are issued by an Islamic cleric after a spirited debate brought about by an unintentional cart crash between Christians, Muslims, and Atheists who shop in the same supermarket aisle. The Atheists point to inconsistent moral applications between *"literary allegory and cherry-picked practices across traditions,"* which enrages those who believe their faith to be:

the one, infallible and final revelation of the divine.] //

⁂

Maj. = 0- THE WEAVER: #1330, 1- THE CARPENTER: #1333
PIZZA: #0775, #0787, #0903, #1018, #1145
ILL: #0147, #1063, #1090, #1135
FAITH: #0001, #0169, #0215, #1201

⁂

#1330 - August 12, 2020 @ 06:00 (Beavercreek, Ohio)

[1330.1 / 3592] [In an aircraft hangar moving at fast speed. I briskly walk through a dining room until halted by a young female server with short black hair. She asks me to turn around and go the other way. Her request makes me angry. I run back the way I came, and briefly encounter THE WEAVER who points at a giant whale-like airship she refers to as a *"Möbius Plane"* that emerges upward from the horizon and floats overhead. Everything on the ground is grey. As the Möbius Plane flies over, we see colorful windows in the middle of the "S" shaped vessel which we infer, *"holds between 800 and 900 passengers."*

As we continue running across the grayscale environment, we encounter THE FUJIYAMA MAMA *(supportive, easy going, and nostalgic)* on a hilltop, who's recently disclosed she's reconnected with a third, older blonde-haired son over email, whom she'd given up for adoption as a teenager. She's en route to meet him at the dining room for lunch. The new fact surprises THE WEAVER.]

[1330.2 / 3593] [I stand outside a wrought iron fence, staring in at a neighborhood of homes built from solid pewter. Waves crash in from all sides and submerge the houses beyond the roofline. I float upward to avoid drowning, looking down on the rippled wavy refractions of the structures that rest solidly beneath the water.]

[1330.3 / 3594] [THE EMT *(firm, helpful, and motherly)* sits on a couch across from me in a large bedroom without a roof. I sit on the bottom bed of a pair of bunks. To the side of the bed sits a stained-glass structure, the size of a pear sapling, with four large equivalently sized stained glass *"sprouts"* which unfold like a pair of giant red and purple dragonfly wings.] //

⁂

Maj. = 0- THE WEAVER: #1333
MOBIUS: #0018, #0540, #0976, #1058
WROUGHT IRON: #0212, #0301, #0511, #0561
SOLID: #0705, #0713, #0763, #0780

⁂

#1331 - August 13, 2020 @ 03:09 (Beavercreek, Ohio)

[1331.1 / 3595] [I'm at an airport at night. I look for my flight, and approach my gate without a boarding pass. I don't remember walking down the jet way to the craft. Inside the cabin of the plane a flight attendant *(petite Black woman with elegant hair braids)* closes the door and invites me to take a seat in first class, without checking my boarding pass. At first, I sit in a seat in row two, but decide to move back to row four. The pilot talks to us as we roll up hilly taxiways. Though speaking from the cockpit, I know the pilot is a middle aged African American man with a mustache.

I text the family to inform them ***"I'm on a first-class flight home."*** We pause at a red light at an intersection in front of a kaleidoscopically lit roller coaster. The wooden frame of the entire ride is covered in colored undulating light emitting diodes. It shimmers like white stars and galaxies in some moments and burns like red-yellow fiery waves in others, very much a *"celestial to hell realm"* seeming moment-to-moment oscillation.

The flight attendant asks me for my drink order. I request an unopened can of ginger ale. She proceeds with order taking from the passengers behind me as I attempt to send an additional text to the family. The light turns green and the plane continues taxiing over an indefinite series of mild ups and downs. Unexpectedly, the plane banks hard to the right into an underground tunnel. The right wing of the plane touches a manmade body of water, sending ripples from the edge to the center of the pool.]

[1331.2 / 3596] [Image of a group of people waving at me from desks in a math class. They await the answer to a question they asked me years ago. I offer an attempt at solving a complex equation that renders a computer image of a young Asian man who texts me the phrase, *"SADAD, FOOL."*] //

⁂

FOOD: #0726
WOODEN: #0699, #0737
RIGHT: #0705, #0720, #0733, #0762
COMPLEX: #0732, #0737, #0767, #0860, #0867, #0895

⁂

#1332 - August 13, 2020 @ 05:02 (Beavercreek, Ohio)

[1332.1 / 3597] [I prepare for my wedding at home. THE LITTLE PRINCE is a baby who sits cooing, smiling, and giggling in a high chair while wearing a pair of lederhosen sewn from my yellow and blue baby blanket. He's dressed to be my ring bearer. His hair's been combed out in a pompadour and is oddly silvered. He babbles back at me after I goofily ask with a poor Louis Armstrong impersonation, ***"Who wore that before you?"***

The chairs in the house need to be reordered for the ceremony. THE ATHEIST helps me, pausing when I ask him to place the one he has in hand, next to a Welsh dresser. The small rectangular floor mat beneath the chair is askew. People spill from a closet in rococo garb. Two girls take keen interest in my gown, and express a desire to publish a short column that poetically attempts to describe the color of the fabric *(which in the moment they jovially riff is a "champagne gold something 'er other.")*

"Darlings, I just don't care and I never have cared to define it. You may proceed as you wish."

A debutante enters with a jeweled fascinator attached to her head. She pauses in the coat room to speak with her friend.

"I love all of your work!" I shout, though not in earshot of the elegantly primped woman.]

[1332.2 / 3598] [A young child runs around the house. The parents chase it. They're filmed as part of a series of *"reality movies."* They break from the script when I direct the child to *"eat some stray kernels of popped corn"* that rest on a square wooden table.]

[1332.3 / 3599] [A Christmas tree has a spinning circular saw blade for a topper.]

[1332.4 / 3600] [I attend a video conference where everyone in attendance is seated in the same conference room. THE GENIUS is among those who sit along a side of a square "O" of thin white tables. The meeting is led by a woman with executive presence. Two additional men participate. One sits on a twin bed. The other sits on the floor with his back against the wall.] //

⁂

Maj. = 8- THE ATHEIST: #1358, 12- THE LITTLE PRINCE: #1333

CORN: #0003, #0189, #0284, #0323, #0787

SPINNING: #0850, #0915, #0939, #1196

BLUE: #0717, #0725, #0727, #0732

⁂

#1333 - August 13, 2020 @ 09:53 (Beavercreek, Ohio)

[1333.1 / 3601] [A group of kids incessantly ask their parents for the same things.

"Will you all just cool it?"

"We're just acting out our characters!" They yell in unison.]

[1333.2 / 3602] [A group of us share a bedroom. I sit with THE WEAVER and THE LITTLE PRINCE. THE LITTLE PRINCE is an infant, yet jumps from the couch and starts a vigorous abdominal workout. As we watch, THE DANCER leans over the couch saying, *"I must've pulled out his umbilical cord prematurely. It obviously compromised his muscular development."*

I pick him up by his feet and ask him to touch his toes as he dangles upside down. I've seen him do this before, but in the moment he refuses.

GRANDMA wears perm curlers in her hair as THE CARPENTER helps her into the shower.] //

⁂

Maj. = 0- THE WEAVER: #1335, 1- THE CARPENTER: #1337, 2- THE DANCER: #1338, 11- GRANDMA: #1356, 12- THE LITTLE PRINCE: #1392

INFANT: #0719, #0895, #0947, #0974, #1000, #1015, #1017

SHOWER: #0808, #0854, #0857, #0910, #0922

⁂

#1334 - August 15, 2020 @ 03:41 (Beavercreek, Ohio)

[1334.1 / 3603] [THE CHILD creates a video for a *"kids contest"* on YouTube. The next day, a camera crew with balloons knocks on the door with a request to interview her. I wasn't told the crew was stopping by and am unprepared to host them. They want to celebrate and document *"her incident in the street."*]

[1334.2 / 3604] [I stand in line at a McDonalds. I'm guided through a line. I run. I don't want to eat.]

[1334.3 / 3605] [I enter a doctor's office. While in line I meet a person with mermaid turquoise hair who invites me to a fundraiser. A pair of doors swing open at the far end of the office. White light pours through and I run full speed towards it.]

[1334.4 / 3606] [I'm in a room with a guy who holds an opened mason jar. Two small crickets released from the jar crawl up my jeans at the ankle and bite my leg. It hurts. I confuse the pain and itch with previous fire ant bites I've endured. The crickets climb down my leg, across the floor, up a table leg and skitter across the gray table top. I realize the guy holding the jar was previously rescued by helicopter, while trapped on a mountainside after unintentionally starting a wildfire.] //

⁂

Maj. = 3- THE CHILD: #1349

BALLOONS: #0094, #0144, #0336, #0618, #0916

ANKLE: #0022, #0245, #0874, #0909

HELICOPTER: #0473, #0500, #0501, #0786, #1033

⁂

#1335 - August 15, 2020 @ 05:52 (Beavercreek, Ohio)

[1335.1 / 3607] [I arrive home to discover THE LAWYER boxing up his property and moving out. THE WEAVER is unexpectedly present and has spent time packing my personal items. The floor in the family room slightly sinks in the center. As we take inventory and continue packing, small bb's, pinballs and a mishmash of large silver and grey marbles collect in a pile at the lowest point of the floor. I reach into a box and pull my hand out covered in a sticky liquid, and small pellets of compressed cat hair.

A curly haired Caucasian couple sit at a table a few feet away. They're evaluating the property and want to live there, though I haven't quite pieced together that I'm supposed to move out. When I ask THE LAWYER what's prompted the sudden move, he closes a door in my face without speaking. I let some time pass before I join him on the couch in a second living room. We watch two episodes of THE SIMPSONS broadcast in Spanish before I ask again about the need for the move, eventually getting a simple response that, *"we need to vacate the premises within a week."* I cry. THE WEAVER reassures me, *"the change in residence is a good thing."* I glance back at the curly haired couple. Once they complete signing a lease, they transform into a pair of elderly African American women who *"shhh"* me and tell me to *"keep it down."*

"The volume of my voice or the TV?" I ask, since I'm not sure how to respond.

The apartment I've lived in is a secondary, duplicative unit bolted on behind the primary residence. From my entirely separate kitchen, I can see another kitchen in a third unit. THE WORLDBRIDGER appears in front of me, and offers a prayer of clarity and ease in discovering a new home. Once I'm assured everything is going to be ok, I know everything is unfolding exactly as intended.]

[1335.2 / 3608] [I stand in the entry of a house behind a door with thick vertical iron bars, taunting a young Nazi who sits on the back of a box truck. He hops to the ground shouting in German and approaches the door. I raise my voice and shout back. He spits in my face through the iron bars. I grab him by his shirt, and pump my arms strongly back and forth. I repeatedly slam his face into the iron bars until he's left broken, bloodied, and missing teeth. With each strike he becomes younger until I have both hands clasped around his neck, and his feet flutter in search of the ground. When he's regressed to age seven, I put him down and spank him. He runs to a double decker bus and returns with a posse who scream *"FAGGOT!"* I'm convinced they will find my family in the upstairs penthouse, and harm them.

I run down a staircase to a basement, turn right, then run up multiple levels of stairs. Once at the top of the building I'm seated at a futuristic mint-white dinner table with my White father, Black mother and numerous siblings. We eat as a family. When the meal concludes, we walk through a salon to a floor-to-ceiling window, pausing in silence while looking down at a library across the street where every book has a turquoise jacket. I remark to White dad that I admire his collection. Black mom is offended and disappointed by my comment and informs me,

"You know all of that's mine, right? It's all here because of me," as she wipes a tear from her left eye.

I'm dismissed by my parents to start preparing for our evening guests. The first to arrive are three Asian women.

"Welcome to breakfast!" I shout as they present me with gifts, which I place on a nearby counter. Non-binary, non-gendered spirits float around the penthouse. More people arrive for the breakfast salon. A couple takes a seat at a cocktail table by a stainless-steel railing.

"I can't get a beer because the BABY here needs to be carded," the man says jokingly pointing at his plus one.

I sit at a table of guests who've just received their plates. THE AD EXECUTIVE *(informed, creative, and trusting)* invites me to sit with him and a trendily dressed group of people. An

Indian man asks if he can take the remaining vacancy on the other side of the table. After he sits, our group savors small portions of dark chocolate.

After breakfast concludes, I realize the angry mob that chased me earlier transformed into our diverse and lively group of guests as they crossed the threshold of the property.]

[1335.3 / 3609] [I walk through a parcel of land that's been leased to a theme park. Strict protocols must be met to ensure it sufficiently mimics a Disney park. Bicycles surrounded by clear plastic globes seem to roll on rainbow Saturn-like rings that softly glow in the dark at a 45-degree tilt. The rainbow mobiles sell candy and ice cream to park guests.]

[1334.4 / 3610] [A big breasted woman confidently walks toward me, fully nude. We're both in the center of a city street.] //

⁂

Maj. = 0- THE WEAVER: #1344, 5- THE LAWYER: #1337, 7- THE WORLDBRIDGER: #1430
IRON: #0176, #0212, #0259, #0285
PENTHOUSE: #0171, #0221, #0236, #0500, #0767
RAINBOW: #0045, #0105, #0106, #0215
FLOAT: #1064, #1123, #1128

⁂

#1336 - August 15, 2020 @ 08:11 (Beavercreek, Ohio)

[1336.1 / 3611] [I ride in a black limousine at dusk accompanied by an older man in the front passenger seat, and a petite old woman named "Mary." We're en route to a fundraiser. She's the host.

"Ritz Carlton - Maritime," she commands as she adjusts the train of her crystal-beaded cream-toned gown to take her seat in the back.

"I've always wanted to ride in a limo and hear someone say that," I say, unintentionally drawing her ire. She now considers me a **Philistine.**

Once we arrive at the venue, she guides us up a gold-lit-white-marble staircase where a woman asks if we'd, *"like to catch shooting stars."* When we ask what that means she points to a group of people gathered by a fireworks display on a green hill as day surrenders to night. The silhouettes of bodies and rockets set along the ridge seem cartoonish in the moments before they're absorbed into the black. Punk is lit. Fuses burn. The *"whoomph"* of explosions in canisters are followed by trails of sparkling light that rise from the horizon. Mortars explode overhead in brilliant sparkling silver spider webs as we reach for rented *"sparkler guns," (which are basic oversized brown cardboard tubes affixed to a red plastic handle)* to catch the hot magnesium filings that explode in a burst of light, equivalent in brilliance to a bundle of 1000 instantly detonating sparklers. I play alongside a group of small children who laugh, *"oooh,"* and, *"ahhh."*

"Mary" asks me to disclose my middle name. I jokingly refuse to give it to her. She responds, *"It didn't matter anyway,"* before walking away.

I drop my "sparkler gun" and run to catch up with her.

"Mary,' it's important we get clear. I don't want to fight."

She lays down on the ground and dies wearing her gown. Her right hand grips a correspondence card with the heading, **"Thank you's"** scribbled across the top, with names and accompanying notes for each unscripted appreciation. The card and envelope are different cream tones that compliment her gown. I find it odd that the envelope is a partially finished work of origami that will not fold close, as is. It falls from her dead hand and unfurls on the ground. I take a moment to gather the components before I read her final written words.] //

⁂

OLDER: #1069, #1091, #1115, #1157, #1205
STARS: #0021, #0367, #0386, #0573, #0597
IMPORTANT: #0298, #0381, #0462
ORIGAMI: #0481

⁂

#1337 - August 16, 2020 @ 02:56 (Beavercreek, Ohio)

[1337.1 / 3612] [I come home. I perch myself in the corner of a room where I watch THE LAWYER's mother sleeping on a mattress on the floor. His dad is asleep in the other bedroom across the hall. THE CARPENTER enters through the front door, walks across the home and into my room. I follow him up to a loft and tuck him in. I turn on the lights to discover THE RAPTOR and THE ROBOT have broken in and pranked me. Every surface of the room is covered in mosaic of different colored Post It notes, each with a cartoon animal or a goofy swear word written in all caps.] //

⁂

Maj. = 1- THE CARPENTER: #1348, 5- THE LAWYER: #1341
Min. = ♦- THE RAPTOR: #1389, ♥- THE ROBOT: #1389
PERCH: #0690
GOOFY: #0185, #0950, #1031, #1131
POST IT: #0396, #0544, #0592, #0971, #0972, #11550

⁂

#1338 - August 16, 2020 @ 07:41 (Beavercreek, Ohio)

[1338.1 / 3613] [THE DANCER sits on the end of her couch, nearest a sliding glass door at the opposite end of the room. She raises her voice.

"Yellow card."

"Don't be so sensitive."

"I'm being honest."

"Well, I'm getting older and slowing down."

I believe my communication is calm and clear. The upset between us is strong enough to wake me up.] //

⁂

Maj. = 2- THE DANCER: #1345
VOICE: #0475, #0480, #0484
UPSET: #1079, #1087
YELLOW: #0532

⁂

#1339 - August 16, 2020 @ 09:35 (Beavercreek, Ohio)

[1339.1 / 3614] [My hair's slicked back, over gelled, and dry. I attempt to run my left hand through my hair. It gets stuck in the crunchy helmet-like mass. I stand in front of a shopping cart near a checkout counter at a red interior walled store. The cart is full of people's personal photos and childhood clothing. A steady stream of people files by, retrieve their items, and smile. The last remaining item is a small square silver frame with a white oval matted photo. I stare at it for some time, unsure of who it belongs to. I lean forward on to the cart and rest on my forearms. I percussively click my tongue on the roof of my mouth and look to the left, spying THE ACTOR approaching from 30 paces. He pauses at the cart while taking a call. I wave at him and say ***"hello,"*** while he remains in conversation. He cordially waves back before grabbing the frame, inspecting it at arm's length with a smirk, and proceeding on his way.] //

⁂

Maj. = 10- THE ACTOR: #1375
FRAME: #0465, #0520, #0556, #0679
HELLO: #0820, #0937, #0972, #1073, #1168, #1236
DRY: #0678, #0768, #0955

⁂

#1340 - August 17, 2020 @ 05:14 (Beavercreek, Ohio)

[1340.1 / 3615] [I jam with DANNY CAREY in the basement of a library. He sets up a *"synthesizer drum kit,"* which seems to take a while, but is worthwhile once we begin playing. Nearby, members of the "Journey of Hope" cycling team stand reading books. THE SQUIRREL gives me a high five. When I ask him how things are going at Google he says,

"I work for ACORN now."

"That's a perfect place for a squirrel to work."]

[1340.2 / 3616] [I pick my adopted teen son up from work. I've misplaced my debit card. We descend an escalator together, then walk to our white-doored apartment. The small space perfectly meets the needs of our tidy little life.]

[1340.3 / 3617] [I ride bikes in the woods with a group of guys. I stop and exclaim, ***"AHA! 'Eric' WAS IN MY CAR!"***]

[1340.4 / 3618] [I take an elevator down to meet a group of friends. No one's there. I logged the incorrect meet-up date on my calendar.] //

⁂

LIBRARY: #0033, #0406, #0484, #0554, #1016
ESCALATOR: #0462, #0493, #0495, #0634
TIDY: #0897, #1073, #1087

⁂

#1341 - August 17, 2020 @ 08:54 (Beavercreek, Ohio)

[1341.1 / 3619] [I move into a split-level dormitory. Off from a common entrance is a partitioned stairwell. One segment leads to a fluorescent-lit basement filled with boxes of old notebooks and papers. The other leads to a rope of sweatshirts tied together at the arms, which must be climbed to get to the upper hallway. Once at the top, I observe members of the US Senate meet with students in a conference room above the basement through a large rectangular window. The walls are made of floor-to-ceiling whiteboards. Team members draw a six-step flow chart in red pen at the top of every white board panel. I wait outside the door for an opportunity to introduce myself to KAMALA HARRIS, but the group breaks into pods of four people who quickly scatter throughout the building before I'm able to do so.

I interact most productively with a group who ask for my help with a *"four eyed check"* of their revised process document, before promptly snaring me in a white plastic bag, flipping me over, filling the bag with white confetti and telling me this was their best *"college try"* to remediate a blizzard disaster recovery protocol.

"I don't get it."]

[1341.2 / 3620] [I'm at home with THE LAWYER, THE DULCE DE LECHE *(diffused, tired, and timid)*, and an unnamed third roommate. Innumerable cats run rampant in the basement. Many are in heat. At dinner we talk about the outcomes of the joint student-senate session, where I learn the primary objective was,*"to catch 18 mice that had previously been declared 'uncatchable.'"*

THE DULCE DE LECHE leaves the house without saying a word. THE LAWYER and I briefly interact and discuss whether or not we'd prefer to live in different dormitories. I could live in a dormitory, but I'd be decades older than my roommate. Anyone I date in the building would insist on fucking other people while we live on premises.] //

⁂

Maj. = 5- THE LAWYER: #1361

CONFETTI: #0215

DIFFERENT: #0464, #0466, #0479

⁂

#1342 - August 18, 2020 @ 05:05 (Beavercreek, Ohio)

[1342.1 / 3621] [I'm a waiter. My shift is ending. I take an order from a couple as a favor to a peer. They're insistent they *"always have orange juice"* and demand I immediately bring it. I tell them it'll be twenty minutes before their food will be ready, and ensure their waiter will bring them their juice. The man is game. The woman prefers I, *"take responsibility and bring her juice now."*] //

⁂

ORANGE: #0486, #0523, #0557, #0560, #0583

GAME: #0472, #0506, #0518, #0524

IMMEDIATELY: #0486, #0517, #0538, #0605

⁂

#1343 - August 18, 2020 @ 07:02 (Beavercreek, Ohio)
Torture and Brutality

[1343.1 / 3622] [A group of people are sequestered and brutalized in increasingly disturbing ways by a militant male captor. Most of the activity occurs in or around a 15-passenger van parked inside a theme park. I move between the roles of observer and captive. As a young man I'm placed in a black-mesh bag by the sliding door side of the van. It's zipped closed and I'm trapped. The body stays there for multiple days, though I'm able to leave it and witness what's happening to other captives. The piece of spirit left in the body becomes broken after the extended period of sensory deprivation.

A brutal encounter unfolds between the brother of the captor *(an aged and balding White man wearing overalls)* and a group of prisoners who revolt. The brother is baited to leave the safety of the van's perimeter, and crosses a lawn populated by county fair food stands. At first, he's accosted from behind and pushed to the ground by two men. Once given a chance to stand, he's challenged to remain upright while another man pokes him in the chest with a wooden broom handle. The handle splinters into a wooden stake, which then pierces the man through the sternum, and ultimately through the heart. The brother reveals himself to be a vampire as he winces, his body smokes, and dies.

A more upsetting scene occurs when the vigilantes gang up around a female prisoner who's discovered to be a mole. Using the same bloody wooden stake, she's first bludgeoned until unable to stand. Appearing to lose consciousness, a revolutionary taps her in the face until she notices the dowel pressing into the left side of her mandible. Pressure on the dowel increases steadily until her jaw snaps and a geyser of blood flows up, as her body depressurizes. The sound overpowers her groans and screams. As my focus moves away from the torturous carnage, I realize a veteran of the Vietnam War holds the other end of the bloodied broomstick. Then I realize ***"it's closing time at the theme park."***

Two other female prisoners escape and flee. They camp in a makeshift tent together in the woods. One is unsure of how much LSD she was given by the militant male captor. The sober woman guides the drugged woman to a safe house where she's previously stayed. It'll surprise the husband and wife who live there, when they find two abused women in their home when they return from vacation.]

[1343.2 / 3623] [I sit on a couch in a filthy apartment with a guy, FRANK ROBINSON, and a woman named "Doris." The area rug sits a full foot above the floor, a result of sweeping years of garbage under it. I tell "Doris" it's my first time in FRANK's house in many years, and that my friend and I would be willing to come back later to clean after we've changed our clothes *(our code for: have sex)*. She's insisted we quickly return because the house smells like *"the corona."*]

[1343.3 / 3624] [I talk to a friend who works in a food truck. He talks about how he was once inspired to learn how to play drums, but after participating in a contest, he realized playing always resulted in him getting angry.]

[1343.4 / 3625] [I set up a multi-dimensional chess board for game play. First, I set small red discs on one half of the board, followed by green ones of similar size on the other. Atop the discs I place plastic-like 4D printed pieces that vary wildly and irrationally in shape and size. Some seem tall. Others seem short. Some adult human sized. Others smaller than a dime.]

[1343.5 / 3626] [I watch a severe storm kick up a wall of brown dust across a great plain. A voice inside ominously whispers: *"the only chance you have to run is when the dust comes."*] //

⁂

BROKEN: #0554, #0562, #0587, #0597, #0607
WOODEN: #0577, #0691, #0695, #0824
SEVERE: #0560, #0623, #0722, #0833

⁂

#1344 - August 19, 2020 @ 08:54 (Beavercreek, Ohio)

[1344.1 / 3627] [I edit a student film in a campus video lab. I change terminals multiple times and have to redo my work. The computer at the far left is reserved for a lesbian graduate assistant who's taken a long lunch. Each of the workstations ha different equipment on which to practice.]

[1344.2 / 3628] [I have an emotional breakdown and cry in front of LADY GAGA. ***"We wasted our entire session. I wasn't able to feel anything."*** After telling her I need her friendship, she pats me on the back. When I look up, we're wearing similar glowing blue-green micro-LED bodysuits.]

[1344.3 / 3629] [I walk through a grocery store with THE CONNECTOR. I pick up saltine crackers, Kraft American singles, and a paper plate, then search for a microwave to melt the oddly long crackers into crunchy *"cheese cracker snacks"* that will congeal once cooled. I'm surprised to find the thin crackers come filled with an even thinner layer of white salty waxy cheese. The first two devices I find on steel baker's racks are DVD players. I don't find a microwave.]

[1344.4 / 3630] [THE POOL BOY *(flirty, social, and virile)* has his first sexual experience with a new lover on a deck chair.]

[1344.5 / 3631] [THE WEAVER and I walk towards a pulled pork food truck, where THE BREAKS DJ *(clear, generous, and fun)* spins a renegade set. *"Is that her?"* THE WEAVER asks as we both raise a hand and wave. THE BREAKS DJ waves back and drops a beat that causes the small crowd around the truck to drop their food and dance.] //

⁂

Maj. = 0- THE WEAVER: #1345, 4- THE CONNECTOR: #1350
CAMPUS: #0556, #0874, #0917, #0979, #1086
BREAKDOWN: #0889
THE POOL BOY: #1366

⁂

#1345 - August 22, 2020 @ 06:31 (Beavercreek, Ohio)

[1345.1 / 3632] [I awaken in a dream, within a dream, where I conclude a conversation with THE HEALER. Nearby, THE WHITE RABBIT gives THE DANCER a roll of cash. From my seat in the office, I can see THE ROMANTIC depart a concert on a screen in the center of my head. He's gathered a stack of rolled up posters and gleefully carries them home, where he leaves them on the table for anyone to take. The posters celebrate the diverse musical expressions of women. He's hopeful his housemates will hang them on their walls to remind them that, *"nights out in the city will soon be back to normal."*]

[1345.2 / 3633] [THE DANCER's recently become a hairstylist. She cuts down the middle of a poster of "The Visible Man" with a pair of shears. The black background poster highlights the cardio-pulmonary system of the human body. I step outside my body and lead her in spirit to a salon where I want to *(eventually)* have my hair cut. ***"When we get around to it, don't cut the top...I still want to keep the hair long until the book is done."***]

[1345.3 / 3634] [THE WEAVER suggests I take $145 from an envelope and pay THE DANCER for *"future services rendered."*

"But that money already belonged to her? She'll know."]

[1345.4 / 3635] [NANCY PELOSI accepts an award at the end of a banquet.]

[1345.5 / 3636] [A house is on fire. The garage burns up through the dormers on the roof. I fly up close to the fire to inspect it. I ask the owners if they know what caused it. A boy with Down Syndrome was left unsupervised while playing with matches. Up the street a dumpster is on fire in front of a mansion. The lid flies off sending embers floating towards the house, putting it in additional jeopardy after the garage fire is brought under control.] //

⁂

Maj. = 0- HE WEAVER: #1350, 2- THE DANCER: #1349,
15- THE ROMANTIC: #1346, 20- THE HEALER: #1412
NANCY PELOSI: #1428
FIRE: #0001, #1231
VISIBLE: #0012, #1120

⁂

#1346 - August 23, 2020 @ 02:46 (Beavercreek, Ohio)

[1346.1 / 3637] [I work with a team to replace a satellite that's been faultily equipped. I fly way up into space and encounter a team member near the device in orbit around Earth. We observe *"the process of communication"* between different nodes in a global network. Our job is to replace hardware.]

. . .

[1346.2 / 3638] [A percussion contest is held over video conference. An instructor guides participants on how to prepare for a lesson, the contest itself, and the assessment portion. I want to participate.]

[1346.3 / 3639] [THE ROMANTIC holds a red solo cup full of blue and black capsules. He claims they will *"calm his nerves"* while he works out on an elliptical machine next to me. He offers me some of his muscle relaxers while eagerly focusing on his physical fitness. He believes the combination will help him to prepare for his next career segment.]

⁂

Maj. = 15- THE ROMANTIC: #1363
LESSON: #0048, #1172
NERVES: #0031, #1028
CAPSULES: #0394, #1185

⁂

#1347 - **August 23, 2020 @ 05:59 (Beavercreek, Ohio)**

[1347.1 / 3640] [Canada's government has decided to place the entire nation on one standard time zone.]

[1347.2 / 3641] [I'm in a house where each room exists in a different time zone. A massive *"clean out"* is underway to prepare for an upcoming election. I find wads of old cash behind a couch. A scientist emerges *(with disheveled hair)* having awakened from his afternoon nap. The portion of the property I inhabit has a large blown glass sculpture on display near the door, which looks like a series of oversized ice cream cones stacked in the shape of an upside down "J." The structure rotates on a slow-turning, circular mirrored platform. The curtains are drawn. When I throw them open, the ceilings and windows grow to 12 feet tall. Limited light flows through horizontally oriented rectangle slits at the top *(that give the look of glowing robot eyes)*. The rest of the windows are obscured by concrete from the neighboring building that buts up against the house.

Another tenant enters *(a man)* and asks me if I want to play. I'm mistaken. He's actually speaking to another person standing ten feet behind me who walks in with a cup of tea. They sit together at a short table and begin playing a board game. Three other women walk into the house believing it's an antique store. One woman has a camera and is eager to take some photos. I suggest they help me mount artwork to the concrete walls of the neighboring building, to repurpose the concrete, viewless windows as *"contemporary frames."* I encourage the women to help me move two pieces of furniture *(a small chest of drawers and the crate at the end of a bed in the living room where the men play)* to another private room.] //

⁂

CANADA: #0254, #0798
GLOWING: #0010, #1172
ZONE: #0168. #0985
INHABIT: #0700, #1168

⁂

#1348 - August 24, 2020 @ 05:33 (Beavercreek, Ohio)

[1348.1 / 3642] [THE CARPENTER and I serve out sentences in the same minimum-security prison. Our captors are friendly and keep the room physically distanced. People in the prison are fit, and enrolled in different creative activities *(dance, gymnastics teams, and cheer)* to keep their bodies physically strong and their minds clear. We're responsible for stocking pantry shelves in the commissary with groceries. He's also responsible for maintaining the tool shed and the tool shop. He doesn't know how much longer he has to serve on his sentence. THE CARPENTER and I stand over a griddle frying bacon, sausage, and other meat for members of our cell block. THE CARPENTER claims he doesn't know what he's going to do when he gets out of prison.]

[1348.2 / 3643] [THE CARPENTER and I hold a small piece of mesh film up to a light that casts a pattern for a secret code on a nearby wall. He's delighted when the number "138" shows up like *"bulbs in a 'Light Bright."* The number unlocks a wall, where after a rush of white light we watch an attractive Black man walk out of jail. The outbound man was a member of our creative team.]

[1348.3 / 3644] [I buy a radio-controlled car to pass the time and keep myself sane, though I've been assigned a maintenance project to work on. While driving the car, I walk across a sidewalk and am asked by an officer to enter a restaurant. People inside are aware I'm a prisoner.]

[1348.4 / 3645] [I follow a large muscular man into a bathroom. He disappears. I sit in a stall next to a glory hole until I wake up.] //

⁂

Maj. = 1- THE CARPENTER: #1350
BULB: #0616, #0701
SANE: #0468, #0974
BLOCK: #0025, #1158

⁂

#1349 - August 25, 2020 @ 03:49 (Beavercreek, Ohio)

[1349.1 / 3646] [THE DANCER and I console KIM KARDASHIAN. I've done something to upset KIM, but I don't know what. I try to make amends.]

[1349.2 / 3647] [We're on a property in rural Wyoming. The woman who owns the ranch is excited a celebrity has recently stopped through to experience her way of life. She's posted photos of her with the celebrity on social media. When she suggests being my friend, I inform her I'm no longer a user of the platform. She's sad. She goes to bed.

We attempt to stay quiet as we look through the cupboards of a small unkempt house while her family sleeps. When I attempt to use a computer, the mouse turns into a phone and activates a stereo. Music turns on at high volume. I don't know how to turn the sound down. Someone I don't recognize rushes over in the dark and helps me bring quiet back to the space. However, the music rouses THE CHILD who stumbles into the room wearing pajamas and rubbing her eyes.

"I wanna watch cartoons," she whimpers.

I'm thirsty. I keep the lights off. I look through the pantry but can't find anything substantial to quench my parched palette. I eventually happen upon small mini-bottles of lemon juice and margarita mix that serve as the components for a stop-gap beverage while I wait for the sun to come up.

I grab THE CHILD's hand and walk with her up a serpentine steel railing maze until we meet a few other people waiting at a turnstile for an attendant to grant them entrance to the park. Screens adjacent to the turnstile display photographs of the ranch. Achingly beautiful spacious blue skies with large rocky mesas in front of a jagged mountain range in the distance prevail.] //

⁂

Maj. = 2- THE DANCER: #1355, 3- THE CHILD: #1350
VOLUME: #0009, #1205
PANTRY: #0541, #0815
SPACIOUS: #0019, #1193

⁂

#1350 - August 25, 2020 @ 06:01 (Beavercreek, Ohio)

[1350.1 / 3648] [THE CARPENTER and I stand next to a swimming pool. He shoots me repeatedly with a squirt gun. I ask him to stop. He immediately shoots me again.

"I just asked you to stop. Please stop."

He shoots me again.

"I can understand why THE CHILD has an anger issue."

Later, when I watch TV with THE WEAVER, THE CARPENTER enters and starts speaking during the middle of a program, unaware that we're watching something. We pause the show.

"Hey we're in something right now. Can you please wait?"]

[1350.2 / 3649] [THE CONNECTOR walks by a bedroom door and through a wall.]

[1350.3 / 3650] [ANDREW W.K. lifts a fist to the air under a banner that reads:

"SILENCE THE VOICE."] //

⁂

Maj. = 0- THE WEAVER: #1353, 1- THE CARPENTER: #1352,
3- THE CHILD: #1351, 4- THE CONNECTOR: #1360
ANGER: #0013, #1236
SILENCE: #0117, #1216

⁂

#1351 - August 26, 2020 @ 03:06 (Beavercreek, Ohio)

[1351.1 / 3651] [I board a flight at an empty airport terminal. I sit next to a woman who engages in humorous banter with her aisle mate. I've been assigned to a "low seat." I reach back behind me to grab my seat belt and errantly strike a small Asian woman in the shin. I apologize when I see her wince with pain, though she doesn't understand what I say.

I have to use the bathroom. I get up from my chair, exit the plane, and proceed past the gate. I pass a woman who's fallen from her wheelchair.

"She's taken an extra severe fall this time," I hear someone say as they attend to the woman. I keep walking.

I pass a couple of sparsely populated restaurants to a bathroom at the far-left end of the terminal. Inside I find a store that sells gimmicks/toys/tricks. A series of plastic bear heads are mounted at waist height beneath the countertop in a glass case. After a moment of confusion, I read a small sign that explains the bear heads are urinals. Patrons pee in the bear's mouth to make a train move across the table behind the register. Suddenly the droll bathroom feels like a carnival midway game. I use the restroom in the suggested manner while making small talk with the clerk *(a man who wears an apron).*

"This is all I can give you today. I'm broke," I say while continuing to pee.

I walk back in the direction of the plane. I never make it back. Instead, I turn out a door and walk down a dusty road towards a small rural Ohio town. A harvest festival is underway. I duck under a line of flags next to a corn field that mark the edge of the road. As I stroll through town like a ghost, I contemplate how I can make a future visit here interesting for THE CHILD. I want her to know I lived here for a number of years before I left for the city. ***"What would be the right year to bring her back here? Would it spur her interest to go to college? I believe she'd love to go to school here, but I have no idea how I'd pay for it."***]

⁂

Maj. = 3- THE CHILD: #1358
SCHOOL: #0033, #1209
CARNIVAL: #0140, #1171
POPULATED: #0015, #1169

⁂

#1352 - August 26, 2020 @ 04:24 (Beavercreek, Ohio)

[1352.1 / 3652] [Two female hotel staff members demonstrate the impossibility of cheating at a high stakes poker game, based on limits placed on player's bets.]

[1352.2 / 3653] [I step away from a table and carry Lucite suitcases full of cash across casino premises.]

[1352.3 / 3654] [I peek in on an office after it's gone through a reorganization. A young blond-haired woman and I take lengths of red yarn and string them between business cards we've posted on different parts of a wall-sized cork board. The red lengths of yarn lead to other business cards, affixed to the exterior of cubicles down a hallway. The yarn model crudely demonstrates person-to-person interactivity within the office. A well-dressed Black man walks up to me and gives me a hug.

"How are things going?"

"Extremely well," he smiles.]

[1352.4 / 3655] [THE CARPENTER leads a discussion on *"wager maximization"* just before competing in a high-stakes poker game. He's won $21MM in jackpots and intends to retain his winnings. Most proceeds will be funneled to, *"home renovations and luxury accommodations."* He hands me his phone, which plays a new track by U2 called, **"go."** We head to an elevator so he can cash out.

"You gonna purchase that special air wicking chair to keep your back dry?"

Without speaking he suggests he might, and implies he'll put it in his top-five-ranked-list of things, *"to buy."*]

⁂

Maj. = 1- THE CARPENTER: #1363

CORK: #0225, #0314

WAGER: #0084, #0573, #0977

LUCITE: #0203, #1163

⁂

#1353 - August 26, 2020 @ 04:51 (Beavercreek, Ohio)

**Waking from a dream within a dream multiple times. Trying to scrape together detail. **

[1353.1 / 3656] [One moment I sit with a young boy who has a profound case of cerebral palsy. His teeth stick out as he turns and gnashes his jaw at me. I hold the side of his head and his jaw begins to chatter. He's responsive to my attention.

In a blink, I'm walking down a ramp with a transgender woman who has not had top or bottom surgery. She wears a black wig with red highlights, goth clothing, and seven-inch platform boots.

"I've attempted this same procession in nine-inch platforms and you don't wanna fall from that height."

She turns left and doubles back. Her hair turns green. As she walks away, she flashes a smile of silver teeth and introduces herself.

"Call me "Steve Jobs."]

[1353.2 / 3657] [I blink, and I'm standing in front of my phone attempting to remember meeting the woman, but I only retain a few shreds of detail at a time before I realize that I'm sleeping.]

[1353.3 / 3658] [I blink and find myself in a cubicle farm, where I see the top of a female admin's head pop up over one of the partitions.]

. . .

[1353.4 / 3659] [I stand by a large picture window and watch fog roll in. It thickens and I realize it's smoke from an approaching wildfire.

"Prepare for things to really intensify when the rain actually comes," THE WEAVER says as she rushes to lay down large deck umbrellas and board up windows.

"Are you seeing this?" I ask THE WEAVER as the thin wisps of smoke bank up and cloud the entire back window of the house. A super-heated blast of air picks up and blows the fog away before the fire and rain arrive.] //

⁂

Maj. = 0- THE WEAVER: #1355
SMOKE: #0012, #1231
CHATTER: #0025, #1033
SLEEPING: #0011, #1142

⁂

#1354 - August 28, 2020 @ 06:00 (Beavercreek, Ohio)

[1354.1 / 3660] [I'm at a house where GAVIN NEWSOM hosts a party. THE OLDEST FRIEND IN THE BOOK *(consistent, logical, and brotherly)* lives in the basement of the building that has multiple "double" floors *(20 foot+ ceilings)*. I'm intrigued because he collects and uses all sorts of vintage electronics, including an original model VHS player, first generation DVD player, and black and white tube TV.]

[1354.2 / 3661] [In a blink, I'm in the back yard standing some distance from a pool where THE OLDEST FRIEND IN THE BOOK points at a 12-foot tiger shark swimming in circles. I jump through the center of a square topiary barrier in the backyard *(that seems large and peculiar for the lot)* to get closer to the pool. Once at the water's edge, I see a thick black outline of a square *(similar in size to the topiary)* floating on the surface of the pool.

"If we can jump to the center of the square, we can safely observe the shark in the water beneath."

We take a leap and splash through unexpectedly thick gelatin-like liquid. When I breach the surface, I notice the pool is full of kelp. I float to the edge, pulling the square floaty along with me, ultimately coming to hang on the edge of the pool with a bunch of people, while we watch the shark troll underneath.

After the swim concludes, GAVIN NEWSOM offers an unexpected apology.

"I just bought you a drink. By the time it arrives you'll be late for your appointment with the movers."

"No. I'm committed, I'm going to stay."

I sit down on the floor with two pillows and inspect the factory-brick walls of the industrial unit, waiting for my cocktail to arrive. I realize my pants are down, so I sheepishly pull them up as inconspicuously as possible.

In a blink, THE OLDEST FRIEND IN THE BOOK and I find ourselves sitting on the ledge of a building rooftop as a caterer drops off our food order. A pelican lands on a cooked turkey that's been left wrapped in foil on the corner edge a few feet away.]

. . .

[1354.3 / 3662] [A woman in an oil painting dances around as she models a mink stole in a mirror. The painting is framed by large solid gold bars.]

[1354.4 / 3663] [An Asian man seated at a pub table makes jokes. He has long wavy black and grey hair, and a Fu Manchu mustache. He tells deadpan anti-jokes that reduce a woman nearby to nervous confusion. He's a prankster.] //

⁂

GAVIN NEWSOM: #1357
BRICK: #0015, #1195
NERVOUS: #0031, #0878
SHARK: #0018, #0564
INDUSTRIAL: #0013, #1205

⁂

#1355 - August 29, 2020 @ 05:47 (Beavercreek, Ohio)

[1355.1 / 3664] [I participate on a movie production crew. THE WEAVER and THE DANCER are present. I climb down a ladder while listening to a new song by DRAKE called **"So what?"** that discusses, *"how much the country sucks now."* The first time I listen to the lyrics I find them sad.]

[1355.2 / 3665] [I work with four guys in an office. We share a dormitory suite as a home. One guy shows up late. I've set out items on his desk that will help him stay motivated today. ***"We have a lot of work to do."***] //

⁂

Maj. = 0- THE WEAVER: #1357, 2- THE DANCER: #1358
COUNTRY: #0007, #1218
WORK: #0006, #1236
LISTENING: #0012, #1077

⁂

#1356 - August 30, 2020 @ 05:12 (Beavercreek, Ohio)

[1356.1 / 3666] [I run through the basement of an old house looking for a white colored ornament. I cross an empty cafeteria, pausing to gather sugar, coffee creamers, and powdered condiments from an abandoned dining room. I put them in a plastic bag, intending to give them to a young chef, to continue motivating him towards his dreams of owning his own restaurant.]

[1356.2 / 3667] [THE SOOTHSAYER buries bunches of bodies in a crawl space beneath the old house. He constantly evades the police, though a strong case is built by local inspectors to take him down. THE SOOTHSAYER hides nothing and tells them exactly where to look, but the inspectors never take action.]

. . .

[1356.3 / 3668] [The rest of the house is filthy and decrepit. After spending most of the evening searching for the woman who occupies, *"the far side of the property,"* I walk upstairs into a dimly-lit room and sit on the foot of a bed. Some time passes and I notice THE CATHOLIC *(talented, withdrawn, and hurt)* sitting in bed with covers pulled up to her nose.

"Did you monetize my tweets?" she asks.

"I don't know what that means."

"I have some early adopting friends who used the platform for fun, and now have their own fiefdoms of millions....by circumstance. They're rich."

"I don't understand it and I don't give it my time."

She understands.

THE CATHOLIC goes on to inform me that, *"GRANDMA and GRANDPA used to be friends with a man named "Albert Fart." He was a bit of a character and always told you exactly where you stood with him."*

As the day concludes, we watch TV in the dark. THE CATHOLIC hands me an address scribbled on a piece of paper I don't recognize. I eventually determine it's the street address for the woman who I was trying to find earlier.] //

⁂

Maj. = 11- GRANDMA: #1379
Min. = ♥- GRANDPA: #1433
FART: #0235, #0646, #0719
PLATFORM: #0014, #1228

⁂

#1357 - August 30, 2020 @ 06:23 (Beavercreek, Ohio)

[1357.1 / 3669] [An administrator at "Guilfoyle College" hands an eager woman a folder in a powder blue envelope. The woman believes it will contain an annual bonus letter. She's surprised to find a cease-and-desist letter accompanied by notice of termination. Her teaching position has been eliminated. She doesn't know why.]

[1357.2 / 3670] [I quickly walk with THE WEAVER to a line that forms outside the Tower of London at night. We're warned by other guests to, *"mind the sheer drop off into the moat,"* a 15-foot drop from a cobblestone walkway that leads to a queue. The walkway splits in two. The path to the right narrows to the width of a balance beam. When we get in line, the distance between the two lines across the **(dry)** moat is vast. The walking pace is brisk. The thinning walkway is said to be less expensive *(a fair tradeoff for shouldering the risk of a catastrophic fall).* The public line at the left is wider and more expensive. The drop off on both sides of the balance beam is sheer. I walk the balance beam all the way to the door. We don't know if we actually want to enter the exhibit. The price differential per line is 15 pounds.

"We were duped...the shorter interior line is the more expensive (and dangerous) of the two!"]

[1357.3 / 3671] [GAVIN NEWSOM is kept on retainer as a bit player on a popular soap opera. Producers need to call his office weeks in advance to ensure his schedule can accommodate shooting as he maintains his role as Governor of California.]

⁂

Maj. = 0- THE WEAVER: #1363
QUEUE: #0745, #1086
SHEER: #0200, #0841

⁂

#1358 - August 31, 2020 @ 07:18 (Beavercreek, Ohio)

[1358.1 / 3672] [I stand with THE DANCER, THE ATHEIST, and THE CHILD. THE DANCER shows THE CHILD a flashcard with three words printed on it. THE CHILD mispronounces the words and reads them in reverse order. THE DANCER sarcastically chastises THE CHILD. I become upset by the teasing. ***"I don't like it when you do that,"*** I say just before I turn and walk away.]

[1358.2 / 3673] [Bifurcation models. Abstract algebra. The Monster Series in 198,366 dimensions. "47x59x71."] //

⁂

Maj. = 2- THE DANCER: #1370, 3- THE CHILD: #1368, 8- THE ATHEIST: #1380
MONSTER: #0352, #1208
REVERSE: #0025, #1044
ABSTRACT: #0010, #1235

⁂

#1359 - September 1, 2020 @ 01:55 (Beavercreek, Ohio)

[1359.1 / 3674] [A cartoonist draws a single crude frame, where a Viking stands next to a blank frame holding a sign that reads:

THINGS JUST AREN'T WHAT THEY USED TO BE.
THINGS AIN'T WHAT THEY USED TO BE."

...Nothing else is in the comic.]

[1359.2 / 3675] [I'm given the last-minute opportunity to sing the lead in a San Francisco Opera production. The conductor asks if it's possible for me to learn all three hours of music by tonight. I accept the offer while in the process of greeting the family on their arrival back to the city. Once I pick them up at the airport, we're taken by bus on a beltway in the opposite direction from the operatic venue. The opera house is at the end of the line.

I want to use my phone to learn the music, but the screen is cracked and dislodged. I hesitate. I doubt myself. I'm unsure I'll be able to learn the music. I figure if I can master the first aria that I'll be able to do the whole thing. I'm eager to invite friends and collaborators, all of whom will receive complimentary tickets, per the conductor.

In a blink, it's 8:31pm. The performance is starting. We're still on the bus. We pull into the parking deck and hear the concierge page over the loudspeaker.

. . .

"ATTENTION STAFF: An out-of-town performer was laid over at the airport, and will arrive late with other musicians. Please keep your eye out for the 'male lead.'"

I ARRIVE at the Opera house with the family, but believe for a moment we're back at the airport. I exit the bus *(which has now turned into a car)*. I walk through the hotel lobby and into a service pit where I overhear a dismissive, *"...even the male lead is late..."* from a woman who polishes silverware and water goblets.

I stop to speak with her when I notice she has a walkie talkie on her belt.

"I heard you ma'am...could you please help me by letting the house know I'm onsite."

silence

"I'm him...I'm the last-minute stand in." She offers no help.

I have the music in my ears, though my phone is cracked, wet and shorting out. I run around a stairwell, across another marble floor, and out to a marble archway when I turn right and funnel down a staircase. I encounter the conductor *(a large African American man with dreadlocks)* ringing two tiny hand bells. He's relieved to see me. ***"I have to perform! I have no prep time! I'm worried! I'm gonna fail! Do I have the right costume on?"*** All manner of doughty comments floods my mind. But then I feel my feet, breathe, and tap into the flow of the opera and let it come through.]

[1359.3 / 3676] [The woman in the hotel restaurant remains unhelpful. I write the manager an email to discuss her unwillingness.]

[1359.4 / 3677] [The performance concludes. I receive a round of applause as I duck, and run, in front of a curtain. I bow and feel energized in the spotlight. I go backstage after the operatic performance knowing I'll have a great weekend warrior story for THE MAGICIAN on our next group video conference.]

⁂

Maj. = 14- THE MAGICIAN: #1368
PERFORMANCE: #0012, #1239

⁂

#1360 - September 1, 2020 @ 03:58 (Beavercreek, Ohio)

[1360.1 / 3678] [THE CONNECTOR drives towards a construction site at night. THE EDUCATOR *(eager, fun, and essential)* rides in the back. I'm happy. I watch them make the trip from the comfort of my couch. Once they arrive, I float nearby as they ascend to an elevated porch and watch a crew. The men unpack a spire and a series of boxes from a semi-truck. The spire is made from chicken wire, and formed from increasingly smaller triangles *(triangles of decreasing size)* as they rise from the base to the top. At the apex, the triangles are tiny. When set upright, the wireframe spire topples over. THE EDUCATOR and THE CONNECTOR rush towards the collapsing structure to help the crew.]

. . .

[1360.2 / 3679] [A woman insists she needs to go back to negotiate a different job and different wage.

"You should just stay here with us."

She actively considers my offer.] //

⁂

Maj. = 4- THE CONNECTOR: #1365

CHICKEN: #0033, #1144

NEGOTIATE: #0007, #1239

⁂

#1361 - September 1, 2020 @ 05:20 (Beavercreek, Ohio)

[1361.1 / 3680] [THE LAWYER expresses he received a reading when he was younger which explained he'd be challenged in partnership.

"Because of that reading, I've never given suitors in business (nor life) a fair shake."

"That's a lot of credit to give someone for a $5 piece of entertainment from 30 years ago."]

[1361.2 / 3681] [My leg dangles off the edge of a ledge of a ten-story building. I adjust the elastic band cuff of my jeans so I can pull my socks up.] //

⁂

Maj. = 5- THE LAWYER: #1377

ELASTIC: #0582, #1089

FAIR: #0209, #0859

⁂

#1362 - September 1, 2020 @ 06:03 (Beavercreek, Ohio)

[1362.1 / 3682] [I work at a blood bank. The intake process is odd. People with appointments are funneled through the same line as walk-ins. When asked the basic intake question again, confusion results. As volunteers greet donors at the door they're immediately placed in line, but no one mentions if they have an appointment. Late in the day, an alarm sounds that turns on awkward synthetic *"nature"* music. A woman waves at me to shut the nature music off. I reach my arm over a high window sill and fumble with the device, scrolling through a variety of different stations and user profiles before I'm able to power it down.

I scribble a bunch of detail in a magazine on "page 355" and mark it with a business reply card. I believe, ***"I've written down a lot, and have remembered quite a bit,"*** that will ultimately be useful when revising an inefficient customer contact process. I'm concerned that suggestions won't be taken.]

[1362.2 / 3683] [I give myself an electrolyte IV drip. I offer to use someone else's needle to save on costs, then realize it's risky, unsanitary, *(and illegal)*.]

. . .

[1362.3 / 3684] [Harmonic sounds with an echo, *"Woooahh pa *click* adoooohhhh pa *click*....woooo hhhhah...."* act as an ephemeral soundtrack to the blood donor needle dream.]

[1362.4 / 3685] [Odd cuts of pork *(bread loaf shaped)* braises in two bread pan drawers beneath a "turkey/pork amalgamation" stewing on the upper rack of a white oven.]

[1362.5 / 3686] [*"You're nowhere, man."*]

⁂

BLOOD: #0021, #1199
NATURE: #0001, #1180
NOWHERE: #0039, #1128

⁂

#1363 - September 2, 2020 @ 07:50 (Beavercreek, Ohio)

[1363.1 / 3687] [My face has been used in an advertising campaign for a, *"six step facial regimen."* The campaign uses an absurd photo of me...for an absurdly named product...produced by an absurd company...and offered at an absurd price. I don't recognize myself at first on a wall-sized poster behind a perfume counter at a mall. When someone points my face out on the wall, I break out in laughter.]

[1363.2 / 3688] [After the face cream hilarity, I sit down next to a woman at a counter. We watch AMY SHUMER give a bunch of community resources to another woman who's recently relocated to the city, and feels uninformed and helpless. The resources are given in a lighthearted and goofily exaggerated way.
"FLORIST? THIS IS WHERE YOU GO! ESTATE PLANNER? THIS IS WHERE YOU GO!"]

[1363.3 / 3689] [I realize I've thrown my reference materials away from all the leadership training things I've done over time. I sit with a scratch pad attempting to remember all the different mental models, thinking models, and motivational models...but I'm left laughing when I begin asking passersby if they've ***"seen the wall sized me,"*** and point at a bottle of face cream on the table. It's silly. I sit across the hall from an office with my name on the door.]

[1363.4 / 3690] [THE WEAVER sits on a couch next to me. We watch an awards program. THE ROMANTIC is presented with an award, and proceeds to give a talk supported by a six-slide presentation. The forward-thinking content deck is positioned for a youthful, socially conscious audience. When I ask THE WEAVER if she's recorded the program, she becomes confused. She'd rather stay in the moment.]

[1363.5 / 3691] [I catch a black snake in the backyard. I grab it around the head. Its mouth opens. I hold the head steady, yet its fangs grow longer and longer and inch nearer my wrist.

The snake nearly bites me just as I pass it to THE CARPENTER. He tosses it over the fence into a neighboring yard. When I express concern about the snake's return, he tells me he saw the serpent, *"slither away."*

⁂

Maj. = 0- THE WEAVER: #1366, 1- THE CARPENTER; #1364, 15- THE ROMANTIC: #1388
MOUTH: #0009, #1238
REFERENCE: #0026, #1157
ABSURD: #0038, #1180

⁂

#1364 - September 3, 2020 @ 02:30 (Beavercreek, Ohio)

[1364.1 / 3692] [I work on a home renovation with THE CARPENTER and a muscle man. The muscle man makes some procedural missteps. We lock him out of the house. THE CARPENTER tells the muscle man he has to find his way back in. The muscle man loops away and around from the sliding glass door we're working to install. He enters through a doorless back entry. When I wave, he doesn't look at me.

"That doesn't seem very good," I say to THE CARPENTER as we watch a storm roll in overhead.] //

⁂

Maj. = 1- THE CARPENTER: #1370
MUSCLE: #0047, #1101
STORM: #0043, #1100

⁂

#1365 - September 3, 2020 @ 04:30 (Beavercreek, Ohio)

[1365.1 / 3693] [THE CONNECTOR washes her hands in a utility sink at a restaurant before I remind her, ***"we're here to eat...not work."***]

[1365.2 / 3694] [I go with THE CONNECTOR to a new sushi restaurant owned by our friends "Brittany and Ava." As we arrive, they go back for a staff meeting. "Brittany" remarks that another interview prevented her from coming to work the other day.]

[1365.3 / 3695] [An obstacle course is set up across a busy intersection. I'm challenged to complete a 30' pole vault without a foam pit to land on.]

[1365.4 / 3696] [I'm in bed and I use my own dick to fuck myself. I moan until the lights come on.] //

⁂

Maj. = 4- THE CONNECTOR: #1374
SUSHI: #0088, #0557

VAULT: #0112, #1183

⁂

#1366 - September 3, 2020 @ 06:12 (Beavercreek, Ohio)

[1366.1 / 3697] [It's my first night back on a university campus. I've been assigned to a single dorm room in a modern building. My roommate has moved into a different room down the hallway and to the left. I can see them in their new room through a courtyard.

All residents leave the dorm and gather together on a bus. A woman in front of me reaches over the top of the seat and places apples in injection molded plastic containers on my vertically oriented binder *(which I've set up to provide a barrier and an impression of privacy for the bus ride)*. She starts a conversation with two guys who sit in the seat behind me. I turn around and see THE POOL BOY *(funny, playful, and gossipy)* and another handsome man. When asked what they want to become they both shout, **"RENT BOYS!"**

The anonymous other man suggests the woman, *"upgrade her eco-consciousness."* He considers her buying apples in heavy plastic a poor choice. Most people seem disinterested in what I have to say. Two guys up at the front watch videos on a phone. The content makes them grimace.]

[1366.2 / 3698] [I give a non-sequitur as I look out the bus window and up toward a group of buildings.

"I haven't seen a school bus since 1997. I've seen six today. Here I am sitting on one. Obviously, there must be something I'm supposed to learn!"

The bus stops at a concert hall where we watch an orchestra composed of members of the US House and Senate rehearse. BERNIE SANDERS plays a tuba. When the orchestra pauses between musical movements, they field questions from students *(and other observing groups)*. Some members are heckled.]

[1366.3 / 3699] [**Headless male mannequin torsos float like carousel horses in a holographic row. **]

[1366.4 / 3700] [I'm very keen to update all my technology so my consciousness can be contained in a *"completely new, and uniform ecosystem."* It feels like I'm about to restart/reboot/redirect my life and the update to my tools is necessary.]

[1366.5 / 3701] [THE WEAVER busies herself with yard work. When she completes, I ask her to move a chair back from a doorway so I can wheel in multiple palettes of letterpress numbers *(stacked tall in square trays)* from a warehouse. Once in position, I tap a "0" in the top right corner, of the top stack of letters with my index finger.

"A zero in the root position. Nothing there. That's the key to moving on to the next level. If any other digit were here, the entire day's work-processing would fail."

"It's good to know how these things work," she replies.]

. . .

[1366.6 / 3702] [THE PHOTOGRAPHIC MEMORY *(divine, exquisite, and powerful)* appears at the end of a driveway.] //

⁂

Maj. = 0- THE WEAVER: #1370
BERNIE SANDERS: #1406
ANONYMOUS: #0092, #0450, #1180
UNIFORM: #0033, #0076, #0108, #0144

⁂

#1367 - September 4, 2020 @ 07:33 (Beavercreek, Ohio)

[1367. 1 / 3703] [I observe a future-human race colonizing a planet. So detailed and nuanced it would fill this entire book ten times over.
"Keep this one just for you," an invisible guide suggests.] //

⁂

FUTURE: #0045, #1212
PLANET: #0014, #0212, #0377, #0474
GUIDE: #1210

⁂

#1368 - September 5, 2020 @ 06:00 (Beavercreek, Ohio)

[1368.1 / 3704] [**Unclear.** I pull out of the cobblestone driveway of a wealthy man's villa. The man leisure's about in a housecoat/bathrobe.]
[1368.2 / 3705] [I clean out a garage.]
[1368.3 / 3706] [I drive down a highway.]
[1368.4 / 3707] [THE CHILD sings a duet with an animatronic macaw.]

[1368.5 / 3708] [I help clean up dishes next to a couple of cubicles in the administrative wing of a palatial estate. A lamp is on, and set on one of the desks, though it's still light out.]

[1368.6 / 3709] [I sit around the table with THE MAGICIAN, THE LALA, THE IRONMAN, THE AWAKENING, THE KIDDO, THE CONJURER and two others. I offer each of them an eye-to-eye ***"thank you"*** with my hands held in prayer at my heart. THE MAGICIAN requests that two new spirits stay after our group adjourns to, *"speak with him privately."*] //

⁂

Maj. = 3- THE CHILD: #1373, 14- THE MAGICIAN: #1386
SPIRITS: #0018, #0357, #0788, #0792, #0886
ANIMATRONIC: #0023, #0561, #1041, #1166

⁂

#1369 - September 6, 2020 @ 06:13 (Beavercreek, Ohio)

[1369.1 / 3710] [My attention is drawn to a horseshoe-shaped driveway in front of a massive home. The lawn within the horseshoe is impeccably mowed in a diamond pattern and edged. The lawn outside the cement horseshoe is populated as far as the eye can see with political propaganda *(lawn signs)*.]

[1369.2 / 3711] [I follow a man on a city bus. I'm his photographer. The bus begins to roll, though the background through the large window behind the man remains completely black. He removes a top hat to reveal a large mouth that sings and chatters on top of his bald head.

"That looks great!" I say as he mugs for the camera. To his right is a constellation of other mouths in the shape of a capital "L" that softly bends to the right. Each mouth holds a different expression, which seem to be interchangeable like facial features for a Mr. Potato Head doll. Some of the mouths look like they've been cut from magazines and toggle between two expressions, in a flickering flutter.] //

⁂

"L": #0130, #0611, #0674, #0821, #0968, #1157
POTATO: #0003, #0243, #0778, #0909
BALD: #0032, #1190

⁂

#1370 - September 7, 2020 @ 04:23 (Beavercreek, Ohio)

[1370.1 / 3712] [I suggest that THE WEAVER and THE CARPENTER update their bathrooms. Their home sits at the high end of the price spectrum, which makes THE WEAVER hesitant to invest. The property has a large back porch with a pool. COLONEL SANDERS exits a closet and suggests I take a dip.]

[1370.2 / 3713] [I pet a dog's belly when it turns over on its back. As I sit on the green of a castle lawn, I look over at a group of people who emerge wearing martial arts gear for a competition. THE CARPENTER is interested in taking photos of some the men as they pass by in their black monochrome guis. One guy is offered some food by hotel staff but is hesitant to take it.]

[1370.3 / 3714] [I walk down a hallway, noting the front stoops of each doorway. The front area I pass has a welcome mat with embroidered cartoon characters from childhood video games. I have an entire conversation in a cardboard box house with a young man who has a child on the way. I encourage him, and reassure him that ***"he has what it takes to be a good dad."*** He might be married to THE DANCER, though he never says. THE DANCER just had an emotional episode and stormed off. Her emotionality had nothing to do with the young man, but he's not convinced.]

[1370.4 / 3715] [I'm in a rehabilitation clinic where a guy's ready to release a book. I'm assigned a case manager who repeatedly asks me my name. We go back and forth for some time until we finally settle on **"JEESH."** Another guy drops his manuscript in a pool. When I look up, I can see charcoal embers blowing up the street catch the road, parking lot, and surrounding buildings on fire. Police sweep in to intervene. Firefighters show up on premises.]

⁂

Maj. = 0- THE WEAVER: #1373, 1- THE CARPENTER: #1374, 2- THE DANCER: #1379
POLICE: #0145, #0161, #0278, #0397, #0513, #0567, #0823, #0917, #0957, #1016
FIREFIGHTER: #0215, #1071

⁂

#1371 - September 7, 2020 @ 06:20 (Beavercreek, Ohio)

[1371.1 / 3716] [I take a service trip to the Balkans, not realizing that when I arrive, the group I've agreed to support is in the midst of a severe conflict with the local community. I don't know how I'm going to get home. I may not be able to leave. Flights to get from where I am, to home don't seem to be scheduled.]

[1371.2 / 3717] [Four women post photos of themselves arm-in-arm at a summer wedding reception that takes place in a known zone of *"high viral transmission."* They post a caption with the photo on social media which reads, *"We've been so good all these months, and we've earned this trip."*] //

⁂

FOUR: #0007, #1234
SEVERE: #0003, #1195
ARRIVE: #0012, #1198

⁂

#1372 - September 8, 2020 @ 03:50 (Beavercreek, Ohio)

[1372.1 / 3718] [I pour cherry pie filling in a blender and mix it up.]

[1372.2 / 3719] [**At a restaurant in New York City.** I eat an entire meal before I feel for my face mask in my trouser pockets. I put it back on, and jump in a cab with THE CONFIDANT. I drive down a hill in the cab with a bunch of people. The energy is frenetic and active. Much of the scene blurs, though I can discern no one in the car is wearing a facial covering.]

[1372.3 / 3720] [**At a store shopping.** A woman who works for an architectural digest publication insists, *"You're Aryan."*

"I assure you I'm not." I say while requesting she pass me a magazine from a shelf behind her, to look through a series of style sheets. I lay the periodical open to a page on the counter before her.

"I only have $5000," she oddly offers.

"That's not a lot if you want to make a life in the city."

Nearby, a handsome actor explores heartbreak to prepare for an upcoming role.
"Let me guess, you're trying to understand what it feels like when you find out your fiancé is fucking your best friend."
"Uh yeah," he affirms.
"Probably the most painful to have her admit it while you're fucking her."
The man looks at me dead eyed and goes silent.
"...Oh, I must be mistaken. I assume you're running a different experiment."] //

⁂

Maj. = 16- THE CONFIDANT: #1376
NEW YORK CITY: #0084, #0142, #0322, #0710
EXPERIMENT: #0228, #0231, #0998, #1006, #1171

⁂

#1373 - September 8, 2020 @ 04:20 (Beavercreek, Ohio)

[1373.1 / 3721] [I sit at a table eating when I hear a doorbell ring. THE WEAVER opens the door. THE CHILD enters and sits on my lap with a giggle.
"Your skin's so soft!" I say as I run a knuckle up her left cheek and continue, ***"How's school going?"***]

[1373.2 / 3722] [I walk up a stone sidewalk and observe men throwing jars of peanut butter and other snack foods from an office kitchenette into a pond, that reflects the image of a small cottage on its still pristine surface. Others approach the pond from the opposite direction. When I get closer to the group, I learn it's a female real estate agent sharing conversation with two other men.
"What's the worst date you've ever been on with a woman?"
Before either of the men have a chance to respond I interject,
"I took a woman to see the movie 'The Bird Cage' and it was a disaster."
The man with curly hair stares at me incredulously and asks, *"Why would you tell her that?"*

⁂

Maj. = 0- THE WEAVER: #1377, 3- THE CHILD: #1388
PEANUT BUTTER: #0021, #0039, #0476, #524, #0562, #0734, #1056
BIRD: #0077, #0682, #0777, #0957, #1055, #1073, #1143, #1218

⁂

#1374 - September 9, 2020 @ 08:41 (Beavercreek, Ohio)

[1374.1 / 3723] [I drive into a garage at a house I share with THE CONNECTOR and another young Asian woman. The Asian woman's family owns the house.]

[1374.2 / 3724] [I'm in a basement of a library where I inspect a map. I attempt to take a photo of a point of interest *(and its GPS coordinates)* with my phone. THE CARPENTER and I had successfully delivered a large-scale complex project at that property. I want to take a photo of it, ***"as a reminder that we're capable of doing genius level work."***]

. . .

[1374.3 / 3725] [I talk to a couple who have moved into a house with a little turret on the second floor and brick facade on the front. They've decided they don't like the standalone house and want to move into a duplex down the street.] //

⁂

Maj. = 1- THE CARPENTER: #1381, 4- THE CONNECTOR: #1376
LIBRARY: #0033, #0406, #0484, #0554, #1016, #1036, #1177
BRICK: #0015, #1195

⁂

#1375 - September 10, 2020 @ 03:21 (Beavercreek, Ohio)

[1375.1 / 3726] [THE EPITOME *(sinewy, precise, and expanded)* is a student at *"the school."* He attends class during the day at an alternative time. We go to a party and become separated when I flirt with myself and wind up narcissistically making out. I briefly encounter THE ACTOR and his partner as we exit later. I wake up at 8:45am on a couch, not knowing where my car is. School is in session. I'm enrolled and afraid I'm going to have to drop out, even though I've finished the curriculum numerous times.

I spend time helping people find their way on campus. I pass a group of kids playing basketball and kick rogue balls back to them up a hill at right when they're over shot. Little spikes shoot up from the ground and impale a few rogue basketballs. A bit further down on campus, a political rally unfolds and becomes a march. I zigzag through buildings. I pass through a boutique where a young guy with a frizzy ponytail sits on a stool, selling hipster clothing. When I express that I've misplaced my grey hat, he guides me to the back to meet another young woman with a short, cropped haircut. Before I shake her hand, she has a large body frame. When our hands part, she instantly becomes petite and dove-boned. I walk with her until she splits into two different people. If I follow her to the left the scene repeats. After a few rounds, I bear right.

I meet the two women who agree to help take me back to my car. ***"I'm pretty sure by this point it's been towed."*** Passing through the boutique,I'm handed a grey hat that the young man found in a box on a top shelf in a back closet. It's similar to what I had, and to get me to leave he says he'll, *"put it on his account."*] //

⁂

Maj. = 10- THE ACTOR: #1426
HIPSTER: #0534, #0687, #0781, #0920, #1084

⁂

#1376 - September 10, 2020 @ 07:42 (Beavercreek, Ohio)

[1376.1 / 3727] [THE CONFIDANT walks with me through the same maze in dream **[1375.1 / 3726]** to help me find my car. We pass through the same series of shops and storefronts. When we open the door out to an upward graded parking lot, we see two women sitting on a bench under a tree. THE CONNECTOR consoles a young woman who's just received a set of test results and cries. When I ask if there's anything I can do, she wipes her tears away as she says, *"I haven't made good decisions."*] //

⁂

Maj. = 4- THE CONNECTOR: #1381, 16- THE CONFIDANT: #1437

MAZE: #0017, #0079, #0089, #0116, #0118, #0149

⁂

#1377 - September 11, 2020 @ 05:14 (Beavercreek, Ohio)

[1377.1 / 3728] [I read a book while lounging on a couch. I'm folded in half *(face towards legs)*. THE LAWYER sits on my back, and waits for me to put a face covering on before letting me sit up straight.]

[1377.2 / 3729] [I stand in a kitchen with THE WEAVER. We discuss the energetic subtleties between being "for" and "against" anything.

"Anything you rally against brings more attention and momentum to it."

"Agreed. It's always best to know what you're for and put your attention there."

⁂

Maj. = 0- THE WEAVER: #1379, 5- THE LAWYER: #1424

FOR: #0001, #1239

AGAINST: #0022, #1218

⁂

#1378 - September 12, 2020 @ 05:53 (Beavercreek, Ohio)

**Enough action for a movie trilogy quickly consolidated into three clear takeaways.* *

[1378.1 / 3730] [I help children solve math problems. I show them three different logical solutions for each item. The challenge is to help them understand, *"there are many paths to the same solution, and at times other solutions."*]

[1378.2 / 3731] [I leap upward and fly over a series of warehouses. THE FOUNDER *(witty, accomplished, and hardworking)* floats at my left as we talk. While over a tan-roofed building, he pulls his knees towards his chest and swiftly drops through the roof of the building like a cannonball. He leaves a perfectly circular hole in the aluminum rooftop. I continue floating for an extended period, until I perch on the branch of a large pine tree and walk through an open third-story window of another building. A group of young adults cook dinner and discuss their upcoming adventures.]

[1378.3 / 3732] [I receive a text message from THE DEVOTEE: *"Hello. I'm answering multiple requests for at home rabbi visits at the moment. I have an appointment next Thursday afternoon or Friday morning if you'd like to talk."*]

⁂

LOGICAL: #0047, #1056

MATH: #0428, #614, #1056, #1093, #1172

⁂

⁂ 15.2 - CONVERGENCE: 1379-1385 ⁂

#1379 - September 13, 2020 @ 06:16 (Beavercreek, Ohio)

[1379.1 / 3733] [I'm a valet. BARBRA STREISAND drives up in a white Mercedes SUV. She tosses me the keys. I park the vehicle while she ascends a short staircase and takes a seat at a restaurant booth with THE WEAVER.]

[1379.2 / 3734] [THE DANCER and I have an argument at a warehouse rave as it's broken up by the cops. She wants to partake in a trendy new intoxicant, distributed from plastic ice chests set by a table that displays cakes of increasing size and ornamentation. I'm not keen on the *purple-and-pink-water-balloon-sized-salmon-roe* revelers bite, and shotgun. The majority of liquid explodes and spills on to the concrete floor, leaving the venue smelling like rotting fish. To get away from the stinky warehouse, I walk along a waist height chain-link fence back toward a parking lot. To the right of the fence rests a scorched field. Whispers of a raging fire rise up in haunting ghostly patterns of white steam against the stark black background. I arrive by my car. As I fumble with the keys, CHRIS PRATT sits on the hood and offers me an audition for a new sitcom he's casting. I would be playing the role of a Marine who's returned from multiple combat deployments. I'm not sold on the notion that a protagonist suffering from PTSD is on comedic pitch for the cultural zeitgeist. Table reads begin next week.

"Dude, regardless if it's carried forward after pilot season, this is your moment to step out into something new. I think you're talented."

"Let me think about this. You're a funny guy. You've found success. You believe in me. Of course, I'll do it," I say with a hand extended.

Later when seated at the table with BARBRA and THE WEAVER, I share my new opportunity.

"Darling, make it about feeling it in your heart before you accept the challenge," BARBRA suggests.

"I waited for it to flow up from my chest before I said, 'yes."

"Good thing you did. He's married to a general's daughter you know," THE WEAVER chortles.

"You're thinking Schwarzkopf. CHRIS married a Schwarzenegger."

Mid-conversation, ROB LOWE jogs by wearing a blue tailored shirt and no trousers, on his way to a "Risky Business" party. THE WEAVER mutters some affirmation about his attractiveness, as I toss BARBRA her keys and leave the table. I sprint up behind him and we jog and talk for a few miles along a fence, where the formerly scorched land has transformed into soccer fields that host youth tournaments under flood lights. Eventually, ROB and I enter the party together. THE DANCER and I reconcile and embrace, as loud house music rumbles around us in the mostly dark room.

[1379.3 / 3735] [THE CARPENTER visits with GRANDMA in her new luxurious apartment, replacing light bulbs and performing other general maintenance.] //

⁂

Maj. = 0- THE WEAVER: #1381, 1- THE CARPENTER: #1381,
2- THE DANCER: #1380, 11- GRANDMA: # 1421
HEART: #0003, #1213

ZEITGEIST: #0007, #0644
SOCCER: #0036, #1155
SALMON: #0008, #1318
⁂

#1380 - September 14, 2020 @ 06:26 (Beavercreek, Ohio)

[1380.1 / 3736] [Most of the scene involves hanging out with DIPLO between major performances. He's quick to admit that he takes anti-anxiety medication to cope with the pressure of delivering chart topping hit-after-hit. He has two pet goldfish that he keeps in separate clear glass bowls the size of basketballs. He admits the daily frequency by which he changes the water, could be considered obsessive. Time runs short, and he decides to place the fish in gallon sized Ziploc bags filled with water, which he hangs over the bottom half of a Dutch door like a saddlebag. DIPLO seems exhausted by the attention paid to the fish.

"You're a drug dealer. Fill these scrips for me."

"I assure you I'm not a drug dealer, dude."

When asked why he thought as much, he admits he was distracted by the program on the TV behind me, which profiles housewives in the heartland of America who are addicted to heroin, and use a pseudo-language to conceal their drug use.

"What really happened at duck pond?"

"Crossed wires and missed communications. 'Dasszit."

He puts on a new track chock full of sirens, honking horns, and ringing phone IDs. Knowing he's giving me a bit of a put on, I submit,

"Expanding the genre, huh. Sounds like an Edgard Varese composition."

My cursory knowledge of 20th century composers amuses DIPLO, which shifts our hangout from music to math. He places three, twelve-inch white circular platters on a table in a row and challenges me to completely cover them with thin brown squares of modeling chocolate, which I can create using a pasta press and kitchen scissors. ***"He's trying to show me an alternative way to solve an integral."***

He's sweet, endearing and quiet one-on-one, though insists he'd, *"rather not talk about 'M.I.A.'"* When a posse of party friends arrive, he throws up a strong emotional barrier, and the quality of conversation returns to the surface. He leaps on to a square ottoman, lifts his hands overhead and screams, *"RAGE!"*]

[1380.2 / 3737] [THE DANCER is fitted for a red two-piece wedding reception dress which will leave her midsection exposed. Wearing it indicates a courageous reclamation of her body identity. She believes it's the sensible option that will allow her and THE ATHEIST to *"perform a water dance together at sunset."* The choreography involves multiple lifts. In their most recent rehearsal, a wave knocked them down, and a rip current dragged them out to sea, resulting in an embarrassing emergency rescue by the US Coast Guard.] //

⁂
Maj. = 2- THE DANCER: #1392
SIREN: #0014, #1224
FISH: #0073, #1149
EXPOSED: #0009, #1205
⁂

#1381 - September 15, 2020 @ 00:00 (Beavercreek, Ohio)
** Dream fragments beckoning to be forgotten. **

[1381.1 / 3738] [THE SLUT and I have sex on a futon on the ground floor of a three-story condo. We're drunk. I take my ring off of my middle finger and place it on a round glass coffee table. He passes out mid-act. I tuck him in. As I walk away and close the door, I notice the futon has turned into my king-sized bed.]

[1381.2 / 3739] [THE CONNECTOR and a woman I don't know, collaborate on a project. THE CONNECTOR is hesitant. She doesn't trust her counterpart.]

[1381.3 / 3740] [A young man fills out a white sticker with the name "RIDLEY SCOTT" and wraps it around the exterior of a pewter chalice. He takes the eighth seat among a group of men sharing a feast and conversation at a round table. They all seem to speak in Middle English with strong accents. They postulate on how *"the management"* would respond to their joke. The feast and partying extend into the wee hours of the night. The stained-glass windows behind them are dazzling and intricate, their details set off by candles in the chandeliers overhead.]

[1381.4 / 3741] [THE WEAVER takes her family to a shopping mall. While browsing, they encounter their next-door neighbors who extend an invitation to join them for a movie. THE CARPENTER agrees to come *"so long as everyone wears the nylons he bought to cover their faces while in the theater."* Once distributed he learns they're sheer and provide no droplet transmission protection *(but look really fun when the zigzag pattern stretches over the children's eyes and mouths).*] //

⁂

Maj. = 0- THE WEAVER: #1384, 1- THE CARPENTER: #1384, 4- THE CONNECTOR: #1386
PEWTER: #0498, #1330
INVITATION: #0009, #1216
JOKE: #0115, #1078

⁂

#1382 - September 16, 2020 @ 08:36 (Beavercreek, Ohio)

[1382.1 / 3742] [I'm seated atop a miniature Choo Choo train on an ovular track. The track runs the length of a hotel ballroom. As the Choo Choo slowly banks on a turn to the left, I pass in front of a conference table where DONALD TRUMP sits with a panel shooting a television ad. Each time I pass by, I whisper a conspiracy theory or an idea that I believe is bodacious enough to cut the take and start over. The director decides to keep rolling. My goal is to get them to shut down the production, but no matter how extreme my language, or ignorant my comment, it seems to bring a greater sense of satisfaction to DONALD. Others in my peer group fear for my life as the rhetoric and sensationalism I spew increases. I dismount the train and walk away, a bit confused because instead of the ideas stifling him, he seems to use all of them without any hesitation, and take them as his own.]

. . .

[1382.2 / 3743] [I make gallon after gallon of fruit smoothie, expressly to use up a 30oz bottle of MCT oil. I drink roughly 20x the suggested daily amount, which brings up some concern among my friends who make their own meals nearby. I know it'll have an adverse effect on my gastro-intestinal tract, but I'd rather not let the bottle go to waste *(even though there's no expiration date, and it'll likely keep for years in a cool, dark pantry).*] //

⁂

DONALD TRUMP: #1416
MINIATURE: #0004, #1267
HESITATION: #0014, #0881
FEAR: #0003, #1271
OIL: #0019, #1354

⁂

#1383 - September 16, 2020 @ 22:57 (Beavercreek, Ohio)

[1383.1 / 3744] [I'm a teenager. I park a small grey car halfway up the driveway of THE BONE's home. As I approach a fence, I see a swimming pool in the front yard composed of a series of overlapping squares. I find it peculiar to find the pool out front when I have strong memories of learning to swim in a kidney bean shaped pool in their backyard more than thirty years ago. I've arrived at the home in response to a family dinner invitation, but become perplexed after I find a handwritten note on the door that reads: *"Let yourself in. Fend for yourself. You're on your own for dinner."* I enter the property and proceed through the kitchen to a bedroom, searching for two young men who live at the home, who I'm not able to find. I'm concerned that the Vietnamese foreign exchange student the family has hosted for the past semester seems to have gone missing, though a collage of crosses he made out of toothpicks, Popsicle sticks, and twigs remains prominently displayed over a hearth. I adjourn to a bedroom and fall asleep on the bottom bunk bed.

While asleep on the bunk bed I fall in to a deeper dream** - I'm a staff member on a cruise ship. I lay on a gurney about to be shrink wrapped for transport by a smiling, bronze-tanned woman. Long, wide vertical ribbons of bubble wrap and plastic cling hang above me. The woman's smile turns to a frown when I say* ***"I don't have the money to pay for the wrapping service." *My hands burst into flames and I begin thrashing back and forth on the gurney, until I awaken in the bunk bed drenched in sweat with an elevated heartbeat.***

A DIGITAL CLOCK radio reads 7:00pm. I stand and stumble towards the kitchen attempting to reorient, pausing with the refrigerator door open to take a few slow breaths as my eyes adjust to the light inside. I take a small navy blue can of "blueberry juice" from the top shelf of the door, and also grab a white can with brown letters that suggests it's a combination of "7Up" and "Dr. Pepper." "7Pepper." "Dr. Up." I walk back to the bedroom and see the work of a cleaning lady, who's tidied up the room while I was in the kitchen. Multiple waste paper baskets are full of single use plastic bottles crudely labeled with black marker as well as **a copy of the manuscript for this book.** Multiple pages have been reviewed and "Ok'd" by THE

BENEFITS ADMINISTRATOR *(helpful, emotive, and anxious)*. She appears in the doorway and begins walking the waste baskets out to the dumpster. I stop her and remove manuscript pages that have yet to be edited. I mention my hands being on fire in the cruise dream, and she laughs.

"It's only seven o'clock? I thought I went to bed hours ago."] //

⁂

HEARTH: #0014, #1066
BUNK BED: #0101, #1153
CRUISE: #0003, #1304
FIRE: #0001, #1353

⁂

#1384 - September 17, 2020 @ 05:15 (Beavercreek, Ohio)

[1384.1 / 3745] [An administrator checks me in for an unwanted surgery. The nurse anesthetist enters and confiscates my phone. THE CANINE SAVIOR *(loving, playful, and sweet)* giggles while sitting in the corner of the room as the intake process proceeds.]

[1384.2 / 3746] [I stand behind an enormous meat grinder, tossing in links of pepperoni that are masticated into a chorizo-like putty and effused onto porcelain dinner plates. THE WEAVER and THE CARPENTER each take a plate, and then another as I keep grinding. Some pieces of half ground meat pop up and out of the grinder, and plop on the floor in a weepy red mess. I believe I'll be left some for dinner, but all is eaten when I bring my plate to the end of the line. ***"There is no food for me."***]

[1384.3 / 3747] [I ride a wooden roller coaster *(without a lap bar or safety restraints)* down a cascading series of hills that pass through a number of different rider "pick up" areas. The further down the hills the train travels, the darker it becomes. At one flat, the train whizzes by THE WEAVER who stands at the gate eager to step on to the ride. She's unable to join the train as it continues to descend. Once at the bottom, I exit the ride to the right and walk through a gallery, where I put small blue-green gemstones in my pocket. Just prior to exiting the building I empty the contents of my pockets into an empty cigar box and place it in a dresser drawer, so the watchful eye of the shopkeeper won't catch me. I know THE BRIGHT SATELLITE is soon to return from a trip and I want to get her a gift. I see her radiant, smiling face in the middle of my head, and grow eager to see her though I know that gap between the mental image and the physical meetup are likely days apart.]

[1384.4 / 3748] [I take a seat behind THE DRAMA QUEEN and family. They occupy a row of steel folding chairs awaiting a new type of relay race that combines elements of horse racing with drag racing.]

⁂

Maj. = 0- THE WEAVER: #1385, 1- THE CARPENTER: #1385
PEPPERONI: #0123, #0696

TRAIN: #0026, #1351

⁂

#1385 - September 18, 2020 @ 05:23 (Beavercreek, Ohio)

[1385.1 / 3749] ["Blue 'L'" and "V.O." help me pack up a messy house in preparation for a move. I cry as I rifle through my old items, deciding what will advance with me to the next life segment. I spend time weeping while sitting on a tile bathroom floor looking at two bath-tubs set in an "L" formation at the perimeter of the room. THE WEAVER and THE CARPENTER are packed up for their own journey. I'm supposed to float across a river, but the mattress I intended to use as a raft has floated away, along with detailed directions I've written on it in marker to guide my trek.

A male companion and I create a different plan to travel across the country, though as yet we haven't set an alternate course. We contemplate a driven path that could take us radically south, though necessary for an effortless passage. Our overall path could look like a giant east to west "V."]

[1385.2 / 3750] [I'm guided to a first-class airline seat. I sit. The plane pushes back, then rolls forward. The main hatch opens and everyone exits the plane. I run with another travel companion to another plane. We grieve the end of an era, which draws to a close as we abandon notions of driving and take our seats on a different flight.] //

⁂

Maj. = 0- THE WEAVER: #1388, 1- THE CARPENTER: #1386

TILE: #0021, #1300

BATH TUB: #0058, #1151

MATTRESS: #0035, #1337

⁂

⁂ 15.3 - IKIGAI: 1386-1420 ⁂

#1386 - September 20, 2020 @ 02:57 (San Francisco, California)

[1386.1 / 3751] [I stand at a white board solving complex statistics equations with BILL GATES.]

[1386.2 / 3752] [THE MAGICIAN calls a meeting on a beach. I wait for him to arrive, twiddling my thumbs and dragging my right big toe in body-sized semicircles. He announces his arrival using a red and white megaphone, followed by a parade of cheering uniformed participants. The aggressive tone of the group suggests a competitive challenge between myself and a short stocky man *(among the sea of those who follow THE MAGICIAN)* is about to unfold.

I was planning to challenge a personal best in a physical stunt. I'm informed today's contest will be composed of, *"two movements evaluated by a panel of judges."*

The first maneuver, referred to as "the bullet" challenges competitors to lunge and leap vertically while rapidly swapping their legs back and forth as many times as possible within sixty seconds **and** concurrently flapping both arms extended overhead like a whale tail, **all** while hovering mere inches from the ground.

The second maneuver referred to as, "spoiled spoils," challenges those who best the first gateway to assess plates of mixed berries and determine which contain, "**the noble rot.**" A platter of blackberries and raspberries are set before me, some covered in a grey furry web of mold. Their sourness stings my nostrils and makes the truly rotten ones easy to differentiate from the highly prized, wine-making fruit.]

[1386.3 / 3753] [While on the back patio of a beachfront property I believe I'm going to be issued a puppy, to raise until it matures].

[1386.4 / 3754] [A curly-silver-haired artist requests I climb down a series of pergolas bolted to the exterior of a building, until I breach the ground and burrow into the soil, eventually descending through a layer of loam and dropping into a hidden basement. While in the basement I'm told I have *"15 minutes to get to the beach meeting with THE MAGICIAN."* The descent from the outside of the building served as, *"a reverse portal through space time."*]

[1386.5 / 3755] [I review blueprints for a temple project with THE ATTRACTOR, THE CONNECTOR, and THE CARPENTER. A host of other faces gather around the drafting table to get their first glimpse of the proposed structure. I express that I want to focus on a particular aspect of the construction, and the crew construes my comment as a desire to leave the engagement entirely. The team remains in a state of mild confusion as I back away from the table and exit the room.] //

⁂

Maj. = 1- THE CARPENTER: #1394, 4- THE CONNECTOR: #1418, 14- THE MAGICIAN: #1430

BILL GATES: #1387

BULLET: #0054, #0146, #0201, #0208, #0466, #0886, #0942

PUPPY: #0255, #0429, #0435, #0555
NOBLE: #0450, #1016
⁂

#1387 - September 20, 2020 @ 04:46 (San Francisco, California)

[1387.1 / 3756] [I run into BILL GATES at a doorway. We share an awkward moment until I break the silence, ***"Excuse me sir, may I please pass you?"***]

[1387.2 / 3757] [I walk down the street with hands in pockets, whistling Handel arias.]

[1387.3 / 3758] [I sit on a bench in a locker room. I catch a glimpse of a disrobing Asian man. When he removes his shirt, he becomes Hispanic. As his trousers drop, he becomes African American. When his socks come off, he's White. His ethnicity continues to shift as I wave at him to come over. I wrap my hands around his torso and pull his crotch towards my face. He turns into a ghost. I perform oral sex on the ghost.

I wake up alone, and find my hands sensually caressing my body. A blue intense light shines radiantly to my left. My penis is shaped like a checkmark and has a friction burn the size of a penny in the *"divit."*]

[1387.4 / 3759] [An older white couple sits in a living room expressing confusion about the concept of institutional racism, but remain eager to learn more.]

[1387.5 / 3760] [Autofellatio on the side of the street. Floppy tofu "old man dick."]

[1387.6 / 3761] [A bent rusted rebar sign swings and creaks in a strong wind. It reads: **"Vortex in the forest."**]

[1387.7 / 3762] [I walk by the "Snakehole" ranch. A boa constrictor sits coiled up at the far end of a dirt driveway. A crystal-clear pond immediately next to the driveway hosts another boa who swims freely. When it spots me, it coils and springs up from the water in my direction.]

[1387.8 / 3763] [A red velvet theater curtain drops as an audience roars with applause. Strobe lights blip as a flurry of flashbangs detonate. A deep masculine voice says, *"Everyone is doing their work. Everyone is playing their part."*]

[1387.9 / 3764] [I informally chat with ERYKAH BADU, acknowledging her connection to the sacred and the flow she generated during a recent Instagram Live concert. The taxidermy bust of a moose mounted on a nearby wall joins our conversation.]

. . .

[1387.10 / 3765] [Rows of pyramid-stacked isosceles triangles stretch until they generate a *"supermassive blackhole."*]

[1387.11 / 3766] [A man is such a fan of a new recording artist "MRE" he flouts social pressures by removing his mask to tell me all the reasons why he loves her.] //

⁂

VORTEX: #0110, #0249, #0479, #1110
RANCH: #0124, #0175, #0323, #0752, #0982, #1223
FRICTION: #0035, #0862, #0940
GENERATE: #0019, #0040, #0060, #0073, #0088

⁂

#1388 - September 21, 2020 @ 02:48 (San Francisco, California)

[1388.1 / 3767] [I briefly encounter THE ROMANTIC. He picks up a piece of candy, and is humored by the printing on the wrapper: **SLEEP TIGHT. SWEET DREAMS.**

"Yeah, I could use more of this. I haven't been sleeping well lately," he admits.

I look down at the used tea bag held by the tag between my right thumb and index finger which offers a similar wish: **SLEEP WELL.** I hand THE ROMANTIC the tea bag. He turns and walks away without saying anything.

"See you later!" I say while walking in the opposite direction down the sidewalk.]

[1388.2 / 3768] [I sit at the back of a movie theater watching trailers for forthcoming films. OPRAH sits with a guest down in the center front row of the venue. Momentarily preoccupied, I miss the preview I was waiting for. I ask the projector operator to replay the reel, who politely refuses because, *"it would irritate other members of the audience."* I offer an apology and take my seat.]

[1388.3 / 3769] [THE TRANSLATOR leads an exercise with a group of students gathered in a high school hallway. She encourages small clusters of students to play *"rock, paper, scissors"* and psychically anticipate each other's answers. For the last round, she encourages everyone to tap in to the common image held by the guides of "the school." Fists pound palms, and every student is left with an extended middle finger.

"Before you run out of here, notice how the energy of the room shifted with a simple lift of a finger," THE TRANSLATOR highlights.

Some people express aversion by saying in unison, *"I just don't like that gesture,"* and leave the school.

The school has a commissary that seems a bit out of place, based on its inventory. Large cuts of meat hang on hooks in a back freezer. I walk through, making a quick round but decide not to purchase anything.]

. . .

[1388.4 / 3770] [THE CHILD drinks Dr. Pepper from an oversized paper cup, while sitting on THE WEAVER's lap, occasionally hopping down and scurrying across the room to refill the cup. She repeats this process a few times. I grab a cup and walk to the dispenser, noticing the syrup has started to run out. I use up the remaining stock and pour it out, then fill my cup with soda water. THE CHILD approaches for another refill.

"A third cup, young lady?"

"No this is but her first," THE WEAVER interjects.] //

⁂

Maj. = 0- THE WEAVER: #1391, 3- THE CHILD: #1391,
15- THE ROMANTIC: #1432, 19- THE TRANSLATOR: #1412
SLEEP: #0979, #1079, #1220
FREEZER: #0394, #0710, #0947, #1107, #1159
ANOTHER: #0396, #0400, #0401

⁂

#1389 - September 22, 2020 @ 01:36 (San Francisco, California)

[1389.1 / 3771] [THE CARTOONIST drives up a steep hill towards a house. I'm the passenger. At the top, the tires squeal, and the car slides along the entire back perimeter of the property, that has a sheer mesa-like drop off. I'm convinced we're about to slip beyond the edge and plummet to our deaths. The car gently slides to a stop and we exit the vehicle.

The front door of the house is open. Once we enter THE CARTOONIST disappears. I walk through the empty home in the direction of a blue-eyed kitten that sits stoically in the center of a family room. I feed the kitten blue pellets of food shaken from a bag placed to its left. As the kitten eats it shrinks. It continues to eat until it shrinks to microscopic size.

When I retrieve my phone from my back pocket, the flashlight momentarily blinds me. The device has recorded hours of blacked-out video. I'm unable to get the phone to stop recording, and believe the device to be hacked.

THE ROBOT and THE RAPTOR sit in a breakfast nook sipping tea and reviewing the daily paper. THE ROBOT becomes anxious when she learns "The President" has taken an action that will result in her father's loss of access to several life sustaining prescriptions. I attempt to get THE ROBOT to sit on a bed with me to talk, though she proceeds to nervously walk the perimeter of the room alternately folding her hands

"This is what happens when you don't exercise your rights. Just like muscles...they lose their strength. Then, you lose choice," she says before posting the same phrase across multiple social media platforms.

I leave the kitchen and exit on to a back driveway where I encounter THE SKYWOLF *(an expression of devoted service).*

"Can I work on the staircase?" she asks.

At first, I don't know what she means. I look off the edge of the mesa and discover zigzag dirt switchbacks that resemble steps.

"Don't act prematurely, best to let the primary crew finish their segment."

[1389.2 / 3772] [*"Sir, we're going to have to amputate your penis,"* a doctor says.

My mouth sours and I decline the procedure.] //

⁂

Min. = ◆- *THE RAPTOR: #1390*
SOCIAL: #0399, #0429, #0453, #0472
PERIMETER: #0446, #0520, #0561
DOCTOR: #0401, #0781, #0847

⁂

#1390 - September 22, 2020 @ 03:11 (San Francisco, California)

[1390.1 / 3773] [**Engaged in a game with THE RAPTOR.** We're summoned to an empty room in a Victorian home by an unseen force. The door slams shut. We engage in an infinite appreciation loop, expressing reasons why we love each other.]

[1390.2 / 3774] [I watch a group of combat warriors on TV make their first attack on a terrorist group, sanctioned by a foreign government. The campaign begins exactly one year after the boat team made an *"overzealous attack on a housing project with solid cement staircases."* They struck the building multiple times with a bazooka, resulting in the killing of numerous civilians living inside the previously-thought-to-be-impervious building.

I jump in to the TV and join the team. We huddle behind a doorway just prior to taking aggressive action. As we wait, two cats run up behind me and bat me with their paws. I playfully knock them away multiple times. They return and repeatedly swipe at my uncamouflaged right forearm.]. //

⁂

EMPTY: #0395, #0422, #0431, #0441
CONCRETE: #0418, #0452, #0473, #0485
CATS: #0581, #0791, #0913, #972, #1000
RETURN: #0400, #0452, #0478, #0500

⁂

#1391 - September 22, 2020 @ 05:31 (San Francisco, California)

[1391.1 / 3775] [*"Hello 'Novum Marcum,'"* an older grey-haired man says. I'm confused for a moment until I determine he's addressing me.

He continues, *"I have plenty of money. Don't worry about how much strain he put on my Tesla. I can buy a dozen more."* I remain perplexed as I accept his dinner invitation at a trendy new restaurant to "celebrate."

We enter the establishment, briefly passing by THE EQUESTRIAN who's huddled and sick beneath a black steel staircase. She's infected with coronavirus. Her breathing is labored. The man places his booted left foot at her side and taps a pile of guano.

"Don't touch that any more. If you do, you'll stay sick. That's infectious waste."

The man's wife greets us. He makes an abrupt about face, and exits the building with her.]

[1391.2 / 3776] [I pick up a toaster-sized wooden box that mysteriously fills with water as I hold it. I repeatedly empty the vessel out a window and into a clear flowing stream at right.

I've placed a set of clean clothes within the box, and am surprised when I remove them dry and unsullied by the water. Jeans. Pajamas. Pillow cases. All bone dry and crisply folded.]

[1391.3 / 3777] [I stand to meet the family in front of another restaurant.
"Do you want to march the rest of the way with THE CHILD?" THE WEAVER inquires.
"Do you want to take a different route? Maybe go a different way?" I ask THE CHILD.
"No! No! No!" THE CHILD repeatedly exclaims as she runs away and leaps into a van with an open sliding door.]

[1391.4 / 3778] [Multiple teams of combat fatigue wearing men leap between levels of a game, using VHS machines as portals. They avoid coiled up snakes set to strike, and fire breathing marble busts as they attempt to assassinate one another. The men alternatively travel through quicksand whirlpools in the corner of each room, to bound between floors of an industrial building in lieu of staircases *(which do not exist in this reality)*.]

[1391.5 / 3779] [SKRILLEX drives the Tesla referenced in **[1391.1 / 3775]**. The vehicle travels at tremendous speed, but SKRILLEX decides to throttle down and shuttles the car near 200mph.
"SLOW DOWN! STOP! YOU'RE GOING TO WRECK!" I frantically scream.
He complies and brings the car down to a reasonable speed, though I'm still upset.
"You took my ability to choose away. What would it be like if you agreed to perform with the audience a certain distance away and then someone leapt up behind you, and put you in a half nelson? Would you like that? It seems like the only relevant comparison I can make."
SKRILLEX holds silent and looks at me incredulously as he brings the car to a stop in front of the bookstore, where a crowd has gathered for a signing. He's a well-respected novelist and has never produced any music in this reality. We exit the car and enter the store together.
"You remind me of a character in my 17th novel," he says walking to a shelf, removing a voluminous multi-thousand-page book, and drops it on a table in front of me.
"When did you have time to write all this? This is epic." I blurt while gleefully flipping through the pages of his magnum opus.] //

⁂

Maj. = 0- THE WEAVER: #1396, 3- THE CHILD: #1424
VESSEL: #0481, #0615, #0887, #0943
TESLA: #1229
REASONABLE: #0543, #0636
EPIC: #0548, #0642, #0885, #0968

⁂

#1392 - September 23, 2020 @ 04:38 (San Francisco, California)

[1392.1 / 3780] [At an airport. I walk towards my gate. I see the backpack I lost during my last trip nestled under an escalator. I grab it and walk to a cafe with a father and daughter who for whatever reason are interested in all the trivia I know about "stroopwafel." They express excessive interest in my instruction to place the cookie atop a hot cup of tea. I order three and place one on each of our beverages as our conversation meanders across a variety of benign topics. I expect a sugary caramel hit from the cookie when I bite it, and am surprised at the taste of raspberry and creme fraiche oozing gently from its center.

At the gate, I'm informed I can only bring one of the two backpacks I'm carrying. I step out of line and empty the contents on the floor. My old work laptop opens. I turn it on, and once the boot up sequence completes, I'm shown a video of every keystroke my hands made during my former career segment. 13 years of typing is shown in time-lapse in a matter of mere moments, and results in a live-feed of me staring at the old computer, streaming online.]

[1392.2 / 3781] [I'm the "hype being" for ARCA, ramping up the crowd in the final moments before she takes the stage. I bounce on jumping stilts, bounding higher, and higher as the crowd's anticipation grows.]

[1392.3 / 3782] [THE DANCER sits under an apple tree, holding THE LITTLE PRINCE on her lap. He's nine and a half months old. He babbles and squeals with delight when he spots another toddler-aged friend sitting with his mom under another tree. He stands with a wobble, and walks towards the friend. I walk over to him. He takes my hand and we walk together down a blacktop path towards a brilliant golden horizon. The sound of angelic choirs increases in volume the more we walk together. So moved by the environment, my eyes well up with tears.

"He's growing up quickly."] //

⁂

Maj. = 2- THE DANCER: #1410, 12- THE LITTLE PRINCE: #1421
RASPBERRY: #0841, #1144, # 1158
GATE: #0472, #1004, #1091

⁂

#1393 - September 26, 2020 @ 05:17 (San Francisco, California)

[1393.1 / 3783] [A family lives in an airstream trailer in savage wintery tundra. They leverage one another's wilderness survival skills to sustain their unique micro-community. Daily at nightfall, the father brings forth a butane blow torch to toast crusts of bread for the children, who in turn use the momentary heat to thaw their freezing cheeks. The family is aware their trailer sits at the far end of a Walmart parking lot, though the store and its abundant contents are encased in a thick layer of ice. They lack the tools to penetrate the ice.]

[1393.2 / 3784] [A video game allows me to change perspective from portrait to landscape. I continue playing the game. Each time the perspective swaps, the perimeter of the game screen grows in size by the golden ratio. The video game controls are clunky and lag in response time.]

[1393.3 / 3785] [THE ANGRY SPRITE and I ascend a staircase. He's supportive and curious about my, *"next steps."* At the top we step towards the door of an RV. A woman leans out of a trailer window and talks to us, while shaking a handful of rice from her palms onto 50lb bags of rice and flour stacked near the rear wheel well of the vehicle.]

[1393.4 / 3786] [I have male-to-female gender reassignment surgery. The procedure is non-invasive and performed in a single office visit. I have long brown hair, ample bosoms, and wear a shiny purple miniskirt as I put on a pair of slingback high heels. I confidently stride up a brown and amber-lit spiral staircase looking for *"my man."*] //

⁂

FLOUR: #0148
MALE: #0394, #0397
FEMALE: #0402, #0405, #0432
TOAST: #0617, #0640, #0841, #0897

⁂

#1394 - September 26, 2020 @ 06:45 (San Francisco, California)

[1394.1 / 3787] [THE CARPENTER and I have agreed to go to a theme park together. I'm in bed. I resist waking up. A playful ghost swings my bedroom door open and reveals a split staircase. One side leads up to a bright sunny level, the other descends to a black, lightless basement. No one's in the basement. The noise causes me to immediately sit up and dart for the door. I'm intrigued by the multiple choices available through a single doorway and veer up and to the left, quickly jumping onto a bike saddle and pedaling toward the park. THE CARPENTER and I whistle at each other in call-and-response, to help locate one another.

As I proceed on the bike, I'm surrounded on both sides of the street by clusters of college students gathered on blue and white checkered blankets spread across a greenspace for a community picnic. It's 9:00am *(a bit early for a picnic)* but the time doesn't dissuade the students from starting to drink. Their mood is friendly and playful. Small waves of laughter roll across the clusters sitting spaced out on the lawn. Multiple steel track roller coasters line the horizon, academic buildings sit in the middle ground, and immediately before me stands a prominently marked "stop" point where people dressed in white hazmat suits block the street and run a rapid testing check point, prior to allowing anyone to enter. The signs are presented in a language I can't read, rendering me unable to discern what the crew tests for. A woman encourages me to lock up my bike and take a seat. I resist, not wanting to be tested.

"I'll stay if I agree with what you're testing for."]

[1394.2 / 3788] [Two nude men embrace in a bathroom, next to a toilet filled with used condoms.

"I'll be your trophy," one whispers in the other's ear with a smile.

"I'd rather you be my rollercoaster," the other whispers back.] //

⁂

Maj. = 1- THE CARPENTER: #1396
HORIZON: #1001
TROPHY: #0007, #0377, #0834, #1083, #1130

⁂

#1395 - September 27, 2020 @ 06:45 (San Francisco, California)

[1395.1 / 3789] [I lay on my stomach as a soft pinkish violet being who calls itself "V.O." gives me a healing. It concurrently touches both my occipital bone and coccyx. The two points of contact send warming sensations through my entire nervous system. I'm given three, multi-minute rounds of sustained touch, each time the sound of "platinum" ringing between my ears *(ultra-high frequency)* raises in volume. I infer my spinal cord is restored from a recent injury, though for a moment I'm reminded, ***"what it was like to be quadriplegic,"*** as I feel motor response in my hands and feet flicker on and off.] //

⁂

HEALING: #0430, #0476, #0498, #0507, #0528
FLICKER: #0611, #0764, #0883, #0894, #0904
VIOLET: #0746, #0815, #0929, #1234
BONE: #0454, #0522, #0528, #0874, #1066

⁂

#1396 - September 28, 2020 @ 03:18 (San Francisco, California)

[1396.1 / 3790] [***"Are you ready to go to Germany?"*** I ask a man.

"I told my partner, 'No,'" he replies as he casually points a chef's knife at his partner who sis at a table five feet away.

He continues trimming a sponge cake.

Saddened by the news they won't be joining me on a trip, I offer once more, ***"Perhaps you'll reconsider when you speak later today?"***

We set to task, raising circus tents that cover a series of industrial ovens in use in an urban parking lot. When opened, the ovens reveal table-sized round chocolate cakes with 5-gallon blobs of heated cherry filling poured on top. THE CARPENTER performs quality control reviews on each cake as they're pulled from the oven.

THE WEAVER asks, *"Where is the shower pocket?"* in reference to burlap shoe holsters slung over the top of steel pole doorways in the tents. I count two of the "shower pockets" on site, but THE WEAVER insists *"there should be three."*

Our tasks are disrupted. The tents transform into a large modern mansion when a group of thieves surprises the crew and begins chasing us around the property. The leader of the assassins is a Black man referred to as "Reggie." He wears a backwards blue ball cap. Their motive is unclear, but it seems they've arrived to steal works of art, and create mayhem with the focused, hardworking crew.

We camouflage ourselves and migrate from the museum-like back wing, descending white marble staircases, and passing through rooms with windows of increasing size. The back of the property is bright and well lit. The front wing is but a series of construction scaffolds and framed walls which have not yet been raised. Some crude tents are sporadically pitched in the otherwise dark and lifeless area. One member of the team scurries through a Zen garden, lays down, and disguises himself in the sand. He narrowly avoids being stabbed.

"Large knives seem to be their preferred weapon." A woman brandishes a big blade and drags it across her tongue to intimidate those who flee. Some are captured and held hostage at knifepoint. "Reggie" takes aim at a woman running backwards and away from him in slow motion, and shoots her once in the right breast.

"That's exactly what we needed to have happen so we can start moving that money around," "Reggie" says as he chews a toothpick and watches the stunned woman collapse.

The violence escalates and results in a standoff. I'm worried more members of the family will be killed. At the last moment, police break down the door and arrest the entire group of thieves. The intensity of the chase leaves me breathless and heaving.] //

⁂

Maj. = 0- THE WEAVER: #1401, 1- THE CARPENTER: #1421
CHOCOLATE: #0406, #0433, #0456, #0476, #0513, #0522, #0529
CHERRY: #0037, #0925, #0939, #0959, #0973, #1041, #1133, #1140

⁂

#1397 - **September 29, 2020 @ 04:34 (San Francisco, California)**

[1397.1 / 3791] [A lobotomized man takes a seat neat to me on a flight.

"Can... Help... Me...Home?" he painstakingly slurs to me and my travel companion.

"Of course, pal," I say with a quiver in my voice and wiping tears from my eyes.

We anticipate the journey to be a challenge. This flight is but the first leg of a multi-segment travel day. We're responsible for getting him home.

The lobotomized man was given priority over 400 other standby passengers, who angrily protest his clearance with the gate agent at the jetway as the plane pushes back and begins to taxi.] //

⁂

TRAVEL: #0394, #0397, #0470, #0549, #0566, #0571
CHALLENGE: #0538, #0568, #0578, #0649, #0732
PROTEST: #0334, #0704, #1124, #1188, #334

⁂

#1398 - **September 29, 2020 @ 05:55 (San Francisco, California)**

[1398.1 / 3792] [I mediate a conflict where men argue about *"the socially appropriate number of napkins to use while attending a picnic."*]

[1398.2 / 3793] [I observe multiple impressions of the same man hold a conversation with himself as "they" walk up and down a staircase. Each time the man ascends, a different version of himself follows, as a seemingly, *"corded copy from the past."*

The current pass finds the man staring at his phone, dismissing the burnt skin man who giggles and taps him on the shoulder while sheepishly laughing. When I zoom in to take a closer look, I learn that both versions of the man look exactly like me.

The trailing version of me is covered in boils and second-degree burns.]

[1398.3 / 3794] [As I rest on my belly, a strange hum and buzz hovering near my right ear *(best described as what a robotic dragonfly may sound like)* increases in volume until I'm jolted from sleep.] //

⁂

VERSIONS: #0664, #0786, #0877, #0966
LAUGHING: #0692, #0699, #0773, #0792, #0799
BUZZ: #0077, #0109, #0189, #0250, #0894

⁂

#1399 - September 29, 2020 @ 06:38 (San Francisco, California)

[1399.1 / 3795] [THE SKEPTIC navigates our course on an unlit woodland trail at night. An emoji of a gold man sitting in lotus position indicates we're on the aligned path. When we deviate, the icon begins to flicker and disappear. I hold his hand as we ascend a steep incline. I take one step too far to the right and begin to stumble into a ditch, perhaps a ravine. I'm not sure how deep the descent will be. My grip is strong, and though I initially feel THE SKEPTIC resist he tumbles overhead, then dangles beneath me. His arm lengthens until the rest of his body is no longer viewable. I don't know how deep he's descended. His hand slips and he disappears into the black. I close my eyes and feel the loss of my friend.

When I open my eyes, he and I are on a giant dung heap surrounded by flies, ants and other pests as the sun rises. We scramble our way to the top of the shit pile. In the light, we come to appreciate how many holes we could have fallen through, and confidently stride along the precarious balance-beam-width edge of a massive honeycomb hexagon mesh. Perhaps we're on the exterior of a giant insect nest. **We don't know where we are.**]

[1399.2 / 3796] [I drive through a part of town where a local celebrity has closed his apothecary. He announces his decision on social media, and discloses he's also returned a book advance. *"I'll have to hustle to make this next life segment work,"* he declares, unaware that his words are driven by a "scarcity being" that triggers his deep-rooted fear of not having enough money. He preaches the prosperity gospel, but doesn't fully believe it...because he loves the game of "the struggle."] //

⁂

LOTUS: #0189, #0394
INSECT: #0917
STRUGGLE: #0049, #0063, #0547, #0571, #0781, #1150, #1158, #1164

⁂

#1400 - September 30, 2020 @ 00:19 (San Francisco, California)

[1400.1 / 3797] [I sit at a round table with a statistician who comedically explains, "$U^p = P_u$." For the first time the concept clicks. I insist he help me work out an explanation. Once I talk through the concept he smiles and says, *"Now you're thinking like a scientist."*] //

⁂

HELP: #0533, #0538, #0552, #0557, #0580
CONCEPT: #0613, #0771, #0787, #0803, #1239
SCIENTIST: #0671, #0912, #1015, #1116, #1130

⁂

#1401 - September 30, 2020 @ 04:31 (San Francisco, California)

[1401.1 / 3798] [I wander around the interior of an aquatics complex. THE GDMF UNICORN finds me zoning out by a pool at 2:00pm and frantically admonishes me for *"being hours late for our group's planned 1:00pm departure."* I follow her up a staircase. She disappears at the top. I proceed to the front of the complex, pausing to watch children slide down bright colored enclosed water slides. I stare off into space again.

"It's time to go. Move it," a grey-haired man I don't know tells me with a nudge to the shoulder. He loads me into a tiny plane with THE GDMF UNICORN, assumes the controls, and flies off. We take off at 7:00pm]

[1401.2 / 3799] [I walk by a man who stares at a computer screen. He's a former rock star, watching a video catalog of his *"happiest moments."* For a moment, he considers calling his former bandmates to discuss the possibility of a reunion show. He jerks away from the desk and looks over his left shoulder when he hears a woman shout his name, *"NOEL!"* I whistle one of his tunes as I turn away, and contemplate why he may have retired.]

[1401.3 / 3800] [I exit a hotel at 7:00pm. A frustrated man expresses his disdain for my actions. He received a call that I had walked through the hotel restaurant in the nude, and the municipal fine for the deed has been applied to his room bill.

"But I had a swimsuit on!" I say in self-defense, though as I recall my lumbering through the restaurant everything seemed to move at half speed. For most of the experience I felt lost, and I likely wandered aimlessly for hours.]

[1401.4 / 3801] [I sit in a salon chair, set up in a church parking lot.

"I have an appointment with 'David,'" I say to the unfamiliar male stylist who takes station behind me.

"You're hours late for your appointment. I'm doing you a favor," the man says as he takes a set of shears to the side of my head, buzzing it to the skin. He goes to my long locks on top. His motions tease that he's about to cut the majority of my hair, but he assures me he's, *"going to (just) nick the ends."*

"What do you do for work?"

"I work with exceptional children, and help them reach their potential."

He silently acknowledges my career choice with a nod.

A small plaque at the edge of the lot offers a whisper; a reminder that in the days preceding the church, the site was a school for the children of indigenous people.]

[1401.5 / 3802] [Mid flight, I look at small squares of spiral notebook paper scotch taped above the window. Upon inspection I discover they're playlists. One with the headline, "THE TATER" has but a single track scribbled on it.]

[1401.6 / 3803] [I help THE WEAVER move living room furniture into a new house. When I remove a blue upholstered chair from its crate, I find a two-inch thick, 18-inch-long infinity symbol made from melted yellow crayon wax draped over the left arm of the chair, and onto the seat cushion.]

[1401.7 / 3804] [A Korean woman wins second place in a *"national noodle bowl"* contest.] //

⁂

Maj. = 0- THE WEAVER: #1409

NOODLE: #0327, #0476, #0597, #0613, #0687, #1226

WHISPER: #0003, #0093, #0163, #0245, #0386, #0405, #0548, #0796, #0833, #0927

TINY: #0573, #0604, #0610, #0622, #0627, #0637

⁂

#1402 - September 30, 2020 @ 07:10 (San Francisco, California)

[1402.1 / 3805] [A woman frantically enters, worried about THE VETERINARIAN's whereabouts. She admits they had a severe argument once she discovered he was casually hooking up with THE JEW. She repeatedly attempts to contact THE VETERINARIAN through Instagram, walking back her earlier shaming with overcompensating praise for his love of *"otters."*

"We had a shouting match at 2:00am, then he took off," she offers without solicitation.

I believe her motives are suspicious. She may have murdered THE VETERINARIAN.

To keep her onsite while the police arrive, I offer to assist with her internet search. I fumble around with the application on my phone, unable to locate THE JEW's profile. I've recently reorganized my contacts into a series of hexagons with a photo in the center, each side with an equilateral triangle that displays photos of **their** six most recent social interactions. The images in the triangles cycle in a clockwise direction, some moving so quickly they blur like a buzzsaw. The aggregate image in the six-pointed star looks like animated collage.

When I glance up from my phone, I see a young mother standing at the top of a staircase who unfurls a coil of party streamers upwards from each palm. She stands motionless as the chains of six pointed stars affix themselves around the wraparound porch at the front of her home. The streamers flung from her right hand are white. Those from her left hand are blue. Final preparations for her children's birthday party are complete.] //

⁂

SIX: #0534, #0563, #0568, #0671, #0672

CONTACT: #0548, #0636, #0640, #0699

COIL: #0397, #0801, #0954, #1087, #1136

WHITE: #1172, #1173, #1175, #1188, #1193

⁂

#1403 - October 1, 2020 @ 06:57 (San Francisco, California)

[1403.1 / 3806] [THE TEACHER decides to purchase *"the school,"* with a cohort of familiar creators. Students scatter in small clusters up a gentle sloping series of grassy hills. Some practice Qi Gong. Others provide student teachers with constructive feedback on their public speaking. Others grapple. Some lay on their backs practicing holotropic breathwork. The environment is lush, friendly, and inviting. Students are encouraged to audit various

activities and supplement their personal practices. "The school" is an open-air amphitheater.]
//

⁂

SCHOOL: #1088, #1109, #1110, #1113, #1142, #1148
FAMILIAR: #0012, #0014, #0016, #0017, #0019
ENCOURAGED: #0005, #0172, #0203, #0400
QI GONG: #0072, #0115

⁂

#1404 - October 1, 2020 @ 07:37 (San Francisco, California)

[1404.1 / 3807] [*"Why do you constantly change up your program?"*
***"Because the body needs to cut new patterns to keep growing, otherwise the organism becomes entrenched."*]**

[1404.2 / 3808] [A woman rapidly darts in and out of her general store's main entrance. Each time she emerges on the porch she wears a different uniform. In one iteration, she wears a starched white Krispy Kreme uniform. In another, she wears a brown, yellow and maroon, Burger King crew shirt and visor. Lastly, she wears a green, white and red horizontally striped polo shirt with the word "MANAGER" embroidered on the left side of her chest *(across her heart)* as she rushes pizzas in blank white boxes to customers who wait in their cars in the parking lot.]

[1404.3 / 3809] [Self. Stimulation.]

[1404.4 / 3810] [THE CHOCOHOLIC indulges.]

[1404.5 / 3811] [THE POINT GUARD practices his "three's."]

[1404.6 / 3812] [It's a bright sunny morning. I lay down on a couch to take a nap. I look out a picture window and witness two men wearing tuxedos walk towards my home. As they approach it becomes clear the men are THE PILOT and THE KIND HEART. Though I've not previously interacted with them within the house, I know they're spouses and occupy the room at the back of the property.

I levitate and slowly float from the couch to my private quarters, and land gently on a white linen pillow top mattress. A slight flick of my wrist from the bed gently closes the door to the room. *"Click."* As I lay on the bed, staring at the door I leave my body, float to the ceiling and look down on myself at rest. Mounds of colorful dirty laundry are piled around the bed. Some are heavy and wet, and seem to be soaked in stale, bile-laden urine.]

. . .

[1404.7 / 3813] [I awaken from the prior dreams into another, where I watch an albino woman with long black hair push her toddler in a white stroller. The room is dazzling white. The air tastes "powdery blue." Light shines in from large square windows in every wall. The woman wears an all-white outfit, constructed from tea doilies. Her child is similarly outfitted. Both have sets of eyes disproportionately large for their heads. Their irises hold a similar sky blue, anime/manga-like tone. Both sets of eyes are dewy with tears.

"I'm the same being split between two bodies," the pair communicate without speaking.

"We want nothing more than to reconnect and be whole, yet we don't know how," they lament.] //

⁂

CLICK: #0227, #0589, #0805, #0832
MANAGER: #0113, #0134, #0154, #0384, #1194
ANIME: #0004, #0786

⁂

#1405 - October 2, 2020 @ 03:20 (San Francisco, California)

[1405.1 / 3814] [Two silverish platinum beings channel a flow of diamond-white light through the center of my forehead. It compresses into a dense magnetic ball in the middle of my skull until it explodes like a gamma ray burst, out through both my ears and the crown of my head. Three equal tunnels of light that look like rapid blasts of golden "O's" fly in straight lines at right angles from my head. When remote viewed, the phenomenon looks like ¾ of a rapidly expanding Maltese cross.]//

⁂

MAGNETIC: #0375, #1023
THREE: #1089, #1099, #1102
RAPID: #0158, #0306, #0400, #0440, #1133, #1168

⁂

#1406 - October 3, 2020 @ 01:24 (San Francisco, California)

[1406.1 / 3815] [*"Use me for sex,"* a young African American man requests of me. Neither of us disrobe. We stand an arm's distance apart.]

[1406.2 / 3816] [I slide down a brass banister to the right of a series of red carpeted stairs. I extend my right arm and grab a hovering bag of junk food. I continue to slide downward as I open the package and indulge in the warm *(and slightly melted)* dark chocolate covered caramels. They melt in my mouth and stick to my teeth.

While continuing down the banister I find a set of dirty dishes in a black tub that I'm inspired to wash, and put away. The dishes were used to plate food *"children cooked for their father"* for a celebratory breakfast. Crumbs from half-munched squares of graham crackers bespeckle the plates. The bin is too heavy to walk from the base of the staircase back to the kitchen at my apartment. I leave the bin at the base of the stairs and walk away.]

. . .

[1406.3 / 3817] [ALEXANDRIA OCASIO-CORTEZ and BERNIE SANDERS encourage my run for sheriff after another public tragedy unfolds. My prospective jurisdiction and extent of local powers are unclear, should I prove victorious at the polls. After contemplation and discussion, I decide to rescind my candidacy. ***"Becoming sheriff would place unnecessary risks on my family."***

"Today is a sad day," I sorrowfully opine, as I turn off the lights at campaign headquarters. BERNIE nods in agreement.]

[1406.4 / 3818] [A preschool teacher lays in a cardboard box with his students and takes multiple lighthearted photos of him positioned head-to-toe in a long line.]

[1406.5 / 3819] [I drink from a plastic cartoon-like vessel in the shape of a 100lb dumb bell. The liquid within is black.

"Was that a gift from my family?" a father asks, as I gulp.

"I'm sorry, no. Someone must've played a prank on you. It runs in my family. I'll replace what I consumed then I'll give it to you."] //

⁂

DRINK: #1120, #1149, #1193, #1222
CAMPAIGN: #0073, #0215, #0395, #0461, #0667
OPINE: #0855, #0909
BREAKFAST: #0017, #0171, #0382

⁂

#1407 - October 3, 2020 @ 04:48 (San Francisco, California)

[1407.1 / 3820] [A group of guys move a stalled vehicle into a garage for repair.]

[1407.2 / 3821] [*"Sketch books FULL of new equations!" "Your kids will be eager to solve them ALL!"*]

[1407.3 / 3822] [I submerge myself in a laboratory pool under the watchful gaze of a group of clipboard-carrying scientists. One squirts an eyedropper's worth of fluid into the tank, which contains a strain of bacteria that rapidly grows to the size of kiwi fruit in the warm, salinized water.]

[1407.4 / 3823] [Hyper-dimensionality of common vitamins is represented by white non-conforming shapes on a black screen. When reduced to three-dimensional observation they rupture. *"That's the cost we pay for only seeing in three,"* an omniscient voice accepts.]

[1407.5 / 3824] [A group of girls sit in rows across from an equivalent-sized group of boys.

"Girls, regardless of what the boys choose, we will remain submerged in the pool," the female teacher-of-the-girls directs.

"Do you boys intend to do 'stuff' tonight or tomorrow?" the girls ask in unison, of the boys.
The boys chatter at low volume among themselves and don't offer a clear answer.]

[1407.6 / 3825] [A person wearing fishnets, a red speedo, a wig, and a red cowboy hat stands across from me.

"That's the exact person who's hit on me a thousand times at Burning Man," I say as snickering breaks out among the group.

"That woman has a nineteen-inch dick!" A voice from the group shouts.]

[1407.7 / 3826] [The bacteria from **[1407.3 / 3822]** and the "vitamin shapes" from **[1407.4 / 3823]** are combined in a tank. The bacteria consume the corners of the shapes. They rapidly increase in size, as the shapes destabilize and explode.]

[1407.8 / 3827] [I ride a train with THE PUBLIC MEDIUM. As it slows to a stop at a station, we pass a long white vehicle that looks similar to the Oscar Meyer Wienermobile.

"What's that place?" he asks, pointing towards a storefront.

"Sort of a cool spot. I dropped my faux fur coat off there, and a week later they turned it into a figurine for THE FIDUCIARY-"

Before I recall the full story, we're interrupted by a group of people who jump and cling to the train after completing their shift at the junkyard.]

[1407.9 / 3828] [I prepay for an appointment with THE DEAR HEART, eager to see his new office. Upon arrival, I find the process onsite unusual. A powder-blue and white checkerboard floor descends on four equal sides to a common center like a Mesoamerican pyramid. People sit around on injection molded furniture, set sporadically across the different steps as they await their session. I remain confused and elect to depart.

"Wait! You left without your complimentary beverage!" THE DEAR HEART calls as I walk away.

I turn and pause as he hands me a small paper cup full of water, then he returns to his office.]

[1407.10 / 3829] [A computer runs its boot up sequence. Once complete, a movie plays in which a group of young men sit on a couch, challenging each other in a battle royal video game, where each try to outdo the next by creating a more nuanced and *"hyphy"* bassline groove.] //

⁂

FAUX: #0306, #0926, #0933
FRUIT: #0024, #0407, #0516, #1158
SPORADICALLY: #0079, #0093

⁂

⁂

#1408 - October 3, 2020 @ 06:52 (San Francisco, California)

[1408.1 / 3830] [I stand at a bathroom sink, rinsing out a beverage vessel lent to me by a friend.

A guide startles me as it floats in through the bathroom window and opens a portal in the wall by the vanity. Higher dimension, abstract geometric forms come briefly in to focus and quickly dissolve. From the scattered particles, a platinum caduceus magnetically comes into being and slowly turns clockwise, lit from behind with a concentrated *(yet soft)* stream of diamond light.

"That's magical."

Once dried, I place the vessel on a couch positioned immediately next to the sink. I look for a stack of lime green Post It notes, on which I wish to write the word, ***"Thanks!"***

As I search for the Post It's, a tall person (6'5" +) asks, *"Who'd you borrow that from?"*

I don't answer when I overhear a woman's voice in the other room. My listening bias suggests *(based on the tone)* she's likely in her early 20's, though I'm not able to confirm as I eavesdrop.

"If you tell me in advance what you're bringing, I'll be able to better prepare for my own travel."] //

⁂

CONFIRM: #0140, #0145, #0166, #0175, #0236
TRAVEL: #1109, #1137, #1139, #1163, #1180, #1187
CADUCEUS: #0999

⁂

#1409 - October 4, 2020 @ 06:52 (San Francisco, California)

[1409.1 / 3831] [I participate in a contest to help THE PHILANTHROPIST and her family reclaim their mansion. The proposed game involves the use of a translucent oversized rubber band, brought to tension between two large dowels. Small discs are placed in the oversized slingshot and fired across a large pool at six targets that bob like buoys. The competition is held in low/no light in a parlor at the far end of property. An unknown count of teams competes, though when asked, the judges claim participation by, *"many many."*

I take aim. I firmly draw the elastic back. "SNAP!"

"You're cheating. You just want to win everything for yourself!" A faceless voice from another team yells.

"No. My sole reason for playing is to help them get their house back."

Between rounds I wander the property. I encounter THE WEAVER in the library who claims a large djembe sized "biscuit barrel" from Zambia would be an appropriate "welcome home" gift for THE PHILANTHROPIST. Initially, she believes the object was previously stolen from the family, and her act of returning it will be considered heroic *(though I confirm it was never their possession).*

The "Master of the House" has purchased all new estate furniture for their assumed return to the home.

While on the top level of the home I follow THE PHILANTHROPIST down *"the grand hallway."* At the doorway to her bedroom, she pauses and thumbs through a folder of loose-leaf paper held under her left arm. As she enters her quarters I back away from her, orienting to the left and descending a staircase in reverse. I take twenty-three steps down, and hit a mass of resistance which renders me unable to move any deeper. I feel uneasy. I know there's a bottom to the staircase and a complementary ascent on the opposite end of the bottom floor. I walk back up and make a turn to the right.

A group of young African American men, recently adopted by THE PHILANTHROPIST, enter the kitchen carrying bags of groceries wanting to share their experience of being racially profiled at the store. Though angered they seem to agree, *"Things suck, but they're better now than they were."*] //

⁂

Maj. = 0- THE WEAVER: #1421
COMPETITION: #0001, #0189, #0265, #0376
ADOPTED: #0115, #0542, #0866, #0902
AGREE: #0007, #0040, #0064, #0072, #0087

⁂

#1410 - October 4, 2020 @ 06:52 (San Francisco, California)

[1410.1 / 3832] [I awaken at a desk on a trading floor, participating in what's assumed to be *"high risk business."* I may be in New York City. I could as easily be in Seattle. I call THE BOSS and thank her for her assistance in, *"getting me the interview."* I'm eager to get to work. I might be placed in an entry level role. Not clear.

I drop a bunch of pencils, crayons and thumbtacks on the floor when I encounter THE DANCER. She's interested in having a friendly spat.

"Stop. Please. Not right now. We're at work."

New faces introduce themselves, though their voices are muffled and garbled. I may have a hearing impairment. I attempt to be cordial while looking at small-pewter name tags with tiny-black-block-letters worn by associates of the firm. At a glance I now know, "Mark," but am too slow to snare the name of the male, curly haired senior executive who hastily greets me on his way to the board room. Next, "Theresa" takes a seat directly across from me and tells me she, *"couldn't be more excited that we managed to book 'Scarlet' for the new marketing campaign."*

"Is this a mass market group? Consumer top of house? Administrative unit? Servicing and fulfillment support? I don't know the lingo around here," I ask another new female coworker who's unable to provide much *(if any)* clarity to my query.

We're called to the board room, home to a metal, thin-bordered square table, lit softly from beneath. Influencers and leaders line the sides, as the curly haired executive provides encouragement and inspiration.

I glance over my left shoulder and see a mature giraffe lumbering through the workspace unencumbered.]

[1410.2 / 3833] [I pass along a promenade lined by carnival game kiosks and concession stands.]

[1410.3 / 3834] [I awaken and realize my phone captures video while lying on the floor. I've recorded one hour and thirty-three minutes of first-person video, where I ride a bike down a golden-lit bike path lined by wheat and cattails; my best attempt to remember a dream within a dream.] //

⁂

Maj. = 2- THE DANCER: #1434
CARNIVAL: #0140, #0390, #0524, #0538
WORK: #1088, #1089, #1101, #1106, #1107
WHEAT: #0104, #0121, #0305, #0678, #0876

⁂

#1411 - October 6, 2020 @ 02:07 (San Francisco, California)

[1411.1 / 3835] [I attend a concert with my girlfriend and a pal named "Steve." We arrive early enough to watch a union crew assemble the semi-circle stage embedded in an outcropping of giant red boulders. The crew head invites us on a backstage tour. We watch the crowd begin to grow as the crew head points to the unique structures that make the stage appear to float. We're encouraged to take a photo. My girlfriend flashes a peace sign with her left hand in front of my face, just as the image is snapped. In a poof, a pair of life-sized blowup dolls mimicking our image hover a few feet away in lieu of a digital photo. *"Creating this goofy and absurd memento is only possible while inside this venue."*

"Gah! I know what you're doing. We're still playing this game?" I smirk and say as I lean in to kiss her on the cheek.

She laughs and grabs my face with both hands as we meet eye-to-eye.

I gently take my hands to her hips and draw her near. We laugh and playfully kiss.

Our attention moves towards a lighting crew, moving trusses and rigs into final position and anchors them down.

"The show's gonna start on time," the crew lead assures us, as we look up at the red semi-circle jutting from the mountain that spins like a saw blade catching light of a half moon.] //

⁂

UNION: #0023, #0033, #0084, #0168, #0336, #0427
FLOAT: #0125, #0135, #0151, #0186, #0193, #0208
EYE TO EYE: #0609, #1001
ATTENTION: #0643

⁂

#1412 - October 6, 2020 @ 03:39 (San Francisco, California)

[1412.1 / 3836] [I attend a "challenge retreat" with a group of 15 other adults. We've agreed to have our problem-solving skills tested, *"en extremis."* Among the challenges that trigger the group the most are, *"puzzles that must be solved in complete darkness within a short period of time."* Our minds race. Our collective blood pressure spikes. Of particular challenge to me is a scenario where I'm seated at a cube shaped desk. As my awareness broadens, I see myself seated at the top right corner of a giant Rubik's cube. As it's cosmically jumbled, my body is sliced in half. I watch my waist and legs sweep quickly to the left and out of sight. Others may be nearby and supportive, though the shock of the action leaves me momentarily despondent and numb. I begin believing members of our group are being picked off one at a time and suggest the others, ***"Run! Escape if you can! Leave me!"***

Overhead lights switch on and reveal a small chain-link fence to the left. Beyond the fence is a body of water with a dingy docked near the shore. THE HEALER and THE WARD OF GAIA rush in and begin taking our vital signs. They assure the group they're facilitators of the program, but we collectively suspect they are trickers. To help us downregulate they assign us to simple, repeatable tasks that also tidy the *"panic room."*

Once calm and coherent, the group is led outside around a property, and told to stand near an open *"back door"* to the house. Participants are encouraged to enter, though once the threshold is crossed, we're surrounded with a looming fear that, ***"we'll never get out."*** One at a time, group members enter, accompanied by THE FLUTIST.

"You know one of you decided to go 'butt first' into the box," THE HEALER mentions, though no one derives any understanding as to whether this is helpful or hurtful to the group's quest.

"What's the quality of the mind's eye when the lights go out? Does it race with thoughts?" THE WARD OF GAIA offers in contrast.]

[1412.2 / 3837] [I stand and inspect a photograph that reanimates a former collegiate scene. A group of friends gather to make evening plans. THE MANAGING DIRECTOR drops cash on the floor. Others scurry to pick it up. With each word spoken, the face of the speaker ages.

"I had to sell my dog!"

"Yeah, but you had to skirt the system."]

[1412.3 / 3838] [THE TRANSLATOR sets the intention for a lecture, moments before THE ADVANCED STUDENTS open the doors to the classroom. A small placard on a round pub table near the door reads: *"Tonight's class will begin promptly at 10:09."*

When questioned about the start time THE TRANSLATOR offers, *"That's when everyone agreed to be here. Our numbers are down and we need them."*] //

⁂

INTENTION: #0644, #0697, #0728, #0746, #0753, #0768, #0792, #0817
PROGRAM: #0748, #0855, #0902, #0935, #0986, #1034, #1103, #1209
CONTRAST: #0170, #0540, #0891, #0927, #0961
THRESHOLD: #0009, #0895, #0904, #0976, #1188

⁂

#1413 - October 6, 2020 @ 05:56 (San Francisco, California)

[1413.1 / 3839] [I stand in the center of a square park, that floods from three sides at the same time. I scurry with a group up a hill to avoid being swept up by the rushing waters.]

[1413.2 / 3840] [I'm young. I attend a boarding school for boys. I ascend to an upper level of a dorm, enter a room and leap up onto a top bunk. The squeak of the springs awakens my neighbor across the hall. Two others and I go back downstairs, and are found by the two female principals of the academy. The elder of the two carries a rolling pin. The younger one turns off a thin vertically mounted black-and-white television that hangs on the door. The only sound in the room is the rolling pin slapping the principal's palm. Does she intend to punish us?

"You don't scare me."

The principal finds my confidence light and humorous, and invites us into the kitchen to help prepare dinner for the rest of the class.

As we advance through the food prep process, members of the class pass by the door to watch. Each face grows slightly older until adult men pause and inspect our activity. The men of increasing age create percussive call-and-response patterns with their mouths. The peculiar tongue flutters sound like spring door stops being plucked.]

[1413.3 / 3841] [I apologize to the boy I awakened upstairs. As he's dismissed by the headmaster, he quickly transforms into a nightgown wearing girl, with long-blond curls. A small drinking straw-sized cardboard tube is placed in each of her nostrils to assist her labored breathing. The further up the tubes go in her sinuses, the longer her hair becomes.] //

⁂

SQUARE: #0648, #0671, #0682, #0698, #0700
TONGUE: #0088, #0175, #0330, #0456, #0615
BREATHING: #0633, #0804, #0893, #0925, #1095

⁂

#1414 - October 7, 2020 @ 03:57 (San Francisco, California)

[1414.1 / 3842] [I riff on guitars with three other guys in a studio. Each of us plays a different model, with a different tone. Four players consistently participate in the jam, casually cycling new musicians in without fanfare. We play a descending minor chord progression for a rock tune that begins on A flat and drops low. We believe the chorus will be an arena anthem that will, *"breathe new life into rock 'n roll."*]

[1414.2 / 3843] [I lead a worship service from the front of a cathedral sanctuary. I dismiss the group when I learn a *"level five"* student has broken a community health-and-safety protocol. During post service discussion with the team, I'm told the rogue congregant was THE PERFORMANCE ARTIST, who was issued a mask and a paper fan, before being asked to leave the building for, *"making a ruckus."*]

[1414.3 / 3844] [**"BUY A PRAYER! SAVE A POLITICIAN!"** a television ad campaign demands. I touch the screen and scroll through a catalog of mantras for sale. Crisp, cogent phrases are priced at a premium. Less clear devotional images of battered saints are offered mid-range. Tones of conflict and disillusion are priced to move mass market volumes of "product."] //

⁂

RIFF: #0230, #0274, #0436, #0887
SANCTUARY: #0042, #0098, #0628
MASS: #0704, #0717, #0721, #0724

⁂

#1415 - October 7, 2020 @ 05:44 (San Francisco, California)

[1415.1 / 3845] [I pass through the doors of a world-renowned chocolatier, into a white marble floored showroom, sparsely populated with jewelry cases presenting premier fare. I've errantly left my credit cards at home and have zero cash on hand. I disclose my circumstances to the sales representatives who welcome me to look around and sample as would any other guest. A trio of young, upwardly-mobile men enter conspicuously espousing their desire to purchase, *"the most ultra-exclusive chocolates in stock,"* at a premium if necessary.

The store has 1000, 10-piece boxes of truffles on hand which retail for $100. One of the three men buys 250 boxes, declaring the impromptu $25,000 expenditure, *"a steal."* Every box nonsensically fits within a single medium paper tote. The man signs the credit card transaction record and departs, as though he's purchased a few pairs of socks and t-shirts.

I'm invited by a tuxedo-wearing clerk to sample a microSD card size portion of "pepper white" chocolate. I'm offered a thumbnail sized cognac truffle as an intermezzo, to neutralize the intense black pepper flavor. I'm subsequently presented with a dried ancho chile dipped in 100% melted cacao, immediately flash-frozen in liquid nitrogen.

A clerk emerges from a cleanroom, wearing white antistatic coveralls and a face shield. He invites the remaining two men to join him in the stock room. He requests they leave their phones in a safe near the register, before leading them back to inspect *ultra-high-end* for the *ultra-high-net-worth* products that are not displayed to the general public.]

[1415.2 / 3846] [I overhear teachers discuss, *"enrollment risk mitigations for the next calendar year at '3DFSD Academy.'"*]

[1415.3 / 3847] [I walk up a narrow stone pathway at first light, lined by a tunnel of lush green vegetation. Once at the top, I see two older gentlemen seated at a white lacquer table on a small, round, well-manicured lawn sipping tea and watching the sun rise. I don't interrupt them as I continue my morning stroll, but overhear them reveling in, *"just how good and miraculous life is!"* Their laughs bring a smile to my face.] //

⁂

CHOCOLATE: #0648, #0654, #0664, #0693
PEPPER: #0074, #0494, #0532, #0938, #1201
LUSH: #0079, #0101, #0265, #0786, #1224
MIRACULOUS: #0658, #824, #0849, #0893

⁂

#1416 - October 8, 2020 @ 05:44 (San Francisco, California)

[1416.1 / 3848] [I attend a joint rally between two opposing political parties. The event occurs in a large indoor arena. Tens of thousands of constituents are present, supporting their candidate and ideology. BARACK OBAMA enters from the left side of the stage. DONALD TRUMP strides in from the right. As both men turn to approach their podiums, BARACK leans forward and awkwardly sprints the final few feet, before frantically tapping the microphone to confirm that it hasn't yet been turned on. As production teams scramble to replace the device, DONALD TRUMP uses the opportunity to deride and spout racial epithets at his opponent. The volume of the crowd crescendos when he says, *"What a loser...would someone just shoot him?"*

I observe the pandemonium from the walkway at the base of an upper deck, stopping to make conversation with a firefighter who threatens to kill me.

"Man, I'm a firefighter too and I have a completely different point of view. Why do you believe what you believe?"

My question is left unanswered. We end our interaction at an impasse.

During an intermission, I feel quite worried a rogue anarchist group has made preparations to blow up the venue and kill everyone inside. I find a cluster of red 50-gallon drums and green 30-gallon garbage cans bound together with clear tape, like giant sticks of dynamite. A thick black, curly wire connects the barrels to a telephone booth nearby. I'm about to clip the wire with a pair of shears with the intent of diffusing the *"bomb,"* but hesitate when I discover it will disconnect the A/V used to deliver a *"sermon on patience"* and *"prayers of peace"* directed toward the incensed and vitriolic crowd.] //

⁂

TELEPHONE: #0273, #0342
PODIUM: #0422, #0573, #0792, #0944
SERMON: #0609, #1088

⁂

#1417 - **October 8, 2020 @ 05:44 (San Francisco, California)**

[1417.1 / 3849] [I voluntarily check into a prison to see how it operates. After passing by an armed guard, I turn left and walk down a long, downward sloping pathway, occasionally glancing left and seeing new intake receiving orientation *(while seated at a conference table)* before being subjected to strip search.

"I've come to visit at an improper time," I mutter to myself while noting I'm likely to miss my scheduled outbound train.

When I close my eyes, I'm shown a map to my aligned end-of-day destination. A large black "X" over a borough called "South Marin" is stamped at the end of a black dotted line that skirts the coast of California.

"Oh right, I forgot how the map changed after 'the big one.'" I continue in self-talk mode.

"REACHABLE ONLY BY TRAIN...NOT BY PLANE," a banner ad scrolls across the mental map.

I know *"South Marin"* is the prospective site for the *"new school,"* but I lack the resources and knowledge to physically travel there.

After walking around the facility, I ascend to the reception area. Employee desks are surrounded by small *"invisible prison"* clear plastic cubes to keep conversations and work product pristine. I take a seat at a desk next to a curvy Black woman, who I quickly learn is responsible for all, *"ins and outs."* She tells a female inmate, *"You will be discharged tonight at 9:00PM. It's currently 8:58AM."* The woman's boss enters seeking answers to questions in outstanding incident reports.

"Why was his throat slit?"

"How many rapes have occurred on your ward in the last month?"

"What can we do that will reduce the number of violent interactions on your ward?"

I don't hear her respond. I have a hearing impairment. She wears a mask that obscures her mouth. The nod of her head suggests she's willing to make the necessary changes to ensure inmate safety.

She's cordial when she eventually notices me typing at the adjacent desk. I become engrossed in my work, until I feel her grip my ponytail and ask, *"What are you doing here?"* When I don't answer she asks, *"How many inches of hair fall past my hand?"*

Telephones begin to ring incessantly and my work comes to a halt.]

[1417.2 / 3850] [I train for a race, and offer fellow participants a psychological performance hack.

"If you start slowly in a wide-open space, and gradually increase your pace as your surroundings narrow it'll feel like you're traveling near the speed of light *(if you complete your training route running through a tunnel).* ***Shrink the space around you. Your body will engage its 'all-natural afterburners.'"***]

[1417.3 / 3851] [I ride a BMX bike up a series of smooth, wave-like escalators that look like a steel-mesh-undulating-body of water while listening to a podcaster discuss his approach of, *"intentionally interviewing the most polarizing characters he can encounter to expand his fiefdom."*]
//

⁂

INCIDENT: #0336, #0602, #0903, #0909
HACK: #0033, ##0624, #0629, #1068
SMOOTH: #0426, #0449, #0534, #0652

⁂

#1418 - October 9, 2020 @ 05:44 (San Francisco, California)

[1418.1 / 3852] [I whisk down a wide, concrete, grey-scalloped slide. On the seemingly infinite descent I pass various cultural icons while waving and blowing them kisses as an acknowledgment of their creative contributions. The slide twists, turns, drops, and dips. It's quite fun. ***"My tummy tickles."***]

[1418.2 / 3853] [I discuss how to best reorganize furniture with five other roommates. We decide to put all the couches in the same room to create a lounge. The freed-up space in the main gathering area will be used to conduct house meetings.]

[1418.3 / 3854] [THE CONNECTOR helps her tenant navigate up and over a sidewalk curve in his wheelchair. The walkway that provides access to the property, at present, is **not** ADA compliant.]

[1418.4 / 3855] [I'm a grade school aged child. I walk with a group of peers through a door into a carpenter's workshop, where we stand in front of an object called, *"the magic desk."* I'm impressed by the beautiful mosaic pattern tools hanging, behind the desk.]

. . .

[1418.5 / 3856] [A young man in his twenties is down on his luck. He's out of money and is about to be evicted. He recently left the armed forces with an honorable discharge. His only assets are his combat fatigues and full-dress uniforms.

"You could get $10,000 for those you know," a friend suggests.

"I can't sell them," the young man replies after pausing for a moment of contemplation.]

[1418.6 / 3857] [My partner joins me in bed. We lay in bed together gently nuzzling and snuggling as we fall asleep.] //

⁂

Maj. = 4- THE CONNECTOR: #1421

INFINITE: #0373, #0398, #1078, #1083, #1085, #1193

MOSAIC: #0396, #0603, #0618, #1181, #1337

COMBAT: #0473, #0500, #0533, #0671, #0712

GENTLY: #0316, #0332, #0396, #0445, #0538

⁂

#1419 - October 10, 2020 @ 06:49 (San Francisco, California)

[1419.1 / 3858] [*"This is an evolutionary blueprint of the Psyche. This is the song of the Soul. Samely singeth the Spirit."*]

[1419.2 / 3859] [I sit at a conference table with THE C-SUITE and her husband discussing, *"the process of creativity."*]

[1419.3 / 3860] [I enter a deserted shopping mall. I pass a middle-aged man wearing a white kimono as he walks toward the only active store frontage *(a dojo)* at the far-left corner of the commercial lot.

"Just passing through," he says with a gentle bow, while keeping his hands together in prayer at his heart.

The door to my condo is at the opposite end of the property.]

[1419.4 / 3861] [THE AVENGER and I are roommates, and incommunicado. Both of us are engrossed in our phones.]

[1419.5 / 3862] [I'm confused when I enter my kitchen and see the contents of the blender replaced with chunks of pumpkin and papaya, prepped for an autumn soup. The smoothie I made must have been discarded, though I find no evidence to confirm my suspicion.]

[1419.6 / 3863] [It's completely dark. I'm in the throes of a sexual encounter, though I'm unable to discern who my intimate partner is.

"It's me."

"No, it's my lover."

I repeat these two phrases as I feel my hands migrate across different body parts shrouded by bed sheets. I'm unsure if I'm touching my erection. ***"Is that my bum?"*** I feel a swell of pressure near my root that suggests penetration is imminent and ecstasy is near.]

[1419.7 / 3864] [I'm momentarily confused when I enter a restaurant restroom with black-and-white checkered flooring. Three shallow steps lead guests up to a large open room with Turkish commodes positioned every few feet around the perimeter of the room, giving it a perforated look. ***"The room isn't filthy, though it's far from pristinely clean."***] //

⁂

PSYCHE: #0560, #0561, #0595
SOUL: #0010, #0045 #0493, #0894
SPIRIT: #0316, #0390, #0433, #0483, #0610
LOVER: #0422, #0558, #0585, #0763, #0856, #1057
THE C-SUITE: #1439

⁂

#1420 - October 11, 2020 @ 03:21 (San Francisco, California)

[1420.1 / 3865] [I take my seat at the community dining table inside GOUGH HOUSE. A group of men eat and make merry.

"Are you the new intake?" a gentleman new to me inquires.

"Yes."

"Which room will you occupy?"

"I can't disclose that just yet."

THE EPICUREAN sits directly across from me, and provides a brief history of the house, its intent, and legacy. After reciting the list of community norms in a song called: "Happy Habits of the People," the residents sound off and declare what they stand for.

"Health and wellbeing."

"Creative expression."

"Compassionate gossip."

I'm given a tour of the property from top-to-bottom through well curated rooms that feel like museum installations. Even elements that appear out of order have been intentionally placed as such. At the top, a series of bedrooms on the West facing side of the house overlook a private club where a few local names of notoriety, converse and rejuvenate.

As we move from the front-to-the-back of the floor, a doorway opens onto a terrace where we observe members of the public queue for their chance to *"jump in the lake."* A large body of water sits at the edge of the deck, though the patrons are focused on quickly dunking in a small two-person jacuzzi tub for a few seconds, before ceding the whirlpool to the next paying guest.

During my first trip across the well-lit basement, I pause to talk to a long brown-haired man. He wears a black porkpie hat and nods his head, while strumming a black polished Les Paul custom.

"You remind me so much of myself when I played bass for that one band," he says with a smile before sweetly excusing himself and gently closing the door. A moment later I hear a gunshot

and assume he's killed himself. Though experienced as brash and traumatic, this seems to be expected.

"Do you know what group he played for in the 60's?" THE EPICUREAN challenges me, in the company of two other housemates.

"Well, based on his tone of voice and description of how he slept, my guess would be THE VELVET UNDERGROUND."

"We've been trying to settle that debate for decades. You arrive and know the answer on the first day? That definitely indicates you belong here."

As we ascend to the main level, I peek into a smoking lounge where a few gentlemen discuss general updates to non-violent communication standards and practices.

The tour concludes and I'm left alone in the entryway.] //

⁂

TOP: #0285, #0293, #0312, #0313
MAIN: #0428, #0443, #0476, #0557
BOTTOM: #0277, #0285, #0324, #0344

⁂

⁂ 15.4 - THE FEAST OF ST. PETER: 1421-1442 ⁂

#1421 - October 11, 2020 @ 23:05 (San Francisco, California)

[1421.1 / 3866] [THE CARPENTER is a rear admiral in the Navy. He walks in front of me towards a podium to deliver remarks at a press conference. An electric sign affixed to his back at my eye level scrolls a phrase in red dot letters: **"EXPECTATIONS ARE A BLOCK."** He turns to me to ask a question before approaching the microphone. A smaller device on his belt loop scrolls: **"HALF CAPACITY."** He turns toward the mic, and taps it twice before addressing the corp. *"I'd like to remind you that America happens."*]

[1421.2 / 3867] [Suffragettes gather to discuss a shared desire to, *"upset the apple cart."* All turn their head in my direction and say in unison, *"Would you like to join?"*]

[1421.3 / 3868] [GRANDMA suggests I immediately remove all my clothing and place it in a black plastic garbage bag.]

[1421.4 / 3869] [THE CONNECTOR texts me, *"I can't believe you're going to leave."*
"I'm still here. I haven't gone anywhere."]

[1421.5 / 3870] [THE WEAVER scatters a box of broken, half-dollar-sized ceramic tiles on a shag carpet covered floor. Some pieces have been reduced to a fine glittering powder. THE LITTLE PRINCE crawls towards the dust. I scoop him up before the ceramic flecks cut his tender palms. The small box of tiles is THE WEAVER's last physical artifact she has to remind her of, *"what childhood was like on 'the farm.'"*] //

⁂

Maj. = 0- THE WEAVER, #1423, 1- THE CARPENTER: #1428,
11- GRANDMA: #1433, 12- THE LITTLE PRINCE: #1437
NAVY: #0315, #0370, #0435, #0479, #0648, #0945, #1190, #1282, #1383
APPLE: #0149, #0309, #0342, #0473, #0701, #0865, #0916
TENDER: #0083, #0379, #0392, #1080

⁂

#1422 - October 12, 2020 @ 00:42 (San Francisco, California)

[1422.1 / 3871] [THE KITKAT *(playful, open, and loving)* asks me if I've seen her specialty insulin pump. *"It's unique to me. N=1. No one else has a similar device. Find it. Please."*]

[1422.2 / 3872] [I stand in a dimly lit bedroom on the opposite side of a queen-sized bed from a woman who wears a zentai suit with a detailed design that illustrates the skeletal muscles of the body. For a moment I'm surprised, because she appears to have been flayed, though she's not bloody. She snaps her fingers to get my attention as she crawls across the bed, *"THE TIGER MOM appears to be having quite an adventure up in the mountains."*]

[1422.3 / 3873] [*"Well that's neighborly,"* I sarcastically say to a man who's taken my seat at a picnic table at a park, during the brief time I stepped away to use the restroom. He refuses to leave. My friends seated around the table say nothing. I crush a beer can in my hand and shake its stale remnants towards the man, lightly spraying him with stale beer spittle. He says nothing and remains seated. I chuck the beer can at him. It bounces off his head and lands in the grass to his left.] //

⁂

PICNIC: #0094, #0188, #0260, #0350, #0648, #0654, #0778, #0876
BEER: #0012, #0375, #0395, #0403, #0602, #0610, #0705, #0718
DETAILED: #0125, #0181, #0189, #0190, #0260, #0269
THE TIGER MOM: #1436

⁂

#1423 - October 12, 2020 @ 02:58 (San Francisco, California)

[1423.1 / 3874] [A blitz of campaign ads runs on television throughout the state of Kansas.]

[1423.2 / 3875] [I'm unjustly detained by Federal officers. They insist I have a gun. I've been mistaken for someone else who boards a flight.]

[1423.3 / 3876] [Children mix Kool-Aid powder in five-gallon jugs of water. They distribute 3oz portions in paper cups to passengers who want to quench their thirst before stepping aboard a plane. Their offering becomes so popular, the kids buy stock in the juice powder company.]

[1423.4 / 3877] [I walk through an airport on my way to the gate. I place a call to THE WEAVER who hurries me off the phone and requests I, *"call back later."* I pass a fast-food kiosk where patrons can purchase "grab-n-go" Big Macs and donuts for $9 each. I've checked a bag, have a roller board, and wear a backpack. I also carry a basket of red apples in my left hand, and a gallon of paint in the other. I leave both at the gate. Before I board, I remove a small plastic package filled with oily garlic covered salami. I eat a couple of pieces, decide it's spoiled, and throw it away. ***"Consuming would be the wrong choice before taking an international flight. Garlic makes me gassy."***]

[1423.5 / 3878] [I'm skidding on an icy track around a blue-ice mountain. I compete with other Russian speaking children in an *"ice block race."* My legs straddle a block of ice that I control with my feet. The wind roars. Much laughter surrounds me. The giggles and joy present among us bring me out of sleep.] //

⁂

FLIGHT: #0002, #0017, #0048, #0079, #0112, #0211, #0247, #0321, #0344
POWDER: #0009, #0035, #0070, #0076, #0189, #0203, #0229
STRADDLE: #0007, #0257, #0263, #0452, #0510

⁂

#1424 - October 12, 2020 @ 05:18 (San Francisco, California)

[1424.1 / 3879] [I'm in the eighth grade. I ski down a four-tier bunny hill, its gentle descent rolls easily toward a club house. Though I see the slushy path home, I call the family and tell them, ***"I feel lost."***]

[1424.2 / 3880] [In a blink, I'm in a hotel suite where a teenage friend's birthday party has just concluded. I missed the entire party. I give my friend a hug, and stay to help clean up.]

[1424.3 / 3881] [I'm briefly confused when I awaken and believe I'm about to miss a flight.
"Are we traveling together for the next bit?" I ask THE LAWYER.
"No. I'm staying put."
I hastily gather my things. I exit the house and open the door to a cab. As the car door clicks closed, I demand the driver, ***"Go fast. Please."***]

[1424.4 / 3882] [THE CHILD sits watching television. Another adult enters and turns the station to an *"art film"* channel, which the adult knows is code for *"sex movies."* After a brief moment I step forward and turn the TV off. I pick up a paint bucket and begin to whistle as I walk out. Multiple elderly couples slowly pack their bags for *"the big staycation"* and insist I don't enter their rooms until they've gone.] //

⁂

Maj. = 3- THE CHILD: #1437, 4- THE LAWYER: #1429
PARTY: #0009, #0023, #0025, #0045, #0083, #0115, #0120
FAST: #0026, #0037, #0044, #0065, #0080, #0089
ELDERLY: #0101, #0376, #0392, #0624, #0787

⁂

#1425 - October 12, 2020 @ 19:28 (San Francisco, California)

[1425.1 / 3883] [A set of stairs between me and THE KANGAROO dips in the shape of a "V." He sits on a stool in front of a bar beneath a buzzing rectangular pink/white neon sign, which shines so brightly the name of the establishment is obscured by light. He inspects fake IDs presented by a string of young people. After providing them with momentary hassle, he allows all of them admission.
"What are you really up to?" I say whilst traversing the stairs in his direction.
"Oh, I think you know," he coyly replies with a giggle as he tips backwards off the stool and tumbles through the butler door at right.
The door swings back and forth. I follow him through.

Once inside, I discover a mixed-use facility partitioned into three equally sized segments; public restroom stalls *(where couples of various genders and sexualities step in to create moments of intimacy)*, an emporium replete with midway games and a full bar, and a library with volumes of books lining floor-to-ceiling shelves made of dense cherry wood.

I pause at a urinal to pee. While in the act, a male attendant approaches me wanting to replace a soiled cloth hand-drying roll mounted in white anodized steel casing at my eye level. He's accustomed to performing the task while patrons relieve themselves, though I find the timing a bit odd and intrusive. He replaces the soiled roll with a spool of pristine cotton fabric and then faces me. He glances down at my genitals while I continue to urinate. He meets me eye-to-eye, bites his bottom lip, and motions as though he's about to fondle me, when another male attendant steps between us and hangs a small purple clear-plastic door hanger from the amorous attendant's nose that reads: **"OUT OF ORDER."**

I look to my right, and watch the silhouette of another man wash his face in a shallow tub of water, positioned in the ball receptacle of a midway basketball free-throw game. The water begins clear, but turns a pinkish beige tone after multiple droplets of blood infiltrate the contents of the basin. It's unclear if he nurses a wound, or a self-inflicted bloody nose.

THE KANGAROO flirtingly advances from behind and grabs my waist. His head cocks down. After a few heavy nostril exhales on the nape of my neck *(he holds the aggressive energy of a bull, or a dragon)*, he leans in to nibble my right ear lobe. The spark of sexual arousal shocks me before his mouth contacts my body, and startles me awake.] //

⁂

ADMISSION: #0021, #0810, #0817
EYE LEVEL: #0040, #0926, #0933, #1322
DRAGON: #0281
AROUSAL: #0059, #0322

⁂

#1426 - October 12, 2020 @ 22:41 (San Francisco, California)

[1426.1 / 3884] [I book a one-hour appointment at a fitness center. Once I've selected the time, I'm unable to change it without putting my membership in jeopardy. The company has a *"one strike"* rule. On the first attempt to change a reservation, *"a client's membership is frozen without recourse, until such time the management deems it appropriate to allow access to the platform."* I'm befuddled, and decide to go run in the park.]

[1426.2 / 3885] [I queue with friends out front of a restaurant ,for its soft opening under new management. A host confirms our reservation, allows us to pass by the maroon velvet rope, and enter the establishment. We're guided to a back patio which has been renovated with tiered snugs that slowly advance up shallow and wide steps. Seven levels of seating are available. The charcoal grey painted woodwork is offset by an intense line of white-light-beams that denote where a *"step up"* occurs. No other lighting sources are present outside *(except for the full moon overhead)*. Banana Trees and Japanese Maple Trees are among the greenery planted to accentuate the transcendent fecundity of the patio.

Once seated, I walk back to the host station to request a book of matches. THE ACTOR and SCARLETT JOHANSSON confirm their reservation as I approach the podium. THE ACTOR looks debonair in a grey suit and fedora, with a single small green feather on the right-hand side of the hat's band. SCARLET hiccups and woozily smiles, seemingly intoxicated, but doesn't say anything. She winks at me. I look at him. He doesn't recognize me.

"The beer. It's something. It'll do that to you," he says quietly as we turn and walk together back toward the patio.

A full-figured bride and her attendants walk down the patio staircase from the top tier in our direction. THE ACTOR and SCARLET stop on the third tier, and take the table to the right. SCARLET stumbles as she takes a seat and lets out a giggle, nearly pulling the white linen and table settings on to the floor. THE ACTOR shrugs his shoulders as if to say, *"I signed up for this. It's cool."*

I feel compelled to follow the bride and turn around, walking all the way back to the host station. I never see her, but I can feel her in the building. Once back at the front, the line of patrons has grown ever longer. My suit has turned into a server's tuxedo. The chef plates a piping hot steak from a grill to the delighted *"oohs and ahhs"* of those who have, *"waited months for a taste."* To assist with the demonstration, I grab a corner of the steak between my thumb and index finger and peel back a thin film the chef describes as the, *"seasoned skin of the fatted calf."*

No longer a guest, but part of the team, I return to my service station on the patio. A glance up and to the right finds THE ACTOR tucking SCARLET into bed *(tables transform into sleeping arrangements, post meal)*. My friends revel above, unaware of my absence, and have a marvelous evening experience under the soft healing white light of the moon.] //

⁂

STRIKE: #0029, #0035, #0140, #0151, #0215, #0249, #0277, #0360
BANANA: #0054, #0183, #0428, #0822, #1023, #1056, #1135
SEVEN: #0014, #0026, #0033, #0105, #0378, #0757, #0791
GUEST: #0015, #0017, #0021, #0045, #0127, #0189

⁂

#1427 - October 13, 2020 @ 04:37 (San Francisco, California)

[1427.1 / 3886] [I awaken in a large Victorian home, which I share with four other male roommates of similar age. Based on the tone of conversation among the group I discern we're all aspiring stand-up comedians and want to transform half of our living space into a public performance venue to better hone our craft.

I actively listen to the debate, while munching on multi-colored segments of bell pepper from a medium sized orange plastic bowl. I use a pair of black chopsticks to flick through the bowl and stab a bite sized portion of yellow pepper.

"You're being too quiet. What do you think?" I'm asked by one of the men.

"I used to be rich. Now I'm wealthy. It's fun to start over," I say with a partially full mouth of veg.

They collectively roll their eyes, seemingly annoyed by what must be my typical non sequitur response to their questions.

In the next few moments, they hire a general contractor, a carpenter, and a bouncer. One roommate with a short-trimmed beard emerges as the lead, and walks the three new hires around the property.

"You're responsible for covering this half of the bar. We'll handle the rest before my set later," he requests before leaving the men to build a stage, and stock the walk-ins with cold beverages.

A sign over the front door in large block letters reads:

"HOUSE RULES: COVER IT. TOUCH IT. PLUG IT."

A tone of nervousness emerges between the five of us, as we discuss how to navigate the transition of our home, *"to a public club, and back to a refuge."* After a few rounds of brainstorming, we decide it's most productive for us to have sex with each other to create a shared connection, before tonight's performances.

THE SOUTHERN GENTLEMAN emerges as one of the four roommates, wearing a backwards ballcap and denim shorts. He smiles, and my mouth falls open like a fish.

"You're a 'new agey' type. Will you tickle my...whatever chakra this is?" he says as he turns and points at his butt.

I nod.

"Cover it."

"So, you know, some would call that your root," I say while dropping my trousers.

"Plug it."

As we lunge towards each other, I wake up.] //

⁂

CHOPSTICKS: #0775
CONNECTION: #0012, #0048, #0059
COVER: #0024, #0037, #0162, #0188, #0281
TOUCH: #0021, #0022, #0031
PLUG: #0359, #0608, #0962

⁂

#1428 - October 13, 2020 @ 05:53 (San Francisco, California)

[1428.1 / 3887] [*"Did you vote 'YES' on ballot prop 112?"* THE CARPENTER asks.

"Yes."

"It means something that you'll take a stand for children's literacy."

He and I stand outside on a lawn, but turn to look at a screen that hovers in the air a few feet away. NANCY PELOSI discusses the need for, *"increased spending, and the benefits of 'Prop 112,'"* at a news conference. After taking questions, she encourages the public to donate and vote. Both actions can be accomplished via text message.

THE CARPENTER is satisfied the initiative will carry with public support, but I know the funds allocated will go towards demolishing libraries to make space for luxury condo projects.]

[1428.2 / 3888] [I run full speed on a sidewalk that follows a highway overpass. Thoughts of the election race as I attempt to leave the still lingering hover-screen behind. I take a right turn on to a banked curve that spills into an empty grocery store parking lot. As I decelerate, the store transforms into a roadside motel.

Upon approach I meet a hillbilly husband and wife, who self-identify as, *"proprietors of the motel."* The wife is much physically larger than the husband. The two front teeth on both her top and the bottom jaws are missing, giving her a hissing lisp as she greets me. The husband distributes hand towels to guests who play tennis matches on invisible courts, spaced at equal intervals across the large vacant parking lot.

"Mah huzzbun and I had err bleedwork durn sisss yerrrs agrrr. I dunneed eh-nee pruf illnessiz er all a hoe-kss" the wife declares as she shows me to a room.

"I promise it's real. My entire family was in the hospital with that 'thing' from the news for a month."

She remains skeptical. The husband overhears and begins to reflect on, *"why he believes what he believes."*]

[1428.3 / 3889] [In a blink, I'm in an empty room. THE DRUMMER appears to my right.

"Both the ADA and childhood literacy props were things I argued for ten years ago. They finally have some public support."

"Has it really taken that long to turn the tide?"

"Remember the news coverage of 'Bradley's Bill' and 'Matt's Prop?' Those were both things I stood for on the statehouse floor. You can watch them all online."

As he reaches for his phone to search for an internet video, I wake up.] //

⁂

Maj. = 1- THE CARPENTER: #1433
NANCY PELOSI: #0907, #0944, #1345
LITERACY: #0902
PROP 112: #1433
VOTE: #0054, #0127, #0520, #0748
VACANT: #0060, #0140, #0142, #0769, #0803

⁂

#1429 - October 13, 2020 @ 20:52 (San Francisco, California)

[1429.1 / 3890] [I'm handed a deck of playing cards, each carrying the visage of a different venomous snake. A warning card included with the deck encourages players to: **"AVOID GETTING BITTEN!"** I deal the entire deck out face up on a table. Upon closer inspection the cards appear to be portals to different dimensions. The snakes are the gatekeepers to these alternative realms; each with its own lethal charm and tactic. A man appears over my shoulder and informs me, *"The albino cobra is the most prized of all. It's incredibly valuable,"* as he points at the card straight down from my chin. The snake snaps at his finger and misses. The serpent's jaw dislodges and folds backwards on itself, inversely swallowing its entire body.]

[1429.2 / 3891] [I'm alone in a completely dark space. A small glowing rectangular screen hovers a few feet from my face flashing gruesome images of death, war, famine and pestilence each in rapid succession. The pace quickens to such an extent, that the images blur and hum in a ball of carnival-glass light. I hold a tone of soft white and gold light with my right palm outstretched, which I offer as a healing to, *"the woundedness of the world."* My hands age and wither, then reconstitute faster than I can count, suggesting that I've offered healing without interruption for many lifetimes. The source is constant. I remain focused.

"In between the two resides an experience of 'the infinite.'"]

. . .

[1429.3 / 3892] [Upon a brilliant white background, a bat transforms into a pelican. The pelican turns into a frog. A pond full of cattails emerges. The frog jumps in the water with a *"bloop,"* as small waves ripple outward in concentric rings.]

[1429.4 / 3893] [THE ARCHITECT and THE DESIGNER invite me to Thanksgiving dinner at their home in wine country.

"THE LAWYER and I are having one last hurrah before I set off on my next adventure. I do hope you'll consider me for the next soiree?" I ask while politely declining.]

[1429.5 / 3894] [Snarling dogs gnash their teeth.]

[1429.6 / 3895] [Upon a jet-black background, the white wireframe of a gecko *(composed of thousands of tiny triangles)* scrambles from the top to the bottom of my field of vision in a serpentine pattern.]

[1429.7 / 3896] [I plot daily road trip destinations on a holographic map of the United States. The challenge of the journey is, *"to only venture through states I've never experienced."* State borders appear to dynamically shift. A constellation of soft white orbs instantly recalibrates each time a border changes, offering a unique series of portals that will allow me to accomplish my goal.]

[1429.8 / 3897] [I hover above a deep purple and obsidian step pyramid, rooted in the center of a spacious black globe. My perspective rotates 360 degrees as I fly over the top. Bolts of electricity erupt like prominences from a large glowing sphere of violet-white light at the top of the pyramid. I marvel at the structure and the abstraction as a low voice booms,

"THE DEVIL WAITS IF YOU PRAY." I'm hurled backwards and tumble head-over-heels for eons through a void.]

[1429.9 / 3898] [I awaken in bed, clutched at the neck by a shadowy figure.

"Perhaps it's the Grim Reaper?"

I'm raised high enough that my feet do not touch the floor. The back side of my body is then repeatedly slammed against my gold-plated wall as the being recites a mantra:

"THIS. IS. WHAT. OPPRESSION. FEELS. LIKE."

The thud of my concussed brain, and crack of my skull rouse me from dreaming.] //

⁂

Maj. = 5= THE LAWYER: #1438
Min. = ♥- THE ARCHITECT: #1432
GRIM REAPER: #0535
HEALING: #0019, #0037

DEVIL: #0875
BRAIN: #0024
⁂

#1430 - October 14, 2020 @ 00:47 (San Francisco, California)
**Hyperreal social scene. Seemed so real it was all nearly forgotten. **

[1430.1 / 3899] [It's night. I'm in a familiar black soundstage-like void. I look at my phone and read an impromptu email from THE MAGICIAN, who's invited me at the last moment to join him as an, *"adjunct professor of ecstatic/cathartic technology."* I type, ***"Yes"*** and when I click *"send"* I'm pulled through a portal generated by the device, and land in a bustling scene where young collegiates register for classes.

I'm unsure what the course curriculum will entail. The hesitation and trepidation suggest THE MAGICIAN is expecting to, *"launch me far beyond known spheres of awareness."*

"I'm happily terrified."

In a blink I'm in line at the Registrar's office behind a group of young women wearing face coverings which read:

"I'M NOT IGNORANT. WE'RE MORE RESILIENT. WE'LL SPREAD IT."

When I arrive at the front of the line, a woman behind a plexiglass shield passes me a hold harmless waiver which declares: *"The undersigned is a change agent, aware of transformational power they may wield on culture and civilization, and are so charged with radical responsibility to know when use of such force is warranted. Misappropriated use or unkind applications of power vested herein, subjects the neophyte to all levels of ethical consequences inherent to (and stemming from) their individual choice making across this and all lifetimes."*

I exit the building and hear a group of students challenge a young woman to stay awake between, *"here and her dormitory."* If she falls asleep, she'll walk off the edge of campus and plummet into an unrecoverable abyss. She accepts the challenge and clasps a pair of brown-bag-wrapped text books at her chest, as she begins her journey down a long diagonal sidewalk towards a residential quad.

I go in the opposite direction. Everything around me turns black *(though I can still see my body).*

"Perhaps I'm the young challenge-accepting woman? Did I leave my body?"

"TIMBER!!!!" A male voice yells as I look up and to the left.

The white venous branches of a large dead tree fall towards me. I quickly back away and out of the path of danger. A group of campus utility employees groom the grounds for the start of the academic year, chopping down trees that each seem to fall in a path where I stand.

"Hey team, a little warning next time would be useful," I say while removing a beveled wooden table leg and a chainsaw from my backpack. I use the table leg to crudely measure carriable lengths of tree trunk *(based on my body strength)* then slog through a number of tree stumps. I leave the lawn empty of stray branches. My chainsaw work is stacked in neat pyramids of 10 logs, easy for their eventual removal and disposal.

I put my tools back in my backpack and walk to a cottage, home to the most popular biergarten on campus. I open the white picket fence, and walk up a series of white switchback staircases to a loft where THE WORLDBRIDGER bartends. His specialty tonight is Hofbräuhaus on draught *(or by the pony keg).* He slides me a scalloped glass one-liter mug full of brew.

"1.5 is my limit before my ethics slide," I admit while looking down at the contents. What begins as beer, shifts to clear carbonated water. The water then becomes still, then reconstitutes as beer.

"It has its observable properties, but those are only as impactful as you make them. Hold the room at a tone of 'diamond rainbow' before you go. Students will opt in when they're willing and able," THE WORLDBRIDGER reminds me.

I walk down the stairs and clink mugs with a tall female Asian student. We both swig and smile as we look around at the white-shaker-patterned lattice that lines the railings and outdoor staircases of the cottage.

"Accepting THE MAGICIAN'S invitation to come here was a good suggestion. Thank you."] //

⁂

OPPOSITE: #0004, #0006, #0009, #0010, #0012, #0027, #0034
BEER: #0940, #1194, #1246, #1301, #1335
DIAMOND: #0170, #0271, #0390, #0431, #0467, #0561, #0572, #0585, #0763

⁂

#1431 - October 14, 2020 @ 03:27 (San Francisco, California)

[1431.1 / 3900] [*"Is the email address on your profile current?"* A landscape architect asks.
"No. Please just use my Gmail addy to communicate with me from here on out."

[1431.2 / 3901] [**Expressions of panic and fear.* *I'm at home awaiting the return of my housemate, THE RECONCILIATOR. My blood runs cold as ice when I hear the front door click open and slowly creak. I race down the entryway and hear a ravenous demonic energy consolidating its power just outside the house. The door begins to swing open as I hurl the full mass of my body toward it at full speed. A hellish chaotic sound erupts, as I force the door to close. Everything immediately falls silent. Drawing short hyper-ventilatory breaths, I look through the peephole. No one's there. All is calm out front. As I take a half step away from the door it flies open and I press it closed once more, with the strength of my legs and the backside of my body. I let out a singular fearful yelp, then place my right hand over my mouth. My left hand places a short piece of surgical tape across my lips to, ***"ensure I will not break noble silence again."***] //

⁂

Min. = ♥- THE RECONCILIATOR #1438
BLOOD: #0021, #0035, #0081, #0145, #0172, #0293, #0518, #0701, #0723
EVERYTHING: #0014, #0027, #0074, #0107, #0128, #0144, #0212
DRAWING: #0163, #0621, #0641, #1144, #1274, #1296
SILENCE: #0117, #0406, #0450, #0600, #0678

⁂

#1432 - October 14, 2020 @ 04:35 (San Francisco, California)

[1432.1 / 3902] [The postman delivers me a package sent by THE ARCHITECT. I tear the brown paper wrapper and inspect three packages of A-Frame T-shirts with a note attached that reads, *"These will hug your body the way I want to."* On the back of the grey set of shirts *(between the black set and the white set)* he's affixed a Polaroid photo of a young muscular man, leaning on a couch and winking at me over his right shoulder. He wears but a white jock strap and happily flaunts his round hairless bubble butt. The ARCHITECT has scribbled, *"I'll share,"* on the bottom of the Polaroid.

I'm pulled into the photograph and stand by THE ARCHITECT as we both salivate over the piece of man-meat splayed out before us on the couch. The young man is quite opinionated, mouthy, and a bit bossy.

"Uh...you guys...you always decide you wanna FUCK at the WRONG time of night," he says looking at his phone, as I suspend his ankles between a pair of stirrups. With him seated upright I walk between his legs, drop my pants, and enter him. He drops his phone. His eyes roll back in his head. I pull out for a moment. In a daze of blissful stupor, he looks at me and requests a guttural, *"Moooorrrre,"* to which I happily acquiesce. After our third shared orgasm he transforms into a Black woman, to whom I am equally attracted.]

[1432.2 / 3903] [A woman takes a seat in front of a microphone to commentate a professional football game. As she makes her first call live on air, I walk to the windows of my corporate skybox at the stadium and close the blinds, ***"so my team can get down to business."***]

[1432.3 / 3904] [An immigrant paddles a self-made pontoon boat around the perimeter of the Roman Colosseum, readied for naumachiae. After completing a lap, he briefly docks a few feet from where I stand and declares himself a *"water devil."* I take a glass bottle of apple juice set beside him on the floor of the boat. The neck of the bottle is absurdly long *(greater than 60 inches)*. I remove the cap and shake it like a salt shaker over the immigrant's mouth. Small droplets of amber-toned liquid splatter on the immigrant's cheeks, brow, and upper lip leaving him with a face full of dripping, watery freckles.]

[1432.4 / 3905] [THE ROMANTIC accepts a cabinet position with the incoming executive administration.

"I thought after doing all that work to get him elected I'd be able to sit back and let the money roll in for a while."

I chase him around an office without a roof. Sun shines down from above.]

[1432.5 / 3906] [**MANTRA:** *"You choose every quality present in your experience. You choose the quantity too."*]

⁂

MANTRA: #0423, #0509, #0649, #0684, #0934, #1414
ROMAN COLOSSEUM: #0172
WINKING: #0254, #0318, #0443

⁂

⁂
⁂

#1433 - October 15, 2020 @ 00:27 (San Francisco, California)

[1433.1 / 3907] [Adult human-sized puppets sing a childlike song: *"Ev-ry tiiiii-me you blink. You taaaa-ke a stehh-p a-way."*]

[1433.2 / 3908] [THE CARPENTER and I watch old films at a drive-in theater while sitting on the hood of his car. We're the only people on site. He rifles through a cardboard box by the side of the car searching for a particular newsreel from when he was in high school.

"Found it! Let's watch it. You'll see nothing changes!" he proudly exclaims, holding the palm-sized object between his thumb and forefinger.

He threads the film into the projector and sets it in motion. After a few clicks, a grainy color film from the 1970's begins to play, showing a row of cars filled with teens forced to leave the school football stadium moments before the big game was scheduled to begin. The stadium closure resulted from a gubernatorial mandate that compelled all residents to declare a preference on *"Prop 112." **"Most are in favor of repealing the law."***]

[1433.3 / 3909] [I wake up believing it's Sunday morning. It's cloudy. I walk across the city intending to serve as a substitute for a fitness instructor friend, who has a family issue to attend to. I arrive at the fitness center and am surprised to see my friend testing his head microphone and ready to begin. I ask him to step outside the classroom, *(moderately annoyed that I made the trip if he didn't need me to).*

"You're here really early," he says lightly.

The clock reads 7:58pm. ***"I'm a full twelve hours early."***]

[1433.4 / 3910] [I sit in a plush orange LA-Z-BOY and turn on the television. In a blink, GRANDMA and GRANDPA appear in chairs on either side of me. I want to share the absurdity of my day, but GRANDPA gently *"shh's"* me and grabs the remote control.

"Turn on the show you wanted him to see, Dad," GRANDMA says to GRANDPA.

With a single click, the antique-rabbit-ears-television displays an image of a pistachio green and white '57 Chevy in a mid-air backwards flip. The camera keeps the vehicle in the center of the frame as it makes contact with a concrete track filled with banked turns and loop-d-loops. I understand the heavy steel car transforms into a child's toy when it's no longer airborne, but looks exactly the same *(though the scale of the object may have dramatically changed).* We watch the car run the track until GREAT GRANDMA appears to the right of the television.

"Well, that's all I've got for you today...have a good night," GREAT GRANDMOTHER says with a wave as she switches off the light.

GRANDMA switches off the TV. She and GRANDPA both stand and walk across the family room to their separate bedrooms. GRANDMA's room is to the left. GRANDPA takes the room to the right.] //

⁂

PUPPETS: #0023, #0033, #0040, #0597, #1254, #1257
STADIUM: #0259, #0872, #1277
LA-Z-BOY: #0001, #0441

PISTACHIO: #0090, #0159, #0350, #0472, #0511, #0545, #1180
'57 CHEVY; #0995

⁂

#1434 - October 15, 2020 @ 02:38 (San Francisco, California)

[1434.1 / 3911] [**Most detail instantly fades** I've lent a custom hand-crafted "Shit Box" to a neighbor. The device is roughly the size of a lobster cage and fashioned from heavy wood. Best I can tell it's a preliminary incarnation of a toilet seat, reserved only for the noble class. The device is "**mine.**" The neighbor wants to sign a contract for purchase after I've installed it over their basement privy. Something feels out of alignment with the exchange, so I uninstall the device, carry it up the stairs, and out of the home.]

[1434.2 / 3912] [I'm seated on a throne made of snow near the back door of a white-walled mountain cabin. Tree limbs sag under the weight of their ice casings. It's likely midday, though the overcast sky presents me with inconclusive natural cues. I playfully shift into a snow leopard, and then to a white lion while perched and waiting for THE DANCER to arrive. Only my pupils remain visible to the trained eye. The rest appears invisible against the snowy backdrop. My need to urinate is strong, though I resist. I know if I leave the snow throne and pee in the woods, the yellow spot will nullify my *body-of-glass* camouflage. I stay where I am. Oddly, the down-and-out pressure in my bladder keeps me present to danger nearby in the woods.

When I see THE DANCER trudge up the stone path behind the house, I return to my human form. She and I get into a white 4x4 truck. She's in the driver's seat. I'm the passenger. Before she turns the key, she shows me a collection of three compact discs given to her at the end of her most recent visit with *"the uncle."* She's quick to point out a series of three icons on the back of the CDs, that appear to be an encoded message. They could be interlocking alien characters...runes...I'm not certain, but the odd puzzle pieces hold the tone of *"true creativity."*

"Let's go to Taco Bell," she says as she drops the CD's in my lap and fires up the ignition. We drive off the snowy property onto a futuristic highway, where vehicles whizz by in short rectangular segments of various colored lights.]

[1434.3 / 3913] [I walk from the far end of a cobblestone promenade in the direction of a basilica. I don't know if it's a cathedral or a municipal building. Waves of pigeons take flight as I stride with purpose toward the urban center. I stop at my favorite family bakery *(which has been in business for the last 400 years),* surprised to **not see** apple tarts and pain au chocolat resting in the window.

I lean through a window and see the bakery replaced with a courtyard cafe on one half, and a dusty out-of-business furniture upholstery restoration shop on the other; the latter covered in dust. Business is booming in the cafe. All the tables are full. The baker now plays the role of head server and expediter at the cafe. A new hire places an order in a paper bag and drops it on the floor next to a male/female couple seated at the table who hold hands and soul gaze.

"Soup goes with that. Don't forget!" the baker-turned-expediter shouts to the young server.]

. . .

[1434.4 / 3914] [I walk through an empty mall food court. Young people dressed like soda jerks are so eager to work, they take orders and prepare meals for one another simply for the practice. After they've exhausted their entire pay checks on meals they can't possibly eat, they contemplate opening up their own sandwich shop.

I continue through the mall, pausing briefly at a doorway to put on a face covering after a man makes me aware I'm *"naked"* by offering a simple hand gesture that sweeps across his face. I pull the swath of black fabric from my right pocket, and place it over my nose and mouth before proceeding through a more densely populated area.

I stop at a kiosk to purchase a pair of movie tickets. One they've printed and I've paid, I place them in my pocket, and walk back the way I came. I pass through the glass doors in the opposite direction and am startled to find SHIRLEY MACCLAINE and a friend seated at a small round table near the door. I continue on my way until I feel the need to stop dead in my tracks. I pull the pair of movie tickets from my pocket and see SHIRLEY's name printed along the bottom of both. Confused that I may have stolen her property, I return to the table and interrupt the women in conversation.

"Hi SHIRLEY! It's been a while. And to your friend, I'm sorry I don't recognize you but I know you're similarly accomplished. I believe these belong to you," I say passing her the tickets.

She remains silent for a moment, then she smiles. Without speaking she reaches in her purse and pulls out another pair of tickets. She stacks all four together and hands them back to me. She and her friend stand up to leave the table. SHIRLEY morphs into CAROL BURNETT. She tugs on her ear and smiles as she walks by, whispering in my ear, *"Tell your mother I say hello."*] //

⁂

LION: #0267, #1134, #1291
PROMENADE: #0032, #0045, #0084, #0408, #0777, #0879
MOVIE: #0016, #0149, #0183, #0334, #0581, #0597
HELLO: #0820, #0937, #0972, #1073, #1168, #1236
SOUL GAZE: #0075

⁂

#1435 - October 15, 2020 @ 04:23 (San Francisco, California)

[1435.1 / 3915] [I enter a cafeteria where clusters of elderly people eat fast food on brown plastic trays. Most seem to have a small pile of McDonalds hamburgers, generally half eaten. I carry my tray of food, pausing briefly at a garbage can to scrape most of the tray's contents into the bin. A scant smattering of cooling French fries and a still-wrapped breakfast sandwich remain as I nosh and take a seat at the table. The cafeteria doubles as a voting center inside a church. The elderly sit in silence as they eat and fill in their ballots.

I quickly complete my ballot and seal it in an envelope, realizing that I've forgotten to log a vote on two federal amendments to the constitution, printed on the back of the fourth page. I'm not able to acquire another ballot, though I want to make sure I voice a grievance. I approach a velvet rope that divides the voting center from the exterior of the building. Beyond the rope sits a group of old people wearing masks and making conversation. NANCY PELOSI walks up to me and grabs my ballot envelope.

"I know what you're doing and you won't get away with it," NANCY says insinuating I'm onsite to pull a prank, or to drum up some sort of mischief.

I glance up and to the right to see a large round clock ticking away the final seconds before midnight, at which time the voting center will close.

A morbidly obese man with a long frizzy grey beard walks in the doorway beneath the clock and raises a black-and-white version of the state flag of Ohio on a pole. Oddly, a single stripe in the flag is crimson red.

"These just arrived today. We don't have the budget to send them where they need to go," the man says as we look up at the flag flapping.]

[1435.2 / 3916] [I ride in a single car on an absurdly long steel roller coaster track, that spreads across a technicolor animated series of emerald green hills with dancing trees and flowers, which celebrate a bright sunny day. The calming voice of a confidant young man narrates as I crest multiple hills, and bank up and around tight turns. Different segments of the track are painted in brilliant saturated solid tones. Corkscrew turns are red. Descents orange. Ascents yellow. Loops green. Banked turns powder blue, and so on. The young man's cues help me to reposition my body in the car to avoid whiplash. I find myself whistling the melodies to different MICHAEL JACKSON pop songs as the ride comes to a stop in a dusty red barn. I believe creating a theme for the ride with the music would be a *"blockbuster attraction"*, and contemplate how to best contact his estate to discuss a licensing deal, as I wait for a ride attendant to loosen my restraints.

A group gathers outside the barn, eager to take the ride. A large framed White woman, likely in her 70's enters the barn using a cane to steady herself. A posse of grade school aged children flood in around her, begging her to, *"let them ride."* As she looks up at me, I can see her wearing black sunglasses. Her face is tattooed, the center of a spiderweb expands out in all directions from the center of her chin giving her a venous, vascular visage.

"You have to go all the way over there to take the ride," I say motioning to my point of origin *(which could be tens of miles away from the barn.)*] //

⁂

McDONALDS: #0148, #0469, #0915, #1334
OHIO: #0339, #0815, #0874
FLOWERS: #0079, #0170, #0189, #0365
WHIPLASH: #0010
OBESE: #0012, #0249, #0547, #0561, #1249

⁂

#1436 - October 15, 2020 @ 22:58 (San Francisco, California)

[1436.1 / 3917] [I'm an executive consultant for a health and fitness start up. I attend an evening board meeting in a dodecagonal room, where most participants attend via video conference. Their faces are presented life-sized on small translucent screens that hover at eye level, creating a sense of interconnectedness. At various conflicted moments during the meeting, select screens begin to glow a peach/tan tone and the edges soften and diffuse from rectangles into amorphous ephemeral shapes. The definition in the faces of the participants on these screens degrades from smooth-skinned human beings, to lower-resolution-polygon-wireframes of *"rubber faced androids."* Once a participant's facial features degrade to an extent that could be evaluated as, *"two orders of magnitude less precise than a believable human face"* the participant is shot in the head by a sniper. No killing physically occurs in the boardroom, but the murders are witnessed by all those in attendance.

The executive team continues with an audit of their forthcoming online content. One half of the team observes, as the other pushes themselves to their anaerobic threshold through forced repetitive exercise *(and excessive use of weights).* As members lag the group, their facial definition degrades, and they're similarly assassinated. The source of the murders is unclear, but I become aware, ***"I've been enrolled as a target if I'm unable to hold pace with the group. Are the killers our competitors?"*** I'm not sure.

The meeting concludes, and I descend a smooth-spiraling escalator to a ground floor. As I exit through clear glass doors onto a dark street, a trench coat wearing security guard offers me an ominous, *"Goodbye."* I ignore him and continue on my way. A few paces further away I hear him shout, *"I'll see you later."*

The next day at dusk I meet my business partner, THE TIGER MOM, at our office. We debrief our prior day's experiences while rifling through and auditing different fitness apparatus suppliers have provided for our potential endorsement. We could be influencers. We could be prominent television personalities. We present a face that people trust as, *"informed and legitimate for things labeled 'good, true, and beautiful.'"* An item provided for consideration is a clear-gel device that looks like a 3D "H" suspended in a cube, intended to provide support to vertebrae, after medical interventions. I place it at different positions on my spinal column and back ribs while keeping in lockstep convo with my partner.

Our meeting adjourns with a pair of head nods. THE TIGER MOM and I walk to the unisex bathroom at the far end of our conference room. We give each other high fives as we disrobe, then proceed through different doors to our own private shower stalls. While bathing, she makes a comment that suggests we're sniper targets. I'm concerned when I see my fingers turn into long smooth cubes.]

[1436.2 / 3918] [DAVE CHAPPELLE and I get word from our agent that we've been booked together for a pair of shows at a small downtown club. He and I sit among a ring of other comedians around a campfire. Joyful at the prospect of playing new material together he jumps up, lights a joint, and puffs it as he walks to my side of the campfire.

"My nigga, let's make this shit a night to remember. Beeeyatch!"

I'm not certain of my race or gender. The group breaks out in laughter. I infer it's my job to find magic mushrooms for the crew, though I don't know who to ask, nor where to look for them. As I start to search, I encounter a young woman in the circle who seems to be losing her mind, though she assures me she, *"can point me in the direction of what I seek."*] //

⁂

SMOOTH: #0005, #0167, #0189, #0194, #0253
MAGIC: #0061, #0070, #0245, #0271, #0485, #0646
MUSHROOM: #0688, #1132
THE TIGER MOM: #1437

⁂

#1437 - October 16, 2020 @ 02:05 (San Francisco, California)

[1437.1 / 3919] [I awaken in a scene where I interact with a community of animated characters from FUTURAMA, TOONTOWN, and SOUTHPARK, who scurry about taking

Polaroids of one another in order, *"to erase themselves from reality."* If captured on film, they cease to exist and evaporate *(similar to characters disappearing from photographs in "Back to the Future").* The vibe is playful and funny. No character seems too concerned by the threat of *"being erased."*]

[1437.2 / 3920] [THE CONFIDANT and I repeatedly pass each other on a loop, at a city street corner on a gray afternoon.

"Did you bring that birthday gift you teased me with all those months back?"

"Gah...I left it at home again. I'm sorry but I've gotta keep some distance," he says, advancing the conversation, though we never seem to get to where we're going.

"I could care less about the gift. I miss the high fives and hugs we used to share before "the thing" happened to our city."]

[1437.3 / 3921] [*"Hey come move your body with us at 1:00pm!"* THE TIGER MOM suggests from her perch atop a circular stage, that fleets gently up roughly six feet over ten shallow mirrored steps on concentric circular platforms. *"Class includes a per diem for lunch,"* she offers as a sweetener.

I politely decline and tell her, ***"I'm scheduled to teach at 6:00pm and plan on eating with my students afterward."***]

[1437.4 / 3922] [An African American woman in a sparkling-red evening gown confidently strides down a catwalk under a beam of light, which prominently displays her ironic-forehead-all-caps-tattoo which reads: **"SUBJECT TO NO ONE."**]

[1437.5 / 3923] [A massive vat of silver-clad coins is pressure washed by streams of superheated water. They pass on a conveyor belt to cool before they're wrapped in paper tubes and shuttled by armor car to banks around town, before eventually being recirculated with the public.]

[1437.6 / 3924] [Still blackness surrounds me, though my body remains illuminated with a soft glow. I crouch to look at a single green sprout planted in a small terracotta cube. As I meditate on the new vulnerable little expression of **powerful life-force,** a voice breathily whispers on the back of my neck, *"Use your body to run all the experiments you want. I'll let you know when they get out of control."*]

[1437.7 / 3925] [I look at the black steel ring worn on my left hand. A tiny bead of white light blinks thrice in rapid succession, which I take as an indication it's been *"overcharged."* I remove it from my finger and place it on its charging stand to confirm. I'm perplexed when the device suggests it now has, *"less than 25% of its battery life remaining."*]

. . .

[1437.8 / 3926] [THE CHILD and THE LITTLE PRINCE sit together in a small circle of gold light in an otherwise still black abyss. They play together without interruption or intrusion. She teaches him *"strength."* He teaches her *"tenderness."*] //

⁂

POLAROID: #0044, #0132, #0266, #0610, #0681, #0786
STRENGTH: #0010, #0850, #1129, #1131, #1154, #1278, #1389
TENDERNESS: #0953

⁂

#1438 - October 16, 2020 @ 03:52 (San Francisco, California)

[1438.1 / 3927] [I help THE LAWYER declutter his flat. I climb up a step ladder to remove some plants from a ledge to dust, and discover a relic from his bohemian days laying inconspicuously flat in a small, simple, black frame beneath one of the ferns planted in a terracotta pot. As I fan the glass with my feather duster, then breathe on it to help clear the dinge, I discern the frame contains a serigraph advertisement from the first known public performance of a global superstar at a storied Greenwich Village theater back in 1979. Text of the artifact reads:

"Avant Garde Open Mic @ 8:00pm
First Porn Reel Screens @ ???
(Better Stay Late and Find Out,
...Ya Buncha Sexy Sinners, xoxo)"

An event ticket is framed with the tri-color silkscreen poster.

For a good time, call ________. #___________.

"**BERNIE**" is printed in all capital letters with black Sharpie pen. I look away before I commit the phone number provided, to memory.

"Where did you get this?" I ask THE LAWYER.

"It was a gift. I used to trade exclusively in 'commercial paper,'" he jokes.

"Who's 'BERNIE?'"

He doesn't answer, but after a couple of breaths continues, *"Such a shame. That venue changed so many lives. It advanced culture. Now no one even remembers the impact it made. It was razed 20 years ago."*

"Where was it?"

"You're standing 'stories above' where the 'stories were once made.'"]

[1438.2 / 3928] [I ascend a red velvet staircase, and am greeted at the top with an embrace by THE REVOLUTIONARY. She silently guides me down a regal hallway and motions at me to enter a ballroom full of purple satin mattresses, where the spirits of old friends from high school have gathered to thumb through photo albums and reminisce. I take a seat on a mattress next to THE PRECIOUS ONE who sits with an album open his lap, coincidentally on a photo where a shirtless, backward blue ball cap wearing teenage version of me makes a *"smoochy mouth"* while flashing the sign for *"Love"* with both hands.

"My god, your abs are better now than they were then. How the EFF do you do it?" he incredulously comments while tapping the album with his right index finger.

"I drink water. I move. I sleep. I pray. The last one I do...when I'm doing the other three."

I stand up and put on my t-shirt. I exit the room, descend the staircase, and drive my old reliable junker of a car home.]

[1438.3 / 3929] [THE RECONCILIATOR hugs me tightly and whispers with sweet excitement, *"I have so much to tell you!"*] //

⁂

THEATER: #0014, #0016, #0021, #0024, #0027
BLUE: #0003, #0005, #0008, #0009, #0010
BALLROOM: #0803, #0904, #0909, #0957, #1222

⁂

#1439 - October 16, 2020 @ 06:32 (San Francisco, California)

[1439.1 / 3930] [THE HYPE MAN helps me prepare for the keynote address of my career.

"Your speaker's notes are over there," he says, actively directing me over to a laser printer.

"This also came for you. I already opened it. It's that thing you've been waiting for," he says handing me my briefcase, while I hold the cooling warmed sheets in my hands.

I set the stack of paper down and draw forth my new "ultra-slim / paper-thin" notebook computer. I open the clamshell case to reveal a peculiar keyboard with unique clusters of letter keys *(and others missing from where they would ordinarily be found)* on a QWERTY configured peripheral. A single keystroke can generate a wide array of characters. Pressing combinations of keys creates contractions and composite "words" that look like alien script.

"I'm sure glad I took that course in transformational stenography, otherwise I'd be helpless."

THE HYPE MAN gently laughs and fits me with a lapel mic, moments before the presentation is scheduled to begin.]

[1439.2 / 3931] [THE ARBITER and I sit at an outdoor cafe catching up on professional exploits after having been on different teams for a decade.

"Do you remember THE C-SUITE when you were running trans-tech?" she asks.

"Know her? I love her! She and I went to high school together. I always thought I was in competition with her but she was always extraordinary. Simply in a league beyond my aptitude. Did you hear she just got 'the big job?'"

"Oh really?!" THE ARBITER responds with a smile.

No sooner do I speak, THE C-SUITE waves to us as she crosses the street from a corporate plaza in the direction of our restaurant patio.

"Would joining be an interruption?" she asks.

We welcome her to the table, where it's soon apparent she's been crying all morning. She politely refuses a tissue when we ask what's wrong.

"Oh, don't feel the least bit bad ladies, these are tears of joy. I want the world to see each droplet that streams down my cheeks."

We sit in silent wonder at the table until she continues, *"I heard what you said. There's no way I could've gotten where I am without you. Your wit. Your contrarianism. Your Holden Caulfield-like acerbic disposition. You inspire me."*

Stunned, I hold the space at the table reverent and quietly, until she speaks again.

"ANNA WINTOUR and GRACE CODDINGTON needed one another to thrive, just like us."

"I believe we're both a healthy blend of both women's best attributes. That's why this friendship works."

Half of my spirit leaves my body and becomes the embodiment of a young boy who's learning to walk and speak. THE C-SUITE and I take each of the boy's hands and leave the table. We walk to a park where we spend the afternoon playing as a group of three.

"Are you complete?" I ask the boy as our time together winds down. The boy begins to cry at my choice of words, certain that, *"playtime is over forever and we're going to leave him."*

"Are we ready for the next part?" I suggest with a different tone and word choice.

He smiles. I hold his left hand as he walks up stacks of banquet chairs that topple like dominoes up a grand white marble staircase. Once at the top of the staircase, he leaps into the ready lap of THE C-SUITE, who then shrouds him with a loving hug and giggling cheek nuzzles. I step up and wrap my arms around both of them, ***"the young innocent boy nestled securely between the artist and the executive."***]

[1439.3 / 3932] ["HERK," a gold being from the non-conditional realm appears in the form of a caduceus in the middle of my eight chakra *(the direct connection to true creativity)* and resonates a healing poem which lightly radiates outward ad infinitum through my entire being and all my creations:

"NO GOAL IS THE PRIZE.
The practice of practice.
A habit of habits.
Turns ignorance, wise."] //

⁂

TRANSFORMATIONAL: #0043, #0417
JOY: #0023, #0125, #0186, #0251, #0579, #0903
CADUCEUS: #0999, #1408, #

⁂

#1440 - October 17, 2020 @ 02:21 (San Francisco, California)

[1440.1 / 3933] [It's well into a balmy night. I'm in the living room of an old apartment. I'm frustrated. The sticky residual heat of the day is making it difficult to fall asleep. I wander like a zombie between recliners, the sofa, and toss and turn while laying naked on the floor in an attempt to get comfortable. I might have roommates, though they're not present. I eventually give up and return to my bedroom. The door mechanism clicks, but it fails to latch, leaving it slightly cracked. I wave a hand at it with a dismissive huff.

The room begins to shake. The walls and windows expand, contract, and rattle. Beams of intense white light blast through the glass, and sear the words off the open pages of books scattered around.

My instinct is to pray as unseen forces continue to shake the space. I chant every mantra I've been taught to stay grounded in the brilliance of such pristine power. My prior frustration boils off and I teem with authentic joy, though a kernel of terror remains intentionally planted in my core.

"I surrender! Use me as a tool! Let the work serve all!" I repeatedly chant with rapturous exasperation as I'm absorbed by the light.]

[1440.2 / 3934] [***"If I'm dreaming, I can fly!"*** I declare while walking through a woodland grove under a brilliant star-filled sky.

I use the ability sparingly, leaping momentarily aloft to grip a white autumnal leafless branch and swing a few gymnastic high bar "giants" beneath the glow of the brilliant white crystal moon. I descend and bound across an expanse of softly rolling grass covered hills, as though I'm dancing on the surface of the heavenly body hovering above. I dance and glide as night surrenders to sunlight. I leave my body, and as spirit watch myself dance into the brilliantly lit horizon before me.]

[1440.3 / 3935] [I take a seat at a lengthy tan wood community dinner table. I feel sad. My new notebook computer refuses to boot up. The screen remains dark.

"Someone else used your new machine while you were away," a helpful female contemporary assists, when she notes my blueness.

I discover the screen lighting has been placed on its minimal setting, optimal for use in low light. I can barely read the content before I scale up the brightness. As I do, the scene dissolves before I can see what the prior user was working on.]

[1440.4 / 3936] [I make repeated trips from the top level of a large manor, to the basement, in search of my journals. The laps happen with increasing quickness. The basement has a single window that shines hues of golden-amber light that makes dust particles in the air shimmer like glitter. My default is to look at a stack of books on the left-hand side, on the middle shelf, of a steel baker's rack. Each time I look, I find a different notebook full of doodles, sketches, insights, scribbles and musings in black ink.

After innumerable attempts, a small flash of magenta light ("V.O.") bumps my attention to the right-hand side of the same shelf where I find my current journals *(black leather cover with a Metatron embossed on the front)* and a pen resting on top. A solid half-an-inch of dust has settled on the book, indicating it's been some time *(perhaps centuries?)* since I last picked it up from the shelf. The most recent entry is a half-composed poem.]

[1440.5 / 3937] [I pass chattering groups of uniform-wearing school children. I give a few who extend their hands "high fives" as I walk in the opposite direction under a Gothically inspired tunnel.]

[1440.6 / 3938] [I come to, at a house party. I know I'm on the third floor of a condo building, though I don't remember how I got there. A young, small-framed-slender-man with a high and tight haircut coyly grips a red solo cup while shooting me a flirty smile. I say nothing. He walks away. This repeats a few times, until he extends an arm and touches the center of my chest.

"You're really cute but you don't share that much," he contends.

"I don't have words that adequately express what I feel when you're around."

THE LOYALIST stands behind the young man.

"Hey what's wrong with that guy? Why doesn't he talk?" the young man asks.

"Let him arrive. He's usually more expressive. He's probably just tired from the 'big trip,'" THE LOYALIST assures, placing his left hand on the young man's right shoulder, while raising his red solo cup full of beer and offering me a concurrent wink and nod.]

[1440.7 / 3939] [I'm in the grand marble entryway of a prestigious museum. I hear the raspy, jovially interrogating voice of an extroverted female friend shout my name in the otherwise silent hallway. ***"Now's not the time for us to connect."*** I float to an upper staircase to avoid her then quickly pivot and glide down a white marble staircase that spirals to the left. My feet hover inches above the stone steps, and don't make contact until I reach the bottom. I exit the building while dusting off my coat lapels and forearms with my hands. I walk up a green hill lined by ancestral trees.]

[1440.8 / 3940] [I crest a hill on foot, and discover myself on the quad of a futuristic university campus. Three backpack wearing students stand on hovering boards on the hilltop roughly 50 feet away, casually discussing plans for the upcoming weekend. ***"I want to know how their boards float."*** The students appear to be of Asian descent. They're polished and smooth skinned, most donning short spiky hair and black form-fitting tank tops that expose sinewy, efficient muscles *(optimally suited for their skeletal frames)* ...specifically not overbuilt. They make a shared hand gesture, and fly away in different directions.

I walk towards a crew of futur-punk-looking students seated a few paces away on a gentle downward slope. Their boards remain strapped to their feet. Most wear all black clothing accented with a small solid stripe of their preferred primary color.

"When are we?" I ask, unable to discern the era.

"Twenty (indecipherable pink noise)," a male student with a single, long, blonde swooping bang on his otherwise bald head responds.

"What?"

"Twenty (garbled static)," he replies with more gusto.

"Huh? Can you divide it into units on a line?" I ask with both palms extended outward, when I remain unable to translate the unit of measure.

"It doesn't make sense to think about it like that," he says while becoming annoyed with my lack of comprehension.

"'After' or 'before' don't exist anymore, once you've surfed the quantum barrel," another offers as the crew stand on their boards to depart.

Instead of flying away, they choose to *"port out."* The posse of students touch a device worn on their wrists, and in a flash, each fold in on themselves like corn kernels popping in reverse. Miniature mushroom clouds of teleporting matter compress to a single point and instantly vanish without leaving a trace.

I glance down at my wrist and discover I've been issued a similar device. I press the button and feel my body flatten, time slow, and then *"an intense flurry of contract renegotiations between the atomic consciousness of my body."* Upon my first *"port"* I leave a *"travel trail"* that looks like a cartoon dust ball, suggesting my understanding and application of the technique is either inefficient, incomplete, or that I **lack the presence required** to effortlessly navigate through space-time.

I bound between various locations within the future world, until I re-materialize in a sunlit library. A studious young Caucasian man with short blond hair wears a pair of glasses that hover in front of his eyes. He's more willing to assist me in assessing *"when"* we are and how to discern my whereabouts.] //

⁂

SURRENDER: #0010, #0215, #0270, #0392, #0438, #0557, #0691, #0799, #0926
FLY: #0005, #0016, #0024, #0059, #0079, #0112, #0141, #0162, #0311, #0394, #0442, #0450
QUANTUM: #0615

⁂

#1441 - October 17, 2020 @ 05:53 (San Francisco, California)

[1441.1 / 3941] [A young woman and man have carefully engineered the circumstances of their wedding engagement. They stand facing one another, eye-to-eye in quiet, gently calm conversation near a large white marble hearth stoked with unlit kindling. A large crystal vase atop a round glass top pub table holds dozens of mature white roses bespeckled with white dots of baby's breath arranged with fecund perfection, bathed in a soft beam of diamond platinum light. They intend to surprise whoever enters the room with the news of their engagement, by enrolling them in the in-the-moment experience.

She wears a black suitcoat and bow tie, her hair pulled back in a tight ponytail. He wears a frilly white gown composed entirely of downturned ostrich feathers. The woman readies herself, allowing the man to brush the dust off the back and shoulders of her suit before taking a knee on the fine Persian rug. She places a large heirloom, square-cut diamond on the man's left ring finger. The jewelry setting seems otherworldly and supernatural. The tone of the diamond gently oscillates, while it turns and hovers like a miniature superconductor. The man gazes meditatively at the ring down the length of his arm and upturned fingers. The light passing over the roses and through the glass table top perfectly refracts to give the jewel its optimal gleam. His attention lovingly turns toward her. She remains ready, on bended knee extending an old-fashioned glass full of an absinthe-green cocktail affirmatively towards him with a winking right eye.

"We're really doing this," they psychically communicate to one another in unison during their final instant of shared privacy.

The heavy oak door to the salon clicks. Is it their parents? Their child? The tone of electrified, vital anticipation permeating the room consolidates to an exquisitely dense grounding "orb" in the exact center of the space. Hearts race. Both keep reverent silence. Though the details of their proposal have been exquisitely appointed down to the exact position of her knee on the rug, the tilt of the white-sand hourglass on the mantle, and the one-eighth turn of the blinds to allow through the **exact hue** of golden light intended through the window, her heart skips with anticipation at the thought of his acceptance of her proposal.

"Will he say yes?" she ponders in the final electric moment, before whoever's behind the door steps past the threshold into the arena of surprise.

I recognize them as the couple I first encountered at the conclusion of their wedding reception in dream **[0999.4 / 2645]**.

"Their love and devotion for each other's spiritual growth is infinite, and all consuming."] //

⁂

DIAMOND: #0013, #0170, #0271, #0390, #0431, #0572, #0585
YES: #0009, #0402, #0414, #0822, #0919
LOVE: #0012, #0017, #0021, #0038
DEVOTION: #0879

⁂

#1442 - October 18, 2020 @ 23:56 (San Francisco, California)

[1442.1 / 3942] [I float from left-to-right over a row of seats ordered by color (ROY G. BIV). Each seat has a plastic bucket set upon it that matches the color of the upholstery.]

[1442.2 / 3943] [I awaken in a blustery winter scene near the top of a mountain range. Numerous beings rush by in a blur of light. The activity and dialog seem complex and nuanced. Though I miss the conversation, I look towards two snowcapped peaks and am drawn towards the bright white ball of light that illuminates the space between them. An ancient female being stands tall to my left, and extends an arm towards the mountain, insisting I, *"Prove it. Take on the impossible task of crossing over into the light."*

I accept the challenge. The grey robed woman instantly vanishes.

I begin a risky journey of traveling uphill through the blizzard without a jacket. Though the blistering cold numbs my skin I effortlessly bound across crevices, avoid deathly drops through pits to the center of the Earth, and slide across glacial ice caps while avoiding evisceration by packs of wild animals. I take photos of my point-to-point journey. The air of impossibility quickly subsides as I play through, stopping to provide my photos as hints before bounding by others who have attempted to cross over, but have gotten stuck en route.

"We're here to walk each other home. We each make it on our own terms," I shout supportively over my shoulder after I pass each person.

I crest the top and descend towards a large village that looks as though it's encased within a massive shaken snow globe. When I make it to the town square, I'm acknowledged by the ancient female who seems legitimately surprised I succeeded with such ease. We converse as I show her my waypoint photos, and selfies I've taken with the others on the mountain who are all a bit *"less stuck,"* after our interactions.

Enough instantly happens on the back side of the mountain to easily fill another entire book as I survey the frenetic scene. I become overwhelmed. I glance back in the direction from whence I came, towards the dark mountain peaks. I look in the other direction and see a watercolor impression of the Golden Gate Bridge softly manifest behind a series of doves as they fly in "V" formation across the bay. Light breaches the dark horizon behind the cityscape causing the waterfront to glisten with gold and platinum sparkles. Between myself and the bridge extends a massive fully stocked buffet, where a man of similar age to me fills a plate. With a laugh he winks at me saying, *"There's always more!"* as I stand tall and absorb the unspeakable beauty of the scene before me.]

[1442.3 / 3944] [***"For the sake of the pious man and his love of the woodland creatures, please let me go back for another look,"*** I pray.

My eyes open, staring up at a white ceiling. I awaken lying in bed with an old man who has long grey hair down to his hips, and an equally long, white, mage-like beard. I soon discover the man is blind. His eyeballs are missing. His eyelids are crudely sewn shut with large black thread "X's." The volume of his voice *(and the extremity of his opinions)* channels the interrogative quality of his lost vision.

A bathrobe wearing housemate enters a kitchen immediately to the left side of the bed. The blind man is unaware the other is nearby, and begins to gossip by critiquing the quality of the rousing man's artwork. I'm unable to hear exactly what he says. My ears are plugged. ***"Perhaps I'm deaf? Maybe my guides "L" and "V.O." each cover an ear to prevent me from reacting?"***

Without drawing a single sip of coffee from his mug, the bathrobe wearing artist turns and ignites a gas burner on the stove. He looks at the two of us lying in bed while plunging his right hand into the flame. He makes a yelping noise seemingly composed of equal parts ecstasy and agony, as he holds his fist firmly in the fire. His eyes widen and become wily when he removes the still burning extremity from the stove and repeatedly waves it back and forth like a flag twirler at a pep rally.

"ONE! TWO! THREE! FOUR..." The bath robed artist counts all whole numbers, up to *"EIGHTY-EIGHT!"*

The flesh is first to sear. Blood hisses and drops in dark syrupy splotches on the vinyl flooring. The bones of his fingers char, eventually becoming small tubes of black ash that disintegrate. The flaming stump continues to split, and hardens into a mass that looks like petrified wood.

"He cares inordinately for the woodland creatures," the blind man repeats as I leap from the bed and rush to the kitchen.

I urge the artist to extinguish the fire, but the damage to his appendage is already done. He holds steady, quiet and unbothered as I field dress his wound. The blind man has no awareness the artist heard him speak, nor that the artist injured himself as a result of hearing the gossip spoken of him.

"Your words matter! Your thoughts are prayers! THEY CHANGE THINGS!" I loudly lament at the blind man to no avail.

"No one's opinion holds as much sway over me. You must be lying," the blind man says, though the scent of burnt flesh hangs acrid in the air.

"You lack vision. You have no idea at all of what just happened. I saw the entire episode unfold as you spoke! He scorched his own hand!"

"Who would show such devotion? No one matters as much to me."

"He's devoted to you. To your growth. He's your seraph!"

"I don't get it. What's in it for him?"

"Grace! Love! Honor! Service! The Divine Spark of Creation! Something shared, good, true and beautiful! All of these and more are given without expectation. All you need do is simply ask."

The verbose old blind man's tongue falls silent. After a pregnant pause, I continue: ***"It's been in front of you in plain sight, the whole time. Angels supporting you. Beings assigned to steward your growth. Entities who heal without hesitation, committed to walking you home regardless of what it takes."***

The blind man's quiet turns reverent as I turn to the self-wounding man and pat him on the back with a simple acknowledgement:

"I see you, "Francis." Thank you for being my teacher."] //

⁂

IMPOSSIBLE: #1249

BLIND: #0001, #0304, #0600
VISION: #1235, #1246, #1251, #1267, #1271
PLEASE: #0056, #0280, #0297, #0382, #0400, #0538, #0611
ANGELS: #0045, #0069, #0141, #0277, #0379, #0599, #0800, #0862, #0998
"L": #0610, #0611, #0658, #0674, #0762, #0821, #0826, #0968, #1157, #1318, #1385
WHOLE: #0008, #0264, #0293, #0411, #0450, #0575, #0703, #0790, #0796, #0917, #0984

⁂

AFTERWORD

"Nowadays more and more people, especially those who live in large cities, suffer from a terrible emptiness and boredom, as if they are waiting for something that never arrives. Movies and television, spectator sports and political excitements may divert them for a while, but again and again, exhausted and disenchanted, they have to return to the wasteland of their own lives. The only adventure that is still worthwhile for modern man lies in the inner realm of the unconscious psyche."

- Man and His Symbols (1964)

That assertion was presented to me by a friend, who said nothing as they held an open book and tapped a page until I read it, unfolding much like a scene in an arthouse film. Curious to explore, I considered the quote to be a novel, *"little 't' truth."* From that morning, through now I've read it daily to prime my mind and set my space before going about activities in the *"wasteland of my life."* Over time, the novelty has waned and the passage itself has transformed into its own sort of koan. As I enter the fourth year of ongoing inquiry and pause to reflect, the subsequent odyssey that's unfolded in both my waking-state and sleep-state lives has immensely grown in its richness and timelessness the more I've given it my full attention.

Candidly: This book contains no answers, yet raises plenty of questions. Perhaps the count of questions generated is a reasonable metric to discern the impact of any work of art. I don't consider myself a traditional novelist, nor even a writer *(and perhaps the syntax chosen and arguable quality of the prose previously contained within the exquisite corpse would welcome strong and just critique which points to that).* I've been guided by the call I was issued on a Peruvian mountain to birth this into being, and delivering on that call has become my daily true north. If anything, I've gained an appreciation for the skill vocational writers employ to stay awake and generate different realities while sitting where they are.

I couldn't do it that way. I had to sleep to collect the stories that wanted to come through, and contribute to, this expression.

The practice of remembering what I dream about has certainly been self-edifying in my quest to better understand what makes me tick, but over time it's expanded from its start in the realm of curious play, into a crucial mechanism that oscillates between experiences of *"doing the hard thing"* and *"listening in selfless surrendered service"* as a moment-by-moment phenomenon. Above all, simply by dedicating a few minutes each day to notice what the language of dreams seems to communicate, a degree of vitalizing effortlessness regularly emerges and offers clues as to:

1) Whether I'm delivering on the terms and conditions of my contract with Creation.

2) How to best deploy remaining breaths and heartbeats while piloting a human body.

If it sounds like a spiritual intention, it is. Contemplating dream state experiences has helped me live at cause as spirit, more of the time.

Language is a useful tool, and in itself an incomplete *(and paradoxically abstract)* model. I've come to love the limitations of my vocabulary, relatively modest understanding of how to present dialog on a page, and what makes for good storytelling. I relish the tradeoffs I made for grit in lieu of elegance, because it more authentically portrays the overt clumsiness of this macro-artistic process. I've found myself in the practice of kicking aside doubt and imposter syndrome with every keystroke.

My hope is that at some breath, you come to know that something as peculiar, fantastic, and unexpectedly delightful *(at every turn)* exists within you, and can be accessed through quality sleep. Should this work inspire but one person to take a second glance at their dreams and curate their own *"hero's journey,"* it'll have fully delivered on its promise. If that's of interest to you, what follows is a loose origin story of *(and subsequent framework for)* the practice illustrated in this book, the meandering path traveled, and some context which hopefully illustrates how the habit of dream recall evolved over time.

As I look back, what's clear is my conscious, analyzing, waking-state mind couldn't have fabricated this work, had I tried. The preceding pages represent the honest, vulnerable, radically imperfect truth of my dreams, with minimal editorializing. They're compiled in the order in which they were experienced.

Preamble: (Not) Doing the Obvious

Sleep. Hydrate. Move the body. Repeat. Obvious. For a protracted period, I paid little attention to what are arguably core practices for any human to remain productive and available for growth. Perhaps my personal narrative prior to undertaking this project wasn't too different from how many others live in this red-hot minute. Hard charging. Self starting. Diplomatic. "The Firefighter." Such valences are culturally relished by teams with large problems to solve. However, I'd lived so long in those personas that I became entrenched in believing I "was" one of many of those things, rather than deploying useful aspects of my identity with just enough buffering to remind me when it's time to remove the costume.

In a nutshell; at the start of this adventure I was 37. I was a workaholic, consistently logging 80-100 hour weeks in my home office, and regularly neglecting sleep. Detached from the core emotion of sadness; I was carrying a lot of it around, and it reflected in my posture and mood. My body began to fail. I had two operations to rebuild my left hand, when stress related illness caused my fingers to contract in to a claw. My left pinky was a candidate for amputation, but luckily the interventions I required didn't come to that. I was certainly **not** in my body, in many ways totally out of personal integrity, and certainly not behaving as a model citizen.

The miracle of the body healed itself, and it came with an intuitive injunction: **change everything**. I had the benefit of fully completing a thirteen year career segment, where I'd been part of teams that consistently *"did the impossible,"* before being jettisoned out on to the perpetually curious, and beautifully wandering road my life continues to follow.

1- Initiate: Take the call

I have certainly held a preference for overtures, and taking epic journeys. I've found retreats are useful tools to assess my central behavioral patterns *(and the depth of their grooves)*. Sometimes it takes a radically different environment and schedule to come in to direct contact with those pictures and programs. With a reforming body, the pending life segment began to unfoldi and beckoned: **Go to Peru**. I didn't know what I would find, but similar to other seminal life choices, my spirit was unrelenting *(and removed every barrier)* to expeditiously get me to the Andes.

A 4,000 acre permaculture retreat center at altitude, tucked away in the mountains along a ridge that leads to the Amazon basin, became the place where I grew my understanding of how depleted, reactive, and technology addicted I'd become. I was fortunate to have the means and circumstances which allowed me a 33 day period away from devices and behaviors, that had become convenient *(and central)* to my life. The absence of a perpetual buzz of a phone against my leg created an awareness of anxiety that, for better or worse, had become normal. Natural sun cycles from dark-to -light became environmental clues to sleep and wake up. By disconnecting from habits I'd created in concert with my devices, I was able to reconnect to nature by throwing myself at its restorative mercy. While my experiences on the mountain could themselves become a novel, what's most germane from that time for our purposes was it became abundantly clear how much vitality, personal empowerment, and freedom I'd traded off by **not** prioritizing quality sleep.

After spending roughly a week on the mountain, creating a new, and more attuned symbiotic set of habits, a facilitator *(and friend)* suggested I start paying attention to what I dream about. The idea was suggested as a corollary to a conversation we'd had about the customs and rituals of different indigenous tribes. Among those were the Achuar, who leverage the language of dreams to inform their choice making and community relationships *(when to hunt, and so on)*. Dreams are in a sense, their unit of exchange.

What was offered in curiosity and inquiry evolved in to its own sort of *"practically mandated"* commandment. I fell asleep. I contemplated ***"what might I dream about,"*** and laid on my back, listening to the Mapacho River while remembering a few scant fragments of recurring dreams I'd had at different stages of my life:

> *"**Ooh!** - The one where I'm the adopted Huxtable child on "The Cosby Show" who lives in a closet under the stairs, and wants **so much** to be part of the family dance numbers, but Claire (the matriarch) consistently says "No, No, No!" before a studio audience laughs and wakes me up."*
>
> *"**Whaddabout** - The one I seem to have before every time I move, where a troll stands on a tree stump. He points and laughs as my teeth fall out, and then my mouth disappears. #weird."*
>
> *"**Hmph** -The one where I'm a superhero who's supposed to be able to fly, but seems to always crash and break my legs (or scrape my face on the concrete) while attempting to help someone in trouble?"*

I glibly giggled and laughed as I playfully recalled these "bizarre" dreams from days of yore, and sauntered off to sleep. I was awakened in the middle of the night by a stern female out-of-body voice who spoke firmly in English, and issued a concise four part edict:

"Remember your dreams."
"Do this 1000 times."
"Write a book."
"Give it away."

From just after midnight on December 20, 2017 through this moment, my life has been principally organized around delivering on that contract. Little did I know at that time, but I'd been given a roadmap to rediscover the lost city of my own tender, heart-centered awareness.

Who was speaking? A muse? Guardian angel? Messenger from a non-conditional realm? My under-expressed maturing feminine, birthing itself? Mother Nature? Holy Spirit?

All possible candidates...*though it ultimately doesn't matter.* I'm ok with not knowing who the owner of "the voice" is and catch myself when attempting to assign it an identity. Such attempts to, *"eff the ineffable,"* provide their own cosmic giggle. I'm perpetually grateful to the energies which conspired to issue the call. My hope is the practice and relationship I've developed with dream state respectfully honors the guidance provided. The creative thrust behind the request has been enough to jolt me from sleep, in service *(with varying degrees of clarity),* hundreds of times.

2 - Wander: Embody True Nature ***(more often)***

As the Peruvian retreat concluded in late January 2018, I departed with roughly 50 dreams scribbled in a journal, and had taken initial steps along what seemed to be a daunting path. How long would it take for me to whittle my way to an eventual 1000 dreams? My analyzing mind was ablaze at the prospect of being sidelined for multiple years, especially after all it had contributed to the circumstances of my life. I gained an understanding of just how capricious that aspect of my being can be, and committed to use this period of psychological self-transformation, to make it more of a humble servant.

I agreed to spend the month of February 2018 in Bucharest, Romania supporting the vision of a pair of friends, who had repatriated from Canada to open the city's only hot power yoga studio. I have a decades long love for yoga asana. I love leading practices that pop participants in to mild non-ordinary states of consciousness. Traveling to Eastern Europe seemed a natural win-for-all to support their nascent community, while retaining and deepening my personal dream practice.

Could I keep attention on my journaling, or would I be swept away by the newness of my short-term expatriation?

Though I spent most of the month alone, I was thrust into a wintry urban environment, regularly leading classes in English to a multi-lingual population. I lived in a tiny fifth floor walk up condo, in an area of the city that served as the seat of the Romanian revolution of the late 1980's. The partial immersion *(and reintroduction)* to social customs, commerce, and technology provided me with a set of circumstances that let me "bridge the gap" between seemingly divergent realities of big nature and city dwelling.

I didn't have to immediately return to the well-worn grooves of my Bay Area reality, and retained the space to gather additional dream experiences, with a steadily broadening cast of imagined characters, moods, and circumstances.

The second month of practice yielded a similar count of dreams as the first. Some nights yielded multiple glimpses, while other stretches of consecutive nights were simply black-out-dead-to-the-world sleep.

Through internal prodding and coaxing, my mind remained oriented towards the longer term objective. Any payoff *(should it come)*, would occur at some future unknowable date. While some experiences left me feeling more exhausted, my commitment to the practice grew night-by-night. I became increasingly eager and curious for where I might go, and what I might experience during dream time. During this wobbly period, I gained tremendous appreciation for how little my words were able to convey the fullness of what I experienced while asleep. Practice made imperfect, and I was largely left in an experience of confusion.

"Why am I doing this?
What will it mean?
Who'll care?"

Personal naysaying set aside, I just kept going. Little by little, I collected more dream data and followed my intuition around Europe. While traversing the continent, I briefly shared seemingly dream-like interactions with friends from various strata of my pre-dreamer's life.

I cherished the opportunity to devote my life during that time to serving the people of Bucharest, who showed up to breathe, move, and sweat. They afforded me a space where I could practice living in heart-centered awareness off the mountain, and out in the world.

3- Root Down: Dropping Anchor

After the enriching month of service in the Eastern Bloc, and sputtering around the European continent, I returned to San Francisco with an opportunity to fully redraw the lines of my life. I had no corporate role to relax back in to. I set up a shared home with a new housemate. With a catalog of ~100 dreams, and a chance to continue living my life in a place I love; I selected an entirely new, quasi-bohemian paradigm. I seized a chance to get unapologetically *"weird,"* in service to my broad spectrum *"why."* San Francisco provided the perfect backdrop.

From the outset it was clear this *"track to 1000"* was shoring up to be a massive data gathering exercise. In my first months back in the city, I tended to focus on scribbling down fragments as remembered without wading too deeply in to meaning-making frames offered by transpersonal psychology, and other oneiric limbs of study.

I became acutely aware of the oscillatory nature of what I would remember, when tracked over time. Periods of sweeping, detailed narrative would rise and fall, followed by eras of short abstraction and quick, punctuated action. In some instances, dreams would emerge as single words, strings of letters, and attempts at onomatopoeia for sounds otherwise undistinguishable. Though threads of my intellect gave rise to their moments of self-judgment; **all** of what I remembered seemed to be necessary and essential at the time, and remains so.

What could be discerned from reviewing "the bullshit of my mind" without acute inner critique? Was what I recalled in my daily journaling as comprehensive as possible? Where would I catch myself avoiding writing something down? With increasing regularity I noticed myself wanting to lean away from dream subject matter I labeled as *"peculiar," "embarrassing,"* or *"taboo."* Those domains became the places to become as honest as possible, and hopefully compellingly conveyed as a core feature of this work. I've never had a better chance to tell on myself.

Can I accept that I'm actually 50% asshole?

What do I do at the end of this, if I discover I'm but a self-indulgent, immature man-boy?
Am I actually a cruel and "mean spirited" person?
Would I ever let my grandmother read tropes incised by my libido?
Above all, am I willing to unconditionally love all those aspects of myself?

Without getting wrapped up in self analysis, I created a buffer that *(to the best of my ability)* allowed me to be candid and responsible, while minimizing editorialization. It was ok, if it didn't make sense. Diving in to those nonsensical places deepened the inquiry.

While as previously stated, the prevailing intention of the work was to generate the reader's curiosity in their own dreams...it oddly required a degree of utter selfishness to continue generating content to support that end.

"What" the book was to be, and its eventual birth, took a back seat to the *"Why"* guiding it.

I remained in service to the contract I was issued on the mountain, and began to develop a unique vocabulary. The novelty of dreaming itself had begun to wane, and new curiosities about how waking-life choices might impact the practice, became a place to ground down ever deeper.

4- Strange Bedfellows: Futzing With Knobs

Through this segment, I was now a few months *(and a couple hundred dreams)* deep within the practice. I started noticing impacts from waking day-to-day urban life experiences bleeding in and "infiltrating" my dreams. Characters from my waking life began making more frequent appearances, with a residual tone. Incomplete conversations from meetings seemed to regularly play out while asleep. Unanswered questions from family discussions took on their own theatrical qualities, as impressions of personality seemed to convene *(and duke it out)* on "spirit time."

I gained an appreciation for the convenience of the service economy and internet of things, which in its own dream-like way yielded the ability to land a meal, an object, or an experience on my door step, basically on demand. For a brief period, my diet backslid a bit. I started checking back in to parts of my life I'd set down while on the mountain *(late nights, socializing, occasional partying)*. While I can't peg it to a specific date or experience, I noticed the slight erosion in basic habits had incrementally taken me further away from dream state experiences, that in other periods felt deep, nourishing, and in a very real sense: **healing**.

I began to wonder just how much of an impact my diet, the type of media, and frequency of which I regularly consumed it, may have on my dream recall. Dream #0200 happened to coincide with the one-year anniversary of leaving my job, so I took it as a chance to celebrate "New Year's" in June. In a very *"quantified-self"* manner I started keeping tabs on the amount of water I drank daily, as well as the times and composition of meals *(arguably to an obsessive extent)*. My dreams were already obtuse and bizarre, but I ran a series of unscientific experiments to test some flimsy concepts I found floating around, as I casually described my practice of dreaming socially:

"Meat makes your dreams aggressive." ***Inconclusive.***

"Eating pork will make you dream you're a cannibal." ***Didn't happen.***

"If I eat salad on Tuesdays, will I regularly dream about being a cow?" ***No.***

For a period of time as I played with diet, sleep, and screen exposure variations, I would catch myself wanting to, *"escape back to the mountain,"* so I could again have, *"better dreams."* But the terms of the contract were exceedingly clear. Only after completing "The Book" would it be aligned for me to take another trip to the mountain. "The Book" would be best presented as a gift to the friend, who suggested I make a start. Becoming a hermit would be a brazen expression of spiritual bypass. ***"Stay where you are and keep practicing,"*** seemed to be whispered quietly in my ear in moments I wanted to avoid my urban life and escape.

Three variables seemed to most erode the quality of dream recall, which I encourage you to consider as you undertake your own dreaming practice:

1) **Eating Late:** Dinners with rich foods and alcohol, soon followed by sleep, mostly resulted in dreamless nights for me. It's probable this is due to the redirection of physiological resources *(blood)* from the brain to support digestion. Dreams were possible over time on nights where meals landed nearer to sleep. I've found that my sweet spot is to eat at least three hours ahead of going to bed, to raise the likelihood of clear recall.

2) **Dehydration:** For a time I thought having a glass of wine or a cocktail was a surefire dream killer. Overindulgence definitely had that effect in my case, but beyond the alcohol, it feels arguable that being optimally hydrated before sleep seemed to contribute to a more vivid dream experience. Consuming four liters of water over the course of a day, with the last liter taken at least two hours before sleep, tends to be the model of best-fit for my body, if my intention that night is to focus on dreaming.

3) **Screen Saturation**. Nights where I keep a device nearby result in a different quality of sleep, and by extension a different quality of dream. I've found something lovingly retro happens on nights where I leave the phone charging in the kitchen, and use an alarm clock to wake up.

I had a phone on my nightstand many nights throughout this project. On nights I stayed up watching hours of videos or doom scrolling, I'd typically have less robust dream recollection. Myriad neuroscience studies show stimulation of the pre-frontal cortex by light from devices near sleep time, can impact the brain's ability to transition, which impacts the quality of sleep, and by extension REM cycles in which most dreaming is assumed to occur.

I'd like to know what variables seem to have the greatest impact on your dreams.

5- Habit Forming: Refining the Model - Zygotic Constellations

As the months progressed, experiences in dreams ran the gamut between realms of the ecstatic, cathartic, and a portion of the time...*utterly banal.* While I was fortunate early on to acquire some base level knowledge of Jungian archetypes, the consistency of practice began to inform the birth of my own dream language dialect, and associated symbols.

With respect to the macro-practice, it's around this period where I believe I'd established a modicum of dream recall *"muscle."* I began moving from an unconsciously incompetent practitioner, to retaining some dimension of conscious incompetence *(aware that I know something, but a scant fraction of what may be discoverable).* I'd created a connection to an increasingly accessible *"hyper-real"* life that spoke to me in new and profound ways.

On my own growth path, this period feels analogous to a toddler learning to walk. **Wonder. Failure. Starting again.**

6- Crash: Traumatic Interruption

Unsubstantiated claim: Trauma to the body impacts one's ability to remember dreams.

The origin of this claim stems from being in a car crash on October 9, 2018 in which my vehicle was T-boned in broad daylight, and lifted on to a median by a white SUV. My damaged car limped to the gates of the Presidio of San Francisco and was later totaled. Thankfully, I didn't sustain any physical injuries. What's interesting, is while maintaining my sleep hygiene and dream practice habits I had three nights *(October 9-11)* where I had no dream recall.

I believe those three nights were required for my overly activated nervous system to recalibrate, based on the relative severity of the incident. I'm curious as to whether or not any conclusive study has been dedicated to this phenomenon.

7- Whispers: Abundant Clues and Guidance

Attention to nuance and subtlety drove ongoing inquiry throughout this segment. I was given a mantra practice by a teacher who asked me to meditate on the word *"vest"* for 117 consecutive days. Through repetition, clarity of purpose for the forthcoming segments of this work began to emerge. I began to precede nightly sleep with the phrase:

"Show me what I'm supposed to know."

I started to draw inferences from my dreams, and apply them to my daily decision making. The few isolated examples of content with brief context that follow, highlight a richness that could be extracted from **any** of the other entries, if I were to sit with, and analyze them.

Dream #0346: Balancing forces: I started noticing the regular emergence of strong women of color in my dreams, a night or two after engaging in fairly rambunctious periods of male:male sexual interaction. While not a hard and fast metric, it's likely if you encounter Oprah or Beyonce in the catalog, it *could be* a lagging indicator that I was sexually active with men in waking-life at some point in the not-so-distant past.

Dream #0370: November 7, 2018 turned out to be an unexpectedly active night of dreaming, where I remembered five between 12:45am and 7:00am. Sandwiched in the middle of the five is a basic trope. *"I meet a friend at a coffee shop and we talk about art."* At the time, I was grappling with whether or not to complete a work of art, and give it to a person I barely knew. I was resistant to the process. Had I not written out this short vignette and contemplated it, it's highly likely I would've shelved the project *(or never completed it)*. I interpret wrapper of THE ROMANTIC *(the recipient of the painting in waking-life)* telling me he, *"doesn't understand abstract art,"* to be a clever *(and subtle)* reflection of my own self doubt, speaking back at me. Getting it on paper allowed for some compassionate confront. I finished the piece, and presented it in December 2018. Tricky!

Dream #0446: Awareness of the *"72 hour reconciliation"* process emerged. Three nights prior to having dream #0446 I shared casual late night conversation with my brother-in-law. We discussed music, games, and other shared interests. He mentioned a forthcoming film starring Christian Bale as former Vice President Dick Cheney. Other than passing commentary, it was an unmemorable, unremarkable portion of our evening. Nights later DICK CHENEY shows up in a dream *(and not again in this data set)*. *headscratch* ***Why might that be?***

Boiled down, I feel attraction to BALE and aversion towards CHENEY.

- ***"Do pairs of opposites mentioned in passing, remain irreconcilable in my unconscious mind?"***
- ***"Perhaps unresolved polarities in my perceptions take a similar amount of time to 'filter through?'"***
- ***"This example's sort of silly, but how does this processing feature of my human organism impact my day-to-day choice making?"***

This phenomenon is not something I regularly tracked, but seems to have some continuity in my overarching experiences whether it be between people, nature, or other dimensions where my integrity and ethics are tested. This awareness keeps me curious as to what sets of mismatched pairs remain kicking around, just beneath my surface.

Dreams #0450-0461: All were gathered during a week of Noble Silence. I highly suggest the practice. Running the experiment while living in a city gave waking-life during this period its own unique, dream-like quality.

8 - Bright Darkness: Pseudo-Scientific Dispositions

Friendly reminder: I am not a therapist, a transpersonal psychologist, nor a formal scientist. I'm an accidental author answering a call to action from a space, far beyond what I understand to be *"myself."* This period carried tones of, *"cleaning house,"* and, *"erasing old programs,"* in an attempt at upgrading to, *"Human 2.0."* The intention for sleep evolved from a germ to a motive:

"Show me what I'm ready to see.
More than I can take, but not so much I break.
Use me as tool."

Additionally, this period found me actively prioritizing sleep, and organizing my days around the habit. I was regularly going to bed at 20:00. On average I would sleep 7.25 hours, bookended with 45 minutes of silent meditation. During a specific period of sleep study between April 4 and May 5, 2019, I saw a slight uptick in the total count of dreams remembered in a month ***(44)***.

I wore an OURA ring to collect basic biofeedback.

In summary, the month yielded:

Average Sleep Efficiency: 87.1% (Min=78%, Max=93%)

- Avg Time Awake (Hrs): 1.17 (13% Time In Bed) (Min=.67, Max=2.58)
- Avg Light Sleep (Hrs): 4.46 (51% Time in Bed) (Min=2.12, Max=8.43)
- Avg REM Sleep (Hrs): 1.71 (19% Time in Bed) (Min=.75, Max=3.03)
- Avg Deep Sleep (Hrs): 1.52 (17% Time In Bed) (Min=.73, Max=2.62)

Vital Signs- In Aggregate

- Avg Resting Heart Rate: 45.43 (Min=41, Max=49)
- Avg Heart Rate Variability:49.9 (Min=39, Max=66)

- Avg Body Temperature Delta: -.05 (Min=-.5, Max=.4)
- Avg Respiratory Rate: 13.16 (Min=12.2, Max=14.6)

9 - Plateau: Chop Wood. Carry Water.

Most of the time on this path to remembrance has been spent, *"on the plateau,"* between peak experiences. Here in the seemingly interminable doldrums of the #0600-#0700 dream range, general fatigue and expressions of boredom seemed to manifest with greater regularity, even though I was on the back side of the mountain to the illusive and arbitrary goal of remembering #1000.

- ***"Complete with quality."***
- ***"Treat every one as the first."***
- ***"Die tonight. Start again tomorrow."***

All were useful thought forms that led to more intimate declarations, and deeper devotion, which helped reframe the practice as my primary inquiry, with its eventual evolution to my living prayer. This period curated the ring-fence required, to transform the mind.

Engage the habit. Relish the task. **Be the wonder of it,**

...with equal parts of effort and ease.

10- I Am That: Oneness & Shadow

"Ha-PIE-yay Con-SON-CHEEZ." - ***"Half of me is you."***

"Oor-PEA-YAY So-COO-yeh." - ***"Doves from my heart."***

Both are rough phonetic spellings of traditional Quechua community greetings, along with their English translations. The phrases are used to generate presence, intimacy, and connection. By practicing them as an introductory custom among my community members on the Peruvian mountain, I experienced fluid access to what some may describe as *"Big Mind"* or *"Collective Consciousness."* While in a closed network of like-minded individuals, this practice of dipping in-and-out of co-creative awareness deeply imprinted upon me, an experience of selflessness, and a sense of *"infinite possibility."*

Now, two years in to my "**new**" life, I found myself quietly longing for *"my people"* or *"the others"* who carry such a practice. In my moment-to-moment life I wanted more of it but it didn't seem available, much less sustainable.

In the murmur of feeling as though life was starting to happen *"to me,"* I started a different experiment. *"Below the line"* moments were bound to continue, but regardless of the situation...*positive/negative affinity, clear/unclear communication, aligned/divergent realities within groups*...what if I practiced 100% responsibility for my role in every interaction as an act of co-creation? From there, what if the opposite of my story is as true *(or perhaps more true)* than my own?

Different wisdom traditions work with this notion. The student and the teacher are essential to the other's existence. Shall I treat everything as a teacher? What happens if I position myself as a perpetual student?

- Abject terror from the capricious ego, sits on one hand.

- *"Causal flow for the spirit to know"* rests on the other.

Perhaps you've experienced this too. Every interaction becomes an opportunity for healing. Every moment becomes a chance to make the highest ethical choice. Here, one gains the possibility of living at cause. During this period, I remembered more clearly I'm THE APERTURE through which a creator of some sort looks back at itself *(which I still have a tendency to forget, or may be programed to not remember).* I was reminded of my time on the mountain, during which I never saw myself in a mirror. My environment was the mirror. The smiling face, the struggling soul, the waterfall, the skyline. **I was that.** Why would it be any different in an urban center?

Waking-state and sleep-state from here, are both sides of the same hand. An awareness appears that conveys when I'm awake and my body's moving, **I'm still dreaming**.

While playing in this space, I've found inquiry shifts to an understanding of multi-variate *(shall I be bold and suggest "quantum")* ethical domains. I'm still here in 3D reality, shuttling around in a body, and playing my role in a marvelous game but...

- *What am I doing at different vibrations?*
- *What tone can I hold, and is most aligned in the moment?*
- *What's most important for me to know, right now?*
- *Where can I exercise greater responsibility?*
- *How consistently do I make the most ethical choices?*
- *Is what I'm shopping for serving the highest good?*
- *How much grief can I metabolize?*

For some, parts of this may be recognizable as the practice of **Tonglen**.

11 - Sonder: Good. True. Beautiful.

Occam's Razor assumes an explanation with the fewest assumptions is usually correct. When in the jointly ecstatic and cathartic throws of sonder, I suggest a mantra as a grounding cord:

"I get what I think about. Life's but a dream."

12 - Feed The Holy: Locating Center

Imagine an equilateral triangle.

1. Put *"Self"* in one corner.
2. Place *"Guidance"* in another.
3. *"Creator / God / Source / Universe"* in the remaining. Pick a neutral moniker.

At the center of the triangle is "**Wholeness**."

Dreams during this period were cultivated with greater awareness of which corner I tend to default to, while leveraging tools from all preceding segments, to move in towards the center. I've held a deeply private relationship with "God" off and on throughout my life; though there's barely any conventional dogmatic entanglement remaining. I'm largely a *"self"* person, growing incrementally in my listening to aligned *"guidance."* Much of the time I still want to do things *"my way."* With guidance at the lead, all bets are off when it comes to ego-centered certainty and control. This work constitutes a reflection of my evolving practice of enrolling, and responding to *"guidance."* It's naturally available to all of us, we just need to ask!

Yoga practitioners could put the Yamas and Niyamas in the *"self corner"* of the triangle. *"Ishvara Pranidhana"* could be a keyhole to peek through at the other two corners.

13- Soul Stirring: Order and Chaos

After dream #0999, I arrived at dream #1000 initially thinking it would be the *"end point."* But what would I do with seven hundred handwritten pages? The stern female voice from the Peruvian mountain returned to the center of my head, as I lounged on a couch staring at an episode of "Parks and Recreation" I'd seen dozens of times, and said: **"Look at the sky."**

I spent time after dusk that evening observing the San Francisco skyline from my rooftop, occasionally glancing up at *(what was on that night)* a clear, starry dome. I was shown a vision of an early stargazer attempting to "map out" the abyss of the heavens. Perhaps it was a glimpse of Ptolemy. Maybe it was an impression of an forgotten astronomical modeler from another ancient civilization.

The little glimpses at the unconscious in my stack of dream journals became analogous to tiny points of light in the vast dark sky. Conveniently, in the historical text "The Amalgest," Ptolemy's 48 ancient constellations were composed from an inventory of ~1026 stars *(some double counted and reducing the total, depending the version referenced)*. Taking a small extension beyond the initial "1000" dreams spurred a continuation in practice, and offered a sense-making frame for the first thirteen parts of this book.

Each book takes the name of an ancient constellation, with a count of dreams equal to the number of stars pegged to the constellation in that initial catalog. In some cases, the chapters foot to the astrological calendar. The homage is intended to honor the bold, yet imprecise beginnings of Astronomy. This work is offered as a similar attempt to frame something largely unknown, and seemingly incomprehensible in the unconscious, dream realm.

At this point I'm living for the questions.

14 - Apophenia: Data Analysis

Dreams experienced during this period teeter-tottered between periods of playfulness and grief, bolstered by a fulcrum of community populated by beings who stood courageously for their own, return to center. Said another way, I was developing a habit of *"generating causal flow."*

I just kept going, mostly because I couldn't stop dreaming. The awareness was established. The proverbial flood gates had opened. Now I lacked a *"kill switch."* Dreams were very much *(and are to this day)*, dreaming me.

During remembrances in the "Book of Ludere" I'd begun tabulating occurrences of people I've met **(THE CHARACTERS)**, public figures, and *"mash ups"* that eventually became "Amalgams, Hybrids, & Spirits." That paved the way for basic stack-ranked lists, and frequency distributions to emerge and create a scatterplot of my own *"inner night sky."* It was astounding to look back and note the degree of significance I gave characters who appeared just fractions of the time. I take delight in BEYONCÉ stopping through 18 times *(the most of any Zeitgeist Valence)*. Though I haven't met her, she feels like a lifetimes-old friend, with very specific goals this time around. I haven't shared her company since dream #1099. I'm eager to dance with her again, to potentially reveal more of my divine, maturing feminine that will land me in ever deeper expressions of tenderheartedness.

For posterity, the "Book of Inanis" represents all dreams from the void, that emerged during the acute phase of the global COVID-19 pandemic, as San Francisco and other major global cities experienced economic shutdowns and residents adapted to stay-at home orders.

15- Fiat Lux: Mythic Mystic

A framework often attributed to Buddha, is people are always choosing one of four transient states of being:

1. Arbiters of Chaos *(dark trending dark).*
2. Optimists *(dark trending light).*
3. Pessimists *(light trending dark).*
4. Stewards of Unity *(light trending light).*

Throughout this final segment, I could place myself in each of those buckets at various moments in time, learning finer discernment when challenged to "locate myself."

During an ebb in the COVID-19 pandemic, I drove from San Francisco, California to Dayton, Ohio. I stopped in a few cities along the way to share some physically-distant conversations *(and a photo op at a RUNZA in North Platte, Nebraska).* After surfing the time-dilated days of June 2020, I arrived at my family's home. I ultimately spent the summer assisting with the chores of my youth, and gaining a deeper appreciation for my parents as they relax in to their autumn years and blossom as grandparents.

I was blessed to spend multiple weeks with my young Godchildren. **With the six year old:** In the morning we'd walk to the pear tree, or ride bikes to see cows in the pasture. Throwing water balloons was a regular afternoon occurrence. **With the infant**: Daily naps, him resting on my chest, while listening to Handel operas or Ashana's singing bowls, were routine.

One day, "Sweet Pea" woke up in a very bad mood. As the morning unfolded she acted out, occasionally in violent ways towards her mother *(my sister).* When "Mommy" needed to leave the house mid-morning to run some errands, "Sweet Pea" became triggered and was convinced, *"Mommy's going to leave me again!"*

The adults were perplexed, since "Mommy" had been an omnipresent character in "Sweet Pea's" world from birth. As she calmed and started telling us more, we learned that she'd had a dream of being left at the grocery that was so real, she believed it happened. She unconsciously carried it in to waking-state, impacting her mood, and seemingly shifting her behavior. By identifying the parts that lived in her dreams *(and what actually happened)* we were able to get "Mommy" to the grocery store, and "Sweet Pea" back to playing.

Coincidental to my dream practice, we began a daily family conversation at breakfast regarding our dream experiences. Marbles rolling down the street. Talking to rainbows. Sometimes a spooky ghost would stop by.

I've heard conjecture *(and it's possibly unknowable),* but I often wonder how much of my daily interpersonal contrast is really a symptom of things left unreconciled from my dreams. If I pay a little more attention, and take incremental steps to be more responsible for how I'm, *"living in my dreams,"* might that just be the thing that lifts me from an imagined perfect waking-state life, to one artfully lived across domains? I suppose how I am anywhere is how I am, everywhere and every**when**.

On 1442: One day = 1440 minutes. Written entries for dreams #0289 and #0766 were missed.

On St. Francis: I'm humbled to claim him as an intercessor. His energy permeates most aspects of my life. The more steps I take, my relationship with him as a guide deepens. I live in a city that bears his name. I portrayed him in a children's cantata. He was an ascetic misfit in his awakened life. In many ways, my current embodiment at the time of this writing, aligns with that expression. His prayer floats in to my life when I've needed a reminder of why I'm here. I graciously accept his help. It was a delightful surprise that he showed up *(partially disguised)* to conclude this segment of work.

"I see you, "Francis." Thank you for being my teacher."

Bold Claims

- Quality sleep is a human right. ***Claim it.***
- Ask for guidance. ***You'll receive it.***
- Let questions lead. ***Tools will follow.***
- The only adventure remaining is to explore your unconscious. ***You're ready now.***
- You could take a waking-life hero's journey.... ***or take one every time you sleep.***

Parting Wishes: *"Om Mani Peme Hung"*

What might the starry sky of your connection to THE UNCONSCIOUS look like? Who might your MAJOR CONSTELLATIONS be? What might you contribute as, *"dreamer of the shared dream?"*

I hope you'll enjoy a similar clumsiness, confusion, failures, and playful invitations from your guides to the eternal return of beginner's mind as you construct your treasure map back to heart-centered awareness, while practicing living at cause.

Perhaps you'll find joy, curiosity and connection to your true north and genius loci as I have, through the simple practice of doing the obvious *(sleeping)*, while holding an intention of remembering what's been forgotten. May what you found here strike an aligned chord from your gut, to your heart, head, higher, to your entire being, that inspires and stokes your unique, connection to true creativity. May you find your **"Paititi."** May your connection to flow, grow ever deeper.

Gather up your wellbeing! Share it all around! Love and compassion to you, and all beings everywhere...and ***everywhen!***

Remember: *"All models lack correctness, though some may be useful...for a time."* [0536.2 / 1319] ;-)

* * *

"Our birth is but a sleep and a forgetting:
The soul that rises with us, our life's star,
Hath had elsewhere its setting, and cometh from afar:
Not in entire forgetfulness, and not in utter nakedness,
But trailing clouds of glory do we come,
From God who is our home."

-William Wordsworth

Intimations of Immortality from Recollections of Early Childhood

MAJOR CONSTELLATIONS (22): DESCRIPTIONS

⁂

~Most frequently encountered reflections and select, non-exhaustive qualities~
Follow a constellation by turning to their dream of origin (#0000).

⁂ **0 - THE WEAVER** ⁂ ***Encountered in 262 dreams between #0010-#1423 (18.2%)*** = [The monad. Mother. Unity. Unconditional love. Infinite light of consciousness. Receptive. Tender. Nurturing. Supportive. Kind. Patient. A steadfast guide which nurtures the walk on the pathway of evolution.

Likely to say: *"True happiness is only possible when shared." "There is always something to learn." "Everything is a product of creative expression."*] //

⁂ **1 - THE CARPENTER** ⁂ ***Encountered in 207 dreams between #0012-#1433 (14.3%)*** = [The dyad. Father. Courageous. Resilient. Consciousness. Aware. Unwaveringly supports true creativity.

Likely to say: *"I am you. You are me." "We're the dream and the dreamer." "Part of me is you." "Namaste." "Om Mani Peme Hung." "Aloha."*] //

⁂ **2 - THE DANCER** ⁂ ***Encountered in 173 dreams between #0002-#1434 (12%)*** = [The self. Invisible force that unifies polarities. Dot connector. Prone to lose sight of itself along its multivariate quest. Highest expression of spirit and creative spark. Access to unconditional love. Unifies and balances aspects of the monad and dyad.

Likely to say: *"Hello Me!" "Love is naturally available to each of us. Our awakening is shared."*] //

. . .

⁂ 3 - **THE CHILD** ⁂ ***Encountered in 107 dreams between #0102-#1437*** *(7.4%)* = [The spark of true nature. The seed of true creativity. Vulnerable, tender, and innocent. Unwaveringly determined. Learns with openness. Plays as an access to ingenuity. Helpless at times. Can't yet engage with life's cruel circumstances. Constantly reminded it's ok to not know. Explores and expresses the evolutionary essence held at its core.

Likely to say: *"Let's do that!" "I don't know." "Can I try? Let me try, please."*] //

⁂ 4 - **THE CONNECTOR** ⁂ ***Encountered in 62 dreams between #0071-#1421*** *(4.3%)* = [The joy of full engagement. Confronts conditioning. Roils against superficiality, avoidance, and coping mechanisms. Essential to the transformation of entitlement and injustice, though occasionally their creative downloads can become distorted and bring overwhelm.

Likely to say: *"I'm in constant motion." "I struggle to find balance in all aspects of life." "This impressive mask hides my most extremely sensitive aspects."*] //

⁂ 5 - **THE LAWYER** ⁂ ***Encountered in 54 dreams between #0080-#1438*** *(3.8%)* = [The armor. Reliant upon form. Reflects the conditioned ego. Often seems like a dictator. Dominating. Masculine. Tends to give power to the mind before the heart. Their growth depends on bringing the mind in service of the heart through compassionate confrontation.

Likely to say: *"I wear this face to engage an uncertain world, and it controls my life." "Much has happened to me. I act in certain ways because I haven't yet fully metabolized unjust trauma."*] //

⁂ 6 - **THE PILOT** ⁂ ***Encountered in 37 dreams between #0129-#1404*** *(2.6%)* = [The friend. Awe. Excitement. Willing to evolve. Alive. Vital. Sees deeper meaning. Fascinated with evolution through play. Smiles. Tastes. Bends. Breaks. Throws. Sees objects through many different sensory capacities. Quickly assimilates knowledge and information.

Likely to say: *"I'm fascinated by learning, exploration, and direct experience." "I'm computation wielding, airplane flying, laser loving, faggot millennial Eurotrash."*] //

⁂ 7 - **THE WORLDBRIDGER** ⁂ ***Encountered in 35 dreams between #0010-#1430*** *(2.4%)* = [The wise one. The elder. The healer. The Bishop. The headmaster. Represents the more transcendental, spiritual aspects of existence. The "at cause" directed energy of the "surrendered spirit in right action." Wizard. Serves the non-conditional. No longer lives for the sake of the world, but attuned to broad spectrum creation. Sets challenges that support various stations of development.

Likely to say: *"Use your tools. Nothing is more powerful than you."*] //

⁂ 8 - **THE ATHEIST** ⁂ ***Encountered in 35 dreams between #0020-#1380*** *(2.4%)* = [Resistant. Intermittently engaged. Righteous. Rational. Tends to protect their vulnerability by overclocking masculinity. Part time relativist. Benefits from invitations to soften. Dutiful spouse, father and ally. Holds strong, fact-based opinions. Occasionally withdraws when threatened. Accustomed to being manipulated and abused. Working to release conditioning. Healing.

Likely to say: *"I'm more bark than bite." "Your argument is invalid." "I'm not wounded...you're wounded."*] //

. . .

⁂ **9 - THE FIDUCIARY** ⁂ ***Encountered in 30 dreams between #0007-#1407 (2.1%)*** = [Conditioned masculinity. Publicly polished. Privately messy. Impulsively paradoxical. Orderly. Compartmentalized. Avoids irrational fears at all costs. Triggered when reminded of unprocessed experiences. Tends to react in a familiar pattern without being aware of the trap of conditioning. Intellectually engages questions.

Likely to say: *"What conditioning?" "What circumstances bring me in and out of integrity."*] //

⁂ **10 - THE ACTOR** ⁂ ***Encountered in 29 dreams between #0066-#1426 (2%)*** = [Soul guide. Anima/Animus. Lover. Calls forth suppressed energy, and things for which the spirit longs. Expressions of intimacy. Spark and flame. Screen on which perfection is projected. Attraction. Magnetic longing. Strides confidently along their own evolutionary path.

Likely to say: *"I'll show you deeper aspects of yourself that other friends avoid."*] //

⁂ **11 - GRANDMA** ⁂ ***Encountered in 27 dreams between #0013-#1433 (1.9%)*** = [Wholeness. Provides a sense of fulfillment and completion. Acknowledges and closes prior evolutionary cycles. Offers an invitation to return to the original state. Often invisible, yet felt along the journey. Playfully points to areas of disintegration behind the scenes. Occasionally takes the role of coach.

Likely to say: *"Don't be overwhelmed and consumed by compulsive states." "Take a deep breath." "Would you like a slice of pie?"*] //

⁂ **12 - THE LITTLE PRINCE** ⁂ ***Encountered in 25 dreams between #0915-#1437 (1.8%)*** = [The joy of curiosity. The sensitive masculine. Steward between epochs. The glimmer of optimism. The single candle shining courageously in the void. The seed of genius. Intrepid spirit. Trusting. Reminder of "tender surrender" among over utilized conditioned expressions.

Likely to say: *"Wow! Wau-wooow! WOW!" *Sings and babbles in a youthfully exuberant developing language**]//

⁂ **13 - THE NURSE** ⁂ ***Encountered in 24 dreams between #0026-#1319 (1.7%)*** = [Conditioned femininity. Witch mother. The area in the subconscious where fears, withholds and traumas are stored. Begs for confrontation. Somewhat defined by the past. Comfortable navigating the swamp, and serving as a guide to those in shadowy parts aching to be made light.

Likely to say: *"The story of my life defines who I am and what I can do." "I'm loyal, hardworking, well intended, empathetic, fearful, loving, forgiving, and introspective."*] //

⁂ **14 - THE MAGICIAN** ⁂ ***Encountered in 22 dreams between #0472-#1430 (1.6%)*** = [Generally emerges as the polychronic trickster. Consistently appears as a gatekeeper between realms of "The Great Game." Proposes challenges to test the character, intention, and motivations of "the rescuer," "the persecutor," and "the victim." Provides playful reminders when backslides into comfortably numb states become areas of risk to mitigate and backstop.

Likely to say: *"Are you sure you're ready?" "You can never go back." "Tempting, isn't it?" "Cause flow. How? You know." "Stay awake. Build stuff."*] //

⁂ 15 - **THE ROMANTIC** ⁂ ***Encountered in 21 dreams between #0318-#1432 (1.5%)*** = [Represents attraction. Clear and eager. Libido. Deeper expressions of friendliness and creative thrust. Wishes for other's happiness without wanting anything in return. Seems fleeting to the conditioned ego. Occurs as fecund, playful, somatic, and a whispering muse to the burgeoning artist.

Likely to say: *"I encourage you." "Take on unimaginable hardship to get closer to meeting your true self." "Get back to basics...and be tender along the way." "Your mind is ridiculous. Let's get naked."*] //

⁂ 16 - **THE CONFIDANT** ⁂ ***Encountered in 20 dreams between #0022-#1437 (1.4%)*** = [Represents liked qualities in others, as yet uncultivated within. Appreciated. Unique. Courageous. Candid. Stable. Present. Possesses the qualities necessary for evolution.

Likely to say: *"You've got this. It's attainable. Go." "Stop. You're doing that bullshit again."*] //

⁂ 17 - **THE LOBBYIST** ⁂ ***Encountered in 18 dreams between #0129-#1296 (1.3%)*** = [The powerful, positive "**NO**" in a sea of inauthentic, cowardly "**YES**." Willing to apply resources when systemic logjams emerge. Unapologetic. Action oriented. Speaks what's wanted into being. Plays the game with nuance and elegance. Though comfortable presenting as bristly and sarcastic, their heart space holds tremendous compassion and broad-spectrum Love for humanity.

Likely to say: *"I'm among the world's most egregious assholes." "People are the worst." "Here. Get this." "Shit."*] //

⁂ 18 - **THE PUBLIC MEDIUM** ⁂ ***Encountered in 17 dreams between #0028-#1407 (1.2%)*** = [A spiritual guide with common past life karma. An ascendant master in training. Has shared trench warfare, far flung extraterrestrial adventures, and healing encounters with entities from unconditional and non-conditional realms in an ethereal, prayerful, and increasingly soft tone.

Likely to say: *"I'm praying for you. Thank you for the opportunity to serve."*] //

⁂ 19 - **THE TRANSLATOR** ⁂ ***Encountered in 17 dreams between #0322-#1412 (1.2%)*** = [Consistently points out pockets of resistance. Teacher. Guide between prime material and non-physical dimensions. Surrendered and in service to God, Guides and Self.

Likely to say: *"The bar is being held for you to tap back in whenever you want." "God embarrasses you? Now that is funny." "I commit to being God's love. I commit to Love as a presence* ***(not as a verb)****. I commit to alignment. I commit to living God's truth. I commit to non-conditional guidance...continuously. I commit to growth. I commit to anchoring to the deep here and now."*] //

⁂ 20 - **THE HEALER** ⁂ ***Encountered in 16 dreams between #0010-#1412 (1.1%)*** = [The pure listener. Unconsciously competent across practiced traditions and modalities. Soul gazer.

Masterfully adept at navigating the "Deep Now." Effortlessly bounds between ecstatic, cathartic, and sober/rational realms.

Likely to say: *"Attempts to label me generally prove futile. None are comprehensive. Healer. Teacher. Facilitator. Steward. Medicine Man. Ayahuascero. All are part time roles. My work is to* ***1)*** *transform the capricious ego into a humble servant of the shared heart of humanity and* ***2)*** *embody True nature." "Love and compassion to all beings now, then, everywhere, and every-When."*] //

⁂ **21 - THE KIND HEART** ⁂ ***Encountered in 15 dreams between #0179-#1404*** *(1%)* = [Commits to co-creative relationship. A voracious and quick learner. Manifests friendships that support their being themselves fully, more of the time. Celebrates its kinks and quirks. Creates space to take refuge within itself, for the benefit of those they love. A being *(purposefully)* of few words

Likely to say: *"Bonjour à tous. De quoi parlerons-nous aujourd'hui? Quel problème est le plus intéressant à résoudre?*] //

CONSTELLATIONS, ASTERISMS, AND BRIGHT STARS

THE ANIMATOR - #0249
THE APIRIST - #0833
THE ARBITER - #1439
THE ARBORIST - #0640
THE ARCHITECT - #0198
THE ARMY ANGEL - #0126
THE ARTIST - #0089
THE ASH - #0498
THE ASSISTANT - #0613
THE ATHEIST - #0020
THE ATTRACTOR - #0254
THE AUDIOLOGIST - #0804
THE AUDITOR - #0033
THE AUSSIE - #0645
THE AVENGER - #0829
THE AWAKENING - #1190
THE AYURVEDIC - #0002

* * *

~B~

THE BAD IDEA - #0841
THE BADASS - #0495
THE BAKER - #0595
THE BANDANA - #0430
THE BANKER - #0076
THE BAPTIZED ONE - #0637
THE BARBIE - #0657
THE BARISTA - #0789
THE BARKEEP - #0323
THE BASS - #1039
THE BENEFITS ADMINISTRATOR - #0901
THE BESTIE - #0719
THE BISEXUAL - #0826
THE BLACK BEAUTY - #0786
THE BLACK KNIGHT - #0402
THE BLUE HAIRED BLOKE - #0284
THE BLUES SINGER - #0019
THE BODHI PUNK - #0539
THE BODY BUILDER - #0593
THE BOND TRADERS - #0009
THE BONES - #1383
THE BONSAI - #0569
THE BOSNIAN - #0202
THE BOSS - #0271
THE BOSTON MARATHONER - #0461
THE BOUNCER - #0701
THE BRAIN - #0656

THE BRAND MANAGER - #0154
THE BREAKS DJ - #0144
THE BREWMASTER - #0204
THE BRIGHT SATELLITE - #0950
THE BRITS - #0670
THE BROKER - #0210
THE BUBBLE - #0117
THE BURLESQUE PERFORMER - #1073
THE BUTCH LESBIAN - #0260

* * *

~C~

THE C-SUITE - #0124
THE CAMERAMAN - #0561
THE CANINE SAVIOR - #1384
THE CARDINAL - #0410
THE CAREGIVER - #0204
THE CAROLER - #1159
THE CAROLINA REAPER - #1207
THE CARPENTER - #0012
THE CARTOONIST - #0284
THE CATALYST - #0712
THE CATCHER - #0703
THE CATERER - #0848
THE CATHOLIC - #0678
THE CENTERLINE - #0836
THE CEO - #0799
THE CHALLENGER - #0071
THE CHAMPION - #0260
THE CHAMPION OF LOVE - #0703
THE CHANNEL - #1078
THE CHARLATAN - #0134
THE CHEERLEADER - #0755
THE CHEF - #0014
THE CHEMISTS - #0150
THE CHICKEN - #0953
THE CHIEF OF STAFF - #1236
THE CHILD - #0102
THE CHOCOHOLIC - #0044
THE CITY EMPLOYEE - #0387
THE CLUB KID - #0037
THE COACH - #0071
THE COCK - #0434
THE COLONEL - #0069
THE COMBAT MEDIC - #0045
THE COMIC - #0082
THE COMMUNITY ORGANIZERS - #0861

THE COMPASS - #0778
THE COMPUTATIONAL LINGUIST - #1155
THE CONCIERGE - #0094
THE CONDUCTOR - #0097
THE CONFIDANT - #0022
THE CONJURER - #1243
THE CONNECTOR - #0071
THE CONSERVATIVE NEIGHBOR - #0744
THE CONSULTANT - #0131
THE CONTRAST JUNKIE - #0170
THE CONVERT - #0009
THE COOK - #0696
THE CORD CUTTER - #0134
THE CORPORATE PLANNER - #1066
THE COSMIC WHITE HEART - #0045
THE COUNSELOR - #0969
THE COUTURIER - #0204
THE COWBOY - #1184
THE COYOTE -#0603
THE CRAZY DIAMOND - #1094
THE CREATOR - #0071
THE CROWN PRINCE - #0528
THE CRUNCH - #0082
THE CRUSH - #0951
THE CUDDLER - #0317

* * *

~D~

THE DANCER - #0002
THE DANDY - #0298
THE DAUGHTER - #0259
THE DEAR HEART - #0624
THE DELIGHT - #0251
THE DENTIST - #0782
THE DESERT NYMPH - #0735
THE DESIGNER - #0472
THE DEVOTEE - #0384
THE DIPLOMAT - #0038
THE DISNEY PRINCE - #0453
THE DOCTOR - #0184
THE DOMINATRIX - #0073
THE DRAGON TAMER - #0281
THE DRAMA QUEEN - #0353
THE DRONE PILOT - #0672
THE DRUM MAJOR - #1166
THE DRUMMER - #0064
THE DULCE DE LECHE - #0363

~E~

THE ECSTASY - #0082
THE EDITOR - #1208
THE EDUCATOR - #1360
THE EDUCATORS - #0716
THE EMPYREAN - #1240
THE EMT - #0939
THE ENGINEER - #0200
THE ENTREPRENEUR - #0969
THE EPICUREAN - #0233
THE EPITOME - #1375
THE EQUESTRIAN - #0401
THE ERROR PROOFER - #0206
THE EVIL TWIN - #0666
THE EXCOMMUNICATED - #0812
THE EXECUTIVE DIRECTOR - #0891
THE EXECUTIVE PRODUCER - #0070
THE EXPAT - #0134
THE EXTERMINATOR - #1003
THE EXTROVERT - #1320

* * *

~F~

THE FAIRY GODMOTHER - #0209
THE FAIRY GODPARENTS - #0392
THE FAITHFUL ONE - #0215
THE FARMHAND - #0201
THE FASHIONISTA - #0170
THE FBI AGENT - #0115
THE FEELER - #0094
THE FELLOW - #0108
THE FIDUCIARY - #0007
THE FIFTY POUND BRAIN - #0710
THE FILM PRODUCER - #0124
THE FIREFIGHTER - #0668
THE FIRST GRADER - #1031
THE FIT BOY - #0650
THE FLASH - #0568
THE FLIRT - #0076
THE FLORIDIAN - #0603
THE FLUFF - #1094
THE FLUTIST - #0023
THE FOUNDER - #0581
THE FRATERNITY MAN - #0237
THE FUJIYAMA MAMA - #1330
THE FUNDAMENTALIST - #0461
THE FUNDRAISER - #0874

THE FUNKY MONKEY - #0598
THE FUR TRAPPER - #1028

* * *

~G~

THE GAME DESIGNER - #0608
THE GAMER - #0307
THE GANG BANGER - #0182
THE GARDENER - #0045
THE GATOR - #0724
THE GDMF UNICORN - #0147
THE GENIUS - #0162
THE GENTLEMAN - #0995
THE GERMAN - #0205
THE GINGER - #0185
THE GODFATHER - #0428
THE GOGO BOY - #0913
THE GOLDEN ONE - #0931
THE GOLDEN SHADOW - #0547
THE GONG MASTER - #0128
THE GOOD WEED - #0917
THE GOTH - #0445
THE GRACE - #0353
THE GRANDDAUGHTER - #1000
THE GRANDSONS - #1000
THE GREASED PIG - #1126
THE GREAT UNCLE - #1066
THE GREEK - #0367
THE GREEN TARA - #0012
THE GREGARIOUS CONSULTANT - #0158
THE GROOMSMAN - #0302
THE GUITARIST - #0025
THE GYM TWINK - #1129
THE GYMNAST - #1202
THE GYPSY - #0066

* * *

~H~

THE HABERDASHER - #0137
THE HIATUS - #0035
THE HANDYMAN - #0021
THE HARBINGER - #0010
THE HEADBANGER - #0899
THE HEADCASE - #0914
THE HEALED WOMAN - #0098
THE HEALER - #0010

THE KENYAN - #0378
THE KETTLE - #0143
THE KIDDO - #0661
THE KINDERGARTENER - #1031
THE KIND HEART - #0179
THE KINKSTER - #1045
THE KINKY MD - #0218
THE KITKAT - #0481
THE KIWI - #0560
THE KOAN - #0557
THE KOKORO - #0512

* * *

~L~

THE LACHRYMOLOGIST - #0573
THE LACROSSE PLAYER - #1080
THE LALA - #0561
THE LAMPLIGHTER - #0972
THE LANDLORD - #0212
THE LANDSCAPE ARCHITECT - #0159
THE LATIN FIREBALL - #0901
THE LAUGHING MONKEY - #0692
THE LAWYER - #0080
THE LEGEND - #0400
THE LINEAGE HOLDER - #1100
THE LINGUIST - #0249
THE LION - #0267
THE LIONESS - #0070
THE LITIGATOR - #1056
THE LITTLE BROTHER - #0029
THE LITTLE PRINCE - #0915
THE LOBBYIST - #0129
THE LOGICIAN - #0126
THE LONGFELLOW - #0957
THE LOVE STORY AUTHOR - #0610
THE LOYALIST - #1440
THE LUCKY MAN - #0025
THE LUMBERJACK - #0021
THE LUTHERAN PASTOR - #0098
THE LYRICIST - #0040

* * *

~M~

THE M&A ATTORNEY - #0106
THE MAGICIAN - #0472
THE MAKE UP ARTIST - #1025

THE MAKER - #0016
THE MALE MODEL - #0799
THE MANAGING DIRECTOR - #0015
THE MARATHONER - #0097
THE MASSEUR - #0868
THE MASSEUSE - #0376
THE MASSIVE HOMOSEXUAL - #0084
THE MBA CANDIDATE - #0620
THE MEDIA TEAM - #0261
THE MEDICINE WOMAN - #0003
THE MEEK - #0302
THE MEME - #0193
THE MIDWESTERN GENT - #0784
THE MIDWIFE - #0226
THE MINIATURE - #1117
THE MINISTER - #0618
THE MIRROR - #0114
THE MODEL - #0144
THE MODERN CAVEMEN - #0563
THE MOTIVATIONAL SPEAKER - #0683
THE MOTO - #0291
THE MUSICAL PANDA - #0794

* * *

~N~

THE NASTY PIG - #0793
THE NAYSAYER - #0048
THE NEIGHBOR - #0672
THE NEIGHBORHOOD WATCH - #1058
THE NEUROSCIENTIST - #0573
THE NEUTRAL GUIDE - #0010
THE NEWLYWEDS - #0556
THE NINERS FAN - #0394
THE NOMINEE - #0803
THE NORSE DEMIGOD - #1016
THE NOWHERE MAN - #0874
THE NUN - #0165
THE NURSE - #0026

* * *

~O~

THE OB/GYN - #0518
THE OBSERVER - #0070
THE OCCUPATIONAL THERAPIST - #0590
THE OFFICE ADMIN - #0394
THE OFFICIANT - #0013

THE PORN STAR - #0393
THE PORTRAIT ARTIST - #0363
THE POSTMASTER - #0201
THE POWER PLAYER - #0234
THE PRACTITIONER - #0980
THE PRAGMATIST - #1003
THE PRANKSTER - #0256
THE PRECIOUS ONE - #0322
THE PRESS SECRETARY - #1124
THE PRETZEL - #0269
THE PRIESTESS - #0391
THE PROFESSOR - #0306
THE PROM DATE - #1104
THE PROMOTER - #0768
THE PROPERTY MANAGER - #0384
THE PSYCHEDELIC STEWARD - #0595
THE PSYCHIATRIST - #0259
THE PSYCHIC - #0241
THE PSYCHIC DOCTOR - #0781
THE PSYCHONAUT - #0030
THE PUBLIC MEDIUM - #0028
THE PUBLIC SERVANT - #0231
THE PYRO IN TRAINING - #0088

* * *

~Q~

THE QUEER - #0263

* * *

~R~

THE RABID RABBIT - #0834
THE RADICAL FAERIE - #0748
THE RADICAL HIPPIE - #0523
THE RAINMAN - #0491
THE RAJNEESH - #1211
THE RAPTOR - #0176
THE RAY OF SUNSHINE - #0717
THE REANIMATOR - #1319
THE REBEL - #0337
THE RECONCILIATOR - #0317
THE REFLECTION - #0007
THE REIKI MASTER - #0010
THE REINCARNATED - #1066
THE RENAISSANCE MAN - #0106
THE RENEGADE - #0085
THE REPATRIATES - #1117

THE REPEATER - #0071
THE RESISTANCE - #0034
THE RESTAURATEUR - #0297
THE RETAILER - #0210
THE REVOLUTIONARY - #0069
THE RICH MAN - #0097
THE RINGMASTER - #0715
THE ROADRUNNER - #0642
THE ROBOT - #0176
THE ROCK STAR SPOUSE - #0281
THE RODIN - #0701
THE ROLLERGIRL - #0495
THE ROMANTIC - #0318
THE RUBY - #0169
THE RUMBLER - #0963

* * *

~S~

THE SAMOAN - #0004
THE SCHOOL TEACHER - #0820
THE SEASON - #0585
THE SEER - #0050
THE SENSOR - #0858
THE SERVANT - #0144
THE SEX FRIEND - #0524
THE SEX THERAPIST - #0647
THE SEX WORKER - #0697
THE SEXUAL SACRED - #0022
THE SHAKTI SISTER - #0143
THE SHARED HEART - #0070
THE SILVER BOYS - #1131
THE SIRENS - #0014
THE SIXTH DEGREE BLACKBELT - #0422
THE SKATER - #0285
THE SKEPTIC - #0656
THE SKYWOLF - #1389
THE SLUT - #0894
THE SMILE - #0532
THE SMOKE SCREEN - #0400
THE SMOKER - #1113
THE SOCCER COACH - #0514
THE SON - #0259
THE SOOTHSAYER - #0135
THE SOUL SISTER - #1275
THE SOUL SINGER - #1185
THE SOUND ENGINEER - #0641
THE SOUTHERN BELLE - #0273

THE SOUTHERN GENTLEMAN - #0698
THE SPECK - #0520
THE SPOTTED DOG - #0237
THE SQUIRREL - #1340
THE STRATEGIST - #0136
THE STUDENT - #0114
THE SUMERIAN - #0964
THE SURGICAL TECH - #0024
THE SURVIVOR - #0400
THE SWAB - #0291
THE SWEET D - #0699
THE SWIM COACH- #0365

* * *

~T~

THE TAR HEEL - #0291
THE TATER - #0705
THE TEACHER - #0144
THE TEAM LEADER - #0239
THE TECHIE - #0117
THE TEETOTALER - #1236
THE TEMPLAR - #0052
THE THEM - #0157
THE THERAPIST - #0579
THE THINKER - #0056
THE TIGER MOM - #0602
THE TINKERBELL - #0862
THE TINY ROMANIAN - #0089
THE TINY TODDLER - #0081
THE TOP OF THE WORLD - #0476
THE TORCH RUNNER - #0070
THE TRAIL RUNNER - #0094
THE TRAINEE - #0595
THE TRAINER - #0532
THE TRANSLATOR - #0322
THE TRANSPARENT HEADCASE - #0075
THE TRAVELER - #0950
THE TRIATHLETE - #0737
THE TRICK - #0887
THE TRINITY - #0589
THE TRIUMVIRATE - #1078
THE TRUST FUND BABY - #1130
THE TWIRLERS - #0219

* * *

~V~

ZEITGEIST VALENCES

~A~

* * *

~B~

* * *

~C~

* * *

~D~

* * *

~E~

* * *

~F~

* * *

~G~

* * *

~H~

* * *

~I~

* * *

~J~

JESUS CHRIST - #0127
JFK JR - #0746
JIMMY PAGE - #0554
JODIE FOSTER - #0405
JOE BIDEN - #0573
JOE ROGAN - #0682
JOE STRUMMER - #0620
JOHN GOSSLING - #1017
JOHN LENNON - #0712
JOHN MCCAIN - #1144
JOHN MYUNG - #0024
JOHN OLIVER - #0944
JOHN PAUL JONES - #0554
JOHN PETRUCCI - #0024
JOHN SPENCE - #1057
JONATHAN DAVIS - #0073
JORDAN PETERSON - #0676
JORDAN RUDESS - #0024
JOSEPH CAMPBELL - #1010
JOSH GROBAN - #0627
JOSH HOMME - #0234
JUDGE JUDY - #0965
JULIA ROBERTS - #1028
JULIA STILES - #0225
JULIE ANDREWS - #0144
JUNYA WANTANABE - #1251
JUSTICE KAVANAUGH - #0341
JUSTIN CHANCELLOR - #0012
JUSTIN TIMBERLAKE - #0466

* * *

~K~

KAMALA HARRIS - #1341
KATIE HENDRICKS - #0247
KATY PERRY - #0897
KELLY CLARKSON - #0079
KELLY OSBOURNE - #1090
KEN RYKER - #0403
KENDRICK LAMAR - #1237
KIM KARDASHIAN - #1349
KMFDM - #0526
KORN - #0073
KRISTI YAMAGUCHI - #0855
KYLIE MINOGUE - #1061

* * *

~L~

LADY GAGA - #0367
LARRY DAVID - #0065
LARS ULRICH - #1071
LAYNE STAYLEY - #0235
LCD SOUNDSYSTEM - #0365
LEONARDO DICAPRIO - #0796
LESLIE JORDAN - #0452
LEWIS CARROLL - #1001
LINDA RONSTADT - #1082
LINDSAY GRAHAM - #0341
LIZZO - #0909
LORIN ASHTON - #0326
LOUIS ARMSTRONG - #0827
LOUIS CK - #0154
LUDWIG VAN BEETHOVEN - #0668
LUKE PERRY - #0568

* * *

~M~

MADONNA - #0266
MARILYN MANSON - #0027
MARC BENIOFF - #1057
MARK ZUCKERBERG - #0113
MARTIN SCORCESE - #1028
MARIANNE WILLIAMSON - #0828
MAYA ANGELOU - #0346
MAYA RUDOLPH - #0457
MAYNARD KEENAN - #0012
MELANIA TRUMP - #1139
MICHAEL BLOOMBERG - #1058
MICHAEL EISENER - #0113
MICHAEL JACKSON - #0515
MICHELLE OBAMA - #1214
MICK JAGGER - #0872
MIKE MANGINI - #0024
MIKE PATTON - #0175
MIKE PENCE - #0255
MITCH MCCONNELL - #0341
MOBY - #0827
MOLLY SHANNON - #0948
MR. BUNGLE - #1092

MR. ROGERS - #0851

* * *

~N~

* * *

~O~

* * *

~P~

* * *

~R~

RICHARD DAVID JAMES - #0774
RICHARD GERE - #0762
RICHARD NIXON - #1188
ROB LOWE - #0055
ROB SCHNEIDER - #0220
ROB ZOMBIE - #0137
ROBERT PLANT - #0914
ROBIN WILLIAMS - #0361
RODNEY DANGERFIELD - #0014
ROSEANNE BARR - #1055

* * *

~S~

SAINT PETER - #0023
SAM NEILL - #1247
SANDRA BULLOCK - #0863
SARA GILBERT - #1055
SARAH PAULSON - #1028
SARAH SILVERMAN - #0541
SCARLETT JOHANSSSON - #1426
SCOTT WEINER - #0220
SELENA GOMEZ - #0683
SERJ TANKARIAN - #0183
SHAKIRA - #1117
SHAQUILLE O'NEAL - #0188
SHARI BAPTISTE - #0482
SHARON OSBOURNE - #1090
SHAUN WHITE - #0126
SHELDON ADELSON - #0218
SHIRLEY MACLAINE - #1434
SID - #1069
SINBAD - #0007
SIR PATRICK STEWART - #1131
SKRILLEX - #0672
SLASH - #0460
SLAYER - #0468
SLIPKNOT - #0666
SOPHIE - #1026
ST. FRANCIS OF ASSISI - #0998
ST. MICHAEL - #1251
ST. RAPHAEL - #1251
ST. THOMAS AQUINAS - #0924
STANLEY KUBRICK - #0405
STEPHEN COLBERT - #0587
STEPHEN KING - #0490
STEVEN TYLER - #0789
STOCKARD CHANNING - #0905

STS9 - #0495

* * *

~T~

THE BEASTIE BOYS - #0770
THE BEATLES - #0935
THE BELKS - #0655
THE BLACK MADONNA - #0350
THE BLUE ANGELS - #0867
THE BUSH PRESIDENTS - #0336
THE CHEMICAL BROTHERS - #0524
THE DALAI LAMA - #0009
THE LONELY ISLAND - #1033
THE NAKED AND FAMOUS - #0784
THE OSBOURNES - #0619
THE QUEEN OF ENGLAND - #0100
THE ROLLING STONES - #0872
THE VELVET UNDERGROUND - #1420
THE VON TRAPPS - #0417
THERESA MAY - #1250
THOMAS EDISON - #0461
THROBBING GRISTLE - #0303
TINA TURNER - #0229
TOM BRADY - #0538
TOM HANKS - #0899
TOM MORELLO - #1275
TOOL - #0012
TRENT REZNOR - #0394
TWIGGY RAMIREZ - #0860
TYPE O NEGATIVE - #1097

* * *

~U~

UNCLE FRED WAHPEPAH - #0396

* * *

~V~

VANILLA FUDGE - #1259
VANNA WHITE - #0773
VICTORIA BECKHAM - #0747

* * *

~W~

WAH! - #0626

* * *

~Y~

* * *

~Z~

AMALGAMS, HYBRIDS, AND SPIRITS

~E~

"ECNIV" - #1286
"Elf Boys" - #0435
"ERIC WHITEMAN" - #0154
"Eric" - #1326
"Eric" - #1340
"Eros - #0558
EROS - #0972

* * *

~F~

"FLEABAG" - #1170
"Francis" - #1442

* * *

~G~

"Gary Marshall" - #0786
“Gatekeeper” - #0169
“Genius” - #0761
GHOSTBUSTERS - #0461
"Gizmo" - #1029
"Greg" - #0069
"Grim Reaper" - #0535

* * *

~H~

"HERK" - #1439
"HRR" - #0496
HAN SOLO - #0875

* * *

~I~

"Ian" - #0910
"ILSE" - #0878

* * *

~J~

"Jacob" - #0637
"Jared and Jaret" - #0600
"JEFF and CHRIS" - #0218
"Jeff" - #0357
"Jeff" - #1155
"Jennifer" - #1168

* * *

~K~

* * *

~L~

* * *

~M~

"MADONNA'S HERO" - #0316
"Maeva" - #1023
"Maggie" - #0979
"Maid Marian" - #1085
"MARK" - #0153
"Mark" - #1410
"Mary" - #1177
"Mary" - #1336
"Matthew" - #0897
"Max" - #0922
"Melanie" - #0302
"Meredith" - #0259
"Mom" - #0317
"Mom" - #0410
"Mr. Beaselman" - #0971
"Mr. Wolf" - #0799
"Mrs. Leavenworth" - #0907
MARTY MCFLY - #0063
MARY POPPINS - #0332
MICKEY MOUSE - #0376
MORPHEUS - #0913

* * *

~N~

"Naomi" - #0175
"NAOMI" - #1187
"Nelson from Norway" - #1073
"NICOTINE" - #0384
NOME KING - #0745

* * *

~P~

"Patrick McFadden" - #0435
"Patrick" - #0975
"Paul" - #0414
"Pete" - #1164
"Phil and Kim" - #0284
PEE WEE HERMAN - #1243

* * *

~Q~

"Q" - #0763

* * *

~R~

* * *

~S~

* * *

~T~

ACKNOWLEDGMENTS

Thanks to every spirit *(in and out of body)* who conspired to bring this vision in to 3D reality. **Half of me is you.**

This work would not have been possible without support from my friends and teachers at:

- Paititi Institute
- Flow Genome Project
- Celebrating Life Ministries
- Conscious Leadership Group
- Baptiste Power Yoga Institute
- Foundation for Spiritual Development

Special shout outs to "VO" and "L."
Your guidance, non-conditional love, and constant support kept me on track.

Thank you.
#NeverHaveIEverBeenBetter

P.S. - Mom & Dad...
so happy that you
brought me through,
and to be a happy blend
of each of you.

Aho!

ABOUT THE AUTHOR

Joshua D. Lundell is an interdisciplinary student and artist, committed to spending increasing proportions of day-to-day life in causal flow, from a space of tender surrender; in service to the shared heart of humanity *(through accessing various zones of genius).*

...phew...that's it...in an out breath.

Joshua:

Loves to play.
Is of great Love.
Knows how to give.
Is a creative visionary.
Is passionate and all in.
Is a spiritual adventurer.
Is an awesome performer.
Loves to be seen and is a great leader.
Brings spirituality in to every moment.
Is willing to read the signs and follow them.
Intentionally creates connection with others.
Takes life experiences and turns them in to art.
Is willing to risk and change everything for aliveness.
Loves to break things down, and put them together again.
Practices resurrection as a moment-to-moment phenomenon.
Likes to touch people, and change people, through aligned service.
Has facility with both the small & individual, and the large & multi-faceted.
...and above all else, practices loving-kindness *(with the same wobbles and foibles as others).*

Beyond that, Joshua:

Resides in San Francisco, CA.
...will eventually have a bulldog.
...and always seems to be shopping for somethin'.

CONSTELLATIONS: An Exquisite Corpse of Dreams is Joshua's first book.

instagram.com/sonderphile

Made in the USA
Monee, IL
18 February 2021